Contents

Horizons

Mathematics 2

Teacher's Guide

by
Sareta A. Cummins

Edited by
David J. Korecki

Illustrated by
Tye A. Rausch

Editorial Assistant
Christine A. Korecki

 AOP

804 N. 2nd Ave. E.   Rock Rapids, IA 51246-1759   800-622-3070   www.aop.com

Horizons Mathematics 2 Teacher's Guide
Published by Alpha Omega Publications, Inc.®
804 N. 2nd Ave. E., Rock Rapids, IA 51246-1759

Printed in the United States of America

Introduction

Before You Start ...

THE CHALLENGE

Today's average high school graduate knows and can do less math than their counterpart of ten, fifteen, or twenty years ago. Basic math skills have deteriorated to the point that many wonder if this country can continue to be a leader in shaping the technology of the future. Unfortunately, the general trend of modern education of all types is downward. Students in private education, while they score higher overall than public school students, still do poorly in math computation skills.

THE GOAL

The goal of this curriculum is to provide the parent and teacher with a tool that will help them effectively combat this deterioration of math skills by raising the level of student performance. Research of the content and methods of other existing curriculums, the concepts evaluated by achievement tests, and typical courses of study resulted in selection of the *Scope and Sequence* starting on page 14. This curriculum was not planned around any particular group of students. Rather, it was determined that the material in this curriculum constituted a reasonable level of performance for second grade students. The curriculum is designed so that the teacher can adapt its use to student(s) of widely varying ability. In

other words, the curriculum is a tool that is capable of performing well over a broad range of student ability to help them achieve a higher minimum level of proficiency. The two major components of the curriculum are the student text (in two volumes) and the *Teacher's Guide*. These are the absolute minimum components for accomplishing the objective of teaching the concepts in the *Scope and Sequence*. Since this guide was designed as an integral part of the curriculum, its use is absolutely necessary. The guide contains activities not found in the student texts that are essential to the accomplishment of the curriculum objectives. As you will see in the following sections, this *Teacher's Guide* contains a significant number of suggestions and helps for the teacher. Unlike first grade, all manipulatives are identified with *italics* so that the teacher may easily see them at a glance.

THE DESIGN

Take a moment to look at the sample chart entitled, *Development of Concepts*, on page 28–29. Take note of how the curriculum concepts are developed. The first presentation is usually a brief familiarization. Then the basic teaching is accomplished as part of three to five lessons. The thoroughness of a presentation depends on how new and how important the concept is to the student's academic development.

THE DEVELOPMENT

Each concept will be reviewed for three to five lessons after the complete presentation. For the next two months the concept will be presented every two weeks as a part of two or three consecutive lessons. After a break in presentation of four weeks, the concept will be thoroughly reviewed as part of the lesson for three to five days. This will be followed by a period of two months where the concept will be reviewed every two weeks as part of two or three lessons. This progression continues until the student(s) have had the opportunity to thoroughly master the concept.

AN EXAMPLE

Some mathematics curriculums might teach *graphs* for two weeks and not go back to it again. In this curriculum it will be introduced and practiced for two weeks. For the next two months, *graphs* will be presented every two weeks as a part of two or three lessons to give the student(s) continual practice to develop mastery of the concept. The third month will be considered a break from presenting the concept and *graphs* will not be taught. In the fourth month, *graphs* will first be thoroughly reviewed and again practiced every two weeks as a part of two or three lessons. By having a series of practices

every two weeks, the student(s) will retain what they have learned to a greater degree. Short periods of exposure repeated many times is much more effective than long periods with fewer exposures. Since there are three types of graphs to study at this level (bar, line, and pictograph), each type is introduced at separate intervals. The *bar graph* is taught at the introduction to the study. *Line graphs* are introduced a month later (following the same progression), and *pictographs* another month later. After each type of graph has been completely introduced individually, the three types are presented together for the remainder of the year. Review the chart on page 29 to see how the concepts are developed.

Readiness Evaluation

WHY EVALUATE READINESS?

Teaching could be defined as the process of starting with what a student knows and guiding him to added knowledge with new material. While this may not be a dictionary definition of teaching, it is descriptive of the processes involved. Determining a student's readiness for second grade mathematics is the first step to successful teaching.

TYPES OF READINESS

True readiness has little to do with chronological age. Emotional maturity and mental preparation are the main components of academic readiness. The teacher who is dealing directly with the student is best able to determine a child's emotional maturity. An emotionally immature student may need special student training in their problem areas. It might be wise, in this case, to delay placing them in the second grade until the next year. A child's mental *preparation* can be more easily discerned with a simple diagnostic evaluation. Observing the child's attitude of confidence or insecurity while taking the evaluation may help determine emotional readiness.

DETERMINING READINESS

The second grade *Readiness Evaluation* on pages 5–8 helps the teacher to determine if student(s) are ready to begin studying math at the second grade level. Complete this evaluation the first or second day of school. The evaluation should take about 30 minutes. It would be helpful to evaluate all of the students to determine what each student knows. However, you may want to evaluate only those student(s) who have not had a thorough first grade program. It is especially important to evaluate any student who is using this curriculum for the first time. The student(s) should be able to complete the test on their own with the teacher making sure they understand the directions for each individual activity.

The answer key is on page 4. Count each individual answer as a separate point except in *Student Activity Twelve* where only the numbers in the boxes, not the circled numbers, are counted. The total for the test is 100 points. The student should achieve a score of 70 or more points to be ready to begin second grade. Be sure to note the areas of weakness of each student, even those who have scored over 70 points. If the student(s) scored under 70 points, they may need to repeat first grade math or do some refresher work in their areas of weakness. For possible review of the identified areas of weakness, refer to the chart "Appearance of Concepts" on page 46 of the *Horizons Mathematics 1 Teacher's Guide*. It will locate lessons where the concepts were taught.

Readiness Evaluation Answer Key

1 Write the numbers.

452 has a ___2___ in the ones place.

918 has a ___9___ in the hundreds' place.

763 has a ___6___ in the tens' place.

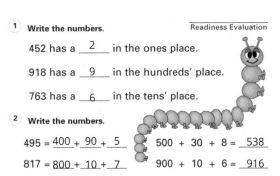

2 Write the numbers.

495 = _400_ + _90_ + _5_   500 + 30 + 8 = _538_

817 = _800_ + _10_ + _7_   900 + 10 + 6 = _916_

3 Write the correct time.

_5:00_   _6:45_   _3:30_   _10:15_

4 Write the value of each coin.

 10 ¢   25 ¢   25 ¢

 5 ¢   1 ¢   10 ¢

 1 ¢   5 ¢

        1 (one)   5

---

5 Add.

29	35	44	13	18	59	37	53
+33	+55	+29	+67	+33	+29	+87	+49
62	90	73	80	51	88	124	102
38	63	58	47	92	97	43	42
+88	+99	+42	+77	+19	+88	+27	+77
126	162	100	124	111	185	70	119

6 Write = or ≠ between each set.

3 + 7 = 10   7 + 9 = 16   5 + 9 ≠ 13

4 + 9 ≠ 12   5 + 3 ≠ 9   6 + 8 = 14

7 Draw a line to match the shape to its name.

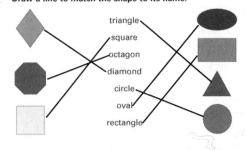

triangle
square
octagon
diamond
circle
oval
rectangle

2 (two)

---

8 Subtract.

11	16	17	12	15	13	11	13
- 9	- 8	- 7	- 6	- 8	- 7	- 3	- 6
2	8	10	6	7	6	8	7
12	14	17	11	15	13	18	16
- 5	- 8	- 8	- 4	- 7	- 4	- 9	- 8
7	6	9	7	8	9	9	8
68	99	72	33	78	55	57	78
-46	-35	-52	-20	-24	-43	-24	-27
22	64	20	13	54	12	33	51

9 Write the fractional part that is shaded.

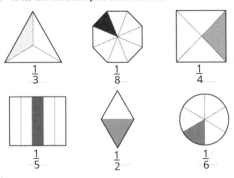

$\frac{1}{3}$ $\frac{1}{8}$ $\frac{1}{4}$

$\frac{1}{5}$ $\frac{1}{2}$ $\frac{1}{6}$

10 How many eggs are in a dozen? 12

3 (three)      7

---

11 Write < or > between each set.

135 < 144   116 < 173

173 > 167   183 < 200

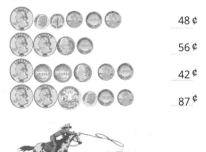

12 Circle every third number after 7.

⑦ 8 9 ⑩ 11 12 ⑬ 14 15

⑯ 17 18 ⑲ 20 21 ㉒ 23 24

㉕ 26 27 ㉘ 29 30 ㉛ 32 33

Write the circled numbers on the blanks.

7 10 13 16 19 22 25 28 31

13 Write the value of each set of coins.

 48 ¢

56 ¢

42 ¢

87 ¢

4 (four)

8

4

① Write the numbers.

452 has a _____ in the ones place.

918 has a _____ in the hundreds' place.

763 has a _____ in the tens' place.

② Write the numbers.

495 = ___+___+___

817 = ___+___+___

500 + 30 + 8 = _____

900 + 10 + 6 = _____

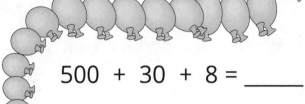

③ Write the correct time.

____ : ____   ____ : ____   ____ : ____   ____ : ____

④ Write the value of each coin.

 _____ ¢   _____ ¢   _____ ¢

 _____ ¢   _____ ¢   _____ ¢

 _____ ¢   _____ ¢

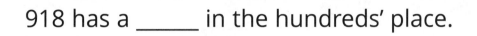
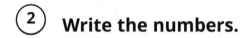

5 Add.

29	35	44	13	18	59	37	53
+33	+55	+29	+67	+33	+29	+87	+49

38	63	58	47	92	97	43	42
+88	+99	+42	+77	+19	+88	+27	+77

6 Write = or ≠ between each set.

3 + 7 _____ 10   7 + 9 _____ 16   5 + 9 _____ 13

4 + 9 _____ 12   5 + 3 _____ 9   6 + 8 _____ 14

7 Draw a line to match the shape to its name.

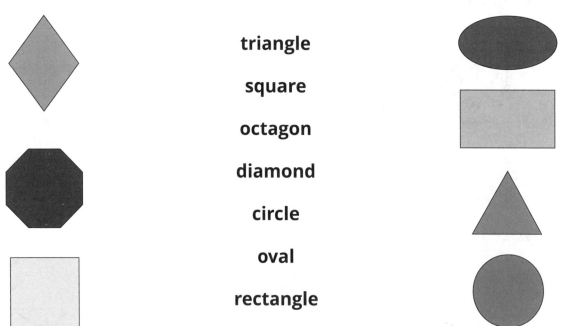

triangle

square

octagon

diamond

circle

oval

rectangle

2 (two)

6

8 Subtract.

11	16	17	12	15	13	11	13
- 9	- 8	- 7	- 6	- 8	- 7	- 3	- 6

12	14	17	11	15	13	18	16
- 5	- 8	- 8	- 4	- 7	- 4	- 9	- 8

68	99	72	33	78	55	57	78
-46	-35	-52	-20	-24	-43	-24	-27

9 Write the fractional part that is shaded.

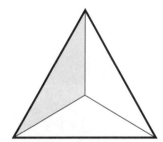
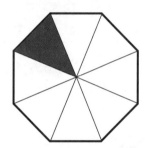
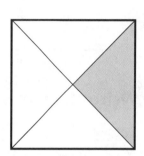

_____ _____ _____

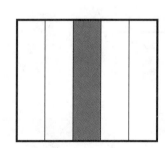
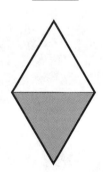
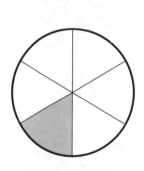

_____ _____ _____

10 How many eggs are in a dozen? _____

Write < or > between each set.

135 _____ 144   116 _____ 173

173 _____ 167   183 _____ 200

12 Circle every third number after 7.

⑦   8   9   10   11   12   13   14   15

16   17   18   19   20   21   22   23   24

25   26   27   28   29   30   31   32   33

Write the circled numbers on the blanks.

_____ _____ _____ _____ _____ _____ _____ _____ _____

13 Write the value of each set of coins.

_____ ¢

_____ ¢

_____ ¢

_____ ¢

4 (four)

Preparing a Lesson

GENERAL INFORMATION
There is some room on the teacher lessons for you to write your own notes. The more you personalize your teacher's guide in this way, the more useful it will be to you.

You will notice that there are 160 student lessons in the curriculum. This allows for the inevitable interruptions to the school year like holidays, test days, inclement weather days, and those unexpected interruptions. It also allows the teacher the opportunity to spend more time teaching any concept that the student(s) may have difficulty with. Or, you might wish to spend a day doing some of the fun activities mentioned in the Teaching Tips. If you find that the student(s) need extra drill, use the worksheets as extra lessons. There are no new concepts introduced after lesson 142. The last eighteen lessons reinforce by application the concepts presented throughout the year.

STUDENT'S LESSONS ORGANIZATION
The lessons are designed to be completed in thirty to thirty-five minutes a day. If extra manipulatives or worksheets are utilized, you will need to allow more time for teaching. Each lesson consists of a major concept and practice of previously taught concepts. If the student(s) find the presence of four or five different activities in one lesson a little overwhelming at the beginning, start guiding the student(s) through each activity. By the end of two weeks, they should be able to work more independently as they adjust to the format. Mastery of a new concept is not necessary the first time it is presented. Complete understanding of a new concept will come as the concept is approached from different views using different methods at different intervals. Because of the way the curriculum is designed, *the student(s) need to do all the problems in every lesson every day*. Directions to the student(s) are given in black type and examples or explanations are presented in blue type. If you expect to have very many students, you will find it extremely helpful to remove all pages from the individual student books and file them (all of Lesson 1 in one file, all of Lesson 2 in another file, etc.) before school starts. This will keep the lessons from being damaged or lost in the students' desks.

Tests
Starting with Lesson 10, tests are included in every tenth lesson. They should require approximately twenty minutes to administer. If your daily schedule time is a major factor, the student lesson may be completed the following day. This will require efficient

scheduling of the lessons throughout the year to complete the program by the end of the school year. The 16 tests and 160 lessons each administered or taught on separate days would bring the scheduled curriculum days to a total of 176.

Do not make the test a special lesson. Allow the student(s) to perceive the test as a regular lesson with no undue pressure. The purpose of testing is not just to measure student progress, although that is an important consideration. A test is also an important teaching tool. It should be returned to the student and any missed items discussed so that it is a true learning experience. For this reason, it is important to grade and return the tests as soon as possible while material is fresh in the student's mind.

The test structure is such that the student(s) will have had sufficient practice with a concept to have learned it before being tested. Therefore, no concept is tested until the initial presentation has been completed. For example, test 2 in lesson 20 covers concepts completed in lessons 6–15. Lessons 16–19 may include the introduction of some new material which will not be covered in test 2. Test 8 in lesson 80 will cover lessons 66–75. The new material from lessons 76–79 will not be covered in test 8.

TEACHER'S LESSONS ORGANIZATION

Each lesson is organized into the following sections: *Concepts*; *Objectives*; *Teaching Tips*; *Materials, Supplies, and Equipment*; *Activities*; *Worksheets*; and occasionally a maxim or proverb. Each of the sections have a distinct symbol to help you locate them on the page of the teacher's lesson. To be a master teacher you will need to prepare each lesson well in advance.

Concepts

Concepts are listed at the beginning of each lesson in the following order: 1.) Concepts taught by the teacher from the activities in the *Teacher's Guide* that do not have a corresponding written activity in the student lesson 2.) New concepts 3.) Concepts that are practiced from previous lessons (listed in the order they appear in the student lesson). Second grade math has twenty-one major concepts. These are developed in a progression that is designed to give the student(s) a solid foundation in the basic math skills while providing enough variety to hold the student's interest. Definitions are given for new terms.

Objectives

The Objectives list criteria for the student's performance. They state what the student should be able to do at the completion of the lesson. You will find objectives helpful in determining the student's progress, the need for remedial work, and readiness for more advanced information. Objectives are stated in terms of measurable student performance so that the teacher has a fixed level of performance to be attained before the student(s) are ready to progress to the next level.

Teaching Tips

Each tip is related to one of the Activities in the lesson. Some Teaching Tips require the teacher to make a manipulative needed to complete the activity. Teaching Tips are optional activities that the teacher can do to enhance the teaching process. You will find them useful for helping the student who needs additional practice to master the concepts or for the student who needs to be challenged by extra work.

Materials, Supplies, and Equipment

Materials, Supplies, and Equipment lists the things you'll need to find before you teach each lesson. Sometimes you will also find instructions on how to make your own materials, supplies, and equipment. When "Number Chart" is listed, it is understood to refer to the chart for 0–99. The number chart for 100–199 will state "Number Chart 100–199." A complete list of all manipulatives and where they are used starts on page 16.

Activities

The teacher's greatest concentration should be on the Activities section. Here the teacher will find step-by-step directions for teaching each lesson. All activities are designed to be teacher directed both in the student lesson and in the teacher's guide. You will need to use your own judgement concerning how much time is necessary to carry out the activities. Be sure, however, that the student(s) do every problem of every lesson. When the activity is part of the student lesson you will find it referred to as *Student Activity One, Student Activity Two,* etc. referring to the number in the circle on the student lesson. If the activity is not part of the student lesson there will be no bold face italic reference and the student will receive the activity from the teacher. Each activity is important to the over all scope of the lesson and must be completed.

Do not omit any portion of the activities unless the student(s) have thoroughly mastered the concept being presented. Please do not put off looking at the activities in the lesson until you are actually teaching. Taking time to preview what you will be teaching is essential. Choose the manipulatives that fit your program best.

Worksheets

There is approximately one worksheet for every two lessons. If worksheets are suggested in a particular lesson you will find them listed in the Worksheets section. Each worksheet has a worksheet number and the number of the lesson with which it is associated. Note that some worksheets will be used over and over as resources, so you'll need to keep a master copy. The *Teacher's Guide* identifies where these resource worksheets are essential to the lessons. All addition, subtraction, and multiplication drill sheets are included in the worksheets. If the Worksheet symbol is on the page, there is a worksheet associated with that lesson. The worksheets will be handy for many purposes. You might use them for extra work for student(s) who demonstrate extra aptitude or ability or as remedial work for the student(s) who demonstrate a lack of aptitude or ability.

You may also make your own worksheets and note where you would use them in the worksheet section on the teacher's lesson.

Maxims

In some lessons you will find a short maxim or proverb at the bottom of the right hand page. These maxims provide a collection of various wise and pithy sayings that deal with character. They are intended for the teacher to share and discuss with the student(s). Ask the student(s) to suggest ways that they could apply the maxim to their day-to-day activities of life. Have them think of a time when their friends may have put the maxim into practice. Tell them to watch for opportunities to practice the maxim in the next week and report the incident to you. You may use or not use them as you wish.

Lesson Summary

The curriculum will work best when you prepare in the following manner. First, note that the teacher's lesson has items that pertain to an overview of the lesson on the left-hand page. The details are on the right-hand page. It is suggested that you first look at the Concepts involved in the lesson. Then study the Objectives to get an idea of the tasks that the student(s) will need to perform to complete the lesson. Next, look at the Activities to get an idea of the presentation of the lesson. If you would like to view the student lessons, the complete student curriculum is included in reduced format in the answer key section. This presentation will allow you to see the whole student lesson in one place as well as all the answers at the same time. You will need more preparation for some of the activities that aren't in the student lessons. Some of the activities will refer to a worksheet which you will find listed in the Worksheet section below the Activities section. You might also want to check the Teaching Tips section for any additional ideas on presenting the lesson. Finally, check the Materials, Supplies, and Equipment for any resources that you may need before you begin the lesson.

ANSWER KEYS
The answer keys section of the *Teacher's Guide* provides answers to the student lessons (reduced so that there are four student pages on each answer key page and printed in black and white). It is suggested that you give the student(s) a grade for tests only. Daily work is to be a learning experience for the student, so do not put unnecessary pressure on them. You should correct every paper, but you should not grade every paper. This means that each lesson should be marked for correct

and incorrect answers, but it is not necessary to record a letter or percentage grade on every lesson. The lessons should then be returned to the student(s) so that they have the opportunity to learn from their mistakes.

WORKSHEETS
The next section contains the worksheets. Note that some worksheets will be used over and over as resources, so you will need to keep a master copy. Worksheets are reproducible and may be copied freely. You will find a complete listing of worksheets, where they are used, and which worksheets are used more than once on pages 20 and 21. Separate packets of all the necessary worksheets for an individual student are also available.

WORKSHEET ANSWER KEYS
Answer keys to the worksheets are provided in the same manner as for the student lessons and reduced so that there are four worksheets on each page of the answer key. The multiple use worksheets do not have answer keys since the answers will vary each time the worksheets are used.

1. COUNTING 1–999
(Recognition)

By 1's, 5's, 10's, 2's, 3's, 6's, 9's, 4's, 8's, and 7's
By 1's from 100–999
One-to-one correspondence
Even and odd numbers
Tally marks
Word numbers to 999
Roman numerals

2. SETS
(Count and Use)

Groups

3. NUMBER ORDER
(Recognition and Use)

Ordinal numbers to 100
The number that comes before and after a given number

4. ADDITION

Carrying in the 1's, 10's, and 100's columns
Two numbers single, double, triple, and four digit
Three numbers single, double, triple, and four digit
Four numbers single and double digit
Horizontal and vertical addition
Word problems
Word sentences
Equations

5. CORRESPONDENCE OF QUANTITIES
(Distinguish Between and Use)

Greater than and less than
Equal and not equal
Greater than, less than, and equal to

6. PLACE VALUE
(Digit Value)

Ones, tens, and hundreds
Thousands

7. SUBTRACTION

Borrowing in the 1's and 10's columns
Two numbers single, double, triple, and four digit
Horizontal and vertical subtraction
Word problems
Word sentences
Equations

8. TIME
(Read and Write)

Hour, half hour, and quarter hour
Five minutes
All times
Equivalents

9. FRACTIONS
(Meaning, Recognition, and Use)

Fractional part of whole
Fractional part of a set
Fraction words

10. MONEY
(Recognition, Value, and Use)

Penny, nickel, dime, and quarter
Half dollar
One, five, ten, and twenty dollar bills
Counting money
Adding, subtracting, and
multiplying money

11. SEQUENCE
(Create and Identify)

Numbers
Shapes
Objects
Events

12. MULTIPLICATION

Readiness
Multiplication facts for 0–10
Word problems

13. SHAPE
(Recognition and Characteristics)

Circle, square, triangle, rectangle,
  oval, diamond, octagon, pentagon,
  hexagon, sphere, cylinder, cube,
  cone, and pyramid
Symmetry

14. CALENDAR
(Memorize and Use)

Months of the year and abbreviations
Days of the week and abbreviations

15. GRAPHS
(Draw and Interpret)

Bar graphs, line graphs,
pictographs, and grids

16. MEASUREMENT
(Practice and Use)

Inches
Centimeters
Equivalents:
  English linear
  English weights
  English liquid
Dozen
Optical illusion
Map reading

17. TEMPERATURE
(Read and Interpret)

Fahrenheit thermometer

18. ESTIMATION
(Practice)

Rounding numbers
Height, length, and time

19. RATIO
(Write)

Comparison of two numbers

20. AREA, PERIMETER, AND VOLUME
(Calculate)

Area
Perimeter
Volume

21. DECIMALS
(Use)

Money

Manipulatives

Manipulative Name	Description	Used In Lesson
Books (5)	any size	130
Brad	one per student	21
Butter	lb.	127
Calendar	picture	54, 69, 70, 71, 73, 74, 126, 135
Clock model	large	18, 19, 20, 21, 22, 23, 24, 25, 26, 27, 28, 38, 39, 40, 42, 43, 44, 45, 46, 47, 48, 49, 62, 63, 72, 73, 74, 75, 76, 77, 88, 89, 101, 102, 103, 124, 125, 126, 135, 152, 153
Clock model	small	21, 22, 24, 25, 28, 38, 39, 40, 44, 45, 47, 48, 62, 63, 75, 88, 89, 90, 102, 103, 124, 152, 153
Cloth	½ yard of burlap or denim	7
Construction paper		21, 150
Counting chips	20 per student	2, 60, 71, 86, 91, 98, 127, 134, 135, 136, 159
Cubes	5	146, 147
Dictionary		98
Dowel rod	½ inch 12 inches long	7
Erasers		119, 129
Flannel board		107, 123, 149, 150, 152
Flannel board materials		107, 123, 149, 150, 152
Flashcards	addition facts	3, 4, 5, 6, 7, 8, 9, 10, 15, 20, 25, 30, 32, 34, 35, 37, 39, 40, 42, 44, 45, 47, 49, 50, 52, 54, 55, 57, 59, 60, 62, 63, 64, 65, 67, 69, 70, 72, 74, 75, 77, 79, 80, 82, 84, 85, 87, 89, 90, 91, 92, 94, 95, 97, 99, 100, 102, 104, 105, 107, 110, 112, 114, 115, 117, 119, 120, 122, 124, 125, 127, 129, 130, 132, 134, 135, 137, 139, 140, 142, 144, 145, 147, 149, 150, 152, 154, 155, 157, 159, 160

Manipulative Name	Description	Used In Lesson
Flashcards	days of the week	130, 132
Flashcards	English weight equivalents	151, 152, 155, 157
Flashcards	= and ≠ symbols	23, 24
Flashcards	< and > symbols	44
Flashcards	English linear equivalents	118, 152, 155, 157
Flashcards	English liquid equivalents	144, 152, 155, 157
Flashcards	months of the year	55, 117, 118
Flashcards	multiplication	61, 62, 63, 64, 65, 66, 67, 68, 69, 70, 71, 72, 73, 74, 75, 76, 77, 78, 79, 80, 81, 82, 83, 84, 85, 86, 87, 88, 89, 90, 91, 92, 93, 94, 95, 96, 97, 98, 99, 100, 101, 102, 103, 104, 105, 106, 107, 108, 110, 111, 112, 113, 114, 115, 116, 117, 118, 119, 120, 121, 122, 123, 124, 125, 126, 127, 128, 129, 130, 131, 132, 133, 134, 135, 136, 137, 138, 139, 140, 141, 142, 143, 144, 145, 146, 147, 148, 149, 150, 151, 152, 153, 154, 155, 156, 157, 158, 159, 160
Flashcards	ordinal numbers	1, 2, 3, 4, 5, 28, 29, 52
Flashcards	Roman numerals	93, 94, 95, 96, 108, 109, 122, 144, 145, 149, 150, 156, 157
Flashcards	shapes	93, 94, 95, 96, 97, 98, 99, 111, 112, 113, 124, 125, 126
Flashcards	solids	114, 115, 128, 140, 151
Flashcards	subtraction facts	16, 17, 18, 19, 20, 21, 22, 23, 24, 25, 26, 27, 28, 29, 30, 31, 33, 35, 36, 40, 41, 43, 45, 46, 48, 50, 51, 53, 55, 56, 58, 60, 61, 63, 65, 66, 68, 70, 71, 73, 75, 76, 78, 80, 81, 83, 85, 86, 88, 90, 91, 93, 95, 96, 98, 100, 101, 103, 105, 106, 108, 110, 111, 113, 115, 116, 118, 120, 121, 123, 125, 126, 128, 130, 131, 133, 135, 136, 138, 140, 141, 143, 145, 146, 148, 150, 151, 153, 155, 156, 158, 160

Manipulative Name	Description	Used In Lesson
Flashcards	tally marks	3, 4, 5, 6, 7, 23
Flashcards	time equivalents	85, 86, 87, 141, 143, 151, 152, 155, 157
Flashcards	word numbers	21, 24, 25, 26, 31, 32, 40, 41, 49, 50, 51, 65, 76
Flour	5 lbs.	127
Fraction materials		82, 83, 84, 85, 89, 90, 91, 103, 104, 113
Graph paper	½ sheet per student	157
Hanger	1 per student	7
Happy face stamp, stickers		13
Liquid measure containers	English	141, 142, 143
Magnetic strips	12 inches	133
Markers	3	130
Meter stick		121
Mirror		138
Multiplication chart		64, 66, 68, 69, 70, 72, 79, 80, 82, 86, 90, 91, 96, 97, 99, 100, 101, 102, 103, 105, 106, 110, 111, 114, 116, 119, 120, 121, 122, 123, 126, 138, 139
Newspaper	magazines or online sources	99, 110
8 1/2 x 11 plain paper		137, 138, 143
Note pads	2	119
Number chart	0–99	1, 2, 3, 4, 5, 6, 7, 8, 9, 10, 12, 13, 14, 15, 17, 18, 19, 22, 23, 24, 25, 26, 27, 28, 29, 30, 31, 32, 33, 34, 35, 36, 37, 38, 39, 40, 41, 42, 43, 44, 45, 55, 56, 57, 58, 59, 61, 62, 63, 64, 67, 68, 74, 76, 77, 85, 109, 113, 146
Number chart	100–199	16, 32, 54, 55, 56, 76, 77, 145
Number line		41, 43, 44
Paper plate	1 per student	21
Pencils or pens		119, 129

Manipulative Name	Description	Used In Lesson
Place value materials		5, 6, 7, 11, 12, 13, 14, 22, 26, 27, 28, 31, 33, 34, 35, 36, 37, 38, 39, 44, 45, 46, 47, 48, 50, 51, 52, 53, 54, 63, 65, 66, 67, 88, 91, 92, 93, 96, 97, 100, 112
Place Value Pockets		7, 31, 32, 33, 47, 97, 141
Play money		68, 69, 70, 71, 74, 75, 76, 82, 83, 84, 85, 87, 88, 90, 92, 93, 94, 95, 105, 106, 107, 108, 119, 127
Posterboard	6 sheets	1, 10, 99, 109, 133, 143, 157
Real money		75, 87
Rubber bands	2 dozen	5, 7, 36
Ruler	12 inch	58, 71, 114, 115, 116, 118, 129, 130, 131, 132, 133, 134, 135, 142
Ruler	30 cm	41, 42, 43, 120, 121, 123, 137, 144
Shoe box		146
Solid models		109, 110, 115, 116, 127, 128, 139, 140, 151, 156
Stickers		13
Straws	20 per student	5, 7, 36, 37, 44, 45
String	8 inches	135
Thermometer	Fahrenheit	142
Thermometer model		143, 144, 145, 153, 154, 155, 159, 160
Yardstick		32, 59, 70, 115, 116, 117

Where To Use
Mathematics Worksheets

*In this handbook you will find eighty worksheets to be used as **Duplication Masters.***

This chart shows where worksheets may be used.
You will need to **duplicate** any worksheet used more than once.

No.	Master Worksheet Name	Lessons Where Worksheets Are Used
1	Number chart 0–99	1, 2, 5, 8, 12, 13, 16, 18, 23, 28, 33, 38, 55
2	Ordinal numbers	3
3	Place value	5
4	Blank number chart	6
5	Number ladder	9
6	Addition drill sheet	11
7	Place value	13
8	Addition drill sheet	16
9	Counting over 100	17
10	Time (hour)	19
11	Addition drill sheet	21
12	Time	23
13	Addition drill sheet	26
14	Number ladder	27
15	Subtraction facts	29
16	Addition and subtraction drill sheet	31
17	Addition with carrying in tens' column	33
18	Addition and subtraction drill sheet	36
19	Place value	39
20	Addition and subtraction drill sheet	41
21	Time for 5 minutes	42
22	Time for 5 minutes	45
23	Addition and subtraction drill sheet	46
24	Addition with ones and tens double-digit answer	48
25	Blank clocks	49
26	Addition and subtraction drill sheet	51
27	Subtraction with borrowing	54
28	Addition and subtraction drill sheet	56
29	More and less	58
30	Addition and subtraction drill sheet	61
31	Multiplication chart	62
32	Missing addend	64
33	Addition and subtraction drill sheet	66
34	Sequences	68
35	Addition and subtraction drill sheet	71
36	Value of coins	74

20

Where To Use Mathematics Worksheets, continued:

No.	Master Worksheet Name	Lessons Where Worksheets Are Used
37	Addition and subtraction drill sheet	76
38	Multiplication by twos	77
39	Word number	79
40	Addition and subtraction drill sheet	81
41	Blank multiplication chart	82
42	Multiplication	84
43	Addition and subtraction drill sheet	86
44	Money (bills)	88
45	Addition and subtraction drill sheet	91
46	Shape sequence	92
47	Money	94
48	Addition and subtraction drill sheet	96
49	Multiplication of pairs	98
50	Bar graph	100
51	Addition and subtraction drill sheet	101
52	Fractions	103
53	Addition and subtraction drill sheet	106
54	Solve equations	107
55	Roman numerals	108
56	Addition, subtraction, and multiplication drill sheet	111
57	Inches	114
58	Addition, subtraction, and multiplication drill sheet	116
59	Solve equations	119
60	Addition, subtraction, and multiplication drill sheet	121
61	Pictograph	122
62	Centimeters	123
63	Addition, subtraction, and multiplication drill sheet	126
64	Fractions	127
65	Addition, subtraction, and multiplication drill sheet	131
66	Adding money	132
67	Fractions	135
68	Addition, subtraction, and multiplication drill sheet	136
69	Line of symmetry	139
70	Multiplication word problems	140
71	Addition, subtraction, and multiplication drill sheet	141
72	Shapes	142
73	Shapes	143
74	Addition, subtraction, and multiplication drill sheet	146
75	Cube pattern	146
76	Addition, subtraction, and multiplication drill sheet	151
77	Area	153
78	Multiplication	155
79	Addition, subtraction, and multiplication drill sheet	156
80	Map reading	159

APPEARANCE OF CONCEPTS

MATHEMATICS 2

1. **COUNTING**	**Appears in Lesson**
By 1's to 100	1, 2, 3
By 5's to 100	4, 5, 6, 66, 67, 68, 69, 70, 72, 73, 74
By 10's to 100	7, 8, 9
By 2's to 100	10, 11, 12, 76, 77, 78, 79, 80, 81, 82, 83, 84
By 3's to 36	13, 14, 15, 16, 17, 86, 87, 88, 89, 90, 91, 92, 93, 94
By 6's to 72	18, 19, 20, 21, 22, 96, 97, 98, 99, 100, 101, 102, 103, 104, 105
By 9's to 108	23, 24, 25, 26, 27, 106, 107, 108, 109, 110, 111, 112, 113, 114, 115
By 4's to 48	28, 29, 30, 31, 32, 117, 118, 119, 120, 121, 122, 123, 124, 125
By 8's to 98	33, 34, 35, 36, 37, 136, 137, 138, 139, 140, 141, 142, 143, 144, 145
By 7's to 84	38, 39, 40, 41, 42, 126, 127, 128, 129, 130, 131, 132, 133, 134, 135
Counting by 1's	
from 100–999	17, 29, 32, 33, 38, 54, 55, 56, 57, 58, 59, 60, 61, 62, 63, 64
One to one	
correspondence	1, 2, 3, 4, 5
Even and odd numbers	
even numbers	55, 67
odd numbers	56, 68
even and odd numbers	77, 78, 98, 113, 114
addition	86, 87, 99
Tally marks	3, 4, 5, 6, 7, 23
Word numbers	
0–100	21, 22, 24, 25, 26, 31, 32, 40, 41, 51, 52, 53, 54, 55, 60, 61, 62, 63, 66, 67, 68, 71, 72, 73, 79, 80, 81, 84, 85, 86, 96, 97, 99, 113, 114, 124, 136, 137
100–999	49, 50, 51, 65, 66, 76, 79, 148, 149
Roman numerals	92, 93, 94, 95, 96, 108, 109, 122, 123, 144, 145, 149, 150, 156, 157

2. **SETS**	
Groups	1, 2, 3, 4, 5,

3. **NUMBER ORDER**	
Ordinal numbers	1, 2, 3, 4, 5, 16, 17, 28, 29, 52, 53, 69, 117, 130
Before and after	
by 1's	1, 2, 3
by 5's	4, 5, 6
by 10's	7, 8, 9
by 2's	10, 12
by 3's	13, 14, 15, 16, 17
by 6's	18, 19, 20, 21, 22
by 9's	25, 26, 27

by 4's	30, 31, 32
by 8's	35, 36, 37
by 7's	40, 41, 42

4. Addition

Without carrying	
two numbers	
single digit	7, 8, 38, 39, 45, 46, 72, 80, 101, 106, 120
two numbers	
double digit	9, 40, 87
two numbers	
triple digit	10, 12, 15
two numbers	
four digit	11, 16
three numbers	
single digit	13
three numbers	
double digit	14
With carrying	
two numbers	
double digit	22, 23, 31, 32, 99
two numbers	
triple digit	24, 25, 33, 34, 35, 47, 48, 49, 50, 51, 52, 57, 58, 59, 60, 61, 62, 98, 130
two numbers	
four digit	26, 27, 37, 38, 39, 41, 53, 54, 55, 63, 64, 65, 66, 67, 68, 100, 101, 102, 103, 104, 106, 107, 108, 109, 110, 112, 113, 114, 115, 116, 123, 124, 125, 126, 129, 131, 132, 133, 135, 136, 139, 140
three numbers	
double digit	28, 29, 30, 73, 74, 75
three numbers	
triple digit	76, 77, 78, 79, 80, 81, 82, 83, 84, 91
three numbers	
four digit	86, 88, 143, 144, 146, 147, 148, 150, 151, 152
four numbers	
single digit	18, 19
four numbers	
double digit	154, 155, 156, 157, 158, 159
Horizontal and	
vertical addition	9, 19, 30, 50, 131
Word problems	21, 22, 23, 27, 28, 29, 31, 33, 34, 35, 43, 44, 45, 46, 47, 48, 49, 61, 62, 63, 71, 123, 147, 154, 159
Word sentences	51, 52, 53, 54, 55, 66, 67, 68, 79, 81, 85, 99, 113, 114, 124, 136, 137, 148, 149
Write own word problems	112, 125, 135, 136, 148, 160
Missing addends	61, 62, 63, 64, 69, 70, 71, 85, 88, 90, 91, 94, 95, 101, 102
Equations	107, 108, 109, 111, 119, 120, 121, 127, 128, 129, 139, 140, 141, 147, 148, 156

5. CORRESPONDENCE OF QUANTITIES

Greater than and less than	
number greater than	15, 16, 18
number less than	31, 32, 33
whole numbers	44, 57, 58, 59
multiplication facts	
and numerals	70, 107
compare money	83, 84, 85, 119
addition and	
subtraction facts	45, 46, 71, 72, 106, 120
compare equivalents	134
Equal and not equal	
addition and	
subtraction facts	24, 38, 39, 40, 52, 65, 101
multiplication fact and	
whole number	78
clock face and	
digital time	26, 51, 64, 77, 102
time equivalents	87
ordinal number	28
shapes with names	100, 126
word numbers with	
numerals	25, 66, 79
numerals with	
tally marks	23
fractions with	
shapes	91, 111, 113
Greater than, less than,	
and equal to	127, 137, 138, 141, 142, 143, 144, 147, 148, 153

6. PLACE VALUE

Ones, tens, and hundreds	5, 6, 7, 8, 9, 10
Thousands	11, 12, 13, 14, 15, 26, 27, 28, 39, 40, 41, 52, 53, 54, 65, 66, 67, 88, 89, 102, 103, 115, 116, 117, 128, 129

7. SUBTRACTION

Review without borrowing	
two numbers	
single digit	11, 17, 18, 19, 20, 23, 24, 25, 26, 27, 29, 30, 35, 40, 48, 52, 65, 71, 101, 106, 120
two numbers	
double digit	16, 17, 18, 19, 31, 33
two numbers	
triple digit	21, 22, 23, 24, 25
two numbers	
four digit	26, 27, 28, 29
Regrouping for borrowing	36, 37, 38, 39, 40, 41, 42, 43, 44, 45, 46, 47, 48, 91, 92, 93

25

Counting money	74, 83, 84, 85, 92, 93, 94, 95, 99, 105, 106, 107, 108
Addition and subtraction	118, 120, 131, 132, 145, 146, 147
Multiplication	119

11. SEQUENCE

Numbers	34, 35, 36, 43, 44, 45, 49, 50, 64, 65, 81, 82, 115, 116, 127, 128
Shapes	92, 93, 94, 152
Objects	67, 68, 69, 139, 140
Events	137, 138, 140, 147, 148, 149, 157, 158

12. MULTIPLICATION

Readiness	56, 57, 58, 59, 60, 63, 66, 67, 76, 77, 78, 86, 87, 88, 89, 96, 97, 98, 106, 107, 108, 109, 116, 117, 118, 119, 120, 126, 127, 136
Facts:	
0, 1	61, 62
0, 1, 10	64, 65
0, 1, 10, 5	68, 69, 70, 72, 73, 74, 76, 78
0, 1, 10, 5, 2	79, 80, 81, 82, 83, 86
0, 1, 10, 5, 2, 3	90, 91, 92, 93, 94
0, 1, 10, 5, 2, 3, 6	99, 100, 101, 102, 103, 104, 105
0, 1, 10, 5, 2, 3, 6, 9	107, 110, 111, 112, 113, 114, 115
0, 1, 10, 5, 2, 3, 6, 9, 4	120, 121, 122, 123, 124, 125
0, 1, 10, 5, 2, 3, 6, 9, 4, 8	128, 129, 130, 131, 132, 133, 134, 135, 137
0, 1, 10, 5, 2, 3, 6, 9, 4, 8, 7	138, 139, 140, 143, 145, 146, 147, 148, 149, 150, 151, 152, 153, 154, 156, 157
Missing fact	158, 159
Word problems	
visualized	104, 105, 106, 116
not visualized	117, 118, 128, 129, 130, 131, 141, 152, 158

13. SHAPES

Review	
7 shapes	93, 94, 95, 96, 97, 111, 112, 113,
9 new shapes	97, 98, 99, 100, 124, 125, 126, 142, 143
Symmetry	137, 138, 139, 140, 149, 150
Geosheet	142, 143
Solids	109, 110, 114, 115, 116, 127, 128, 139, 140, 151, 153, 154, 156

14. CALENDAR

Months of the year and abbreviations	54, 55, 56, 117, 118, 119
Days in the week and abbreviations	69, 70, 71, 130, 132
"Thirty Days Hath September"	117, 118, 119

15. **GRAPHS**	
Bar graphs	98, 99, 100, 141, 156
Line graphs	109, 110, 111, 112, 118, 119, 142, 155
Pictographs	121, 122, 127, 128, 133, 134, 143, 157
Grids	144, 145, 150, 151, 156, 157

16. **MEASUREMENT**	
Inches	
whole	114
half	115, 116, 117, 118
quarter	129, 131, 132, 133, 134, 142, 143
Centimeters	120, 121, 122, 123, 130, 137, 144
English linear equivalents	116, 117, 131, 152, 155, 157, 158, 160
English weights equivalents	126, 127, 134, 151, 152, 155, 157, 158, 160
English liquid equivalents	141, 142, 143, 144, 152, 155, 157, 158, 160
Dozen	153
Optical illusion	132
Map reading	46, 159, 160

17. **TEMPERATURE**	
Fahrenheit thermometer	142, 143, 144, 145, 153, 154, 155, 159, 160

18. **ESTIMATION**	
	41, 42, 43, 44, 46, 47, 48, 58, 59, 70, 71, 84, 85, 109, 121, 122, 126, 133, 134, 145, 146

19. **RATIO**	
Compare two sets	105, 106, 107, 117, 118, 119, 129, 130, 138, 139, 150, 151

20. **AREA, PERIMETER, AND VOLUME**	
Area	131, 132, 133, 141, 142, 153
Perimeter	135, 136, 137, 138, 144, 154
Volume	146, 147, 148, 155

21. **DECIMALS**	
Money	131, 132, 145, 146, 147

Development of Concepts

GENERAL PATTERN:

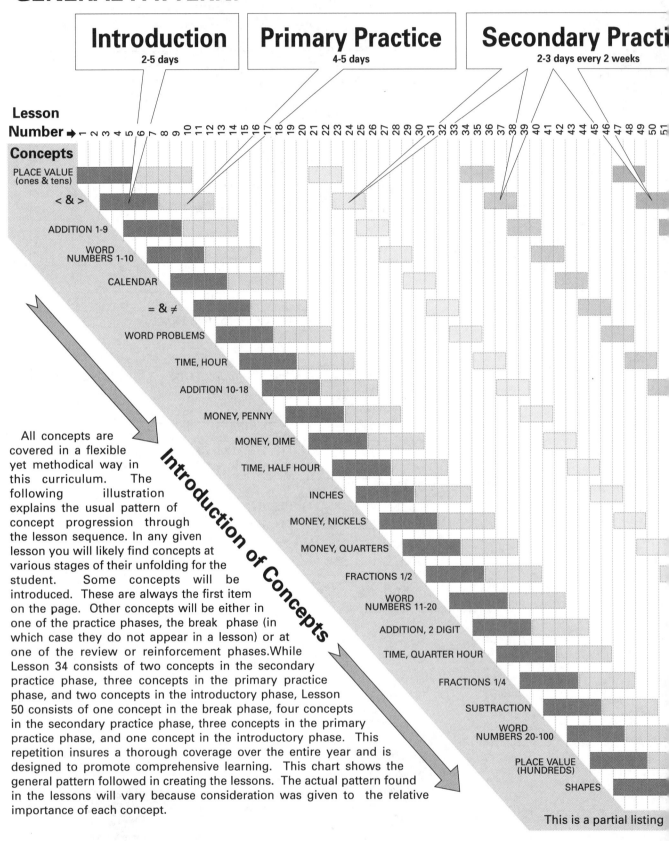

Introduction	Primary Practice	Secondary Practi
2-5 days	4-5 days	2-3 days every 2 weeks

Lesson Number → 1 2 3 4 5 6 7 8 9 10 11 12 13 14 15 16 17 18 19 20 21 22 23 24 25 26 27 28 29 30 31 32 33 34 35 36 37 38 39 40 41 42 43 44 45 46 47 48 49 50 51

Concepts

PLACE VALUE (ones & tens)
< & >
ADDITION 1-9
WORD NUMBERS 1-10
CALENDAR
= & ≠
WORD PROBLEMS
TIME, HOUR
ADDITION 10-18
MONEY, PENNY
MONEY, DIME
TIME, HALF HOUR
INCHES
MONEY, NICKELS
MONEY, QUARTERS
FRACTIONS 1/2
WORD NUMBERS 11-20
ADDITION, 2 DIGIT
TIME, QUARTER HOUR
FRACTIONS 1/4
SUBTRACTION
WORD NUMBERS 20-100
PLACE VALUE (HUNDREDS)
SHAPES

Introduction of Concepts

All concepts are covered in a flexible yet methodical way in this curriculum. The following illustration explains the usual pattern of concept progression through the lesson sequence. In any given lesson you will likely find concepts at various stages of their unfolding for the student. Some concepts will be introduced. These are always the first item on the page. Other concepts will be either in one of the practice phases, the break phase (in which case they do not appear in a lesson) or at one of the review or reinforcement phases. While Lesson 34 consists of two concepts in the secondary practice phase, three concepts in the primary practice phase, and two concepts in the introductory phase, Lesson 50 consists of one concept in the break phase, four concepts in the secondary practice phase, three concepts in the primary practice phase, and one concept in the introductory phase. This repetition insures a thorough coverage over the entire year and is designed to promote comprehensive learning. This chart shows the general pattern followed in creating the lessons. The actual pattern found in the lessons will vary because consideration was given to the relative importance of each concept.

This is a partial listing

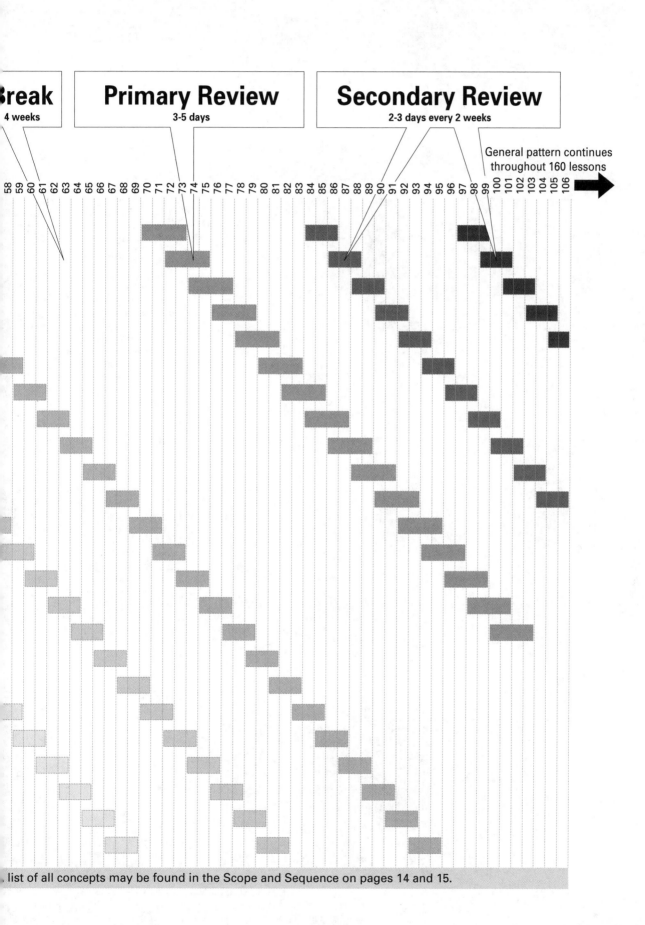

Break
4 weeks

Primary Review
3-5 days

Secondary Review
2-3 days every 2 weeks

General pattern continues
throughout 160 lessons

list of all concepts may be found in the Scope and Sequence on pages 14 and 15.

Lessons

Lesson 1

Concepts:

Counting by ones, sets, one-to-one correspondence, the number that comes before and after by ones, and ordinal numbers

Definitions: Cardinal numbers are counting numbers.

Ordinal numbers are numbers that show order like first, second, third, and fourth.

Objectives:

1. The student shall be able to count out loud by ones to 100.
2. The student shall be able to correctly count the objects in a given set and write the number.
3. The student shall be able to write the missing numbers from 0 to 49.
4. The student shall be able to write the numbers that come before and after a given number when counting by ones.
5. The student shall be able to correctly place a set of letters, numbered ordinally, on blanks corresponding to the appropriate ordinal numbers.
6. The student shall be able to draw a circle around the larger of two given numbers.

Teaching Tips:

1. The student(s) will be using *Worksheet 1* several times throughout the year. Have the student(s) place it in a folder to keep in their desks for easy access. Or you may want to collect the worksheet each time and hand it to the student(s) as the need arises. Be sure to keep the master copy for later use.

Materials, Supplies, & Equipment:

1. Number chart 0–99

2. Flashcards for ordinal numbers

3. Posterboard

Note: For a complete listing of materials and where they are used in the curriculum, see page 16 in the introduction.

Activities:

1. Have the student(s) count to 100 using the *number chart* if necessary. Remind them that the numbers used in counting are called cardinal numbers.

2. Have the student(s) read the directions for **Student Activity One**. Count out loud, together, each of the objects in the first set. They should be able to count the remaining sets by themselves.

3. Ask the student(s) to write the numbers 0–10 on a clean sheet of paper. Check each number to see that it is correctly formed. When the student(s) can form the numbers 0–10 correctly, let them complete **Student Activity Two** on their own using a *number chart* only if needed.

4. Using the *number chart*, point to several numbers and have the student(s) tell the number that comes before and after each number. Remind them that the number that comes before is one less, one taken away, or one subtracted from the given number. The number that comes after is one more, plus one, or one added to the given number. *Worksheet 1* may be used by the student(s) for **Student Activity Three**.

5. Have the student(s) read and spell the words on both sides (first, 1st) of the *flashcards for ordinal numbers* 1–10. Notice the spelling for the words "fifth" ("ve" changed to "f") and "ninth" (the "e" has been dropped). After putting the flashcards out of order, place the card that says "first" on the board rail. Ask a student to choose the next card that should be placed on the board rail to put them in order. Continue in the same way until all the cards have been arranged in correct order. Have the student(s) point to the first ordinal number in **Student Activity Four**. Have them point to the second blank and tell you what letter should be placed on that blank (E). Continue helping those who need it until all blanks have been filled.

6. Since this may be the first time many student(s) have worked a cross-number puzzle, make a large copy of the puzzle in **Student Activity Five** on *posterboard* or on the board before class time. Have the student(s) read "1 across" and tell the answer. Write the answer for "1 across" on your cross-number puzzle as a guide for the student(s) to follow. The *number chart* may be useful. Complete the puzzle in the same manner.

7. After doing the first two sets of numbers with the student(s) in **Student Activity Six**, they should be able to continue without further help.

Worksheet:

1. *Worksheet 1* – Number chart 0–99

Lesson 2

Concepts:
  Counting by ones, before and after by ones, ordinal numbers, sets, and one-to-one correspondence

Objectives:
  1. The student shall be able to count out loud by ones to 100.

  2. The student shall be able to draw a circle around the smaller of two given numbers.

  3. The student shall be able to write the missing numbers from 50 to 99.

  4. The student shall be able to write the numbers that come before and after a given number when counting by ones.

  5. The student shall be able to draw a line to match a written ordinal number to the corresponding abbreviated form of the ordinal number.

  6. The student shall be able to correctly count the objects in a given set and write the number.

Teaching Tips:
  1. When doing activity 6, discuss with the student(s) the different places they have seen and used ordinal numbers and their abbreviations. Suggest the newspaper, street signs, grades, names of companies, names of churches, and anniversaries.

Materials, Supplies, & Equipment:
  1. Number chart 0–99

  2. Flashcards for ordinal numbers

  3. Counting chips

Activities:

1. Count out loud with the student(s) from 1 to 100 without the use of the *number chart*.

2. The student(s) should be able to complete **Student Activity One** independently once they have found the starting point at the number "1." Make the *number chart* available for those who need it. You may want to give the student(s) time to color the picture after completing the entire lesson.

3. After discussing the directions, the student(s) should be able to complete **Student Activity Two** on their own.

4. Allow the student(s) to complete **Student Activity Three** using *Worksheet 1* only if necessary.

5. Using the *number chart*, point to several numbers and have the student(s) tell the number that is one less and the number that is one more than each number. Discuss with them how the number that comes before is one less than the given number and the number that comes after is one more than the given number. *Worksheet 1* may be used by the student(s) in completing **Student Activity Four** if needed.

6. Using the *flashcards for ordinal numbers*, drill 1–10 and discuss with the student(s) the abbreviated form of ordinal numbers. Remind them of the difference between cardinal numbers (counting numbers) and ordinal numbers (order or which one). Together, read out loud the directions and each of the ordinal numbers in **Student Activity Five**. Instruct the student(s) to draw the necessary lines without further help.

7. Have the student(s) count 15 *counting chips* and then several other sets at their desk. Remind them to say only one number as they point to each chip. Allow the student(s) to count each set in **Student Activity Six** by themselves. If any of them have a difficult time keeping the counting of objects clear in their minds, have them draw a line through each object as they count off the numbers to themselves.

Worksheet:

1. *Worksheet 1* – Number chart 0–99

Since courtesy is contagious, we need a good epidemic.

Lesson 3

Concepts:
 Counting by ones, tally marks, before and after by ones, ordinal numbers, sets, and one-to-one correspondence

Objectives:
 1. The student shall be able to count out loud by ones to 100.

 2. The student shall be able to make a tally mark for each given object.

 3. The student shall be able to write the number that is one more or one less than a given number.

 4. The student shall be able to correctly place a set of letters, numbered ordinally, on blanks corresponding to the appropriate ordinal numbers.

 5. The student shall be able to circle a given number of objects.

 6. The student shall be able to correctly arrange a given set of numbers in the proper sequence.

Teaching Tips:
 1. When doing activity 6, discuss with the student(s) the difference between ordinal numbers and cardinal numbers. Ordinal numbers tell which one. Cardinal numbers or counting numbers tell how many. Say several ordinal and cardinal numbers and have the student(s) tell if they show which one or how many.

Materials, Supplies, & Equipment:
 1. Flashcards for addition facts, tally marks, and ordinal numbers

 2. Number chart 0–99

Activities:

1. Count out loud with the student(s) from 1 to 100 without the use of the *number chart*.

2. Using *flashcards for addition facts*, drill 1–18 with the answers showing to give the student(s) an accurate review. These would include sums that total 18 or less. After the next two lessons, the drill will be done without the answers showing.

3. Review with the student(s) how to make tally marks for one through ten. Remind them to make one mark for each object in the set. Pay special attention to the tally marks for five and ten. *Tally mark flashcards* may be a help. After reading the directions for **Student Activity One**, complete the first three tally marks together. With the tally marks for one through ten on the board, the student(s) should complete the activity on their own.

4. Discuss with the student(s) the meaning of "the number that comes after" (one more, plus one, or one added). Point to several numbers on the *number chart* and have the student(s) tell the number that is one more. With the aid of the *number chart*, they should be able to complete **Student Activity Two** by themselves.

5. Discuss with the student(s) the meaning of "the number that comes before" (one less, one taken away, or one subtracted). Point to several numbers on the *number chart* and have the student(s) tell the number that is one less. With the aid of the *number chart*, they should be able to complete **Student Activity Three** independently.

6. Have the student(s) read and spell the words on both sides (first, 1st) of the *flashcards for ordinal numbers* 10–20. Notice the spelling of the word "twelfth" ("ve" changed to "f" as in five and fifth). Have the student(s) say the first ordinal number in **Student Activity Four**. Have them point to the seventeenth blank and tell you what letter should be placed on that blank (E). Continue helping those who need help until all blanks have been filled.

7. Read the directions for **Student Activity Five** with the student(s). They should be able to finish drawing one circle around each set without further help.

8. After reading the directions, have the student(s) choose the smallest number listed in **Student Activity Six** and make an "X" on that number. Then write the number on the first blank. Now the student(s) need to choose the next smallest number listed, make an "X" on that number, and write the number on the second blank. The "X's" will enable the student(s) to know what numbers they have used. Continue with the same procedure until the student(s) can proceed on their own.

Worksheet:

1. *Worksheet 2* – Ordinal numbers

Lesson 4

Concepts:
>   Counting by fives, tally marks, ordinal numbers, before and after by fives, sets, and one-to-one correspondence

Objectives:
1. The student shall be able to count out loud by fives to 100.

2. The student shall be able to make tally marks for each given number.

3. The student shall be able to draw a line to match a written ordinal number to the corresponding abbreviated form of the ordinal number.

4. The student shall be able to write the numbers that come before and after a given number when counting by fives.

5. The student shall be able to correctly arrange a given set of numbers in the proper sequence.

6. The student shall be able to circle a given number of objects.

7. The student shall be able to write the missing numbers when counting by ones and by fives.

Teaching Tips:
1. As another method of doing activity 6, find the smallest number (23). Then have the student(s) find all the numbers that are in the thirties and arrange them in correct order. Find all the numbers that are in the forties and arrange them in correct order. Follow the same procedure with the fifties.

Materials, Supplies, & Equipment:
1. Number chart 0–99

2. Flashcards for addition facts, tally marks, and ordinal numbers

Activities:

1. Count out loud with the student(s) by fives to 100 using the *number chart*.

2. Using *flashcards for addition facts*, drill sums 1–18 with the answers showing to give the student(s) an accurate review. After the next lesson, the drill will be done without the answers showing.

3. Discuss with the student(s) the procedure used in making tally marks for the numbers from ten to twenty (e.g., eleven would be 2 groups of five plus 1 mark). *Tally mark flashcards* may be a help (tally marks on one side and numerals on the other side). Write the number "18" on the board. Allow the student(s) to tell how to make the tally marks for 18 (3 groups of 5 plus 3 marks). Continue to make the tally marks for the numbers to 20. Allow the student(s) to complete **Student Activity One** on their own but provide help where needed.

4. Have the student(s) read the *ordinal number flashcards* 10–20. This should be done out loud and together. Read the instructions for **Student Activity Two** to the student(s). They should be able to complete the activity without any further help.

5. Point to several multiples of five on the *number chart* as you discuss the meaning of "the number that comes before by fives" (five less, five taken away, or five subtracted) and "the number that comes after by fives" (five more, plus five, or five added). With the aid of the *number chart*, the student(s) should be able to complete **Student Activity Three** independently.

6. To begin **Student Activity Four**, read the directions and have the student(s) find the smallest number to write on the first blank. They should be able to complete the activity without further help.

7. After making sure that the student(s) understand the directions, they should be able to complete **Student Activity Five**, **Six**, and **Seven** by themselves. Allow the student(s) to refer to the *number chart* if necessary.

It is a grand person who can laugh at himself with others and enjoy it as much as they do.

Lesson 5

Concepts:
Counting by fives, place value, tally marks, ordinal numbers, before and after by fives, sets, and one-to-one correspondence

Objectives:
1. The student shall be able to count out loud by fives to 100.

2. The student shall be able to write the correct number for a given set of place value blocks made of hundreds, tens, and ones.

3. The student shall be able to draw a line to match a given set of tally marks with their corresponding numbers.

4. The student shall be able to write the abbreviated form for the given ordinal numbers.

5. The student shall be able to write the numbers that come before and after a given number when counting by fives.

6. The student shall be able to draw an object a given number of times.

Teaching Tips:
1. If *place value materials* are not available for activity 3, you may use several groups of ten *straws* with *rubber bands* around them for tens. For the one hundreds, take ten groups of ten and put a large *rubber band* around them. Use single *straws* for the ones.

Materials, Supplies, & Equipment:

1. Flashcards for addition facts, tally marks, and ordinal numbers

2. Place value materials

3. Number chart 0–99

4. Straws and rubber bands

Activities:

1. Count out loud with the student(s) by fives to 100 without using the *number chart*.

2. Using *flashcards for addition facts*, drill sums 1–18 with the answers showing to give the student(s) an accurate review. This is the last lesson the drill will be done with the answers showing.

3. Illustrate a three-digit number (364) using *place value materials* for hundreds, tens, and ones. Have the student(s) tell the number that has been illustrated by counting the hundreds by 100's, counting the tens by 10's, and counting the ones by 1's (e.g., 100, 200, 300, 310, 320, 330, 340, 350, 360, 361, 362, 363, 364). Do several illustrations of three-digit numbers in this manner. With the student(s), write the value of the first set of place value blocks in **Student Activity One**. Allow them to complete the remaining sets of place value blocks on their own.

4. Using several different combinations of *tally mark flashcards* (e.g., the ten card, the five card, and the three card to represent 18), have the student(s) count by fives and ones to determine the number corresponding to the tally marks (count 5, 10, 15, 16, 17, 18). Count the first three sets of tally marks in **Student Activity Two** together and have the student(s) match the tally marks to the correct numbers. The student(s) should be able to count and match the remaining tally marks by themselves.

5. Show the student(s) the *ordinal number flashcards* and have them write the shortened form (abbreviation) for each number on a sheet of paper. Turn the *flashcards* over to enable the student(s) to check their answers. **Student Activity Three** should be completed by the student(s) without further help.

6. Using the *number chart*, point to several multiples of five. Have the student(s) tell the number that is five less and the number that is five more than each number. Remind them that "before" and "after" means to subtract and to add. The student(s) should be able to complete **Student Activity Four** independently using *Worksheet 1* if needed.

7. After reading the directions together, the student(s) should be able to complete **Student Activity Five** on their own.

Worksheets:

1. *Worksheet 3* – Place value

2. *Worksheet 1* – Number chart 0–99

Lesson 6

Concepts:
Counting by fives, place value, before and after by fives, and tally marks

Objectives:

1. The student shall be able to count out loud by fives to 100.

2. The student shall be able to write the value of a given number of ones, tens, and hundreds.

3. When given three numbers, the student shall be able to circle the number that is greatest.

4. The student shall be able to write the number that is five more or five less than a given number.

5. The student shall be able to write the correct number for a given set of tally marks.

6. The student shall be able to correctly arrange a given set of numbers in the proper sequence.

Teaching Tips:

1. When doing activity 1, have the student(s) fill in the missing numbers on *Worksheet 4* and circle the numbers used when counting by fives. Tell them to write the numbers used in counting by fives in sequence at the bottom of the worksheet.

Materials, Supplies, & Equipment:

1. Flashcards for addition facts and tally marks

2. Place value materials

3. Number chart 0–99

Activities:

1. Count out loud with the student(s) by fives to 100 without using the *number chart*.

2. Using *flashcards for addition facts*, drill sums 1–18 without the answers showing. The addition facts will be drilled for five lessons without the answers showing. Then the drill will be done using drill sheets from the worksheets.

3. Using *place value materials*, demonstrate for the student(s) that 4 tens equal 10 + 10 + 10 + 10. To find the value of 4 tens, count 10, 20, 30, 40. 4 tens equal 40. Ask the student(s) what 6 tens equal, 3 tens, 8 tens, etc. Follow the same procedure for 5 hundreds (5 hundreds equal 100 + 100 + 100 + 100 + 100). Have the student(s) tell the first answer of each column in **Student Activity One** together. They should be able to complete the activity alone.

4. Write several sets of three numbers (26, 28, 24) on the board. Ask the student(s) to choose the number that is the largest and the number that is the smallest. Then have them arrange the three numbers in sequence. Read the directions for **Student Activity Two** with the student(s). They should be able to complete the activity by themselves.

5. Point to several multiples of five on the *number chart* and have the student(s) tell the number that is five less and five more. Allow the student(s) to use a *number chart* if necessary when completing **Student Activity Three** and **Four**.

6. Using several different combinations of *tally mark flashcards*, have the student(s) count by fives and ones to determine the number corresponding to the tally marks. After counting the first set of tally marks in **Student Activity Five** with the student(s), they should be able to complete the activity independently.

7. Ask the student(s) to read the directions and look at the first row of numbers in **Student Activity Six**. They need to find the smallest number, put an "X" on it and write the number on the first blank. Now the student(s) need to choose the next smallest number listed, make an "X" on that number, and write the number on the second blank. Continue with the same procedure until the student(s) can proceed on their own.

8. The student(s) should be able to complete **Student Activity Seven** without assistance.

Worksheet:

1. *Worksheet 4* – Blank number chart

Lesson 7

Concepts:

Counting by tens, place value, tally marks, before and after by tens, and addition

Objectives:

1. The student shall be able to count out loud by tens to 100.

2. The student shall be able to write the value of a given number of hundreds, tens, and ones as a sum and the number it represents.

3. The student shall be able to write the correct tally marks for each given number.

4. The student shall be able to write the numbers that come before and after a given number when counting by tens.

5. The student shall be able to write the correct letter above a corresponding number that is the answer to an addition fact.

6. When given three numbers, the student shall be able to circle the number that is greatest.

7. The student shall be able to correctly arrange a given set of numbers in the proper sequence.

Teaching Tips:

1. Here are instructions for making *Place Value Pockets* for activity 3. On a heavy piece of 20" x 10" burlap or denim, sew three rows of three pockets each using three 5" x 10" strips of material (hemmed on one 10" side). Leave the extra length at the top to fold over a *hanger* or *½" wooden dowel* and stitch. Hem the other three edges. Label the first column of three pockets on the left "hundreds," the next "tens," and the right hand column "ones." Use single *craft sticks* or *straws* in the pockets for ones, ten *rubber banded* together for tens, and ten groups of ten *rubber banded* together for hundreds. This aid may also be used when teaching carrying and borrowing.

Materials, Supplies, & Equipment:

1. Flashcards for addition facts and tally marks

2. Place value materials

3. Number chart 0–99

4. Place Value Pockets – cloth material 35" x 10", hanger or ½" wooden dowel, craft sticks or straws, and rubber bands

44

Activities:

1. Count out loud with the student(s) by tens to 100 using the *number chart*.

2. Using *flashcards for addition facts*, drill sums 1–18 without the answers showing. The addition facts will be drilled for three more lessons without the answers showing. Then the drill will be done using drill sheets from the worksheets.

3. Write "3 hundreds + 8 tens + 6 ones = ____ + ____ + ____ + = _____" on the board. Use *place value materials* to aid the student(s) as they tell the value of each place and the number represented (300 + 80 + 6 = 386). Do this for several other groups of hundreds, tens, and ones. As the student(s) complete **Student Activity One**, check to see that they are not making any repetitious mistakes.

4. Have the student(s) choose the necessary *tally mark flashcards* needed to represent several given numbers. If the first number is 27 guide them in choosing the twenty, five, and two cards (count by fives to the largest number without going over 27 and then count by ones). Use the *number chart* as an aid for the student(s) to see that 27 is two more than 25. Complete the first two numbers in **Student Activity Two** with the student(s) before allowing them to finish on their own.

5. Point to several multiples of ten on the *number chart* as you discuss the meaning of "the number that comes before by tens" (ten less, ten taken away, or ten subtracted) and "the number that comes after by tens" (ten more, plus ten, or ten added). With the aid of the *number chart*, the student(s) should be able to complete **Student Activity Three** independently.

6. To decode the message in **Student Activity Four**, the student(s) must solve the addition fact and put the letter associated with the fact on the blank that has the sum beneath it. Have the student(s) look at the first addition fact (3 + 5) and write the sum beside it (8). Ask them what letter they will put on the blank above the number 8 (N). Then ask them what (7 + 6) equals and write the sum beside it (13). Have the student(s) tell what letter they will put on the blank above the number 13 (E). Allow them to complete the activity on their own if they are capable.

7. The student(s) should be able to complete **Student Activity Five** and **Six** independently.

Lesson 8

Concepts:
>Counting by tens, place value, before and after by tens, and addition

Objectives:
1. The student shall be able to count out loud by tens to 100.

2. The student shall be able to write the number of hundreds, tens, and ones in a given number and write their value as a sum.

3. The student shall be able to write the numbers that come before and after a given number when counting by tens.

4. When given three numbers, the student shall be able to circle the number that is least.

5. When given three digits, the student shall be able to write the smallest triple-digit number possible.

6. The student shall be able to write the correct answer for addition problems of two single-digit numbers.

Teaching Tips:
1. For variety when introducing ***Student Activity One***, write "638 = 6 _____ + 3 _____ + 8 _____" on the board. Have the student(s) tell where to write the words "hundreds," "tens," and "ones." Then have them tell the value of 6 hundreds, 3 tens, and 8 ones. Discuss with them what digit is in the hundreds' place, tens' place, and ones' place. Then name the digit and have the student(s) tell if it is in the hundreds', tens', or ones' place.

Materials, Supplies, & Equipment:
1. Flashcards for addition facts

2. Number chart 0–99

Activities:

1. Count out loud with the student(s) by tens to 100 without using the *number chart*.

2. Using *flashcards for addition facts*, drill sums 1–18 without the answers showing. The addition facts will be drilled on a daily basis for two more lessons without the answers showing. Then the drill will be done using drill sheets on the worksheets and flashcards.

3. Write "473 = ___ hundreds + ___ tens + ___ ones = ___ + ___ + ___" on the board. Ask the student(s) how many hundreds, tens, and ones are in 473. Write the numbers in the blanks. Then ask them what the value of the hundreds', tens', and ones' digit is. Do several more examples like this on the board. The student(s) should then be able to complete **Student Activity One** on their own after they do the first set of blanks together.

4. Using the *number chart*, point to several multiples of ten. Have the student(s) tell the number that is ten less and ten more than each number. Remind them that "before" and "after" means to subtract and to add. The student(s) should be able to do **Student Activity Two** independently using *Worksheet 1* if needed.

5. Write several sets of three double-digit numbers (43, 47, 41) on the board. Ask the student(s) to choose the number that is the greatest and the number that is the least. Explain that the number that is least is the number that is smallest. Then have them arrange the three numbers in sequence. Read the directions for **Student Activity Three** with the student(s). They should be able to complete the activity by themselves.

6. Write three single-digit numbers on the board (4, 2, 7). Ask the student(s) to see how many different three-digit numbers they can make from the given numbers (427, 472, 274, 247, 724, 742). Have them choose the smallest number (247). Discuss the relationship of the value of each digit (smallest to largest). Ask "How do you find the smallest number possible using the three digits?" (Arrange the digits smallest to largest.) Put several other sets of three single-digit numbers on the board (include the zero which must be the second digit not the first) and allow the student(s) to tell the smallest three-digit number they can make. After finding the first two numbers in **Student Activity Four**, allow the student(s) to finish without any further help.

7. Use **Student Activity Five** as a quick check to see which student(s) have not mastered their addition facts and may need some further drill on an individual basis.

Worksheet:

1. *Worksheet 1* – Number chart 0–99

Lesson 9

Concepts:
>   Counting by tens, place value, before and after by tens, and addition (horizontal to vertical)

Objectives:
1. The student shall be able to count out loud by tens to 100.

2. The student shall be able to write the correct number when given the value of the digits in the hundreds', tens', and ones' place.

3. The student shall be able to write the number that is ten more or ten less than a given number.

4. When given three numbers, the student shall be able to circle the number that is least.

5. The student shall be able to write the missing numbers when counting by tens.

6. The student shall be able to write the correct sum of a horizontal addition problem rewritten vertically.

Teaching Tips:
1. When doing activity 5, suggest that the student(s) look at the digit in the tens' place when comparing three double-digit numbers. The smallest digit in the tens' place is the smallest number. The largest digit in the tens' place is the greatest number. If two numbers have the same digit in the tens' place, then they must compare the numbers in the ones' place.

Materials, Supplies, & Equipment:
1. Flashcards for addition facts

2. Number chart 0–99

Activities:

1. Count out loud with the student(s) by tens to 100 without using the *number chart*.

2. Using *flashcards for addition facts*, drill sums 1–18 without the answers showing. The addition facts will be drilled on a daily basis for one more lesson without the answers showing. Then the drill will be done using drill sheets from the worksheets and with flashcards.

3. Write several problems on the board similar to those in ***Student Activity One*** (e.g., 400 + 60 + 3 = ___, 700 + 20 + 0 = ___, etc.). Have the student(s) tell what number is represented by asking what digit will go in the hundreds', tens', and ones' place and write the digits on the corresponding blanks. Have the student(s) do the first two problems in ***Student Activity One*** together and finish the remaining ones by themselves.

4. Point to several multiples of ten on the *number chart* and have the student(s) tell the number that is ten less and ten more. Allow the student(s) to use a *number chart* if necessary when completing ***Student Activity Two*** and ***Three***.

5. Write several sets of three double-digit numbers (e.g., 52, 38, 29) on the board. Ask the student(s) to choose the number that is the greatest and the number that is the least. Explain that the number that is least is the same as the number that is smallest. Then have them arrange the three numbers in sequence (least to greatest). Have the student(s) read the directions carefully before starting ***Student Activity Four***.

6. The student(s) should be able to complete ***Student Activity Five*** on their own.

7. Write a horizontal double-digit addition problem on the board. Discuss with the student(s) how to write this problem vertically. Write the first double-digit number by itself. Underneath it, write the second double-digit number being careful to place the tens and ones in their corresponding columns. Write the answer by first adding the ones' column and then adding the tens' column. Write "57 + 8" on the board. Discuss the placing of the number "8" in the ones' column (under the "7" of 57) when the problem is written vertically. Work the first two problems in ***Student Activity Six*** together and then let them do the remaining ones independently.

Worksheet:

1. *Worksheet 5* – Number ladder

Lesson 10

Concepts:
Counting by twos, place value, before and after by twos, and addition

Objectives:
1. The student shall be able to count out loud by twos to 100.

2. The student shall be able to write the correct digit in the hundreds', tens', or ones' place in a given number.

3. The student shall be able to write the missing numbers when counting by twos.

4. The student shall be able to write the numbers that come before and after a given number when counting by twos.

5. When given three digits, the student shall be able to write the smallest triple-digit number possible.

6. The student shall be able to write the correct sum of two triple-digit numbers.

Teaching Tips:
1. When doing activity 3, do a careful check with the student(s) to determine which ones have not mastered their addition facts by using the *flashcards for addition facts*. Make provisions for those who still need drill time. Student(s) could drill student(s), teacher drill student(s), brother/sister drill student(s), or parent drill student(s). Those who still need it should make a practice of drilling 10 minutes extra each day.

Materials, Supplies, & Equipment:
1. Number chart 0–99

2. Flashcards for addition facts

3. Posterboard

Activities:

1. Administer **Test 1**. There is no time limit for the tests. If you choose, you may administer the test one day and complete the lesson the following day. If you plan to give the test and complete the lesson on the same day, make sure to plan for sufficient time.

2. Count out loud with the student(s) by twos to 100 using the *number chart*.

3. Using *flashcards for addition facts*, drill sums 1–18 without the answers showing. This is the last day for daily drill of the addition facts using flashcards. In the next lesson, the drill will be done using drill sheets from the worksheets and flashcards.

4. Write several three-digit numbers on the board. Ask the student(s) what digit is in the tens', the hundreds', and the ones' place changing the order each time. In **Student Activity One**, do the first three sentences together to be sure that the student(s) understand the directions. Let them finish the activity on their own.

5. Using the *number chart*, show the student(s) how counting by twos is adding two to the number each time. On the number chart, they count over two numbers to find the next number each time. Some student(s) may need to use the *number chart* when doing **Student Activity Two**.

6. Point to several multiples of two on the *number chart* as you discuss the meaning of "the number that comes before by twos" (two less, taken away, or subtracted) and "the number that comes after by twos" (two more, plus two, or two added). Using the *number chart*, they should be able to complete **Student Activity Three** independently.

7. Write several sets of three single-digit numbers on the board. Ask the student(s) to tell how they write the smallest number possible using the three digits (arrange the digits smallest to largest). On a sheet of paper, have the student(s) write the answers for the sets written on the board. Let the student(s) say the answers as you write them on the board. Give help if needed as the student(s) do **Student Activity Four**.

8. As the student(s) begin **Student Activity Five**, remind them to add the ones' column first, then the tens' column, and last the hundreds' column. Check the procedure the student(s) use.

9. Guide the student(s) through each step of **Student Activity Six**. Be sure they understand the concepts of "across" and "down." Have them point to the "1" on the puzzle and tell how many boxes are going across (2) and down (3). Using a sheet of *posterboard* or the board, draw the number puzzle large enough to show the student(s) how to write the answers in the boxes.

Lesson 11

Concepts:
Counting by twos, place value (thousands), addition, and subtraction

Objectives:
1. The student shall be able to count out loud by twos to 100.

2. The student shall be able to write the correct number of thousands, hundreds, tens, and ones that make up a given set of place value blocks.

3. The student shall be able to write the correct sum of two four-digit numbers.

4. The student shall be able to write the correct letter above a corresponding number that matches the sum or difference of two numbers.

Teaching Tips:
1. When doing activity 3, discuss with the student(s) how many ones equal one ten, how many tens equal one hundred, and how many hundreds equal one thousand. Ask them what is the greatest number of ones they can have, the greatest number of tens they can have, the greatest number of hundreds they can have, and the greatest number of thousands they can have in any one number. Then ask them what happens when they have ten ones (they become one ten), ten tens (they become one hundred), and ten hundreds (they become one thousand).

2. Although the use of a comma is optional in **_Student Activity Two_**, Horizons curriculum will use the comma throughout with a four-digit number. The comma is used to separate the hundreds from the thousands. The purpose of the comma will be explained further in third grade when place value is extended beyond the thousands' place.

Activities:

1. Count out loud with the student(s) by twos to 100 without using the *number chart*.

2. Use *Drill # 1, Worksheet 6* for the addition drill. You will save time by giving the whole worksheet to the student(s) at once and not cutting it apart. Have the student(s) keep it neat in a special folder for quick access when drill time comes. When the drill is over, remind them to return the drill sheet to the folder and place the folder in a special place in their desk. After all four drills have been completed, make sure they are removed from the folder. The drills should be one minute long. As the student(s) become accustomed to them, the time can be shortened.

3. Have the student(s) look at **Student Activity One**. Read the example at the top of the page together. Go over the meaning of the number "1,387" with the student(s). Do several other four-digit numbers with the student(s) using the *place value materials*. Let them tell what number you have represented. When they are ready to begin **Student Activity One**, do the first place value problem together counting the thousands, hundreds, tens, and ones separately. The student(s) should then be able to complete the remaining problems by themselves.

4. Tell the student(s) to always add the ones' column first, then tens', then hundreds' and then the thousands' column. The student(s) should be able to complete **Student Activity Two** on their own.

5. To decode the message in **Student Activity Three**, have the student(s) look at the first fact (4 + 2) and write the sum beside it. Ask them what letter they will put on the blank above the number 6 (O). Then ask them what (6–2) equals and write the difference beside it. Have the student(s) tell what letter they will put on the blank above the number 4 (L). Discuss with the student(s) how the subtraction and addition facts are the same as "before" and "after" by twos. Allow them to complete the activity on their own if they are capable.

Worksheet:

1. *Worksheet 6* – Addition drill sheet

*Faithfulness in the little things will
bring trust in bigger things.*

Lesson 12

Concepts:
Counting by twos, place value (thousands), before and after by twos, and addition

Objectives:
1. The student shall be able to count out loud by twos to 100.

2. The student shall be able to write the correct number of thousands, hundreds, tens, and ones that make up a given set of place value blocks.

3. The student shall be able to write the number that is two more and two less than a given number.

4. When given three digits, the student shall be able to write the greatest triple-digit number possible.

5. The student shall be able to write the correct sum of two three-digit numbers.

Teaching Tips:
1. When doing activity 1, give each student a copy of *Worksheet 1*. Have the student(s) color the numbers used in counting by twos. Color the ones family red, the tens family blue, the twenties family green, the thirties yellow, the forties orange, the fifties brown, the sixties purple, the seventies gray, the eighties pink, and the nineties tan.

Materials, Supplies, & Equipment:
1. Place value materials

2. Number chart 0–99

Activities:

1. Count out loud with the student(s) by twos to 100 without using the *number chart*.

2. Drill the addition facts using *Drill #2, Worksheet 6*.

3. Using *place value materials*, demonstrate the number "2,574." As the student(s) count the number of thousands, write the number on the board. Continue in the same manner as the students count the hundreds, tens, and ones. Ask the student(s) to tell what number they have. Follow the same procedure with several other four-digit numbers. When starting **Student Activity One**, complete the first set of place value blocks together. Allow those who are able to continue on their own to do so. Give help to those who need it.

4. Point to several multiples of two on the *number chart* and have the student(s) tell the number that is two less and two more. Allow the student(s) to use a *number chart* if necessary when completing **Student Activity Two** and **Three**.

5. Write three single-digit numbers on the board. Ask the student(s) to see how many different three-digit numbers they can make from the given numbers. Have them pick the greatest or largest number. Notice the value of the digits decrease as they go from the hundreds' place to the ones' place. Put several other sets of three single-digit numbers on the board including a zero. Have the student(s) tell the greatest three-digit number they can make. After reading the directions for **Student Activity Four**, find the first three-digit number together. Allow the student(s) to finish without further help.

6. The student(s) should be able to complete **Student Activity Five** independently. Check to see that they add the ones' column first and continue to work from right to left.

Worksheets:

1. *Worksheet 6* – Addition drill sheets

2. *Worksheet 1* – Number chart 0–99

Pulling your own weight is better than throwing it around.

Lesson 13

Concepts:
> Counting by threes, place value (thousands), before and after by threes, and addition

Objectives:
1. The student shall be able to count out loud by threes to 36.

2. The student shall be able to write the number represented by a given number of place value blocks in thousands, hundreds, tens, and ones.

3. The student shall be able to write the numbers that come before and after a given number when counting by threes.

4. When given three numbers, the student shall be able to circle the number that is greatest.

5. When given three digits, the student shall be able to write the greatest triple-digit number possible.

6. The student shall be able to write the correct sum of three single-digit numbers.

Teaching Tips:
1. Using *Worksheet 1*, have the student(s) circle all the numbers used in counting by threes in activity 1.

2. A great motivator for activity 2 is to put a *happy face stamp* or *sticker* in the upper right hand corner of the drill each time the student(s) complete the drill in the allotted time and have no errors. This should be done daily. You can then see at a glance when the student(s) have completed all four of the drills satisfactorily.

Materials, Supplies, & Equipment:
1. Number chart 0–99

2. Place value materials

3. Happy face stamp or stickers

Activities:

1. Count out loud with the student(s) by threes to 36 using the *number chart*. The student(s) will count to 36 which includes all the multiplication facts they will be learning for three.

2. Drill the addition facts using *Drill #3, Worksheet 6*.

3. Demonstrate a four-digit number (2,514) using *place value materials*. Have the student(s) count the place value blocks to arrive at the number (1,000; 2,000; 2,100; 2,200; 2,300; 2,400; 2,500; 2,510; 2,511; 2,512; 2,513; 2,514). Do the same with other four-digit numbers. The student(s) should then be able to complete **Student Activity One** on their own.

4. Point to several multiples of three on the *number chart* as you discuss the meaning of "the number that comes before by threes" (three less, taken away, or subtracted) and "the number that comes after by threes" (three more, plus, or added). With the aid of the *number chart*, the student(s) should be able to complete **Student Activity Two** independently.

5. Write "23, 67, 45, 17" on the board. Have the student(s) tell the largest and the smallest number in the set. Arrange the four numbers in their numerical sequence. The student(s) should complete **Student Activity Three** by themselves.

6. Write several sets of three single-digit numbers on the board. Ask the student(s) to tell how they write the greatest number possible using the three digits (arrange the digits largest to smallest). On a sheet of paper, have the student(s) write the greatest number for the sets written on the board before you write the answer. Give help only where needed as the student(s) complete **Student Activity Four**.

7. Write several sets of three single-digit numbers vertically on the board for addition. Be sure that the sum of the first two numbers is not over 9. Add the first two numbers with the student(s) and then add the third number to the total. Show them how they can check their answer by adding the bottom two numbers and then add the top number to the total. They should be able to complete **Student Activity Five** without further help.

Worksheets:

1. *Worksheet 7* – Place value

2. *Worksheet 6* – Addition drill sheets

3. *Worksheet 1* – Number chart 0–99

Lesson 14

Concepts:
Counting by threes, place value (thousands), before and after by threes, and addition

Objectives:

1. The student shall be able to count out loud by threes to 36.

2. The student shall be able to write the value of a given number of thousands.

3. When given three numbers, the student shall be able to circle the number that is greatest.

4. The student shall be able to write the missing numbers when counting by threes.

5. The student shall be able to write the numbers that come before and after a given number when counting by threes.

6. The student shall be able to correctly arrange a given set of numbers in the proper sequence.

7. When given four digits, the student shall be able to write the greatest four-digit number possible.

8. The student shall be able to write the correct sum of three double-digit numbers.

Teaching Tips:

1. For enrichment in activity 7, discuss with the student(s) the principle used to write the smallest four-digit number (arrange the digits in order from smallest to largest). By applying the principle, allow them to discover that they can easily write the smallest number possible if given eight digits. Arrange the eight digits in order smallest to largest. If one of the digits is zero, it will always be the second digit following the next smallest digit because the number should not begin with zero.

Materials, Supplies, & Equipment:

1. Number chart 0–99

2. Place value materials

Activities:

1. Count out loud with the student(s) by threes to 36 using the *number chart*.

2. Drill the addition facts using *Drill #4, Worksheet 6*.

3. Tell the student(s) that 5 thousands means to add 1,000 five times (1,000 + 1,000 + 1,000 + 1,000 + 1,000) or to count by one thousand five times (1,000; 2,000; 3,000; 4,000; 5,000). *Place value materials* would be a help to demonstrate this. Ask the student(s) what 8 thousands would equal, 3 thousands would equal, etc. If they need to count 3 place value cubes by thousands, allow them to do so. They should now be able to complete **Student Activity One** by themselves.

4. Write several sets of three triple-digit numbers on the board (642, 845, 147). Ask the student(s) to choose the number that is greatest and the number that is smallest. Point out that if the hundreds' digits are all different, they only have to compare the hundreds' digits. If the hundreds' digits are the same, they have to compare the tens' digits. When starting **Student Activity Two**, complete the first set of numbers together. They should be able to finish on their own.

5. The student(s) should be able to complete **Student Activity Three** and **Four** independently using a *number chart* if necessary.

6. To begin **Student Activity Five**, have the student(s) pick out the numbers in the teens and put them in order, pick out the twenties and put them in order, the thirties and put them in order, etc. until all numbers have been used.

7. Write four single-digit numbers on the board. Have the student(s) arrange them in such a way that they will form the smallest four-digit number possible (putting them in order smallest to largest). They should complete **Student Activity Six** without further help.

8. **Student Activity Seven** should be completed by the student(s) independently. Insist they check their answers by adding from the bottom up and from the top down.

Worksheet:

1. *Worksheet 6* – Addition drill sheet

Lesson 15

Concepts:
Counting by threes, place value (thousands), before and after by threes, greater than, and addition

Objectives:
1. The student shall be able to count out loud by threes to 36.

2. The student shall be able to write the value of a given number of thousands.

3. The student shall be able to write the numbers that come before and after a given number when counting by threes.

4. The student shall be able to circle the given numbers greater than 36.

5. The student shall be able to correctly arrange a given set of numbers in the proper sequence.

6. The student shall be able to write the correct sum of two triple-digit numbers.

7. The student shall be able to write the missing numbers from 100–199.

Teaching Tips:
1. Encourage the student(s) to do **Student Activity Seven** without help from you or a *number chart*. If some student(s) cannot write their numbers to 199, they need to be given daily practice filling in the numbers on a *number chart* or writing them on a clean sheet of paper (100–109 on the first row, 110–119 on the second row, etc.) until they can do it successfully on their own.

Materials, Supplies, & Equipment:
1. Flashcards for addition facts

2. Number chart 0–99

Activities:

1. Count out loud with the student(s) by threes to 36 without using the *number chart*.

2. Have the student(s) take a clean sheet of paper on which to write the answers for their addition facts. Select ten *addition flashcards*. Show each card for 5 seconds as the student(s) write the answers in a column. Check the answers before you begin a second set of ten cards. Do as many sets as time permits in 7 minutes.

3. Allow the student(s) to read the directions for **Student Activity One** and complete the work on their own.

4. Before beginning **Student Activity Two**, discuss the different meanings of the words "before a number" and "after a number" (subtract, take away, or less and add, plus, or more). Using the *number chart*, point to several multiples of three and have the student(s) tell the number when you subtract or add three. The student(s) should be able to complete the activity by themselves.

5. Point to several numbers on the *number chart* and ask the student(s) if the numbers are greater than 50. The student(s) should have little difficulty completing **Student Activity Three** independently.

6. Put a chart similar to **Student Activity Four** on the board. As the student(s) tell the answer when each number is added or subtracted, write the sum or difference in the box after the number. Use that sum or difference as they add or subtract the next number. Complete the chart together. Put a second chart on the board. Allow the student(s) to complete it by themselves and compare their answers. They should then be able to complete the activity alone.

7. The student(s) should be able to complete **Student Activity Five**, **Six**, and **Seven** on their own.

*A fellow can love his enemies easier than
he can make them love him.*

Lesson 16

Concepts:
Counting by threes, ordinal numbers, before and after by threes, greater than, addition, and subtraction

Objectives:
1. The student shall be able to count out loud by threes to 36.

2. The student shall be able to write a given number on a mailbox in a given ordinal position of a given row.

3. The student shall be able to write the numbers that come before and after a given number when counting by threes.

4. The student shall be able to circle the given numbers greater than 126.

5. The student shall be able to write the correct sum of two four-digit numbers.

6. The student shall be able to write the difference of two double-digit numbers.

Teaching Tips:
1. When doing activity 3, be sure the student(s) say the complete subtraction fact and not just the answer. They should say, "Eight minus (or take away) three equals five."

2. If the student(s) have difficulty working with the four-digit numbers in *Student Activity Four*, suggest they cover all columns except the one they are adding. They need to concentrate on one column at a time.

Materials, Supplies, & Equipment:
1. Flashcards for subtraction facts

2. Number chart 100–199

Activities:

1. Count out loud with the student(s) by threes to 36 without using the *number chart*.

2. Drill addition facts using *Drill #1, Worksheet 8*.

3. Drill the *subtraction facts with minuends 1–18* using *flashcards* with the answers showing to give the student(s) an accurate review. After the next four lessons, the drill will be done without the answers showing.

4. Give the student(s) *Worksheet 1* for preparation for **Student Activity One**. Tell them to point to the sixth number in the first row and raise their hand. Ask them what the number is. Continue with the same type of instructions (the second number in the eighth row, the third number in the seventh row, etc.). Read the directions for **Student Activity One** with the student(s). Allow them to work on their own after completing the first two sentences together.

5. The student(s) should be able to complete **Student Activity Two** by themselves.

6. Using the *number chart 100–199*, point to several numbers and have the student(s) tell if they are greater than 140. The student(s) should be able to complete **Student Activity Three** on their own.

7. The student(s) should be able to complete **Student Activity Four** and **Five** independently.

Worksheets:

1. *Worksheet 8* – Addition drill sheet

2. *Worksheet 1* – Number chart 0–99

*It is better to use a little talent faithfully
than to waste great talent.*

Lesson 17

Concepts:
Counting by threes, ordinal numbers, before and after by threes, counting over 100, and subtraction

Objectives:
1. The student shall be able to count out loud by threes to 36.

2. The student shall be able to write the name of a given box in respect to its ordinal position.

3. The student shall be able to write the number that is three more and three less than a given number.

4. The student shall be able to write the missing numbers when counting over 100.

5. The student shall be able to write the missing numbers when counting by threes.

6. The student shall be able to write the correct difference of two double-digit numbers.

Teaching Tips:
1. If any student(s) have received a smiley face stamp every day on their drill sheets, you should reward them by allowing them to not do the next drill sheet.

Materials, Supplies, & Equipment:
1. Flashcards for subtraction facts

2. Number chart 0–99

Activities:
1. Count out loud with the student(s) by threes to 36 without using the *number chart*.

2. Drill addition facts using *Drill #2, Worksheet 8*.

3. Drill the *subtraction facts with minuends 1–18* using *flashcards* with the answers showing to give the student(s) an accurate review. After the next three lessons, the drill will be done without the answers showing.

4. Have the student(s) look at **Student Activity One** and read each of the names on the boxes. Read the first three sentences and fill in the blanks together. Then allow the student(s) to continue on their own.

5. Point to several multiples of three on the *number chart* and have the student(s) tell the number that is three less and three more. Allow the student(s) to use a *number chart* if necessary when completing **Student Activity Two** and **Three**.

6. Using the *number chart 0–99,* demonstrate to the students how they can count as high as 999 by putting the hundreds digit in front of each number on the *number chart*. Ask them to start counting at 452 and go to 462, at 523 to 533, at 786 to 796, etc. When starting **Student Activity Four**, point out to the student(s) that each row starts at a new number.

7. The student(s) should be able to complete **Student Activity Five** and **Six** independently.

Worksheets:
1. *Worksheet 9* – Counting over 100

2. *Worksheet 8* – Addition drill sheet

*Jealousy does the same to the soul as
sickness does to the body.*

Lesson 18

Concepts:
  Counting by sixes, time (hour), greater than, before and after by sixes, addition, and subtraction

Objectives:
  1. The student shall be able to count out loud by sixes to 72.

  2. The student shall be able to write the correct time displayed on the face of the clock by the hour.

  3. The student shall be able to circle the given numbers greater than 383.

  4. The student shall be able to write the numbers that come before and after a given number when counting by sixes.

  5. The student shall be able to write the correct sum of four single-digit numbers.

  6. The student shall be able to write the difference of two double-digit numbers.

Teaching Tips:
  1. When doing activity 1, use *Worksheet 1* and have the student(s) circle all the numbers used in counting by threes, Then have them color all the numbers used in counting by sixes. Point out to the student(s) how all the numbers used in counting by sixes are also used in counting by threes.

  2. When doing activity 7, suggest to the student(s) that it may be easier to find numbers that add to 10 and then add the remaining numbers to 10. (e.g., 4 + 3 + 5 + 7 could be added 3 + 7 = 10, 10 + 5 = 15, and 15 + 4 = 19).

Materials, Supplies, & Equipment:
  1. Number chart 0–99

  2. Flashcards for subtraction facts

  3. Clock model

Activities:

1. Count out loud with the student(s) by sixes to 72 using the *number chart*.

2. Drill addition facts using *Drill #3, Worksheet 8*.

3. Drill *subtraction facts with minuends 1–18* using *flashcards* with the answers showing. After two lessons, drill will be done without the answers showing.

4. Discuss the short hand (the hour hand) and the long hand (the minute hand) on the clock with the student(s). Talk about the length of a day being 24 hours and 60 minutes equaling an hour. Ask them where the hour hand and the minute hand are located when the clock reads 5:00 o'clock. Using a *clock model*, demonstrate 2 o'clock, 8 o'clock, and 11 o'clock. When starting **Student Activity One**, have the student(s) check to see if the minute hand is on 12. Then have them look at the hour hand to determine the correct time.

5. Using the *number chart 0–99*, have the student(s) pretend that it represents counting from 300–399 by putting a 3 in front of each number. Then point to several numbers on the chart and have the student(s) tell if the number is greater or less than 369. Write "156, 284, 429, and 507" on the board and ask the student(s) to tell if they are greater or less than 369. When starting **Student Activity Two**, discuss with the student(s) if the first four numbers are greater than 383 or not. After circling those that are, allow the student(s) to complete the remaining numbers by themselves.

6. Point to several multiples of six on the *number chart* as you discuss the meaning of "the number that comes before by sixes" (six less, taken away, or subtracted) and "the number that comes after by sixes" (six more, plus, or added). With the aid of the *number chart*, the student(s) should be able to complete **Student Activity Three** independently.

7. Write several sets of four single-digit numbers (sum less than 20) on the board as vertical addition problems. Have the student(s) orally add the first two numbers and say the answer. Let them add that sum to the third number and say the answer. Then add that sum to the last number and say the answer. Insist the student(s) add from the bottom up to check their answers as they complete **Student Activity Four**.

8. The student(s) should be able to complete **Student Activity Five** on their own.

Worksheets:

1. *Worksheet 8* – Addition drill sheet

2. *Worksheet 1* – Number chart 0–99

Lesson 19

Concepts:
 Counting by sixes, time (hour), before and after by sixes, subtraction, and addition (horizontal to vertical)

Objectives:
 1. The student shall be able to count out loud by sixes to 72.

 2. The student shall be able to write the correct time displayed on the face of the clock by the hour.

 3. The student shall be able to write the missing numbers when counting by sixes.

 4. The student shall be able to write the numbers that come before and after a given number when counting by sixes.

 5. The student shall be able to write the difference of two double-digit numbers.

 6. The student shall be able to write the sum of four horizontal single-digit numbers rewritten vertically.

Teaching Tips:
 1. If the student(s) have mastered telling time on the hour in the first grade, have them do *Worksheet 10* along with activity 4. Remind them to draw the minute hand first (on the 12) and then the hour hand as the placement of the hour hand is dependent on where the minute hand in located. Be sure they make a good distinction between the length of the hour and minute hand.

Materials, Supplies, & Equipment:
 1. Number chart 0–99

 2. Flashcards for subtraction facts

 3. Clock model

Activities:

1. Count out loud with the student(s) by sixes to 72 using the *number chart*.

2. Drill addition facts using *Drill #4, Worksheet 8*.

3. Drill the *subtraction facts with minuends 1–18* using *flashcards* with the answers showing to give the student(s) an accurate review. After the next lesson, the drill will be done without the answers showing.

4. Set the *clock model* for several times on the hour as the student(s) write the correct time on a sheet of paper. Have them check their answers with the correct answer you write on the board. The student(s) should be able to complete **Student Activity One** on their own.

5. Allow the student(s) to use the *number chart* when completing **Student Activity Two** and **Three** if necessary.

6. The student(s) should be able to complete **Student Activity Four** independently.

7. Write several sets of four single-digit numbers on the board as a horizontal addition problem. Demonstrate to the student(s) how the horizontal problem is written vertically. Express the importance of putting all of the ones in the same column. After working the first two problems together in **Student Activity Five**, allow them to complete the remaining problems by themselves.

Worksheets:

1. *Worksheet 10* – Time (hour)

2. *Worksheet 8* – Addition drill sheet

You may think revenge is sweet,
but it will leave a bitter taste.

Lesson 20

Concepts:
Counting by sixes, time (half hour), before and after by sixes, and subtraction

Objectives:
1. The student shall be able to count out loud by sixes to 72.

2. The student shall be able to write the correct time displayed on the face of the clock by the half hour.

3. The student shall be able to write the numbers that come before and after a given number when counting by sixes.

4. The student shall be able to correctly arrange a given set of numbers in the proper sequence.

5. The student shall be able to write the correct answers for 78 subtraction facts.

Teaching Tips:
1. When doing activity 5, tell the student(s) telling time on the half hour can be expressed in four different ways. "6:30" may also be expressed as "half past six," "30 minutes after six," or "30 minutes before seven."

2. When doing activity 7, suggest that the student(s) who are having difficulty with the subtraction facts spend 10 minutes each night practicing them. It could be done orally with flashcards or as a written exercise.

Materials, Supplies, & Equipment:
1. Flashcards for addition and subtraction facts

2. Clock model

Activities:

1. Administer **Test 2**. Use the test as a learning experience for the student(s). Give individual help to those who were not successful by going over the test with them after it has been graded. Some re-teaching may have to be done.

2. Count out loud with the student(s) by sixes to 72 without using the *number chart*.

3. Have the student(s) take a clean sheet of paper on which to write the answers for their addition facts. Select ten *addition flashcards*. Show each card for 5 seconds as the student(s) write the answers in a column. Check the answers before you begin the second set of ten cards. Do as many sets as time permits in 7 minutes.

4. Drill the *subtraction facts with minuends 1–18* using *flashcards* with the answers showing to give the student(s) an accurate review. This is the last lesson the drill will be done with the answers showing.

5. Discuss with the student(s) how a clock can have the 60 minutes in an hour cut in half. Find the minutes in a half hour by counting by fives beginning at one and ending at six, the half way point. Each half hour is 30 minutes. When the time is 3:00 o'clock, the minute hand is on the 12. When 30 minutes have passed on the clock, the minute hand is then on the six and the hour hand is half way past the three. It is now 3:30. Show on a *clock model* the distance the two hands move with the passage of 30 minutes. Set the *clock model* for several half hour times. Have the student(s) tell where the minute hand is and what that means (30 minutes past the hour), where the hour hand is and what that means (30 minutes past that hour), and write the answer on a sheet of paper. When starting **Student Activity One**, determine the correct time for the first three clocks with the student(s). Allow them to write the time for the remaining clocks on their own.

6. The student(s) should be able to complete **Student Activity Two** and **Three** by themselves.

7. Use **Student Activity Four** as a quick check for mastery of the subtraction facts. Make arrangements for additional drill with answers for those student(s) who were not successful with this activity. This could be done at recess, lunch hour, before school, or after school with teacher and student or student and student.

One way to have a better world is to be kinder than is necessary.

Lesson 21

Concepts:
    Counting by sixes, time (half hour), word numbers, before and after by sixes, subtraction, and word problems

Objectives:

1. The student shall be able to count out loud by sixes to 72.

2. The student shall be able to write the correct time displayed on the face of the clock for the half hour.

3. The student shall be able to draw a line to match a given word number to its corresponding number.

4. The student shall be able to write the numbers that come before and after a given number when counting by sixes.

5. The student shall be able to write the correct difference of two triple-digit numbers.

6. The student shall be able to write the addition fact necessary to solve a word problem and label the answer.

Teaching Tips:

1. When doing activity 4, have the student(s) make their own clock from a *paper plate*, *construction paper*, and a *brad*. Have them write the numbers on the face of the clock around the edge of the paper plate, make a minute and an hour hand from construction paper, and attach the hands to the center of the plate with the brad.

Materials, Supplies, & Equipment:

1. Flashcards for subtraction facts and word numbers

2. Clock model

3. Small clock model for student(s)

4. Paper plate, construction paper, and brad

Activities:

1. Count out loud with the student(s) by sixes to 72 without using the *number chart*.

2. Drill addition facts using *Drill #1, Worksheet 11*. Since there are only four drills a week, you may omit drilling on whichever day of the week you choose. Just be sure that you do four drills every week. Do not skip more than one day a week. If any student(s) successfully complete all of the four drills in the allotted time, you might allow them the option of doing only the last drill the next week.

3. Drill the *subtraction facts with minuends 1–18* using *flashcards* without the answers showing. This drill will be done for ten lessons without the answers showing. Then the drill will be done using drill sheets from the worksheets and with flashcards.

4. Have the student(s) tell how many hours are in a day, how many minutes are in an hour, and how many minutes are in a half hour. Give the student(s) a *small clock model*. Write four half hour times on the board. Tell the student(s) to set their clock for the given times. Have them place the minute hand first and then the hour hand. The student(s) should check their clocks with your *clock model*. Allow them to complete **Student Activity One** by themselves.

5. Using *word number flashcards*, read and spell each of the word numbers from one to twenty with the student(s). After they read the directions for **Student Activity Two** together, allow them to complete the matching on their own.

6. The student(s) should be able to complete **Student Activity Three** and **Four** independently.

7. Have the student(s) read the first word problem in **Student Activity Five** to themselves. Ask them to tell the key word, if they add or subtract, and what the label should be. Tell them to write the addition fact necessary to solve the word problem and label their answer. As the student(s) complete the next two word problems, be sure they write the addition fact and label their answer.

Worksheet:

1. *Worksheet 11* – Addition drill sheet

*A friend who always has to stand up for you
may tire and sit down.*

Lesson 22

Concepts:
Counting by sixes, addition, time (half hour), before and after by sixes, word numbers, subtraction, and word problems

Objectives:
1. The student shall be able to count out loud by sixes to 72.

2. The student shall be able to write the correct sum for two double-digit numbers when the ones' column has a double-digit answer.

3. The student shall be able to draw a line to match a given time to the time displayed on the face of a clock.

4. The student shall be able to write the number that is six more and six less than a given number.

5. The student shall be able to write the corresponding number for a given word number.

6. The student shall be able to write the correct difference of two triple-digit numbers.

7. The student shall be able to write the addition fact necessary to solve a word problem and label the answer.

Teaching Tips:
1. When doing activity 5, ask the student(s) to find as many pictures of different types of clocks as they can in the newspaper, magazines, catalogs or other sources. Have them bring the pictures to class and discuss where you would most likely find each type of clock.

Materials, Supplies, & Equipment:
1. Flashcards for subtraction facts

2. Place value materials

3. Clock model

4. Small clock model for student(s)

5. Number chart 0–99

Activities:

1. Count out loud with the student(s) by sixes to 72 without using the *number chart*. Then have the student(s) take a clean sheet of paper and write the numbers used in counting by sixes.

2. Drill addition facts using *Drill #2, Worksheet 11*.

3. Drill the *subtraction facts with minuends 1–18* using *flashcards* without the answers showing.

4. On the board write "54 + 29" as a vertical addition problem. After the student(s) add the ones' column (13), discuss the value of the "3" in 13 and the value of the "1" in 13. Using *place value materials* would be helpful. If the "1" has the value of "1" ten, then it should be added with the tens' column. Remind them that they must always add the ones' column first, write the "3" under the ones' column, and write the "1" above the tens' column. Now they are ready to add the three numbers in the tens' column (1 + 5 + 2) and write "8" under the tens' column. Do several examples of two double-digit numbers with carrying in the ones' column. As the student(s) begin **Student Activity One**, check to see that they add the ones' column first and then write the one to be carried above the tens' column.

5. Give the student(s) *small clock models*. Have them set their clocks to match the times you have written on the board. They should check their clocks with your *clock model*. Encourage them to set the minute hand first and then the hour hand. After reading the directions for **Student Activity Two**, instruct the student(s) to draw a line from each clock to its correct time.

6. Point to several multiples of six on the *number chart* and have the student(s) tell the number that is six less and six more. Allow the student(s) to use a *number chart* if necessary when completing **Student Activity Three** and **Four**.

7. After saying and spelling the word numbers for one to twenty, the student(s) should be able to complete **Student Activity Five** and **Six** on their own.

8. Discuss with the student(s) the key word (altogether) in the word problem in **Student Activity Seven**. Ask them if they add or subtract, what the addition fact is, and what the label should be.

Worksheet:

1. *Worksheet 11* – Addition drill sheet

Lesson 23

Concepts:
Counting by nines, time (quarter hour), addition, subtraction, equal and not equal, tally marks, and word problems

Objectives:
1. The student shall be able to count out loud by nines to 108.

2. The student shall be able to write the correct time displayed on the face of the clock for the quarter hour.

3. The student shall be able to write the correct sum for two double-digit numbers when the ones' column has a double-digit answer.

4. The student shall be able to write the correct difference of two triple-digit numbers.

5. The student shall be able to write the correct symbol (= or ≠) between a number and tally marks.

6. The student shall be able to write the addition fact necessary to solve a word problem and label the answer.

Teaching Tips:
1. Using *Worksheet 1*, have the student(s) circle all the threes, color the sixes blue, and put a box around the nines. Discuss with them how every other three is used in counting by sixes and every third three is used in counting by nines. Have the student(s) write the threes to 36, the sixes to 72, and the nines to 108 as a sequence at the bottom of the page.

Materials, Supplies, & Equipment:
1. Number chart 0–99

2. Flashcards for subtraction facts, = and ≠, and tally marks

3. Clock model

Activities:

1. Count out loud with the student(s) by nines to 108 using the *number chart*. They need to count to 108 since they will soon be using the first 12 multiples in multiplication.

2. Drill addition facts using *Drill #3, Worksheet 11.*

3. Drill the *subtraction facts with minuends 1–18* using *flashcards* without the answers showing.

4. Show the student(s) a *clock model* set at 8:15. Remind them that the hour is always the number that the hour hand has just passed. To find the minutes, have the student(s) begin to count by fives at the number 1 and stop at the number 3. Show them a *clock model* set at 5:45. Have them determine the hour and then count by fives to find the minutes. Do this several times for 15 minutes and 45 minutes after the hour. After determining the time on the first two clocks together in **Student Activity One**, allow the student(s) to write the remaining times on their own.

5. Write several sets of two double-digit numbers on the board with carrying in the ones' column. As the student(s) work the problems, see that they add the ones' column first, write the one to be carried above the tens' column, and then add the tens' column. After the student(s) complete **Student Activity Two**, check each student's work for correct procedure.

6. The student(s) should be able to complete **Student Activity Three** by themselves.

7. With the aid of *flashcards*, discuss the meaning of the = and ≠ symbols. Equal (=) means the same. Not equal (≠) means not the same. Review *tally marks* using *flashcards* of varied combinations. Put several examples of tally marks and numerals on the board, some equal and some not equal. Have the student(s) count the tally marks and determine if they need an = or ≠ symbol between the quantities. The student(s) may need your help completing the first problem in each column in **Student Activity Four**, before completing the remaining ones on their own.

8. Have the student(s) read the first word problem in **Student Activity Five** out loud. Check to see that they write the addition problem vertically and label their answer.

Worksheets:

1. *Worksheet 12* – Time

2. *Worksheet 11* – Addition drill sheet

3. *Worksheet 1* – Number chart 0–99

Lesson 24

Concepts:
    Counting by nines, word numbers, equal and not equal, addition, time (quarter hour), and subtraction

Objectives:

1. The student shall be able to count out loud by nines to 108.

2. The student shall be able to draw a line to match a given word number with its corresponding number.

3. The student shall be able to write the correct symbol (= or ≠) between a given addition fact and a number.

4. The student shall be able to write the missing numbers when counting by nines.

5. The student shall be able to write the correct sum for two triple-digit numbers when the ones' column has a double-digit answer.

6. The student shall be able to write the correct time displayed on the face of the clock for the quarter hour.

7. The student shall be able to write the correct difference of two triple-digit numbers.

Teaching Tips:

1. Since this is the last day for the addition drill sheet in activity 2, encourage the student(s) that have not learned their addition facts thoroughly to spend at least 10 minutes of additional drill time with flashcards each day.

Materials, Supplies, & Equipment:

1. Number chart 0–99

2. Flashcards for subtraction facts, word numbers, and = and ≠

3. Clock model

4. Small clock model for student(s)

Activities:

1. Count out loud with the student(s) by nines to 108 using the *number chart*.

2. Drill addition facts using *Drill #4, Worksheet 11.*

3. Drill the *subtraction facts with minuends 1–18* using *flashcards* without the answers showing.

4. Using *word number flashcards* for one through twenty and the multiples of ten to one hundred, say several numbers less than one hundred and have the student(s) choose the cards necessary to write the word numbers. Remind them that a hyphen must be used when a multiple of ten is used with another word number. After reading and spelling the word numbers in **Student Activity One**, the student(s) should be able to complete the matching on their own.

5. Review the meaning of the symbols = and ≠ using *flashcards*. Write several problems similar to **Student Activity Two** on the board. Insist the student(s) say the answer to the addition fact (e.g., 6 + 8 = 14) and then compare the two numbers. They should be able to complete **Student Activity Two** independently.

6. The student(s) should be able to complete **Student Activity Three** and **Four** by themselves with you helping those who need individual attention.

7. Give the student(s) *small clock models* to set at given times for the quarter hour. Remind them that the hour is always the number the hour hand has just passed and not the number to which it is closer. Let the student(s) check their clocks with your *clock model*. They should be able to complete **Student Activity Five** without further help.

8. **Student Activity Six** should be completed by the student(s) by themselves.

Worksheet:

1. *Worksheet 11* – Addition drill sheet

*The sooner folks find out that life
is a do-it-yourself job, the better they'll do.*

Lesson 25

Concepts:
   Counting by nines, word numbers, before and after by nines, time (quarter hour), equal and not equal, addition, and subtraction

Objectives:

1. The student shall be able to count out loud by nines to 108.

2. The student shall be able to write the corresponding number for a given word number.

3. The student shall be able to write the number that comes before and after a given number when counting by nines.

4. The student shall be able to write the correct time displayed on the face of the clock for the quarter hour.

5. The student shall be able to write the correct symbol (= or ≠) between a word number and a number.

6. The student shall be able to write the correct sum for two triple-digit numbers when the ones' column has a double-digit answer.

7. The student shall be able to write the correct difference of two triple-digit numbers.

Teaching Tips:

1. When the student(s) are doing activity 4, have them spell the word numbers out loud together from one to twenty and the multiples of ten to one hundred. Take special note of the spelling of the words "thirteen, fifteen, thirty, forty, and fifty."

Materials, Supplies, & Equipment:

1. Flashcards for addition facts, subtraction facts, and word numbers

2. Number chart 0–99

3. Small clock model for student(s)

4. Clock model

Activities:

1. Count out loud with the student(s) by nines to 108 without using the *number chart*.

2. Have the student(s) take a clean sheet of paper on which to write the answers for their addition facts. Select ten *addition flashcards*. Show each card for 5 seconds as the student(s) write the answers in a column. Check the answers before you begin the second set of ten cards. Do as many sets as time permits in 7 minutes.

3. Drill the *subtraction facts with minuends 1–18* using *flashcards* without the answers showing.

4. Display the *word number flashcards* on the board rail. Write several numbers less than 100 on the board and have the student(s) write the corresponding word numbers on a sheet of paper. The *flashcards* should be used as reference for spelling. Allow the student(s) to choose the correct *flashcards* to correspond to each number as a check for their work. They should be able to complete **Student Activity One** on their own.

5. Point to several multiples of nine on the *number chart* as you discuss the meaning of "the number that comes before by nines" (nine less, nine taken away, or nine subtracted) and "the number that comes after by nines" (nine more, plus nine, or nine added). Allow the student(s) to use the *number chart* if necessary to complete **Student Activity Two**.

6. Give the student(s) *small clock models* to set for several quarter hour times. Allow them to check their work by your *clock model*. They should be able to complete **Student Activity Three** independently.

7. After discussing the meaning of the symbols = and ≠, the student(s) should be able to complete **Student Activity Four** by themselves.

8. When starting **Student Activity Five**, check to see that the student(s) add the ones' column first, write the "1" above the tens' column, and then add the tens' column.

9. The student(s) should be able to complete **Student Activity Six** on their own.

The more patience a person has the more it will be tested.

Lesson 26

Concepts:
> Counting by nines, place value (thousands), word numbers, equal and not equal, time (quarter hour), before and after by nines, addition, and subtraction

Objectives:
1. The student shall be able to count out loud by nines to 108.

2. The student shall be able to write the correct value of a given number of thousands.

3. The student shall be able to write the word number that corresponds to a given number.

4. The student shall be able to write the correct symbol (= or ≠) between the time displayed on the face of a clock and a time written in digital form.

5. The student shall be able to write the numbers that come before and after a given number when counting by nines.

6. The student shall be able to write the correct sum for two four-digit numbers when the ones' column has a double-digit answer.

7. The student shall be able to write the correct difference of two four-digit numbers.

Teaching Tips:
1. When doing activity 1, have the student(s) create their own dot-to-dot drawings using the numbers necessary to count by nines. Then have the students exchange their drawings with a friend, allowing the friend to complete the drawing.

Materials, Supplies, & Equipment:
1. Flashcards for subtraction facts and word numbers.

2. Place value materials

3. Clock model

4. Number chart 0–99

Activities:

1. Count out loud with the student(s) by nines to 108 without using the *number chart*.

2. Drill addition facts using *Drill #1, Worksheet 13*.

3. Drill the *subtraction facts with minuends 1–18* using *flashcards* without the answers showing.

4. Write several problems similar to those in **Student Activity One** on the board (e.g., 3 thousands = ___, 5 hundreds = ___, 4 tens = ___). Using *place value materials*, have the student(s) count 3 thousands to equal 3,000 (1,000; 2,000; 3,000), 5 hundreds to equal 500 (100, 200, 300, 400, 500), and 4 tens to equal 40 (10, 20, 30, 40). The student(s) should be able to complete **Student Activity One** by themselves.

5. Place the *word number flashcards* for the multiples of ten on the board rail to provide a spelling reference for the student(s) as they complete **Student Activity Two**.

6. Write the same time on the board as is displayed on the face of the *clock model*. Have the student(s) tell if the two times are the same (=) or not the same (≠) by stating the time on the clock face and comparing the two times. Do this for several other quarter hour times with some times the same and some not the same. The student(s) should be able to complete **Student Activity Three** on their own.

7. Using the *number chart*, point to several multiples of nine. Have the student(s) tell the number that is nine less and the number that is nine more than each number. Remind them that "before" and "after" mean to subtract and to add. The student(s) should be able to complete **Student Activity Four** independently using the *number chart* if needed.

8. The student(s) should be able to complete **Student Activity Five** and **Six** independently. Check to see they begin with the ones' column in both addition and subtraction.

Worksheet:

1. *Worksheet 13* – Addition drill sheet

Friends are hard to keep if you treat them wrong.

Lesson 27

Concepts:
Counting by nines, place value (thousands), before and after by nines, word problems, time, addition, and subtraction

Objectives:

1. The student shall be able to count out loud by nines to 108.

2. The student shall be able to write the value of a given number of thousands, hundreds, tens, and ones as a sum.

3. The student shall be able to write the number that is nine more and nine less than a given number.

4. The student shall be able to write the addition fact necessary to solve a word problem and label the answer.

5. The student shall be able to write the correct time displayed on the face of the clock for the hour, half hour, and quarter hour.

6. The student shall be able to write the correct sum for two four-digit numbers when the ones' column has a double-digit answer.

Teaching Tips:

1. When the student(s) do activity 7, allow them to set the *clock model* for given times. Remind them the hour is always the number the hand has just past and not the number to which it is closer. Ask them where the minute hand is on the hour, on the half hour, and on the two quarter hours.

Materials, Supplies, & Equipment:

1. Flashcards for subtraction facts

2. Place value materials

3. Number chart 0–99

4. Clock model

Activities:

1. Count out loud with the student(s) by nines to 108 without using the *number chart*.

2. Drill addition facts using *Drill #2, Worksheet 13*.

3. Drill the *subtraction facts with minuends 1–18* using *flashcards* without the answers showing.

4. "4 thousands + 5 hundreds + 2 tens + 6 ones = __ + __ + __ + __" should be written on the board. Have the student(s) tell the value of 4 thousands to write in the first blank, 5 hundreds to write in the second, 2 tens to write in the third, and 6 ones to write in the last blank. *Place value materials* should be helpful. Explain to the student(s) this is the expanded form (4,000 + 500 + 20 + 6) of a number. Put several more problems similar to the one above on the board to be completed by the student(s). They should be able to complete **Student Activity One** by themselves.

5. Point to several multiples of nine on the *number chart* and have the student(s) tell the number that is nine less and nine more. Allow the student(s) to use a *number chart* if necessary when completing **Student Activity Two** and **Three**.

6. In **Student Activity Four**, notice that the key word is "joined." Have the student(s) read the word problem, tell the key word, decide if they add or subtract, write the fact, and label the answer.

7. Using the *clock model*, display several times for the hour, half hour, and quarter hour. Instruct the student(s) to write the times on a piece of paper. Check their answers by writing the correct time on the board. They should be able to complete **Student Activity Five** independently.

8. The student(s) should be able to complete **Student Activity Six** on their own.

9. Have the student(s) look at **Student Activity Seven**. Point them to the answer that is given for "12 – 3" (9). Instruct them to continue around the flower petals by finding the answer to "12 – 6," "12 – 9," etc. and writing the answer on the big petal.

Worksheets:

1. *Worksheet 14* – Number ladder

2. *Worksheet 13* – Addition drill sheet

Lesson 28

Concepts:
    Counting by fours, place value (thousands), time, ordinal numbers, equal and not equal, addition, subtraction, and word problems

Objectives:
1. The student shall be able to count out loud by fours to 48.

2. The student shall be able to write the value of a given number of thousands, hundreds, tens, and ones as a sum.

3. The student shall be able to write the correct time displayed on the face of the clock for the hour, half hour, and quarter hour.

4. The student shall be able to write the correct symbol (= or ≠) between an ordinal number and an ordinal number abbreviation.

5. When given three numbers, the student shall be able to circle the number that is least.

6. The student shall be able to write the correct sum for three double-digit numbers when the ones' column has a double-digit answer.

7. The student shall be able to write the correct difference of two four-digit numbers.

Teaching Tips:
1. Using *Worksheet 1*, have the student(s) circle all the twos and color all the fours blue. Discuss with them how every other two is used in counting by fours. Have the student(s) write the twos to 24 and the fours to 48 as a sequence at the bottom of the page.

Materials, Supplies, & Equipment:
1. Number chart 0–99

2. Flashcards for subtraction facts and ordinal numbers

3. Place value materials

4. Clock model

5. Small clock model for student(s)

Activities:

1. Count out loud with the student(s) by fours to 48 using the *number chart*.

2. Drill addition facts using *Drill #3, Worksheet 13*.

3. Drill the *subtraction facts with minuends 1–18* using *flashcards* without the answers showing.

4. "2 thousands + 7 hundreds + 4 tens + 5 ones = __ + __ + __ + __" should be written on the board. Have the student(s) tell the value of each and write it in the blanks. *Place value materials* should be helpful. Explain to the student(s) this is the expanded form (2,000 + 700 + 40 + 5) of a number. Put several problems, similar to the one above, on the board to be completed by the student(s). They should be able to complete **Student Activity One** by themselves.

5. Give the student(s) the *small clock models*. Write several hour, half hour, and quarter hour times on the board. Have the student(s) set their clocks and check the time by your *clock model*. Remind them to set the minute hand first and then the hour hand. The student(s) should now be able to complete **Student Activity Two**.

6. Review with the student(s) *ordinal numbers* and their abbreviations using *flashcards*. After completing the first problem in each column of **Student Activity Three**, they should be able to finish without further help.

7. Using the *number chart*, point to three numbers from the same family (twenties, thirties, etc.) and have the student(s) choose the largest or greatest number and smallest or least number. Look at the directions for **Student Activity Four**. Explain the meaning of the word "least" as being the same as smallest. The student(s) should be able to complete the activity on their own.

8. In **Student Activity Five** have the student(s) check their answers by adding up and then adding down.

9. The student(s) should be able to complete **Student Activity Six** and **Seven** independently.

Worksheets:

1. *Worksheet 13* – Addition drill sheet

2. *Worksheet 1* – Number chart 0–99

Lesson 29

Concepts:

Counting by fours, ordinal numbers, word problems, counting over 100, addition, and subtraction

Objectives:

1. The student shall be able to count out loud by fours to 48.

2. The student shall be able to write the name of a given book in respect to its ordinal position.

3. The student shall be able to write the missing numbers when counting by fours.

4. When given three numbers, the student shall be able to circle the number that is least.

5. The student shall be able to write the missing numbers when counting by ones over one hundred.

6. The student shall be able to write the correct sum for three double-digit numbers when the ones' column has a double-digit answer.

7. The student shall be able to write the correct difference of two four-digit numbers.

Teaching Tips:

1. You will want to take time today to check all student(s) proficiency in the subtraction facts, determine their area of weakness, and make arrangements for further drill if needed. *Worksheet 15* could be used to help determine the areas of weakness. Further drill could be arranged before or after school, at lunch or recess, with student and student, teacher and student, or volunteer help (maybe an older student or parent) and student.

Materials, Supplies, & Equipment:

1. Number chart 0–99

2. Flashcards for subtraction facts and ordinal numbers

Activities:

1. Count out loud with the student(s) by fours to 48 using the *number chart*.

2. Drill addition facts using *Drill #4, Worksheet 13*.

3. Drill the *subtraction facts with minuends 1–18* using *flashcards* without the answers showing. The next lesson will be the last time the subtraction drill will be done with flashcards on a daily basis. The drill will then be done using drill sheets from the worksheets and with flashcards.

4. Say and spell each *ordinal number* and its abbreviation with the aid of *flashcards*. Have the student(s) read the names on each of the books in **Student Activity One**. Read the first three sentences together with the student(s) and fill in the blanks. Allow them to continue on their own.

5. The student(s) should be able to complete **Student Activity Two** by themselves using the *number chart* if necessary.

6. Write several sets of three double-digit numbers on the board (e.g., 59, 36, 40). From each set, have the student(s) choose the greatest number and the least number. Ask them what the word "least" means (smallest). After going over the directions for **Student Activity Three**, the student(s) should be able to finish without further help.

7. After allowing the student(s) to complete **Student Activity Four** with no help, discuss the key word (more), if they added or subtracted, the addition fact, and the correct label.

8. Allow the student(s) to count out loud from 245 to 260, 382 to 395, 510 to 523, etc. by adding the hundreds digit to each number on the *number chart 0–99*. After the student(s) count the first row of **Student Activity Five** together, have them complete the remaining rows independently.

9. The student(s) should be able to complete **Student Activity Six** and **Seven** by themselves remembering to check the addition by adding up and down.

Worksheets:

1. *Worksheet 15* – Subtraction facts

2. *Worksheet 13* – Addition drill sheet

Lesson 30

Concepts:
> Counting by fours, addition (horizontal to vertical), before and after by fours, and subtraction

Objectives:
1. The student shall be able to count out loud by fours to 48.

2. The student shall be able to write the correct sum of a horizontal addition problem of three double-digit numbers rewritten vertically.

3. The student shall be able to write the numbers that come before and after a given number when counting by fours.

4. When given three numbers, the student shall be able to circle the number that is least.

5. The student shall be able to correctly arrange a given set of numbers in the proper sequence.

Teaching Tips:
1. When doing activity 5, have the student(s) copy the horizontal addition problems from the board and practice writing them in correct columns on their own sheet of paper and find the answers. This assures you that every student is attempting to work the problem correctly. As they work it together on the board they need to check their own work. Encourage them to ask questions if they did not write the numbers in the correct columns or find the correct answer. For student(s) with consistent problems in lining up their columns, let them use graph paper as a practice sheet.

Materials, Supplies, & Equipment:
1. Flashcards for addition and subtraction facts

2. Number chart 0–99

Activities:

1. Administer *Test 3*.

2. Count out loud with the student(s) by fours to 48 without using the *number chart*.

3. Have the student(s) take a clean sheet of paper on which to write the answers for their addition facts. Take ten *addition flashcards*. Show each card for 5 seconds as the student(s) write the answers in a column. Check the answers before you begin the second set of ten cards. Do as many sets as time permits in 7 minutes.

4. Drill the *subtraction facts with minuends 1–18* using *flashcards* without the answers showing. This is the last lesson subtraction facts will be drilled by flashcards on a daily basis. The drill will then be done using drill sheets from the worksheets and with flashcards.

5. Write several sets of three double-digit numbers on the board as a horizontal addition problem (e.g., 36 + 23 + 17). Demonstrate to the student(s) how to write the problem vertically. Write the first double-digit number by itself. Underneath it, write the second double-digit number, being careful to place the tens and ones in their corresponding columns. Then place the third number underneath the first two, lining up the ones' and tens' columns. Remind them if the number is a single digit it must be placed in the ones' column. In **Student Activity One**, have the student(s) complete the first two problems together and then finish on their own.

6. Point to several multiples of four on the *number chart* as you discuss the meaning of "the number that comes before by fours" (four less, four taken away, or four subtracted) and "the number that comes after by fours" (four more, plus four, or four added). Allow the student(s) to use the *number chart* if necessary to complete **Student Activity Two**.

7. After the student(s) find the number that is least in the first group in **Student Activity Three** together, they should be able to finish by themselves.

8. The student(s) should be able to complete **Student Activity Four** independently.

9. In **Student Activity Five**, have the student(s) fill in the answers for the subtraction problems in the first box together. They should then be able to complete the remaining boxes on their own.

Lesson 31

Concepts:
Counting by fours, addition, less than, subtraction, before and after by fours, word numbers, and word problems

Objectives:

1. The student shall be able to count out loud by fours to 48.

2. The student shall be able to write the correct sum for two double-digit numbers when the tens' column has a double-digit answer.

3. The student shall be able to circle the given numbers less than 54.

4. The student shall be able to write the difference of two double-digit numbers on the cross-number puzzle.

5. The student shall be able to write the correct numbers that come before and after a given number when counting by fours.

6. When given three numbers, the student shall be able to circle the number that is least.

7. The student shall be able to write the word number that corresponds to a given number.

Teaching Tips:

1. You may want to use the *Place Value Pockets* described in the Teaching Tips for lesson 7 to demonstrate carrying to the hundreds' place in activity 4. Use craft sticks in the first and second rows to represent the numbers to be added. Add the ones' column by combining the sticks from the ones' column and putting them in the ones' column in the third row. Then add the tens' column by combining the sticks from the ten's column and putting them in the tens' column in the third row. Discuss combining 10 tens with a rubber band to make one hundred and putting them in the hundreds' column in the third row. The third row now represents the answer.

Materials, Supplies, & Equipment:

1. Flashcards for subtraction facts and word numbers

2. Place value materials

3. Number chart 0–99

4. Place Value Pockets

Activities:

1. Count out loud with the student(s) by fours to 48 without using the *number chart*.

2. Drill addition facts using *Drill #1, Worksheet 16*.

3. Using *flashcards for subtraction facts*, drill minuends 1–18 without the answers showing.

4. On the board, write several sets of two double-digit numbers with carrying in the tens' column as vertical addition problems (e.g., 66 + 72). Place a small box above the hundreds' column similar to what is done in **Student Activity One**. Have the student(s) copy the problems on their paper. Tell them to add the ones' column and write the answer (8) as you write it on the board. Now have them add the tens' column (13). Ask if the tens' column can hold 13 tens. Demonstrate with *place value materials* the 13 tens regrouped into 10 tens or 1 hundred and 3 tens. Ask how many hundreds are in 13 tens (1) and how many tens are left over (3). Tell them to write the "3" in the tens' column and write the "1" in the small box in the hundreds' column as you do the same on the board. Now they are ready to add the hundreds' column (1). Give the same explanation for each of the addition problems written on the board. Allow the student(s) to work on their own in **Student Activity One** checking each student for proper procedure.

5. Point to several numbers on the *number chart* and have the student(s) tell if the number is less than 62. Remind them that the numbers before 62 are less and the numbers after 62 are more. After reading the directions for **Student Activity Two**, the student(s) should be able to finish by themselves.

6. In **Student Activity Three**, have the student(s) find the difference and write the answer in the cross-number puzzle. Give individual help where needed.

7. The student(s) should be able to complete **Student Activity Four** and **Seven** independently.

8. After discussing the meaning of the word "least" (smallest), the student(s) should be able to complete **Student Activity Five** without further help.

9. Display the *word number flashcards* on the board rail as a spelling reference as the student(s) complete **Student Activity Six**.

Worksheet:

1. *Worksheet 16* – Addition and subtraction drill sheet

Lesson 32

Concepts:
> Counting by fours, addition, before and after by fours, less than, counting over 100, and word numbers

Objectives:
1. The student shall be able to count out loud by fours to 48.

2. The student shall be able to write the correct sum for two double-digit numbers when the tens' column has a double-digit answer.

3. When given three numbers, the student shall be able to circle the number that is least.

4. The student shall be able to write the number that is four more and four less than a given number.

5. The student shall be able to circle the given numbers less than 128.

6. The student shall be able to write the missing numbers when counting over 100.

7. The student shall be able to write the answer for a given question as a word number.

Teaching Tips:
1. When the student(s) begin activity 2, remind them that they will now be doing subtraction for their timed drill twice a week. Arrange for additional drill time, with flashcards, for those who are not proficient in subtraction.

2. You may want to use the *Place Value Pockets* from Teaching Tips, lesson 31, when doing activity 4.

Materials, Supplies, & Equipment:
1. Flashcards for addition facts and word numbers

2. Number chart 0–99 and 100–199

3. Yardstick

4. Place Value Pockets

Activities:

1. Count out loud with the student(s) by fours to 48 without using the *number chart*.

2. Drill subtraction facts using *Drill #2, Worksheet 16*.

3. Using *flashcards for addition facts*, drill sums 1–18 without the answers showing.

4. On the board, write several sets of two double-digit numbers with carrying in the tens' column as vertical addition problems. Follow the same step by step explanation for each problem as was done in lesson 31. Be sure the student(s) begin by adding the ones' column first. Allow them to complete **Student Activity One** independently. Spend extra time with those who benefit from the extra personal attention.

5. Using the *number chart 100–199*, point to two numbers and have the student(s) tell which number is least. Now point to several groups of three numbers and have the student(s) choose the number that is least. **Student Activity Two** should be completed by the student(s) on their own.

6. Point to several multiples of four on the *number chart* and have the student(s) tell the number that is four less and four more. Allow the student(s) to use a *number chart* if necessary when completing **Student Activity Three** and **Four**.

7. Point to several numbers on the *number chart 100–199* and have the student(s) tell if the number is less than 135. Remind them that the numbers before 135 are less and the numbers after 135 are more. After reading the directions for **Student Activity Five**, the student(s) should be able to finish by themselves.

8. Beginning with the number 364, have the student(s) count by ones for at least fifteen numbers. Do the same for several other numbers over 100. The student(s) should be able to write the missing numbers in **Student Activity Six** without further help.

9. Discuss the directions for **Student Activity Seven** with the student(s). Answer each question with the student(s) but allow them to write the correct word number on their own. If the student(s) do not know the answers to some of the questions, help them discover what the answer is (e. g. look at a *yardstick* to see how many inches are on it). The *word number flashcards* would be a help in spelling the words correctly.

Worksheet:

1. *Worksheet 16* – Addition and subtraction drill sheet

Lesson 33

Concepts:
>   Counting by eights, addition, less than, word problems, subtraction, and counting over 100

Objectives:
1. The student shall be able to count out loud by eights to 96.

2. The student shall be able to write the correct sum for two triple-digit numbers when the tens' column has a double-digit answer.

3. The student shall be able to circle the given numbers less than 376.

4. The student shall be able to write the correct letter above a corresponding number that matches the difference of two numbers.

5. The student shall be able to write the missing numbers when counting over 100.

Teaching Tips:
1. Using *Worksheet 1*, have the student(s) circle all the twos, color the fours blue, and put a box around the eights. Discuss with them how every other two is used in counting by fours and every other four is used in counting by eights. Have the student(s) write the twos to 24, the fours to 48, and the eights to 96 as a sequence at the bottom of the page.

2. You may want to use the *Place Value Pockets* from Teaching Tips, lesson 31, when doing activity 4.

Materials, Supplies, & Equipment:
1. Number chart 0–99

2. Flashcards for subtraction facts

3. Place value materials

4. Place Value Pockets

Activities:

1. Count out loud with the student(s) by eights to 96.

2. Drill addition facts using *Drill #3, Worksheet 16*.

3. Using *flashcards for subtraction facts*, drill minuends 1–18.

4. On the board, write several sets of two triple-digit numbers with carrying in the tens' column as vertical addition problems (e. g. 367 + 481). Place a small box above the hundreds' column. Have the student(s) copy the problems on their paper. Tell them to add the ones' column and write the answer (8) as you write it on the board. Now have them add the tens' column (14). Ask if the tens' column can hold 14 tens. Demonstrate with *place value materials* the regrouping of the 14 tens into 10 tens or 1 hundred and 4 tens. Tell them to write the "4" in the tens' column and write the "1" in the small box in the hundreds' column as you do the same on the board. Now they are ready to add the three numbers in the hundreds' column. Tell them to write "8" in the hundreds' column as you write it on the board. Give the same explanation for each of the addition problems written on the board. Allow the student(s) to work on their own in **Student Activity One** checking each student for proper procedure.

5. Write several three-digit numbers (some greater than 350 and some less than 350) on the board. Have the student(s) tell which numbers are less than 350. Remind them that when counting the numbers that come before 350 are less and the numbers that come after 350 are more. The student(s) should be able to complete **Student Activity Two** on their own.

6. **Student Activity Three** should be completed by the student(s) by themselves.

7. In **Student Activity Four**, have the student(s) find the difference for the first subtraction problem. Then ask them what letter they are going to put above the 22 (S). Allow them to complete the secret code giving help only when needed.

8. Begin counting out loud by ones with the student(s) at several numbers over 100 for 15 consecutive numbers. The student(s) should then be able to do **Student Activity Five** independently.

Worksheets:

1. *Worksheet 17* – Addition with carrying in tens' column

2. *Worksheet 16* – Addition and subtraction drill sheet

3. *Worksheet 1* – Number chart 0–99

Lesson 34

Concepts:
> Counting by eights, number sequence, addition, and word problems

Objectives:
1. The student shall be able to count out loud by eights to 96.

2. The student shall be able to write the next three numbers in a given sequence of numbers.

3. The student shall be able to write the missing number when adding or subtracting a given number in a sequence.

4. The student shall be able to write the missing numbers when counting by eights.

5. The student shall be able to write the correct sum for two triple-digit numbers when the tens' column has a double-digit answer.

Teaching Tips:
1. Before starting activity 2, do some mental drill with the student(s) similar to the problems in *Student Activity Two* (e. g. $7 + 4 = \underline{} - 6 = \underline{} + 8 = \underline{} - 9 = \underline{} + 5 = \underline{}$). Increase the speed just a little each time.

2. When doing activity 4, draw the first square on the board. As the student(s) tell the answers write them in the boxes as a guide for the student(s) to follow.

Materials, Supplies, & Equipment:
1. Number chart 0–99

2. Flashcards for addition facts

3. Place value materials

Activities:

1. Count out loud with the student(s) by eights to 96 using the *number chart*.

2. Drill subtraction facts using *Drill #4, Worksheet 16*. Remind the student(s) that this is a subtraction drill.

3. Using *flashcards for addition facts*, drill sums 1–18 without the answers showing.

4. Count out loud three numbers by ones and have the student(s) count out loud the next three numbers (e.g., 73, 74, 75, __, __, __). Do several numbers over 100 up to 999 in the same manner. After completing the first sequence with the student(s) in **Student Activity One**, allow them to finish by themselves.

5. Start **Student Activity Two** by working the first problem with the student(s). Then have them do the remaining problems alone. Give individual help where needed.

6. Allow the student(s) to use the *number chart* if necessary when completing **Student Activity Three**.

7. Tell the student(s) to add going across (4 + 5 and 3 + 2) in the first box in **Student Activity Four** and write the answers in the empty boxes to the right. Now have them add going down (4 + 3 and 5 + 2) and write the answers in the empty boxes at the bottom. The student(s) should now add the answers going down and across (9 + 5 and 7 + 7). They will discover that the sums for the answers going across and down are the same (14). Have them write that answer in the last empty box on the right in the third row. Ask the student(s) to complete the remaining boxes on their own. Check to see that they get the same number for the last box on the right in the third row.

8. Use *place value materials* to review carrying in the tens' column. Notice there are no longer any little boxes above the hundreds' column. As the student(s) are completing **Student Activity Five**, spot check their answers to detect any reoccurring errors. Remind them to always add the ones' column first, then the tens' column, and last the hundreds' column.

9. The student(s) will need to write the addition facts in **Student Activity Six** vertically. Be sure they label their answers.

Worksheet:

1. *Worksheet 16* – Addition and subtraction drill sheet

Lesson 35

Concepts:
    Counting by eights, number sequence, before and after by eights, subtraction, addition, and word problems

Objectives:

1. The student shall be able to count out loud by eights to 96.

2. The student shall be able to write the next three numbers in a given sequence of numbers.

3. The student shall be able to write the numbers that come before and after a given number when counting by eights.

4. The student shall be able to write the correct sum for two triple-digit numbers when the tens' column has a double-digit answer.

5. The student shall be able to correctly arrange a given set of numbers in the proper sequence.

Teaching Tips:

1. When doing activity 2, you may want to adjust the time to meet the needs of the student(s). If doing three sets of addition and then three sets of subtraction better meets your needs than doing one of each, do so. A variety in drill method, through the use of other senses, will enhance learning by making it more thorough and more permanent.

Materials, Supplies, & Equipment:

1. Flashcards for addition and subtraction facts

2. Number chart 0–99

3. Place value materials

Activities:

1. Count out loud with the student(s) by eights to 96 without using the *number chart*.

2. Have the student(s) take a clean sheet of paper on which to write the answers for their addition and subtraction facts. Take ten *addition flashcards*. Show each card for 5 seconds as the student(s) write the answers in a column. Check the answers before you begin the next set of ten *subtraction flashcards*. Do as many sets as time permits in 7 minutes.

3. Count out loud three numbers by twos and have the student(s) count out loud the next three numbers (e.g., 52, 54, 56, __, __, __). Do several numbers over 100 up to 999 in the same manner. After completing the first sequence with the student(s) in **Student Activity One**, allow them to finish by themselves.

4. Point to several multiples of eight on the *number chart* as you discuss the meaning of "the number that comes before by eights" (eight less, eight taken away, or eight subtracted) and "the number that comes after by eights" (eight more, plus eight, or eight added). Allow the student(s) to use the *number chart* if necessary to complete **Student Activity Two**.

5. Have the student(s) look at **Student Activity Three**. Point them to the answer that is given for "9 − 0" (9). Instruct them to continue going around the flower petals by finding the answer for "9 − 5," "9 − 7," etc. and writing the answers on the big petals.

6. Use *place value materials* to demonstrate carrying in the tens' column. As the student(s) are completing **Student Activity Four**, check their first three answers for accuracy. Watch for common mistakes made by the student(s).

7. The student(s) should be able to complete **Student Activity Five** and **Six** on their own.

*It is easier to turn over a new leaf than
to tear out some of the old pages.*

Lesson 36

Concepts:
Counting by eights, subtraction regrouping, before and after by eights, and number sequence

Objectives:
1. The student shall be able to count out loud by eights to 96.

2. The student shall be able to write the regrouping of one ten to ten ones for borrowing in subtraction.

3. The student shall be able to write the numbers that come before and after a given number when counting by eights.

4. The student shall be able to write the next three numbers in a given sequence of numbers.

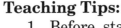

Teaching Tips:
1. Before starting activity 4, give each student a bundle of ten *straws* held together by a *rubber band*. Discuss with the student(s) how the one bundle of ten represents one ten in the tens' place. When the *rubber band* is taken off then the one group of ten becomes ten ones in the ones' place. Do the same with three groups of ten and change them to two groups of ten and ten ones.

2. When doing activity 7, draw a ladder (the same as the first one in **Student Activity Four**) on the board. As the student(s) tell the answers to the first three steps, write the answers on the correct steps. This will give the student(s) a concrete example to follow in filling in the answers.

Materials, Supplies, & Equipment:
1. Flashcards for subtraction facts

2. Place value materials

3. Number chart 0–99

4. Straws and rubber bands

Activities:

1. Count out loud with the student(s) by eights to 96 without using the *number chart*.

2. Drill addition facts using *Drill #1, Worksheet 18*.

3. Using *flashcards for subtraction facts*, drill minuends 1–18 without the answers showing.

4. Use *place value materials* to demonstrate how 2 tens can be regrouped to equal 1 ten and 10 ones, 4 tens to equal 3 tens and 10 ones, and 8 tens to equal 7 tens and 10 ones. Be sure the student(s) grasp the fact that 1 ten is the same as 10 ones. When adding, 10 ones must be changed to 1 ten and when subtracting, 1 ten often has to be changed to 10 ones. This is the introductory work for borrowing in subtraction. Have the student(s) do the first problem in **Student Activity One** together and finish the remaining ones by themselves.

5. Using the *number chart*, point to several multiples of eight. Have the student(s) tell the number that is eight less and the number that is eight more than each number. Ask them what "before" and "after" mean (subtract and add). The student(s) should be able to complete **Student Activity Two** independently using the *number chart* if needed.

6. Write "115 118 121 ___ ___ ___" on the board. Have the student(s) tell the sequence used to form the first three numbers (adding 3). Then have them tell the next three numbers in the sequence. Do several sequences using numbers from 200 to 999 and a sequence of adding three. Allow the student(s) to complete **Student Activity Three** independently. Be available to help those who need it.

7. Ask the student(s) to look at the ladders in **Student Activity Four**. Complete the first three steps on the first ladder together with the student(s) (9 − 3 = 6 − write "6" on the first step, 9 + 6 = 15 − write "15" on the second step, and 9 − 7 = 2 − write "2" on the third step). Allow the student(s) to continue the remaining steps on the ladders by themselves.

Worksheet:

1. *Worksheet 18* – Addition and subtraction drill sheet

*Patience is displayed when you count down
before you blast off.*

Lesson 37

Concepts:
Counting by eights, subtraction regrouping, before and after by eights, and addition

Objectives:

1. The student shall be able to count out loud by eights to 96.

2. The student shall be able to write the regrouping of one ten to ten ones for borrowing in subtraction.

3. The student shall be able to write the number that is eight more and eight less than a given number when counting by eights.

4. The student shall be able to write the correct sum for two four-digit numbers when the tens' column has a double-digit answer.

Teaching Tips:

1. Allow the student(s) to use the *place value materials* when doing activity 4, if available. If not, give them *straws* in bundles of ten and ones. Have them follow the steps for regrouping with *straws* while you do it with the *place value materials*.

2. Before doing activity 7, draw a triangle similar to the one in **Student Activity Five** and write a single-digit number in each angle of the inner triangle. Following the steps in activity 7, have the student(s) tell the sum to be written in each angle of each remaining triangle. Then have them find the total of the three angles in the largest triangle.

Materials, Supplies, & Equipment:

1. Flashcards for addition facts

2. Place value materials

3. Number chart 0–99

4. Straws

104

Activities:

1. Count out loud with the student(s) by eights to 96 without using the *number chart*.

2. Drill subtraction facts using *Drill #2, Worksheet 18*.

3. Using *flashcards for addition facts*, drill sums 1–18 without the answers showing.

4. Use *place value materials* to demonstrate how the student(s) can regroup 3 tens and 4 ones to equal 2 tens and 14 ones, 6 tens and 6 ones to equal 5 tens and 16 ones, and 5 tens and 3 ones to equal 4 tens and 13 ones. Ask the student(s) how many ones in one ten. Have the student(s) complete **Student Activity One** on their own.

5. Point to several multiples of eight on the *number chart* and have the student(s) tell the number that is eight less and eight more. Allow the student(s) to use a *number chart* if necessary when completing **Student Activity Two** and **Three**.

6. On the board, write two four-digit numbers as an addition problem with carrying in the tens' column. Have the student(s) copy the problem on a sheet of paper and find the answer. Then let a student tell you how to work the problem. The student(s) should be able to complete **Student Activity Four** without further help.

7. Have the student(s) look at **Student Activity Five**. Ask them to find the numbers 6 and 5 at two of the vertices on the inner triangle. Tell them to add the numbers and notice where the sum is written (D). Find the numbers 6 and 9 and ask the student(s) where to write the sum (F). After writing the sum of 9 and 5 at B, have them look at D and F, add the two numbers (11 + 15), and write the sum for E (26), A (29), and C (25). Allow the student(s) to do the second triangle on their own.

Worksheet:

1. *Worksheet 18* – Addition and subtraction drill sheet

The greatest of all faults is to say that
you have none at all.

Lesson 38

Concepts:
Counting by sevens, time (hour), subtraction regrouping, equal and not equal, addition, and counting over 100

Objectives:
1. The student shall be able to count out loud by sevens to 84.

2. The student shall be able to draw both hands on the face of the clock for the hour.

3. The student shall be able to write the regrouping of one ten to ten ones for borrowing in subtraction.

4. The student shall be able to write the correct symbol (= or ≠) between two addition facts.

5. The student shall be able to write the correct sum for two four-digit numbers when the tens' column has a double-digit answer.

6. The student shall be able to write the missing numbers when counting by sevens and ones over 100.

Teaching Tips:
1. If the student(s) have difficulty in being accurate when doing *Student Activity Three*, have them write the answer for each addition fact on their paper above the fact before they attempt to choose the correct symbol.

2. Using *Worksheet 1*, have the student(s) circle all the sevens when doing activity 1. Have them write the sevens to 84 as a sequence at the bottom of the page. The student(s) would find *Worksheet 1* helpful when doing *Student Activity Five*.

Materials, Supplies, & Equipment:
1. Number chart 0–99

2. Clock model

3. Small clock model for student(s)

4. Place value materials

Activities:
1. Count out loud with the student(s) by sevens to 84 using the *number chart*.

2. Drill addition facts using *Drill #3, Worksheet 18*.

3. Using *flashcards for subtraction facts*, drill minuends 1–18 without the answers showing.

4. Give the student(s) a *small clock model*. Write several times for the hour on the board and have them set their clocks to match the hour times. Remind them to place the minute hand in position first and then the hour hand since the placement of the hour hand depends on where the minute hand is located. Allow them to check their time by your *clock model*. As the student(s) begin **Student Activity One**, remind them to also draw the minute hand first and then the hour hand.

5. Discuss with the student(s) how you can take 1 group of ten and regroup it as 10 ones using *place value materials*. Write "9 tens + 0 ones = 8 tens + __ ones" on the board. Ask the student(s) what they should do with the 1 ten that was taken away from the 9 tens to make the sentence a true statement (regroup it as 10 ones). Do several similar sentences for the student(s) to fill in the blanks. They should be able to complete **Student Activity Two** by themselves.

6. Write "5 + 3 __ 7 + 2" on the board. Have the student(s) tell if the addition facts are equal or not equal. Insist that they say the answer to each fact before they decide to write equal or not equal. Do not allow them to guess. Do several examples before you have the student(s) complete **Student Activity Three** independently.

7. The student(s) should be able to complete **Student Activity Four** on their own.

8. Have the student(s) look at **Student Activity Five**. Help them fill in the boxes in the first column beginning with the 7. Then have them do the first row which also begins with 7. Tell them that all rows and columns do not begin with 7. For some boxes, they will have to write the number for 7 less to find the correct answer. Continue to help those who need it until the puzzle is completed.

9. The student(s) should be able to complete **Student Activity Six** by themselves.

Worksheets:
1. *Worksheet 18* – Addition and subtraction drill sheet

2. *Worksheet 1* – Number chart 0–99

Lesson 39

Concepts:
Counting by sevens, place value, time (half hour), addition, subtraction regrouping, and equal and not equal

Objectives:
1. The student shall be able to count out loud by sevens to 84.

2. The student shall be able to write the value of a given number of thousands, hundreds, tens, and ones and the number it represents.

3. The student shall be able to draw both hands on the face of the clock for the half hour.

4. The student shall be able to write the sum for two four-digit numbers when the tens' column has a double-digit answer.

5. The student shall be able to write the regrouping of one ten to ten ones for borrowing in subtraction.

6. The student shall be able to write the missing numbers when counting by sevens.

7. The student shall be able to write the correct symbol (= or ≠) between two addition facts.

Teaching Tips:
1. Award those student(s) who have completed all four drills on *Worksheet 18* without errors.

Materials, Supplies, & Equipment:
1. Number chart 0–99

2. Flashcards for addition facts

3. Clock model

4. Small clock model for student(s)

5. Place value materials

Activities:

1. Count out loud with the student(s) by sevens to 84 using the *number chart*.

2. Drill subtraction facts using *Drill #4, Worksheet 18*.

3. Using *flashcards for addition facts*, drill sums 1–18 without the answers showing.

4. "4 thousands + 8 hundreds + 3 tens + 6 ones = __ + __ +__ + __= __" should be written on the board. Have the student(s) tell the value of 4 thousands and write it in the first blank, 8 hundreds in second blank, etc. Then have them tell the number the expanded form represents. Do this for several similar problems. Work the first two problems in **Student Activity One** with the student(s). Allow them to complete the remaining ones on their own.

5. Write several times for the half hour on the board. Have the student(s) set their *small clock models* to match the half hour times. Ask them which hand they should place first and why (minute hand – because the position of the hour hand depends on where the minute hand is located). Set your *clock model* for the student(s) to verify the placement of their clock's hands. The student(s) should be able to complete **Student Activity Two** by themselves.

6. After you remind the student(s) to add the ones' column first, they should be able to complete **Student Activity Three** without further help.

7. Give the student(s) *place value materials*. Have them demonstrate 3 tens and 2 ones. Ask them how many ones they will have if they take 1 group of ten and add it to the 2 ones (12). Have them tell how many tens and how many ones they now have. Write "7 tens + 4 ones = 6 tens and __ ones" on the board. Ask them how many ones they will have when one ten is changed to ones and added to the 4 ones they already have. Do several more problems of this nature with the student(s) before they complete **Student Activity Four**.

8. Allow the student(s) to use the *number chart,* if needed, as they do **Student Activity Five**.

9. Remind the student(s) to find the sum of both addition facts (write it down if necessary) before they choose which is the correct symbol in **Student Activity Six**.

Worksheets:

1. *Worksheet 19* – Place value

2. *Worksheet 18* – Addition and subtraction drill sheet

Lesson 40

Concepts:
Counting by sevens, place value, word numbers, addition, equal and not equal, time (quarter hour), before and after by sevens, and subtraction regrouping

Objectives:

1. The student shall be able to count out loud by sevens to 84.

2. The student shall be able to write the correct digit for the thousands', hundreds', tens', and ones' place in a given number.

3. The student shall be able to write the word number that corresponds to the answer for a given addition problem.

4. The student shall be able to write the correct symbol (= or ≠) between a subtraction fact and a whole number.

5. The student shall be able to draw both hands on the face of the clock for a given quarter hour.

6. The student shall be able to write the numbers that come before and after a given number by sevens.

7. The student shall be able to write the regrouping of one ten to ten ones for borrowing in subtraction.

Teaching Tips:

1. Take time to draw the puzzle in **Student Activity Two** on the board before class begins. As the student(s) give the answer to the first addition problem, write the word number on the puzzle as a guide for them to follow. Show them where the word number needs to be written for the second addition problem.

Materials, Supplies, & Equipment:

1. Flashcards for addition facts, subtraction facts, and word numbers

2. Clock model

3. Small clock model for student(s)

4. Number chart 0–99

Activities:

1. Administer *Test 4*.

2. Count out loud with the student(s) by sevens to 84.

3. Have the student(s) take a clean sheet of paper on which to write the answers for their addition and subtraction facts. Take ten addition flashcards. Show each card for 5 seconds as the student(s) write the answers in a column. Check the answers before you begin the next set of ten *subtraction flashcards*. Do as many sets as time permits in 7 minutes.

4. Write several four-digit numbers on the board. Have the student(s) tell what number is in the thousands', hundreds', tens', and ones' place. Then ask them to tell the value of each digit as you write it on the board in expanded form. The student(s) should be able to complete *Student Activity One* on their own.

5. Ask the student(s) to find the answer to the first addition problem in *Student Activity Two*. Tell them to point to number "1" on the puzzle and write the word number for the answer going across (forty-nine). After the student(s) have found the answer to the second problem, have them point to number "2" and write the word number going down (fifty-seven). As they finish the puzzle, help those who need it. The *word numbers flashcards* would aid in spelling.

6. Write several subtraction facts on the board horizontally with some answers correct and some not correct. Have the student(s) tell if they should put an = or ↑ symbol between the fact and its answer. The student(s) should be able to complete *Student Activity Three* by themselves.

7. Write several times for the quarter hour on the board. Give the student(s) the *small clock models*. Have them set the hands on the clock to represent the given times. Let them check their clock by your *clock model*. *Student Activity Four* should be completed by the student(s) without further help.

8. Point to several multiples of seven on the *number chart* as you discuss the meaning of "the number that comes before by sevens" and "the number that comes after by seven" Allow the student(s) to use the number chart if necessary to complete *Student Activity Five*.

9. Write several problems similar to those in *Student Activity Six* on the board. Ask the student(s) how many ones have been added to the ones (10). Then see if they can tell from where the 10 came. Discuss how many tens are left and write the number in the blank. Have the student(s) complete the first two equations together in *Student Activity Six* and then finish independently.

Worksheets

Lesson 41

Concepts:
Counting by sevens, estimation, word numbers, subtraction regrouping, place value, before and after by sevens, and addition

Objectives:
1. The student shall be able to count out loud by sevens to 84.

2. The student shall be able to write the correct number (0 or 10) to which a given number is closer.

3. The student shall be able to write the word number that corresponds to a given number.

4. The student shall be able to circle the correct regrouping of one ten to ten ones for borrowing in subtraction.

5. The student shall be able to write the correct value of the thousands', hundreds', tens', and ones' digit in a given number in expanded form.

6. The student shall be able to write the numbers that come before and after a given number when counting by sevens.

7. The student shall be able to write the sum for two four-digit numbers when the tens' column has a double-digit answer.

Teaching Tips:
1. If some student(s) have difficulty when starting **Student Activity One**, have them use a *centimeter ruler* if a number line is not readily available to them.

Materials, Supplies, & Equipment:
1. Flashcards for subtraction facts and word numbers

2. Number line

3. Number chart 0–99

4. Centimeter ruler

Activities:

1. Count out loud with the student(s) by sevens to 84 without using the *number chart*.

2. Drill addition facts using *Drill #1, Worksheet 20*.

3. Using *flashcards for subtraction facts*, drill minuends 1–18 without the answers showing.

4. On a *number line*, point to the numbers 0 and 10. Tell the student(s) they are going to discuss the numbers that fall between 0 and 10. Ask them what number falls in the middle between 0 and 10 and therefore not closer to one than the other (5). Point to each of the other numbers at random and have the student(s) tell if the number is closer to 0 or 10. The student(s) should be able to complete **Student Activity One** on their own using a *number line* if needed.

5. Point to several numbers on the *number chart* and have the student(s) say and spell the word numbers. Place the *word number flashcards*, for the multiples of ten, on the board rail for the student(s) to use as spelling reference as they complete **Student Activity Two**.

6. Write "3 tens + 6 ones = __ tens + __ ones" on the board. Ask the student(s) how many ones they will have if they take 1 ten, change it to 10 ones, and add the 10 ones to the 6 ones (16). Discuss how many tens they will have left (2). Write the answers in the blanks. Do several equations asking the same questions. The student(s) should then be able to complete **Student Activity Three**.

7. Discuss with the student(s) the value of each digit in several four-digit numbers and write the values in expanded form. The student(s) should be able to complete **Student Activity Four** without further help.

8. Allow the student(s) to use the *number chart* if needed when completing **Student Activity Five**.

9. **Student Activity Six** should be completed by the student(s) on their own.

Worksheet:

1. *Worksheet 20* – Addition and Subtraction drill sheet

Lesson 42

Concepts:

Counting by sevens, time (5 minutes), estimation, before and after by seven, and subtraction regrouping

Objectives:

1. The student shall be able to count out loud by sevens to 84.

2. The student shall be able to circle the correct time displayed on the face of the clock for given five minute increments.

3. The student shall be able to write the correct number (10 or 20) to which a given number is closer.

4. The student shall be able to write the number that is seven more and seven less than a given number.

5. The student shall be able to write the correct regrouping of one ten to ten ones for borrowing in subtraction.

Teaching Tips:

1. Remind the student(s) that *Drill #2* in activity 2 is a subtraction drill.

2. If you feel the student(s) need more practice reading the clock for five minutes with the minutes written on the clock in activity 4, *Worksheet 21* is available.

Materials, Supplies, & Equipment:

1. Flashcards for addition facts

2. Clock model

3. Number chart 0–99

4. Centimeter ruler

Activities:

1. Count out loud with the student(s) by sevens to 84.

2. Drill subtraction facts using *Drill #2, Worksheet 20*.

3. Using *flashcards for addition facts*, drill sums 1–18 without the answers showing.

4. Using the *clock model*, show the student(s) how to count the minute numbers (in a clockwise direction) by fives using the numbers 1–12. Set the clock for 10 o'clock. Have them tell what time it is. Then move the minute hand and the hour hand so that the clock says 10:05. Set the clock for 10:10, 10:20, and 10:40 and have the student(s) tell what time the clock says. Discuss the movement of the hour hand. As the minute hand makes one complete revolution, the hour hand only moves from one number to the next. Look at **Student Activity One** with the student(s). Have them write the numbers necessary for counting by fives beginning at "1" on the second clock. To read the first clock, check to see what number the hour hand has just passed and write it. Then begin counting by fives at the number "1" until they reach the number to which the minute hand is pointing and write it. Have them tell what time is displayed on the clock. Guide the student(s) in finding the hour and the minutes for the first four clocks in **Student Activity Two**. Allow them to then finish the page on their own.

5. Point to the numbers 10 and 20 on the *number chart*. Ask what number is in the middle or half way between 10 and 20 (15). Tell the student(s) the number will be closer to 10 if it is less than 15 and closer to 20 if it is greater than 15. Choose several numbers at random and have the student(s) tell if each number is closer to 10 or 20. The student(s) should be able to complete **Student Activity Three**. Allow the use of the *number chart* or a *centimeter ruler* if necessary.

6. Point to several multiples of seven on the *number chart* and have the student(s) tell the number that is seven less and seven more. Allow the student(s) to use a *number chart* if necessary when completing **Student Activity Four** and **Five**.

7. Work the first two problems in **Student Activity Six** with the student(s). Allow them to continue by themselves.

8. The student(s) should be able to complete **Student Activity Seven** independently.

Worksheets:

1. *Worksheet 21* – Time for 5 minutes

2. *Worksheet 20* – Addition and subtraction drill sheet

Lesson 43

Concepts:
Time (5 minutes), number sequence, estimation, subtraction regrouping, and word problems

Objectives:
1. The student shall be able to write the correct time displayed on the face of the clock for given five minute increments.

2. The student shall be able to write two addition and two subtraction facts when given three numbers.

3. The student shall be able to write the next three numbers that come in a given sequence of numbers.

4. The student shall be able to write the correct number (20 or 30) to which a given number is closer.

5. The student shall be able to write the correct regrouping of one ten to ten ones for borrowing in subtraction.

Teaching Tips:
1. If your *number line* does not go to 20, use the *number chart* to demonstrate activity 6 for the student(s). They may use a *number chart* or their *centimeter ruler* as an aid when they complete the activity.

Materials, Supplies, & Equipment:
1. Flashcards for subtraction facts

2. Clock model

3. Number line

4. Number chart 0-99

5. Centimeter ruler

Activities:

1. Drill addition facts using *Drill #3, Worksheet 20*.

2. Using *flashcards for subtraction facts*, drill minuends 1–18 without the answers showing.

3. On the *clock model*, count the minute numbers by fives using the numbers 1–12. Set the clock for 8:25. Ask the student(s) what number the hour hand has just passed (8). Write the hour on the board. Then begin counting by fives at the number 1 until they reach the number to which the minute hand is pointing and write the minutes on the board. Do this several times on the *clock model* so that the student(s) can write the time on their own paper. They should be able to complete **Student Activity One** by themselves.

4. Write the numbers "4, 5, and 9" on the board. Ask the student(s) to tell two addition facts and two subtraction facts that can be written using the three numbers (4 + 5 = 9, 5 + 4 = 9, 9 − 4 = 5, 9 − 5 = 4). Do several examples similar to this one. Help the student(s) get started on **Student Activity Two** by completing the first column together.

5. Write three consecutive numbers on the board counting backwards (e.g., 15, 14, and 13). Ask the student(s) by what number (ones) they are counting. Then have them tell the next three numbers. Do several examples using numbers from 100–999. The student(s) should be able to complete **Student Activity Three** on their own.

6. Discuss with the student(s) the numbers between 20 and 30 (middle number, those greater than 25, those less than 25) with the aid of the *number line*. Choose numbers at random between 20 and 30 and have the student(s) tell if the number is closer to 20 or 30. They should be able to complete **Student Activity Four** without further help.

7. Work the first problem in **Student Activity Five** with the student(s). If they are capable, allow them to finish the activity by themselves.

8. Have the student(s) read the word problem in **Student Activity Six**. Ask them what the key word is, if they add or subtract, and what the label would be. Make sure they add the problem vertically and write the label.

Worksheet:

1. *Worksheet 20* – Addition and subtraction drill sheet

Lesson 44

Concepts:
Greater than and less than, time (5 minutes), subtraction regrouping, estimation, number sequence, and word problems

Objectives:

1. The student shall be able to write the correct symbol (< or >) between two numbers.

2. The student shall be able to write the correct time displayed on the face of the clock for given five minute increments.

3. The student shall be able to write the correct regrouping of one ten to ten ones for borrowing in subtraction.

4. The student shall be able to write the correct number (60 or 70) to which a given number is closer.

5. The student shall be able to write two addition and two subtraction facts when given three numbers.

6. The student shall be able to write the next three numbers that come in a given sequence of numbers.

Teaching Tips:

1. If the student(s) have difficulty doing activity 3, locate the numbers on the *number line* or *number chart* when making the comparisons.

2. Using *place value materials* or *straws* to demonstrate activity 5 may be a help to the student(s).

Materials, Supplies, & Equipment:

1. Flashcards for addition facts and < and >

2. Number line

3. Small clock model for student(s)

4. Clock model

5. Number chart 0–99

6. Place value materials or straws

118

Activities:

1. Drill subtraction facts using *Drill #4, Worksheet 20*.

2. Using *flashcards for addition facts*, drill sums 1–18.

3. Discuss the meaning and how to read the *< and > flashcards*. Remind the student(s) to refer to the *number line* to help distinguish between the less than and the greater than symbols. The arrow at the end of the number line where the numbers are increasing is the greater than arrow and the arrow at the end where the numbers are decreasing is the less than arrow. When placing the symbol between two numbers, the arrow always points towards the number that is less. Write several sets of two numbers on the board and have the student(s) choose which symbol should be placed between each. After the student(s) place the symbols in **Student Activity One**, have them read the sentences out loud.

4. Write several times for 5 minutes on the board. Have the student(s) set the *small clock models* for the given times. Allow them to check their clocks by your *clock model*. Give help where needed as the student(s) complete **Student Activity Two**.

5. Write "89 = __ tens + __ ones = __ tens + __ ones" on the board. In the first two blanks have the student(s) tell how many tens and ones are in the number. Then have them tell how many tens and ones they would have if they regrouped one ten to equal ten ones and write the answers in the next two blanks. Using *place value materials* or *straws* to demonstrate this may be a help to the student(s). Complete the first two sentences in **Student Activity Three** with the student(s) before they continue on their own.

6. Say the numbers 30 and 40. Ask what number is in the middle or half way between 30 and 40 (35). Tell the student(s) the number will be closer to 30 if it is less than 35 and closer to 40 if it is greater than 35. Choosing the numbers at random, have them tell if each number is closer to 30 or 40. The student(s) should be able to complete **Student Activity Four**.

7. Write "5, 8, and 13" on the board. Have the student(s) tell two addition facts, and two subtraction facts using the three numbers. Write them on the board. Use as many combinations as is necessary for them to be able to complete **Student Activity Five** on their own.

8. Point to three consecutive numbers used in counting by twos going backwards on the *number chart* (e.g., 12, 10, and 8). Ask the student(s) what sequence is being used. Then have them name the next three numbers in the sequence. After practicing several sequences by twos backwards, the student(s) should be able to complete **Student Activity Six** by themselves.

9. The student(s) should do **Student Activity Seven** independently.

Worksheet:

1. *Worksheet 20* – Addition and subtraction drill sheet

Lesson 45

Concepts:
> Greater than and less than, subtraction regrouping, time (5 minutes), number sequence, and word problems

Objectives:
1. The student shall be able to write two addition and two subtraction facts when given three numbers.

2. The student shall be able to write the correct symbol (< or >) between an addition fact and a number.

3. The student shall be able to write the correct regrouping of one ten to ten ones for borrowing in subtraction.

4. The student shall be able to write the correct time displayed on the face of the clock for given five minute increments.

5. The student shall be able to write the next three numbers that come in a given sequence of numbers.

Teaching Tips:
1. If the student(s) have difficulty with **Student Activity Two**, have them write the answer above the addition fact before they make a comparison to determine which symbol to write.

2. When doing activity 5, ask the student(s) to tell how many minutes it will take for the minute hand to move from 12 to 2, from 12 to 5, from 12 to 9, etc.

Materials, Supplies, & Equipment:
1. Flashcards for addition and subtraction facts

2. Place value materials or straws

3. Clock model

4. Small clock model for student(s)

5. Number chart 0–99

Activities:

1. Have the student(s) take a clean sheet of paper on which to write the answers for their addition and subtraction facts. Take ten *addition flashcards*. Show each card for 5 seconds as the student(s) write the answers in a column. Check the answers before you begin the next set of ten *subtraction flashcards*. Do as many sets as time permits in 7 minutes.

2. Take several *addition flashcards* with the answers showing and have the student(s) tell the other addition and the two subtraction facts that use the same three numbers. Write three numbers "7, 11, and 4" on the board. Have them tell two addition and two subtraction facts using the three numbers. The student(s) should be able to complete **Student Activity One** by themselves.

3. As you show the student(s) an *addition flashcard* without the answer showing, name a number that is greater or less than the fact. Do several examples having the student(s) tell if one is greater than or less than the other. The student(s) should now be able to complete **Student Activity Two** on their own.

4. Write "67 = ___ tens + ___ ones = ___ tens + ___ ones" on the board. Have the student(s) tell the numbers to write in the blanks. Do as many sentences as are necessary for them to gain understanding. The student(s) should be able to complete **Student Activity Three** by themselves.

5. Give the student(s) sm*all clock models*. Write several times for 5 minutes on the board. Have the student(s) set the clocks for each of the given times. Allow them to check their clocks by your *clock model*. Give help where needed as the student(s) complete **Student Activity Four**.

6. Point to three consecutive numbers used in counting by threes going backwards on the *number chart* (21, 18, and 15). Ask the student(s) what sequence is being used. Then have them name the next three numbers in the sequence. After practicing several sequences by threes backwards, the student(s) should be able to complete **Student Activity Five** by themselves.

7. The student(s) should be able to complete **Student Activity Six** independently.

Worksheet:

1. *Worksheet 22* – Time for 5 minutes

Lesson 46

Concepts:
   Estimation, greater than and less than, subtraction regrouping, word problems, time (5 minutes), and map reading

Objectives:
1. The student shall be able to circle the estimated time for several given situations.

2. The student shall be able to write the correct symbol (< or >) between a number and an addition fact.

3. The student shall be able to write the correct regrouping of one ten to ten ones for borrowing in subtraction.

4. The student shall be able to draw a line to match the time displayed on the face of the clock with a given digital time for 5 minutes.

5. The student shall be able to write the given number of miles between two locations on a map.

Teaching Tips:
1. When doing activity 8, discuss the distances to certain locations around you (e.g., Daddy drives to work, Grandma lives, Mother buys groceries, etc.). Tell the student(s) that these are estimated distances and not exact. Using the above information, make a map on the board similar to the one in *Student Activity Six*. Ask the student(s) the distance from one location to another including some distances that require addition.

Materials, Supplies, & Equipment:
1. Flashcards for subtraction facts

2. Place value materials

3. Clock model

Activities:

1. Drill addition facts using *Drill #1, Worksheet 23*.

2. Using *flashcards for subtraction facts*, drill minuends 1–18 without the answers showing.

3. Discuss the word "estimation" with the student(s) (an approximate time or educated guess about when you think something happened or is going to happen). Have the student(s) tell when they get up, what time they leave for school, when they eat lunch, when they go to bed, etc. When doing **Student Activity One**, discuss each of the situations with the student(s) and determine the answer together.

4. After reviewing how to read the symbols (compare with the arrows on the number line) and how to write the symbols correctly (the point always goes towards the smaller number), the student(s) should be able to complete **Student Activity Two** on their own.

5. Using *place value materials*, demonstrate the following statement: 91 = 8 tens + __ ones. After the student(s) have a clear understanding of regrouping one ten as ten ones and adding the ten ones to the number of ones given, they should be able to complete **Student Activity Three** by themselves.

6. Ask the student(s) to identify the key word in the word problem for **Student Activity Four**, tell if they add or subtract, and what the label should be. Check each step once they have found the answer.

7. Show the student(s) several 5 minute times on the *clock model*. Have them write the correct time on a piece of paper. Write the correct time on the board by which the student(s) may check their answers. Have the student(s) read the directions for **Student Activity Five** together before they complete the activity.

8. Have the student(s) look at **Student Activity Six**. Discuss the distance from Jack's house to Roy's house, Ken's house to Roy's house, Chuck's apartment to Jack's house, and from Chuck's apartment to Roy's house by way of Ken's house. Allow the student(s) to answer the first two questions on their own, giving direction for the third question where needed.

Worksheet:

1. *Worksheet 23* – Addition and subtraction drill sheet

Lesson 47

Concepts:
    Addition, time (5 minutes), subtraction regrouping, estimation, and word problems
    Definition: The sum is the answer in addition.

Objectives:
1. The student shall be able to write the sum of two triple-digit numbers when the ones' and the tens' columns have double-digit answers.

2. The student shall be able to write the correct time displayed on the face of the clock for given 5 minute increments.

3. The student shall be able to write the correct regrouping of one ten to ten ones for borrowing in subtraction.

4. The student shall be able to draw a line to match a given event to the estimated time that event would take place.

Teaching Tips:
1. Activity 3 could be demonstrated with the *Place Value Pockets* described in Teaching Tips for lesson 7 and enlarged upon in Teaching Tips for lesson 31.

2. Notice **Student Activity One** has different directions for addition. Discuss with the student(s) the meaning of the word "sum." The sum is the answer in addition.

Materials, Supplies, & Equipment:
1. Flashcards for addition facts

2. Place value materials

3. Clock model

4. Small clock model for student(s)

5. Place Value Pockets

Activities:

1. Drill subtraction facts using *Drill #2, Worksheet 23*.

2. Using *flashcards for addition facts*, drill sums 1–18 without the answers showing.

3. On the board, put several sets of two triple-digit numbers as an addition problem with the sum in the ones' and tens' columns being double-digit answers (e.g., 468 + 357). Place small boxes above the tens' and the hundreds' columns. As they add the ones' column, ask them what they will do with the 15 ones (change them to 1 ten and 5 ones). *Place value materials* may be helpful here. Write the "1" in the box above the tens' column and put the "5" in the answer under the ones' column. Now have them add the three numbers in the tens' column. Ask them what they are going to do with 12 tens (change them to 1 hundred and 2 tens). Write the "1" in the box above the hundreds' column and write the "2" in the answer under the tens' column. Have the student(s) tell the sum of the three numbers in the hundreds' column and write the number "8" in the answer under the hundreds' column. Write a similar problem on the board and have the student(s) copy it onto a sheet of paper. As you work through the problem this time have the student(s) work it on their paper before you write each step on the board. Have the student(s) work the first three problems of **Student Activity One** together. Continue to help those who need further guidance for the remainder of the problems.

4. Give the student(s) *small clock models*. Write several 5 minute times on the board. Have the student(s) set the clocks for each of the given times. Allow them to check their clocks by your *clock model*. The student(s) should need no further help to complete **Student Activity Two**.

5. Demonstrate "56 = ___ tens + 16 ones" using *place value materials*. If the student(s) have a clear understanding of regrouping one ten as ten ones and adding the ten ones to the number of ones given, they should be able to complete **Student Activity Three** on their own.

6. Discuss with the student(s) the events given in the pictures for **Student Activity Four**. Help them discover together which of the given times is the best estimate for each event.

7. The student(s) should be able to complete **Student Activity Five** independently.

Worksheet:

1. *Worksheet 23* – Addition and subtraction drill sheet

Lesson 48

Concepts:
Time (5 minutes), estimation, subtraction regrouping, word problems, addition, and subtraction

Objectives:

1. The student shall be able to draw the minute hand on the face of the clock for given five minute increments.

2. The student shall be able to write the correct regrouping of one ten to ten ones for borrowing in subtraction.

3. The student shall be able to write the sum of two triple-digit numbers when the ones' and the tens' columns have double-digit answers.

4. The student shall be able to write the estimated time after a given number of hours have past.

Teaching Tips:

1. *Worksheet 24* is available for the student(s) who need further practice in addition when the ones' and tens' columns have double-digit answers. You may want to use it as extra practice doing just two rows at a time. The sheet could then be used over a period of three or four days. Or you may want to use the problems when you are working with a student on a one-to-one basis. Have the student(s) do the problems while you watch so that you can help them correct their mistakes.

Materials, Supplies, & Equipment:

1. Flashcards for subtraction facts

2. Small clock model for student(s)

3. Clock model

4. Place value materials

126

Activities:
1. Drill addition facts using *Drill #3, Worksheet 23*.

2. Using *flashcards for subtraction facts*, drill minuends 1–18 without the
   answers showing.

3. Give the student(s) *small clock models*. Write several times using 5 minute intervals on the board. Have the student(s) determine where to place the minute hand and then where to place the hour hand. The student(s) should check their clocks with your *clock model*. They should be able to complete **Student Activity One** on their own.

4. Write "94 = __ tens + __ ones" on the board. With *place value materials*, demonstrate the regrouping of one ten to ten ones and add the ten ones to the number of ones given in the ones' place. Ask the student(s) what numbers should be written in the blanks. Do several similar sentences with them. They should then be able to complete **Student Activity Two** by themselves.

5. Discuss the thought process necessary to complete the second word problem after the student(s) have completed **Student Activity Three** independently.

6. On the board, write several sets of two triple-digit numbers as addition problems. Have the student(s) work each problem on a sheet of paper and then the student(s) check their answers as you work the problems on the board with them. Help those student(s) who need further assistance as they complete **Student Activity Four**.

7. Discuss with the student(s) what time it was 2 hours ago and 6 hours ago, and what time it will be in 3 hours and in 8 hours. Allow the student(s) to count on the clock to arrive at their answers if necessary. The student(s) should be able to complete **Student Activity Five** with little help.

8. Discuss with the student(s) the answer (1) written on the first subtraction wheel in **Student Activity Six**. Allow them to complete the wheel on their own once they have clear understanding of the procedure.

Worksheets:
1. *Worksheet 24* – Addition with ones and tens double-digit answers

2. *Worksheet 23* – Addition and subtraction drill sheet

Lesson 49

Concepts:
> Subtraction, time (5 minutes), word numbers (over one hundred), addition, number sequence, and word problems
> *Definition*: The answer in subtraction is called the difference.

Objectives:
1. The student shall be able to write the difference of two double-digit numbers when borrowing from the tens' column.

2. The student shall be able to draw both hands on the face of the clock for given five minute increments.

3. The student shall be able to write the correct number for the corresponding word number over one hundred.

4. The student shall be able to write the sum of two triple-digit numbers when the ones' and the tens' columns have double-digit answers.

5. The student shall be able to correctly circle every third number in a sequence of numbers and then write the circled numbers in correct sequence.

Teaching Tips:
1. Notice **Student Activity One** has different directions for subtraction. Discuss with the student(s) the meaning of the word "difference." The answer in subtraction is called the difference.

2. Give the student(s) *Worksheet 25* to use for practice when they begin activity 4. Save the unused clocks on the worksheet for future use.

Materials, Supplies, & Equipment:
1. Flashcards for addition facts and word numbers

2. Clock model

Activities:

1. Drill subtraction facts using *Drill #4, Worksheet 23*.

2. Using *flashcards for addition facts*, drill sums 1–18.

3. Write "80 – 27" as a vertical subtraction problem on the board. Ask the student(s) if they can take 7 from 0. Tell them they need to regroup 80 = 7 tens and 10 ones. This is done by making a slanted line through the 8 and writing a 7 above the 8. Then put a 1 beside the 0 to make the 0 a 10. Now they have 80 as 7 tens and 10 ones. Subtract 7 from 10 and write the answer in the ones' column. Subtract 2 from 7 and write the answer in the tens' column. Do several subtraction problems similar to the one above with a 0 in the ones' place of the top number. As the student(s) look at **Student Activity One**, point out that the first two problems have the regrouping done for them. Insist they show the regrouping on their paper as they do each problem.

4. After writing a time on the board for 5 minutes, tell the student(s) to draw the minute hand on their own clock and tell why they placed it there. Then have them draw the hour hand. Be sure that the minute hand is longer than the hour hand. The placement of the hour hand will be approximate but insist that it is closer to the correct number. Set the *clock model* for the student(s) to check their work. The student(s) should be able to complete **Student Activity Two** on their own.

5. Say several numbers between 100 and 999 and have the student(s) choose the *word number flashcards* necessary to write the numbers. The student(s) should be able to complete **Student Activity Three** by themselves.

6. Allow the student(s) to complete **Student Activity Four** independently. Check their first three answers to see that they are following the correct procedures.

7. To start **Student Activity Five**, have the student(s) count the third number after 3 and circle that number (6). Then count to the third number after 6 and circle that number (9). Let them continue circling every third number and write the sequence of the circled numbers below. Ask the student(s) if they recognize the sequence (counting by threes).

8. The student(s) should complete **Student Activity Six** alone.

Worksheets:

1. *Worksheet 25 –* Blank clocks

2. *Worksheet 23 –* Addition and subtraction drill sheet

Lesson 50

Concepts:
 Addition (horizontal to vertical), number sequence, time, subtraction, and word numbers

Objectives:
1. The student shall be able to write the sum of a horizontal addition problem of two triple-digit numbers rewritten vertically when the ones' and the tens' columns have double-digit answers.

2. The student shall be able to correctly circle every fourth number in a sequence of numbers and then write the circled numbers in correct sequence.

3. The student shall be able to write the correct time displayed on the face of the clock.

4. The student shall be able to write the difference of two double-digit numbers when borrowing from the tens' column.

5. The student shall be able to draw a line to match the correct number to the corresponding word number over one hundred.

Teaching Tips:
1. When doing activity 7, give each student one *word number flashcard*. When you say a number over one hundred, have the student(s) who have part of the number come to the front of the room and arrange themselves in the correct order to represent the number. Allow the remaining student(s) to determine if the number is correct. Or you may want to have one student choose the cards that would be needed to represent the number and arrange them in the correct order.

Materials, Supplies, & Equipment:
1. Flashcards for addition facts, subtraction facts, and word numbers

2. Place value materials

Activities:

1. Administer **Test 5.**

2. Have the student(s) take a clean sheet of paper on which to write the answers for their addition and subtraction facts. Take ten *addition flashcards*. Show each card for 5 seconds as the student(s) write the answers in a column. Check the answers before you begin the next set of ten *subtraction flashcards*. Do as many sets as time permits in 7 minutes.

3. Write several sets of two triple-digit numbers on the board as a horizontal addition problem with carrying in the tens' and the ones' places. Have the student(s) copy the problems vertically from the board onto a sheet of paper and add. Then work the problems on the board as a check for the student(s). They should be able to complete **Student Activity One** on their own. Check their vertical alignment of the last two problems.

4. Have the student(s) count the fourth number after 4 and circle the number (8) to start **Student Activity Two**. Then count to the fourth number after 8 and circle that number (12). Let them continue circling every fourth number and write the sequence of the circled numbers below. Ask the student(s) if they recognize the sequence (counting by fours).

5. The student(s) should be able to complete **Student Activity Three** independently.

6. Write "60 – 23" as a vertical subtraction problem on the board. Ask the student(s) if they can take 3 from 0. Tell them they need to regroup 60 = 5 tens and 10 ones. *Place value materials* may help here. Remind them to make a slanted line through the 6 and writing a 5 above the 6. Then put a 1 beside the 0 to make the 0 a 10. Now they have 60 as 5 tens and 10 ones. Subtract 3 from 10 and write the answer in the ones' column. Subtract 2 from 5 and write the answer in the tens' column. Do several subtraction problems similar to the one above with a 0 in the ones' place of the top number. As the student(s) look at **Student Activity Four**, insist they show the regrouping on their paper as they do each problem.

7. Say several word numbers over one hundred and have the student(s) write the numbers on a sheet of paper. They need to check their papers as you write the answers on the board. **Student Activity Five** should be completed with no further help.

A thrown stone and a spoken word cannot be recalled.

Lesson 51

Concepts:
Word sentences, time, equal and not equal, addition, word numbers, and subtraction

Objectives:

1. The student shall be able to rewrite an addition word sentence as a number sentence.

2. The student shall be able to write the correct symbol (= or ≠) between the time displayed on the face of a clock and a given digital time.

3. The student shall be able to write the sum of two triple-digit numbers when the ones' and the tens' columns have double-digit answers.

4. The student shall be able to write the word number that corresponds to a given number.

5. The student shall be able to write the difference of two double-digit numbers when borrowing from the tens' column.

Teaching Tips:

1. Discuss with the student(s) the answer to the last sentence in **Student Activity One** (5 + 12 = 17). Some student(s) may write 12 + 5 = 17 which is also a true statement because the order can be changed in addition without changing the value. But this is not true for subtraction or division. They need to learn at the beginning that they are starting with the 5 and that the 12 is being added to the 5. Ask them what is being added on. That number must come second. This thought process will be very important when they have a sentence like, "Twenty-one subtracted from forty-six is twenty-five."

Materials, Supplies, & Equipment:

1. Flashcards for subtraction facts and word numbers

2. Place value materials

Activities:

1. Drill addition facts using *Drill #1, Worksheet 26*.

2. Using *flashcards for subtraction facts*, drill minuends 1–18 without the answers showing.

3. Discuss with the student(s) the different ways the word "add" can be expressed (plus, added to, sum, more than, increased, etc.). Write several word sentences on the board that describe an addition problem (e.g., Twenty-four and thirty-seven equals sixty-one). In some sentences use the word "is" in place of the word "equal." Ask the student(s) to tell what numbers and symbols they should use to write the same sentence as a number sentence or equation (24 + 37 = 61). The student(s) should do all of **Student Activity One** together as you write the answers they suggest on the board.

4. After discussing the meaning of equal and not equal, the student(s) should be able to complete **Student Activity Two** on their own.

5. **Student Activity Three** should be completed by the student(s) without assistance.

6. Display the *word number flashcards*, for the multiples of ten and the one hundred card, on the board rail as a spelling reference while the student(s) complete **Student Activity Four**.

7. Write "64 – 39" as a vertical subtraction problem on the board. Ask the student(s) if they can take 9 from 4. Tell them to regroup the 6 tens to equal 5 tens and 10 ones. *Place value materials* would be helpful here. This is done by making a slanted line through the 6 and writing a 5 above the 6. The 10 ones are then added to the 4 ones to become 14. Show the 14 by placing a small 1 beside the 4. Subtract 9 from 14 and write the answer in the ones' column. Subtract 3 from 5 and write the answer in the tens' column. Do several subtraction problems similar to the one above. As the student(s) look at **Student Activity Five**, point out that the first problem has the regrouping done for them. Insist they show the regrouping on their paper as they do each problem.

Worksheet:

1. *Worksheet 26* – Addition and subtraction drill sheet

Lesson 52

Concepts:
> Place value, ordinal numbers, addition, word sentences, word numbers, equal and not equal, and subtraction

Objectives:
1. The student shall be able to correctly write the value of each digit of a four-digit number in expanded form.

2. The student shall be able to correctly place a set of letters numbered ordinally on blanks corresponding to the appropriate ordinal numbers.

3. The student shall be able to write the sum of two triple-digit numbers when the ones' and the tens' columns have double-digit answers.

4. The student shall be able to rewrite an addition word sentence as a number sentence.

5. The student shall be able to write the correct symbol (= or ≠) between a number and a subtraction fact.

6. The student shall be able to write the difference of two double-digit numbers when borrowing from the tens' column.

Teaching Tips:
1. Suggest to the student(s) they add their answers in **Student Activity One** vertically on another sheet of paper. If they have written the correct answer the sum for the addition problem will be the same as the given number.

2. In **Student Activity Five,** suggest the student(s) write the answer to the subtraction fact above the fact before they make the comparison if accuracy is a problem.

Materials, Supplies, & Equipment:
1. Flashcards for addition facts and ordinal numbers

2. Place value materials

Activities:

1. Drill subtraction facts using *Drill #2, Worksheet 26*.

2. Using *flashcards for addition facts*, drill sums 1–18 without the answers showing.

3. Write several four-digit numbers on the board and have the student(s) tell the value of each digit as you write it in expanded form. Use *place value materials* as an aid if needed. The student(s) should be able to complete **Student Activity One** by themselves.

4. Count out loud by *ordinal numbers* to 25th. You may want to use *flashcards*. Discuss the spelling of the abbreviations for 1st, 2nd, 3rd, 21st, 22nd, and 23rd. As the student(s) look at **Student Activity Two**, have them point to the 17th blank and tell what letter they are to write in that blank (G). Once you are sure the student(s) can follow the directions, allow them to continue on their own.

5. The student(s) should be able to complete **Student Activity Three** independently.

6. Review with the student(s) the different ways the word "add" can be expressed (plus, added to, sum, more than, increase, etc.). Write several word sentences on the board that describe an addition problem (e.g., The sum of thirty-one and twenty-five is fifty-six). In some sentences use the word "equal" in place of the word "is." Ask the student(s) to tell what numbers and symbols they should use to write the same sentence as a number sentence or equation (31 + 25 = 56). Spend some time on the phrase "added to." "Seven added to five equals twelve" should be written "5 + 7 = 12" They start with 5 and add 7 to it. The student(s) should do all of **Student Activity Four** together as you write the answers they suggest on the board.

7. The student(s) should be able to complete **Student Activity Five** without help.

8. Write several sets of two double-digit numbers as subtraction problems with borrowing from the tens' place. Have the student(s) copy the problems on a sheet of paper. Ask them to work the problems at their desks before you work them on the board. Answer any questions concerning method. Give help where needed as the student(s) complete **Student Activity Six**.

Worksheet:

1. *Worksheet 26* – Addition and subtraction drill sheet

Lesson 53

Concepts:
Ordinal numbers, place value, addition, word sentences, word numbers, and subtraction

Objectives:
1. The student shall be able to color a shape the correct color corresponding to its appropriate ordinal position.

2. The student shall be able to write the correct number when given the value of the digit in the thousands', hundreds', tens', and ones' places.

3. The student shall be able to write the sum of two four-digit numbers when the ones' and the tens' columns have double-digit answers.

4. The student shall be able to rewrite an addition word sentence as a number sentence.

5. The student shall be able to write the difference of two double-digit numbers when borrowing from the tens' column.

Teaching Tips:
1. When doing activity 6, visualize the phrase "added to" with counting chips. Show the student(s) how they can demonstrate "five added to two" by giving them two chips and then adding five more to equal seven. Ask them how many chips they had to start with and what they added to the amount. Then have them write the addition fact to represent the problem.

2. When doing activity 7, discuss with the student(s) how they can check their subtraction problems by adding the answer and the bottom number (subtrahend) and it will equal the top number (minuend). After they have mastered the procedure used in borrowing, they will be requested to check all of their subtraction problems in this manner.

Materials, Supplies, & Equipment:
1. Flashcards for subtraction facts

2. Place value materials

Activities:

1. Drill addition facts using *Drill #3, Worksheet 26*.

2. Using *flashcards for subtraction facts*, drill minuends 1–18 without the answers showing.

3. Have the student(s) point to the sixth shape in **Student Activity One** and color it red. They should be able to color the remaining shapes by reading the instructions.

4. Write "1,000 + 900 + 50 + 7 = __ __ __ __" on the board. When writing the number represented, ask the student(s) what digit would go in the thousands' place and in which blank to write the digit. Do the same for the hundreds', tens', and ones' places. Demonstrate this with *place value materials*. The student(s) may then add the four numbers to check their answer. They should be able to complete **Student Activity Two** alone after working the first two problems together.

5. The student(s) should be able to complete **Student Activity Three** by themselves.

6. Major on the phrase "added to" when you review with the student(s) the different ways the word "add" can be expressed. Say several examples of word sentences that have one number "added to" another number. "Fifty-one added to sixty-four equals one hundred fifteen" should be written "64 + 51 = 115." Explain how they are starting with 64 and adding 51 to it. This principle will be very important when they work with the different ways the word "subtract" can be expressed. Have the student(s) complete **Student Activity Four** together with your guidance.

7. Insist the student(s) show the regrouping on their paper as they do each problem in **Student Activity Five**.

8. Give assistance to those student(s) who need it as they complete **Student Activity Six**.

Worksheet:

1. *Worksheet 26* – Addition and subtraction drill sheet

One is seldom criticized for keeping his mouth shut.

Lesson 54

Concepts:
> Counting from 100 to 200, months of the year, place value, addition, word sentences, word numbers, and subtraction

Objectives:
1. The student shall be able to count out loud from 100 to 200.

2. The student shall be able to circle the correct date or day of the week requested in the given questions.

3. The student shall be able to write the correct number when given the value of the digit in the thousands', hundreds', tens', and ones' places.

4. The student shall be able to write the sum of two four-digit numbers when the ones' and the tens' columns have double-digit answers.

5. The student shall be able to rewrite an addition word sentence as a number sentence.

6. The student shall be able to write the difference of two double-digit numbers when borrowing from the tens' column.

Teaching Tips:
1. Using a picture calendar, make a bulletin board display of the 12 months to go with activity 4. Have the student(s) identify the month in which they were born, the month school started, the month school is out, the month it is the coldest, the month it is the warmest, the month the leaves turn colors, and the spring month it is suppose to rain the most.

2. *Worksheet 27* should be used for those student(s) who need extra practice in subtracting when borrowing.

Materials, Supplies, & Equipment:
1. Flashcards for addition facts

2. Number chart 100–199

3. Calendar

4. Place value materials

138

Activities:
1. Drill subtraction facts using *Drill #4, Worksheet 26.*

2. Using *flashcards for addition facts*, drill sums 1–18 without the answers showing.

3. Count out loud from 100 to 200 using the *number chart 100–199.*

4. Have the student(s) recite the twelve months of the year in order. Use a picture *calendar* to discuss on what day a given date is, on what date a given day is, and on what month certain holidays occur. Have the student(s) read each of the questions in **Student Activity One**. Give them guidance as they discover the answers together.

5. The student(s) should be able to complete **Student Activity Two** and **Three** on their own.

6. Write "fourteen plus three equals seventeen" on the board. Under fourteen write "14". Under plus write "+." Under three write "3." Under equal write "=." Under seventeen write "17."

   Fourteen plus three equals seventeen
   14 + 3 = 17

   This is the simplest word sentence to write as a number sentence. When they write a symbol for the words "added to," they need to remember that the "added to" tells them the "+" must be in front of the number (e.g., Two added to six is eight – Under the two write "2." "Added to" tells them the "+" must go in front of the 2. The "6" must go in front of the "+." Under the equal write "=." Under eight write "8."). Discuss each sentence in **Student Activity Four** with the student(s) as they determine what number sentence to write on the blank.

7. Insist the student(s) show the regrouping on their paper as they do each problem in **Student Activity Five**. Use *place value materials* to reinforce the thought process in borrowing for the student(s) having difficulty.

Worksheets:
1. *Worksheet 27* – Subtraction with borrowing

2. *Worksheet 26* – Addition and subtraction drill sheet

Because the road to success is always under construction, it has many detours.

Lesson 55

Concepts:
Counting from 100 to 200, even numbers, months of the year, subtraction, word sentences, word numbers, and addition
Definition: Even numbers are the numbers used in counting by twos.

Objectives:
1. The student shall be able to count out loud from 100 to 200.

2. The student shall be able to write the missing even numbers from 2 to 60.

3. The student shall be able to number the months of the year in consecutive order.

4. The student shall be able to write the difference of two double-digit numbers when borrowing from the tens' column.

5. The student shall be able to rewrite an addition word sentence as a number sentence.

6. When given three numbers, the student shall be able to circle the greatest number.

7. The student shall be able to write the sum of two four-digit numbers when the ones' and the tens' columns have double-digit answers.

Teaching Tips:
1. When doing activity 3, have the student(s) circle all of the even numbers on *Worksheet 1*.

2. For enrichment with activity 7, see how many of the given shapes can be readily identified by the student(s).

Materials, Supplies, & Equipment:
1. Flashcards for addition facts, subtraction facts, and months of the year.

2. Number chart 0–99 and 100–199

Activities:
1. Have the student(s) take a clean sheet of paper on which to write the answers for their addition and subtraction facts. Take ten *addition flashcards*. Show each card for 5 seconds as the student(s) write the answers in a column. Check the answers before you begin the next set of ten *subtraction flashcards*. Do as many sets as time permits in 7 minutes.

2. Count out loud from 100 to 200 using the *number chart 100–199*.

3. Discuss with the student(s) the meaning of even numbers. Point out that even numbers are the same numbers used in counting by twos. They will always end in 2, 4, 6, 8, or 0. Point to several numbers on the *number chart* and have the student(s) tell if the numbers are even or not. The student(s) should be able to complete **Student Activity One** by themselves.

4. Have the student(s) recite the months of the year in consecutive order. Arrange the *months of the year flashcards* on the board rail in random order. Ask the student(s) to come to the board rail and rearrange them in the correct order. Point out that January is the first month, February the second, March the third, etc. As the student(s) begin **Student Activity Two**, have them find the first month and put a 1 by it, the second and put a 2, etc. until they can finish on their own.

5. The student(s) should be able to complete **Student Activity Three** independently.

6. Allow the student(s) to complete **Student Activity Four** without help. Once they have completed the activity, discuss with the student(s) why they wrote each number sentence as they did.

7. After the student(s) have completed **Student Activity Five** independently, discuss the answers with them.

8. The student(s) should be able to complete **Student Activity Six** on their own.

Worksheet:
1. *Worksheet 1* – Number chart 0–99

The best way to hide ignorance is to keep silent.

Lesson 56

Concepts:
Counting from 100 to 200, multiplication readiness, odd numbers, and months of the year
Definition: An odd number is a whole number that is not even.

Objectives:
1. The student shall be able to count out loud from 100 to 200.

2. The student shall be able to circle groups of a given number and write the number of groups as an addition fact and a multiplication fact.

3. The student shall be able to write the missing odd numbers from 1 to 59.

4. The student shall be able to write the months of the year in the correct order.

5. When given three numbers, the student shall be able to circle the smallest number.

Teaching Tips:

1. When doing activity 4, point out to the student(s) how the word "of" means to multiply in the expression "3 groups of 2." Anytime the word "of" appears between two quantities, it can be replaced by a multiplication sign (e.g., ½ of 8 means ½ x 8).

2. When reciting the months of the year in activity 6, say "Thirty Days Hath September" with the student(s).

> Thirty days hath September,
> April, June, and November,
> All the rest have thirty-one
> Except February alone
> Which has twenty-eight
> Until leap year gives it twenty-nine.

Materials, Supplies, & Equipment:
1. Flashcards for subtraction facts

2. Number chart 0–99 and 100–199

Activities:

1. Drill addition facts using *Drill #1, Worksheet 28*.

2. Using *flashcards for subtraction facts*, drill minuends 1–18 without the answers showing.

3. Count out loud from 100 to 200 using the *number chart 100–199*.

4. Have the student(s) look at the set of squares in **Student Activity One**. Ask them to circle groups of 2's. Now count the groups and write the number in the blank. Discuss how 3 groups of 2's is the same as 2 added 3 times (2 + 2 + 2) and equals what number (6). Discuss how multiplication is a short cut for addition. 3 groups of 2's can also be expressed as 3 x 2 and equals 6. Next, look at the set of circles. Instruct the student(s) to circle groups of 3's and tell how many groups they circled. 2 groups of 3's can be expressed as 3 + 3 or 2 x 3 and both expressions equal 6. Continue to work with the student(s) following the same procedure for each set. Allow those who are capable to work ahead on their own.

5. Discuss with the student(s) the meaning of odd numbers. Point out that odd numbers are all counting numbers that are not even numbers. They will always end in 1, 3, 5, 7, or 9. Point to several numbers on the *number chart* and have the student(s) tell if the numbers are odd. The student(s) should be able to complete **Student Activity Two** by themselves.

6. Orally recite the months of the year in order with the student(s). Have them tell something special about each month. Allow the student(s) to say the months of the year individually. They should be able to complete **Student Activity Three** independently.

7. The student(s) should be able to complete **Student Activity Four** without help.

Worksheet:

1. *Worksheet 28* – Addition and subtraction drill sheet

With ability comes great responsibility.

Lesson 57

Concepts:
> Counting from 200 to 300, greater than and less than, multiplication readiness, addition, and subtraction

Objectives:
1. The student shall be able to count out loud from 200 to 300.

2. The student shall be able to write the correct number on each side of a greater than or less than symbol.

3. The student shall be able to write the correct multiplication fact corresponding to a given addition problem.

4. The student shall be able to write the sum of two triple-digit numbers when the ones' or the tens' column has a double-digit answer.

5. The student shall be able to write two addition and two subtraction facts when given three numbers.

6. The student shall be able to write the difference of two double-digit numbers when borrowing from the tens' column.

Teaching Tips:
1. To cover one of the addends in activity 2, take a strip of heavy paper the width of a number on the flashcard. Fold the strip around the flashcard and tape the strip on the back. This will enable you to slip the sleeve up and down to cover a different addend at different times. Although it will take a little time to make one for each of the addition cards, the value of the drill makes it worth the time.

2. When doing activity 3, be sure you do not allow the student(s) to put an "and" in their numbers when they are counting. "And" is used only when a decimal point is present and must not be used any other time.

Materials, Supplies, & Equipment:
1. Flashcards for addition facts

2. Number chart 0–99

Activities:

1. Drill subtraction facts using *Drill #2, Worksheet 28*.

2. Using *flashcards for addition facts*, drill sums 1–18 with the answers showing and covering one of the two addends. Have the student(s) supply the missing number (e.g., __ + 5 = 13 and they say "8 + 5 = 13" or 7 + __ = 14 and they say "7 + 7 = 14"). At first you will have to do the drill at a slower pace until the student(s) become accustomed to thinking in this manner.

3. Count out loud with the student(s) from 200 to 300 using the *number chart 0–99*. Instruct the student(s) to say two hundred in front of each number.

4. Write two numbers on the board. Write the greater than or less than symbol below the two numbers. Ask the student(s) to place the correct number on each side of the symbol to make a true statement. Do several examples for the student(s) to complete. Have them complete the first problem in each row in **Student Activity One** together. They should then be able to finish on their own.

5. On the board, write "4 groups of 5's, 6 groups of 7's, and 3 groups of 8's." Ask the student(s) how many 5's are being added together if they have 4 groups (4). 4 groups of 5's represents what addition problem (5 + 5 + 5 + 5 = 20). Discuss the equivalent multiplication problem (4 x 5 = 20) for the addition problem. Ask the student(s) to tell the equivalent addition and multiplication problems for each of the other groups. Work the first two problems in **Student Activity Two** together with the student(s). Allow them to continue on their own if they are capable.

6. The student(s) should be able to complete **Student Activity Three** independently.

7. Have the student(s) complete the first problem in **Student Activity Four** together. They should be able to complete the activity with no further help.

8. The student(s) should be able to complete **Student Activity Five** by themselves.

Worksheet:

1. *Worksheet 28* – Addition and subtraction drill sheet

Lesson 58

Concepts:
　　Counting from 300 to 400, estimation, multiplication readiness, addition, greater than and less than, and subtraction

Objectives:
1. The student shall be able to count out loud from 300 to 400.

2. The student shall be able to circle the animals that are about 12" tall.

3. The student shall be able to write the addition fact and multiplication fact that correspond to a given set of numbers.

4. The student shall be able to write the sum of two triple-digit numbers when the ones' or the tens' column has a double-digit answer.

5. The student shall be able to write the correct number on each side of a greater than or less than symbol.

6. The student shall be able to write two addition facts and two subtraction facts when given three numbers.

7. The student shall be able to write the difference of two double-digit numbers when borrowing from the tens' column.

Teaching Tips:
1. Discuss with the student(s) some different ways to remember how to read the < and > symbols when doing activity 7. The comparison with the arrows on the number line was mentioned before. The greater than symbol has the large opening first (>). The less than symbol has the small point first (<). When placed between two numbers, the large opening always goes next to the larger number and the point always points to the smaller number.

Materials, Supplies, & Equipment:
1. Flashcards for subtraction facts

2. Number chart 0–99

3. 12-inch ruler

Activities:

1. Drill addition facts using *Drill #3, Worksheet 28*.

2. Using *flashcards for subtraction facts*, drill minuends 1–18 without the answers showing.

3. Count out loud with the student(s) from 300 to 400 using the *number chart 0–99*. Instruct the student(s) to say three hundred in front of each number.

4. Have the student(s) use their hands to demonstrate how tall various animals are. Show them a *12-inch ruler* and ask if they know any animals that would be about that tall. Discuss the height of the animals pictured in **Student Activity One**. Tell the student(s) to circle the animals they think are about 12" tall.

5. Write "5 groups of 7's, 7 groups of 5's, 4 groups of 6's, and 6 groups of 4's" on the board. Ask the student(s) how many 7's are being added together if they have 5 groups of 7's (five 7's). Write the addition problem on the board. Have them tell the multiplication fact that corresponds to the addition problem. Write the multiplication fact on the board. Follow the same procedure for 7 groups of 5's. Discuss the similarity of the two multiplication facts (same answer, same numbers multiplied together but in different order). The order can be changed in multiplication and the answer stays the same. 7 x 5 and 5 x 7 have the same answer. Have the student(s) tell the addition facts and multiplication facts for 4 groups of 6's and 6 groups of 4's. Compare the multiplication facts. Have the student(s) complete the first two problems in **Student Activity Two** together. Give help on the remaining problems only when needed.

6. The student(s) should be able to complete **Student Activity Three** by themselves.

7. Write the greater than and less than symbols on the board. Say two numbers to the student(s) and have them tell which symbol (< or >) should go between them. Write the correct number on each side of the symbol and have the student(s) read the statement. Give the student(s) two more numbers. Using the other symbol, tell them to put the two numbers in the correct order to give a true statement. The student(s) should be able to complete **Student Activity Four** on their own.

8. The student(s) should be able to complete **Student Activity Five** and **Six** independently.

Worksheets:

1. *Worksheet 29* – More and less

2. *Worksheet 28* – Addition and subtraction drill sheet

Lesson 59

Concepts:

Counting from 400 to 500, multiplication readiness, addition, estimation, and greater then and less than

Objectives:

1. The student shall be able to count out loud from 400 to 500.

2. The student shall be able to write two addition facts and two subtraction facts when given three numbers.

3. The student shall be able to write the multiplication fact that corresponds to a given group of numbers.

4. The student shall be able to write the sum of two triple-digit numbers when the ones' or the tens' column has a double-digit answer.

5. The student shall be able to draw three objects about 36 inches tall.

6. The student shall be able to write the correct number on each side of a greater than or less than symbol.

Teaching Tips:

1. Since some of your student(s) may be about 36" tall, measure their height while doing activity 7.

Materials, Supplies, & Equipment:

1. Flashcards for addition facts

2. Number chart 0–99

3. Yardstick

Activities:

1. Drill subtraction facts using *Drill #4, Worksheet 28.*

2. Using *flashcards for addition facts*, drill sums 1–18 with the answers showing and covering one of the two addends. Have the student(s) supply the missing number (e.g., __ + 7 = 13 and they say "6 + 7 = 13" or 5 + __ = 14 and they say "5 + 9 = 14"). At first you will have to do the drill at a slower pace until the student(s) become accustomed to thinking in this manner.

3. Count out loud with the student(s) from 400 to 500 using the *number chart 0–99.* Instruct the student(s) to say four hundred in front of each number.

4. The student(s) should be able to complete **Student Activity One** independently.

5. Write "four 5's, five 4's, and two 7's, seven 2's" on the board. Discuss with the student(s) the meaning of four groups of 5's as being four 5's added together (5 + 5 + 5 + 5 = 20) or four and 5 multiplied together (4 x 5 = 20). Have the student(s) tell what multiplication fact corresponds to five 4's (5 x 4 = 20). Point out that 4 x 5 and 5 x 4 both equal 20. Follow the same procedure for the other groups you have written on the board. Work the first two problems in **Student Activity Two** with the student(s). Allow those who are capable to continue on their own.

6. The student(s) should be able to complete **Student Activity Three** by themselves.

7. Discuss with the student(s) about how tall 36 inches is. Then show them a *yardstick* and tell them it is 36 inches tall. Discuss what other things they can see in the room that are 36 inches tall. They may want to go beyond the room and discuss anything they can think of that is 36 inches tall. After discussing the directions for **Student Activity Four**, allow them to draw their pictures on their own.

8. The student(s) should be able to complete **Student Activity Five** without assistance.

Worksheet:

1. *Worksheet 28* – Addition and subtraction drill sheet

It is better to use a little ability well than to make poor use of much ability.

Lesson 60

Concepts:
Counting from 500 to 600, word sentences, word numbers, multiplication readiness, addition, and subtraction

Objectives:

1. The student shall be able to count out loud from 500 to 600.

2. The student shall be able to rewrite a subtraction word sentence as a number sentence.

3. The student shall be able to write the multiplication fact that corresponds to a given set of shapes.

4. The student shall be able to match corresponding number families.

5. The student shall be able to write the sum of two triple-digit numbers when the ones' or the tens' column has a double-digit answer.

6. The student shall be able to write the difference of two double-digit numbers when borrowing from the tens' column.

Teaching Tips:

1. When doing **Student Activity Two**, have the student(s) arrange 12 *counting chips* to represent 3 x 4 by putting them in three rows of four each. Next have them arrange the *counting chips* to represent 4 x 3 by putting them in four rows of three each. Tell the student(s) to try 2 x 6 and 6 x 2.

Materials, Supplies, & Equipment:

1. Flashcards for addition and subtraction facts

2. Counting chips

Activities:

1. Administer **Test 6**.

2. Have the student(s) take a clean sheet of paper on which to write the answers for their addition and subtraction facts. Take ten *addition flashcards*. Leave the sleeves over one addend. Show each card for 5 seconds as the student(s) write the answers in a column. Check the answers before you begin the next set of ten *subtraction flashcards*. Do as many sets as time permits in 7 minutes.

3. Count out loud with the student(s) from 500 to 600 using the *number chart 0–99*. Instruct the student(s) to say five hundred in front of each number.

4. Review with the student(s) the different ways the word "subtraction" can be expressed (minus, subtracted from, difference, less than, decreased, take away, etc.). Write several word sentences on the board that describe a subtraction problem (e.g., The difference of thirty-one and twenty-five is six). In some sentences use the word "equal" in place of the word "is." Ask the student(s) to tell what numbers and symbols they should use to write the same sentence as a number sentence or equation $(31 - 25 = 6)$. Spend some time on the phrase "subtracted from." "Five subtracted from twelve equals seven" should then be written "$12 - 5 = 7$." They start with 12 and subtract 5 from it. The student(s) should do all of **Student Activity One** together as you write the answers they give on the board.

5. Have the student(s) count the first set of triangles in **Student Activity Two**. Then have them tell how many rows there are and how many in each row. Write the answers in the blanks. Now have them tell the multiplication fact that is represented by the triangles. Allow those student(s) who are capable to complete the activity by themselves. Help those who need assistance.

6. Give individual help where it is needed as the student(s) complete **Student Activity Three**.

7. The student(s) should be able to complete **Student Activity Four** and **Five** independently.

*We learn many things from adversity and
few things from prosperity.*

Lesson 61

Concepts:

Counting from 600 to 700, multiplication, word sentences, word numbers, word problems, addition, and subtraction

Objectives:

1. The student shall be able to count out loud from 600 to 700.

2. The student shall be able to write the missing addend in an addition fact.

3. The student shall be able to write the product of the multiplication facts for zero and one.

4. The student shall be able to rewrite the subtraction word sentence as a number sentence.

5. The student shall be able to write the sum of two triple-digit numbers when the ones' or the tens' column has a double-digit answer.

6. The student shall be able to write the difference of two triple-digit numbers when borrowing from the tens' column.

Teaching Tips:

1. If there are student(s) who are having difficulty with activity 5, suggest they look at the problems as subtraction problems. For example $6 + \_\_ = 13$ can also be stated as $13 - 6 = \_\_$. Then have them say the addition fact $6 + 7 = 13$ as a check for their answer.

Materials, Supplies, & Equipment:

1. Flashcards for subtraction and multiplication facts

2. Number chart 0–99

Activities:

1. Drill addition facts using *Drill #1, Worksheet 30*.

2. Using *flashcards for subtraction facts*, drill minuends 1–18 without the answers showing.

3. Using *flashcards for multiplication facts*, drill 0's and 1's with the answers showing. When a card shows "6 x 1 = 6," have the student(s) say "Six times one equals six and one times six equals six." It is important for them to learn the facts in pairs every time. By doing this, the number of facts left to learn when they start the 7's, 8's, and 9's will be very few.

4. Count out loud from 600 to 700 using the *number chart 0–99*.

5. Write several addition facts on the board leaving one of the addends blank (e.g., 6 + __ = 13). Teach the student(s) to find the answer by thinking "What do I add to 6 to get 13 or 6 plus what equals 13." The addition drill with the sleeve over one addend should help the student(s) think in this manner. The student(s) should be able to complete **Student Activity One** by themselves although it may take them a little longer than usual.

6. Zero times any number is always zero. If they have six groups of 0's, they have zero. Any number times one is the same number. If they have four groups of 1's, they have 4. Remembering these two facts enables the student(s) to have learned their 0's and 1's facts for multiplication. The student(s) should be able to complete **Student Activity Two** on their own.

7. Say several examples of word sentences that have one number "subtracted from" another number. "Fifty-two subtracted from sixty-five equals thirteen" should be written "65 – 52 = 13." Explain how they are starting with 65 and subtracting 52 from it. Have the student(s) complete **Student Activity Three** together with your guidance.

8. The student(s) should be able to complete **Student Activity Four, Five**, and **Six** by themselves.

9. Have the student(s) look at **Student Activity Seven**. Ask them to find the number at A (25). If they want the number at B (14) plus the number at F to equal 25, what must they do with 25 and 14 (subtract them). Tell them to write the difference in the vertex of the smaller triangle at F (11). Now F + B = A. If they want F + D to equal E, what must they do with the numbers at F and E (subtract them). Check to see if D + B = C. What must they do to find the number at H (subtract G from D) and at I (subtract G from F). Have the student(s) check their answers by adding. Allow those who are capable to complete the second triangle on their own, helping those who need your help.

Worksheet:

1. *Worksheet 30* – Addition and subtraction drill sheet

Lesson 62

Concepts:
Counting from 700 to 800, time (5 minutes), addition, multiplication, word problems, word sentences, and word numbers

Objectives:
1. The student shall be able to count out loud from 700 to 800.

2. The student shall be able to write the correct time displayed on the face of the clock for given five minute increments.

3. The student shall be able to write the missing addend in an addition fact.

4. The student shall be able to match pairs of multiplication facts.

5. The student shall be able to rewrite the subtraction word sentence as a number sentence.

6. The student shall be able to write the product of the multiplication facts for zero and one.

7. The student shall be able to write the sum of two triple-digit numbers when the ones' or the tens' column has a double-digit answer.

Teaching Tips:
1. Teach the student(s) how to read the multiplication chart on *Worksheet 31*. Across the top have them point to the number 1. Going down the first column have them point to the number 3. Tell them to bring their finger down from 1 until the finger is in the same row as 3. The number in that box should be the answer (3). Try other facts (5 x 3, 6 x 8, etc.) and see if the student(s) can tell you the answers. The chart will be used by them until all multiplication facts have been mastered.

Materials, Supplies, & Equipment:
1. Flashcards for addition and multiplication facts

2. Number chart 0–99

3. Small clock model for student(s)

4. Clock model

154

Activities:

1. Drill subtraction facts using *Drill #2, Worksheet 30*.

2. Using *flashcards for addition facts*, drill sums 1–18 with the answers showing and covering one of the addends. Have the student(s) supply the missing number (e.g., __ + 6 = 15 and the student(s) say "9 + 6 = 15" or 5 + __ = 14 and the student(s) then say "5 + 9 = 14").

3. Using *flashcards for multiplication facts*, drill 0's and 1's without the answers showing. When a card shows 1 x 4 = __, have the student(s) say "One times four equals four and four times one equals four." The student(s) should learn the facts in pairs every time.

4. Count out loud from 700 to 800 using the *number chart 0–99*.

5. Give the student(s) *small clock models*. Say several 5 minute times and have them set their clocks for that time. Set the *clock model* for the student(s) to use to check their time. If a student's clock is incorrect, take time to help that student individually. They should be able to complete **Student Activity One** by themselves.

6. Use the *addition flashcards* with the sleeve over one addend to review the thought process for **Student Activity Two** (7 + __ = 12). "What do they add to 7 to get 12 or 7 plus what equals 12." The student(s) should be able to complete the activity on their own.

7. The student(s) should be able to complete **Student Activity Three** by matching the top row to the bottom row.

8. The student(s) should be able to complete **Student Activity Four** independently.

9. Write "Fourteen minus three equals eleven" on the board. Under fourteen write "14". Under minus write "-." Under three write "3." Under equal write "=." Under eleven write "11." When the student(s) write a symbol for the words "subtracted from," they need to remember that the "subtracted from" tells them the "-" must be in front of the number (e.g., Six subtracted from eight is two: Under the six write "6." "Subtracted from" tells them the "-" must go in front of the 6. The eight must go in front of the "-." Under the equal write "=." Under two write "2."). Discuss each sentence in **Student Activity Five** with the student(s) as they determine what number sentence to write on the blank.

10. The student(s) should be able to complete **Student Activity Six** and **Seven** without assistance.

Worksheets:

1. *Worksheet 31* – Multiplication chart

2. *Worksheet 30* – Addition and subtraction drill sheet

Lesson 63

Concepts:
Counting from 800 to 900, multiplication, time (5 minutes), addition, word sentences, word numbers, subtraction, and word problems

Objectives:
1. The student shall be able to count out loud from 800 to 900.

2. The student shall be able to draw a line to match corresponding number families.

3. The student shall be able to draw both hands on the face of the clock for given five minute increments.

4. The student shall be able to write the sum of two four-digit numbers when the ones' or the tens' column has a double-digit answer.

5. The student shall be able to write the missing addend in an addition fact.

6. The student shall be able to rewrite the subtraction word sentence as a number sentence.

7. The student shall be able to write the difference of two triple-digit numbers when borrowing from the tens' column.

Teaching Tips:
1. Show the student(s) the relationship between counting by tens and the tens' facts in multiplication when doing activity 5. Give them *place value materials* for tens. Have them take a set of five 10's and tell the corresponding multiplication fact (5 x 10). Then have them count the five 10's by tens (10, 20, 30, 40, 50). Do the same for several other sets of ten.

Materials, Supplies, & Equipment:
1. Flashcards for subtraction, multiplication, and addition facts

2. Number chart 0–99

3. Small clock model for student(s)

4. Clock model

5. Place value materials

Activities:

1. Drill addition facts using *Drill #3, Worksheet 30*.

2. Using *flashcards for subtraction facts*, drill minuends 1–18 without the answers showing.

3. Using *flashcards for multiplication facts*, drill 0's and 1's without the answers showing. Remember when a card is 6 x 0 = __, have the student(s) say "Six times zero equals zero and zero times six equals zero." It is important for them to learn the facts in pairs every time.

4. Count out loud with the student(s) from 800 to 900 using the *number chart 0–99*.

5. Write "10 + 10 + 10 = 30" on the board. Ask the student(s) how many 10's are being added together (three 10's). Then ask them what multiplication fact corresponds to three 10's (3 x 10). Write "6 x 10" on the board. Ask the student(s) how many tens are being added together (6). Discuss multiplying by 10 means they add a zero to the number. When the student(s) start **Student Activity One**, complete the first two matches together. Then allow them to continue on their own.

6. Give the student(s) the *small clock models*. Write several 5 minute time intervals on the board. Remind the student(s) to set the minute hand first and then the hour hand on their clocks. Have them check their clocks by the *clock model*. They should be able to complete **Student Activity Two** by themselves.

7. The student(s) should be able to complete **Student Activity Three** independently.

8. Review the thought process for **Student Activity Four** with the student(s) by using the *addition flashcards* with the sleeve over one addend. They should be able to complete the activity without further help.

9. Allow the student(s) to complete **Student Activity Five** without help. Once they have completed the activity, discuss with the student(s) why they wrote each number sentence as they did.

10. The student(s) should be able to complete **Student Activity Six** and **Seven** alone.

Worksheet:

1. *Worksheet 30* – Addition and subtraction drill sheet

Lesson 64

Concepts:

Counting from 900 to 1,000, time, equal and not equal, addition, subtraction, multiplication, and sequence

Objectives:

1. The student shall be able to count out loud from 900 to 1,000.

2. The student shall be able to write the correct symbol (= or ≠) between the time displayed on the face of a clock and a given digital time.

3. The student shall be able to write the missing addend in an addition fact.

4. The student shall be able to write the difference of two triple-digit numbers when borrowing from the tens' column.

5. The student shall be able to write the product of the multiplication facts for zero, one, and ten.

6. The student shall be able to write the next three numbers after a given sequence of numbers.

7. The student shall be able to write the sum of two four-digit numbers when the ones' or the tens' column has a double-digit answer.

Teaching Tips:

1. When the student(s) are doing activity 8, have them count out loud by 10's to 100 several times. Then have them say "One 10 is 10, two 10's are 20, three 10's are 30, etc. This exercise will help solidify the idea of putting a zero after the number when multiplying by 10's.

Materials, Supplies, & Equipment:

1. Flashcards for addition and multiplication facts

2. Number chart 0–99

3. Multiplication chart

Activities:

1. Drill subtraction facts using *Drill #4, Worksheet 30*.

2. Using *flashcards for addition facts*, drill sums 1–18 with the answers showing and covering one of the two addends.

3. Using *flashcards for multiplication facts*, drill 0's, 1's, and 10's without the answers showing. It is important for them to say the facts in pairs every time.

4. Count out loud from 900 to 1,000 using the *number chart 0–99*.

5. Discuss the meaning of equal and not equal (same and not the same). The student(s) should be able to complete **Student Activity One** by themselves.

6. Drill ten *addition flashcards* with the sleeve over one addend to prepare the student(s) for completing **Student Activity Two**.

7. The student(s) should be able to complete **Student Activity Three** without assistance.

8. Review the multiplication rules by asking the student(s) the following questions. "What does zero times any number equal?" (0) "What does one times any number equal?" (the same number) "To multiply 10 times any number, what is placed beside the number?" (0) If the student(s) can remember these three rules, they can do their multiplication facts for 0's, 1's, and 10's. If the student(s) have any difficulty with any of the multiplication facts in **Student Activity Four**, encourage them to use the *multiplication chart*. This chart will be used by the student(s) until all multiplication facts have been mastered. Have the student(s) place it in a special place in their desk. The folder they keep their drill sheet in would be a good place. Lamination of the page would preserve it.

9. Write several sequences of digits on the board. Make each sequence a repeat of two or three digits (e.g., 242424 __ __ __, 258258 __ __ __). Ask the student(s) to identify the pattern used and tell the next three digits. Be sure they can identify the patterns in **Student Activity Five** before they attempt to complete the activity on their own.

10. The student(s) should be able to complete **Student Activity Six** independently.

Worksheets:

1. *Worksheet 32* – Missing addend

2. *Worksheet 30* – Addition and subtraction drill sheet

Lesson 65

Concepts:
Place value, multiplication, addition, subtraction, word numbers, sequence, and equal and not equal

Objectives:
1. The student shall be able to write the digit in the thousands', hundreds', tens', and ones' places in a given number.

2. The student shall be able to write the product of the multiplication facts for zero, one, and ten.

3. The student shall be able to write the sum of two four-digit numbers when the ones' or the tens' column has a double-digit answer.

4. The student shall be able to write the difference of two triple-digit numbers when borrowing from the tens' column.

5. The student shall be able to draw a line to match a word number and its corresponding number.

6. The student shall be able to write the next three numbers after a given sequence of numbers.

7. The student shall be able to write the correct symbol (= or ≠) between two subtraction facts.

Teaching Tips:
1. If any student is having difficulty with borrowing in subtraction in **Student Activity Four**, use the *place value materials* with them individually. Begin by taking 6 from 20. Show the regrouping of 2 tens to 1 ten and 10 ones. Then have the student take 6 of the ones away and count to see how many ones and tens are left. Repeat the steps for marking the regrouping on the problem itself with the student.

Materials, Supplies, & Equipment:
1. Flashcards for addition facts, subtraction facts, multiplication facts, and word numbers

2. Place value materials

160

Activities:

1. Have the student(s) take a clean sheet of paper on which to write the answers for their addition and subtraction facts. Take ten *addition flashcards*. Leave the sleeves over one addend. Show each card for 5 seconds as the student(s) write the answers in a column. Check the answers before you begin the next set of ten *subtraction flashcards*. Do as many sets as time permits in 7 minutes.

2. Using *flashcards for multiplication facts*, drill 0's, 1's, and 10's without the answers showing. It is important for them to say the facts in pairs every time.

3. Write several four-digit numbers on the board. As you point to each digit of a number in random order, have the student(s) tell if the digit is in the ones', tens', hundreds', or thousands' place. Then have them tell what digit is in the ones' place, the tens' place, etc. The student(s) should be able to complete **Student Activity One** by themselves.

4. Review the rules for multiplying by 0's, 1,'s, and 10's. If any student is having difficulty with multiplying by 10 use *place value materials* to re-enforce what three 10's equal, what four 10's equal, etc. The student(s) should be able to complete **Student Activity Two** on their own.

5. **Student Activity Three** and **Four** should be completed by the student(s) without assistance.

6. Write several three-digit numbers on the board. Ask the student(s) to write the word numbers for each. Have the *word number flashcards* available for spelling reference. The student(s) should be able to complete **Student Activity Five** independently.

7. Write several sequences of digits on the board. Make each sequence a repeat of two or three digits (e.g., 363636 __ __ __, 246246 __ __ __). Ask the student(s) to identify the pattern used and tell the next three digits. **Student Activity Six** should be completed by the student(s) on their own.

8. Insist that the student(s) say the answers to both subtraction facts in **Student Activity Seven** before they decided which symbol to put in the blank. Have them write the answer above the fact if necessary.

Adversity brings out talents that would have lain dormant during prosperity.

Lesson 66

Concepts:
Counting by fives, multiplication, place value, addition, word numbers, equal and not equal, word sentences, and subtraction

Objectives:
1. The student shall be able to count out loud by fives to 60.

2. The student shall be able to write a given number of fives as an addition problem, a multiplication problem, and the product.

3. The student shall be able to write the place value name for any digit in a given four-digit number.

4. The student shall be able to write the sum of two four-digit numbers when the ones' or the tens' column has a double-digit answer.

5. The student shall be able to write the correct symbol (= or ≠) between a word number and its corresponding number.

6. The student shall be able to rewrite an addition word sentence as a number sentence.

7. The student shall be able to write the difference of two triple-digit numbers when borrowing from the tens' column.

Teaching Tips:
1. If a student is having difficulty with the subtraction drill in activity 2, suggest that they think of the problem as an addition problem. __ − 4 = 8 is the same as 8 + 4 = __.

Materials, Supplies, & Equipment:
1. Flashcards for subtraction and multiplication facts

2. Multiplication chart

3. Place value materials

Activities:

1. Drill addition facts using *Drill #1, Worksheet 33*.

2. Using *flashcards for subtraction facts*, drill minuends 1–18 with the answers showing and covering the minuend or the subtrahend. Have the student(s) supply the missing number (e.g., __ – 6 = 9 and the student(s) say "15 – 6 = 9" or 14 – __ = 6 and the student(s) say "14 – 8 = 6").

3. Using *flashcards for multiplication facts*, drill 0's, 1's, and 10's without the answers showing. It is important for them to learn the facts in pairs every time.

4. Count out loud with the student(s) by fives to 60 from memory.

5. Write "two 5's, three 5's, four 5's, etc." on the board. Ask the student(s) how to write two 5's as an addition problem. Then have them tell how to write two 5's as a multiplication problem. Now have them look at the *multiplication chart* for the answer to 2 x 5 if they do not already know it (5 + 5 should give them the answer). Follow the same procedure for three 5's, four 5's, etc. The student(s) should be able to complete **Student Activity One** with the help of the *multiplication chart*.

6. Write several four-digit numbers on the board. Have the student(s) tell in random order what digit is in the ones' place, the tens' place, etc. As you point to each digit in a number, have them tell if the digit is in the ones', tens', hundreds', or thousands' place. *Place value materials* may be a help here. The student(s) should be able to complete **Student Activity Two** by themselves.

7. The student(s) should be able to complete **Student Activity Three** and **Four** on their own.

8. Discuss the words that tell the student(s) to add. Pay special attention to "added to" by showing them how to write the number sentence. Give the student(s) guidance as they complete **Student Activity Five**.

9. To check the answers in **Student Activity Six**, have the student(s) draw a line under the answer and add the answer to the subtrahend. This sum should be the same as the minuend. The student(s) should be able to complete the subtraction independently.

Worksheet:

1. *Worksheet 33* – Addition and subtraction drill sheet

Lesson 67

Concepts:

Counting by fives, sequence, multiplication, even numbers, word sentences, word numbers, place value, addition, and subtraction

Objectives:

1. The student shall be able to count out loud by fives to 60.

2. The student shall be able to circle the next picture that would appear in a sequence of pictures.

3. The student shall be able to draw a line to match corresponding number families.

4. The student shall be able to circle the even numbers.

5. The student shall be able to rewrite an addition word sentence as a number sentence.

6. The student shall be able to circle the digit for a given place value position in a four-digit number.

7. The student shall be able to write the sum of two four-digit numbers when the ones' or the tens' column has a double-digit answer.

8. The student shall be able to write the difference of two triple-digit numbers when borrowing from the tens' column.

Teaching Tips:

1. When drilling the fives' multiplication facts in activity 3, ask the student(s) if they can discover a pattern – 5 x 4 will equal one half of 4 with a 0 added (2, 20), 5 x 6 is one half of 6 with a 0 added (3, 30), and 5 x 8 is one half of 8 with a 0 added (4, 40). Another pattern can also be found – 5 x 3 is 5 x 2 + 5, 5 x 5 is 5 x 4 + 5, etc.

Materials, Supplies, & Equipment:

1. Flashcards for addition and multiplication facts

2. Number chart 0–99

3. Place value materials

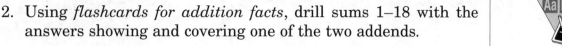

Activities:

1. Drill subtraction facts using *Drill #2, Worksheet 33*.

2. Using *flashcards for addition facts*, drill sums 1–18 with the answers showing and covering one of the two addends.

3. Using *flashcards for multiplication facts*, drill 0's, 1's, and 10's without the answers showing and 5's with the answers showing. It is important for them to learn the facts in pairs every time (e.g., 2 x 5 = 10, 5 x 2 = 10).

4. Count out loud with the student(s) by fives to 60 from memory.

5. Have the student(s) look at **Student Activity One**. Ask them to determine what the next picture in the first activity should be and circle the picture. Together let them determine what the next picture in the second activity should be and circle it. Allow those who are capable to continue on their own, helping those who need help.

6. Ask the student(s) to write three 5's as an addition problem and as a multiplication problem on a sheet of paper. Then let them tell you what to write on the board for them to use to check their answer. Do several groups of 5's in the same manner. The student(s) should be able to complete **Student Activity Two** by themselves.

7. Discuss with the student(s) the meaning of even numbers. Point to several numbers on the *number chart* and ask the student(s) if the number is even. The student(s) should be able to complete **Student Activity Three** on their own.

8. Allow the student(s) to complete **Student Activity Four** without assistance. Discuss the number sentences after they complete them.

9. Write several four-digit numbers on the board. Name the place value of each digit with the student(s). *Place value materials* may be a help here. Then have them name the digit that is in each place. After going over the directions for **Student Activity Five**, the student(s) should be able to complete the activity independently.

10. The student(s) should be able to complete **Student Activity Six** and **Seven** with no help. Be sure they check their answers in **Student Activity Seven**.

Worksheet:

1. *Worksheet 33* – Addition and subtraction drill sheet

Lesson 68

Concepts:
Counting by fives, pennies, sequence, multiplication, odd numbers, word sentences, word numbers, addition, and subtraction

Objectives:
1. The student shall be able to count out loud by fives to 60.

2. The student shall be able to write the value of the given number of pennies.

3. The student shall be able to circle the next picture that would appear in a sequence of pictures.

4. The student shall be able to write the product of the multiplication facts for zero, one, ten, and five.

5. The student shall be able to circle the odd numbers.

6. The student shall be able to rewrite an addition word sentence as a number sentence.

7. The student shall be able to write the sum of two four-digit numbers when the ones' or the tens' column has a double-digit answer.

8. The student shall be able to write the difference of two triple-digit numbers when borrowing from the tens' column.

Teaching Tips:
1. If the student(s) are not familiar with the penny in activity 5, discuss in detail the color, picture on front (Abraham Lincoln), building on back (Lincoln Memorial), monetary value (one cent on back), "IN GOD WE TRUST" and "LIBERTY" on front, and date it was minted. Our country is identified on the back.

Materials, Supplies, & Equipment:
1. Flashcards for subtraction and multiplication facts

2. Play money

3. Multiplication chart

4. Number chart 0–99

Activities:

1. Drill addition facts using *Drill #3, Worksheet 33*.

2. Using *flashcards for subtraction facts*, drill minuends 1–18 with the answers showing and covering the minuend or the subtrahend. Have the student(s) supply the missing number (e.g., __ – 6 = 4 and the student(s) say "10 – 6 = 4" or 14 – __ = 8 and the student(s) say "14 – 6 = 8").

3. Using *flashcards for multiplication facts*, drill 0's, 1's, and 10's without the answers showing and 5's with the answers showing. It is important for them to learn the facts in pairs every time.

4. Count out loud with the student(s) by fives to 60 from memory.

5. Give the student(s) pennies. Discuss the different characteristics of the penny (color, front, back, date, etc.). Ask them to count out several sets of pennies and tell how many cents they have in each set. The student(s) should be able to complete **Student Activity One** on their own.

6. Have the student(s) look at **Student Activity Two**. Ask them to determine what the next picture in the first row should be and circle the picture. If the student(s) have difficulty with this, have them look at the last picture. Find that picture again towards the first of the pictures and see what picture comes after it. The same picture will come after a given picture each time. Together let them determine what the next picture in the second row should be and circle it. Allow those who are capable to continue on their own, helping those who need help.

7. Tell the student(s) to use their *multiplication chart* to find the answers for the facts they do not know in **Student Activity Three**.

8. Discuss with the student(s) the meaning of odd numbers. Point to several numbers on the *number chart* and ask the student(s) if the number is odd. The student(s) should be able to complete **Student Activity Four** on their own.

9. The student(s) should be able to complete **Student Activity Five, Six,** and **Seven** by themselves. Be sure they check their answers in **Student Activity Seven**.

Worksheets:

1. *Worksheet 34* – Sequences

2. *Worksheet 33* – Addition and subtraction drill sheet

Lesson 69

Concepts:
Counting by fives, days of the week, ordinal numbers, multiplication, nickels, addition, and sequence

Objectives:
1. The student shall be able to count out loud by fives to 60.

2. The student shall be able to write the names of the days of the week according to their ordinal position, the number of days for a given day in a month, and the date for a given occurrence of a day of the week.

3. The student shall be able to write the product of the multiplication facts for zero, one, ten, and five.

4. The student shall be able to write the value of the given number of nickels.

5. The student shall be able to write the missing addend in an addition fact.

6. The student shall be able to circle the next picture that would appear in a sequence of pictures.

Teaching Tips:
1. If the student(s) are not familiar with the nickel in activity 7, discuss in detail the color, picture on front (Thomas Jefferson), building on back (Monticello, Thomas Jefferson's home), monetary value (five cent on back), "IN GOD WE TRUST" and "LIBERTY" on front, and date it was minted. Our country is identified on the back.

Materials, Supplies, & Equipment:
1. Flashcards for addition and multiplication facts

2. Calendar

3. Multiplication chart

4. Play money

Activities:

1. Drill subtraction facts using *Drill #4 Worksheet 33*.

2. Using *flashcards for addition facts*, drill sums 1–18 with the answers showing and covering one of the two addends.

3. Using *flashcards for multiplication facts*, drill 0's, 1's, and 10's without the answers showing and 5's with the answers showing. It is important for them to learn the facts in pairs every time (e.g., 4 x 5 = 20, 5 x 4 = 20).

4. Count out loud with the student(s) by fives to 60 from memory.

5. Show the student(s) the days of a week on a *calendar*. Discuss what day today is, how many times there is a day the same as today in a month, and what date is the third Wednesday of the month. Read the questions together in **Student Activity One**. Allow the student(s) to answer the questions on their own and then discuss their answers.

6. Have the student(s) complete **Student Activity Two** by themselves using their *multiplication chart* when needed.

7. Give the student(s) nickels. Discuss the different characteristics of the nickel (color, front, back, date, value, etc.). Ask them to count out several sets of nickels and tell how many cents (by counting by 5's) they have in each set. Equate this with having five 5's or 5 x 5 = 25. Choose different sets of nickels and equate them to the equivalent multiplication facts. The student(s) should be able to complete **Student Activity Three** on their own.

8. Review the thought process for **Student Activity Four** with the student(s) by using the *addition flashcards* with the sleeve over one addend. They should be able to complete the activity without further help.

9. Allow the student(s) to complete **Student Activity Five** by themselves discussing their answers upon completion.

Worksheet:

1. *Worksheet 33* – Addition and subtraction drill sheet

> *It takes a bigger man to take advice than to give it.*

Lesson 70

Concepts:

Counting by fives, dimes, estimation, subtraction, days of the week, greater than and less than, multiplication, and addition

Objectives:

1. The student shall be able to count out loud by fives to 60.

2. The student shall be able to write the value of the given number of dimes.

3. The student shall be able to write two addition facts and two subtraction facts when given three numbers.

4. The student shall be able to circle the animal that is about 30 inches long.

5. The student shall be able to write the difference of two triple-digit numbers when borrowing from the tens' column.

6. The student shall be able to number the days of the week in the correct order.

7. The student shall be able to write the correct symbol (< or >) between a multiplication fact and a number.

8. The student shall be able to write the missing addend in an addition fact.

Teaching Tips:

1. If the student(s) are not familiar with the dime in activity 5, discuss in detail the color, picture on front (Franklin D. Roosevelt), back (torch and sprigs of laurel and oak), monetary value (on back), "IN GOD WE TRUST" and "LIBERTY" on front, and date it was minted.

Materials, Supplies, & Equipment:

1. Flashcards for addition, subtraction, and multiplication facts

2. Play money

3. Yardstick

4. Calendar

5. Multiplication chart

Activities:

1. Administer **Test 7**.

2. Have the student(s) take a clean sheet of paper to write the answers for their addition and subtraction facts. Take ten *addition flashcards*. Leave the sleeves over one addend. Show each card for 5 seconds as the student(s) write the answers in a column. Check the answers before you begin the next set of ten *subtraction flashcards*. Do as many sets as time permits in 5 minutes.

3. Using *flashcards for multiplication facts*, drill 0's, 1's, and 10's without the answers showing and 5's with the answers showing. It is important for them to learn the facts in pairs every time.

4. Count out loud with the student(s) by fives to 60 from memory.

5. Give the student(s) dimes. Ask them to count several sets of dimes and tell how many cents they have in each set. Equate this with having five 10's or 5 x 10 = 50. Choose different sets of dimes and equate them to the equivalent multiplication facts. The student(s) should be able to complete **Student Activity One** on their own.

6. Have the student(s) give the answers to several *addition fact flashcards*. Then have them tell another addition fact and two subtraction facts using the same three numbers. The student should be able to complete **Student Activity Two** by themselves.

7. Ask the student(s) to demonstrate with their arms how long 30 inches is. Ask them to name some animals that they think are about 30 inches long. Show them on a *yardstick* the length and height of 30 inches. See if there is anything in the room that looks about that long. The student(s) should be able to complete **Student Activity Three** independently.

8. The student(s) should be able to complete **Student Activity Four** without assistance. They must check their answers.

9. Review the days of the week using a *calendar*. See how many of the student(s) can say them in the correct order by themselves. After going over the directions, they should be able to complete **Student Activity Five** alone.

10. Review the meaning and how to read the greater than and less than symbols (< and >). Allow the student(s) to use the *multiplication chart* where needed as they complete **Student Activity Six** and **Seven**.

Lesson 71

Concepts:
Quarters, days of the week, word sentences, word numbers, addition, estimation, greater than and less than, subtraction, and word problems

Objectives:
1. The student shall be able to write the value of a given number of dimes.

2. The student shall be able to write the days of the week in the correct order.

3. The student shall be able to draw a line to match a subtraction word sentence and a number sentence.

4. The student shall be able to write the missing addend in an addition fact.

5. The student shall be able to draw three objects that are about twelve inches long.

6. The student shall be able to write the correct symbol (< or >) between two subtraction facts.

Teaching Tips:
1. If the student(s) are not familiar with the quarter in activity 4, discuss in detail the color, picture on the front (George Washington), back (eagle), monetary value (quarter dollar on back), "IN GOD WE TRUST" and "LIBERTY" on front, and date it was minted. Our country is identified on the back.

Materials, Supplies, & Equipment:
1. Flashcards for subtraction and multiplication facts

2. Play money

3. Calendar

4. 12-inch ruler

5. Counting chips

Activities:

1. Drill addition facts using *Drill #1, Worksheet 35*.

2. Using *flashcards for subtraction facts*, drill minuends 1–18 with the answers showing and covering the minuend or the subtrahend.

3. Using *flashcards for multiplication facts*, drill 0's, 1's, and 10's without the answers showing and 5's with the answers showing.

4. Give the student(s) quarters. Ask them to count several sets of quarters and tell how many cents they have in each set. Discuss the value of 4 quarters as being 100¢ or $1.00. The decimal point separates the dollars from cents and is read "one dollar." 5 quarters would be 125¢ or $1.25 and is read "one dollar and twenty-five cents." The student(s) should be able to complete **Student Activity One** by themselves.

5. Recite the days of the week in order from memory with the student(s). Using a *calendar*, discuss with them the date of the third Thursday, second Tuesday, the date the 16th is on, the 27th is on, today's date, today's day, etc. The student(s) should be able to complete **Student Activity Two** on their own.

6. Review with the student(s) the different ways the word "subtraction" can be expressed (minus, subtracted from, difference, less than, decreased, take away, etc.). Write several word sentences on the board that describe a subtraction problem. Use the expression "subtracted from" in a word sentence. Have the student(s) read each sentence in **Student Activity Three**. After they finish the activity, discuss it with them.

7. The student(s) should be able to complete **Student Activity Four** independently.

8. Show the student(s) how long 12 inches is with an *12-inch ruler*. See if they can name some objects that are about 12 inches long. Then have them draw the objects for **Student Activity Five**.

9. For accuracy, have the student(s) write the answer for each subtraction fact above the fact before they determine which symbol they should use in **Student Activity Six**.

10. After the student(s) read the first word problem to themselves in **Student Activity Seven**, have them choose the key word (left). Ask them to determine if they add or subtract (their first subtraction word problem). Demonstrate the concept with *counting chips* using smaller numbers (14 − 6 = 8 pages). Remind the student(s) to label their answers for both problems.

Worksheet:

1. *Worksheet 35* – Addition and subtraction drill sheet

Lesson 72

Concepts:

Counting by fives, time equivalents, multiplication, subtraction, greater than and less than, addition, word sentences, word numbers, and word problems

Objectives:

1. The student shall be able to count out loud by fives to 60.

2. The student shall be able to write the equivalents for seconds, minutes, hours, days, weeks, months, and a year.

3. The student shall be able to write the product of the multiplication facts for zero, one, ten, and five.

4. The student shall be able to write two addition facts and two subtraction facts when given three numbers.

5. The student shall be able to write the missing subtrahend in a subtraction fact.

6. The student shall be able to write the correct symbol (< or >) between two addition facts.

7. The student shall be able to rewrite a subtraction word sentence as a number sentence.

Teaching Tips:

1. If it is necessary for accuracy for the student(s), encourage them to write the answers to the addition facts above the facts in **Student Activity Five** before they determine the correct symbol to place between the two facts.

Materials, Supplies, & Equipment:

1. Flashcards for addition and multiplication facts

2. Clock model

3. Multiplication chart

Activities:

1. Drill subtraction facts using *Drill #2, Worksheet 35.*

2. Using *flashcards for addition facts*, drill sums 1–18 with the answers showing and covering one of the two addends.

3. Using *flashcards for multiplication facts*, drill 0's, 1's, and 10's without the answers showing and 5's with the answers showing. It is important for them to learn the facts in pairs every time (e.g., 2 x 5 = 10, 5 x 2 = 10).

4. Count out loud with the student(s) by fives to 60 from memory.

5. Discuss with the student(s) the sequence of time from a second to a year. The *clock model* would be a help here. Have them give the answers for **Student Activity One** together. It is important that they write the correct answers in the blanks since this is the first time they have answered these questions. Use 365 days in a year but discuss leap year as 366 days.

6. Discuss the rules for multiplying by zero, one, and ten. Allow the student(s) to use the *multiplication chart* for fives when doing **Student Activity Two**.

7. The student(s) should be able to complete **Student Activity Three** on their own.

8. Write "12 – __ = 8" on the board. When the subtrahend is missing, have the student(s) subtract the answer from the minuend (12 – 8 = 4 so 12 – 4 = 8). Or they can think, "What do I add to 8 to get 12?" The student(s) should not rush but think through each problem when they complete **Student Activity Four**.

9. The student(s) should be able to complete **Student Activity Five** and **Seven** by themselves.

10. Discuss the answers with the student(s) after they complete **Student Activity Six**.

Worksheet:

1. *Worksheet 35* – Addition and subtraction drill sheet

One who needs advice most is most likely to like it least.

Lesson 73

Concepts:
Counting by fives, subtraction, time equivalents, addition, word problems, multiplication, word sentences, and word numbers

Objectives:
1. The student shall be able to count out loud by fives to 60.

2. The student shall be able to write the missing subtrahend in a subtraction fact.

3. The student shall be able to write the equivalents for seconds, minutes, hours, days, weeks, months, and a year.

4. The student shall be able to write the sum of three double-digit numbers when the ones' column has a double-digit answer.

5. The student shall be able to write the difference of two four-digit numbers when borrowing from the tens' column.

6. The student shall be able to write the product of the multiplication facts for zero, one, ten, and five.

7. The student shall be able to rewrite a subtraction word sentence as a number sentence.

Teaching Tips:
1. Notice that ***Student Activity Three*** has new directions for the addition problems. It will no longer say to add. "Find the sum" tells the student(s) to add by re-enforcing the meaning of the word "sum" (the answer for an addition problem).

Materials, Supplies, & Equipment:
1. Flashcards for subtraction and multiplication facts

2. Clock model

3. Calendar

Activities:

1. Drill addition facts using *Drill #3, Worksheet 35*.

2. Using *flashcards for subtraction facts*, drill minuends 1–18 with the answers showing and covering the minuend or the subtrahend.

3. Using *flashcards for multiplication facts*, drill 0's, 1's, and 10's without the answers showing and 5's with the answers showing. It is important for them to learn the facts in pairs every time.

4. Count out loud with the student(s) by fives to 60.

5. Write a subtraction fact on the board with the subtrahend missing (e.g., 13 – __ = 5). Remind the student(s) to either subtract the difference from the minuend (13 – 5) or to ask "What do I add to the difference to get the minuend?" (5 + __ = 13) The student(s) must think carefully when they work each problem in **Student Activity One**.

6. Review the time equivalents with the aid of the *model clock* and a *calendar*. Encourage the student(s) not to guess when they do **Student Activity Two**, but to ask about the correct answer if they do not know.

7. On the board write three double-digit numbers as an addition problem with carrying only in the ones' column. Remind the student(s) to add down and then to check their answer by adding up. Be sure they check their answers when completing **Student Activity Three**.

8. After reading the word problem in **Student Activity Four**, have the student(s) choose the key word which determines if they are to add or subtract. Remind them to label their answer.

9. The student(s) should be able to complete **Student Activity Five**, **Six**, and **Seven** independently. Discuss **Student Activity Seven** once they have written their answers.

Worksheet:

1. *Worksheet 35* – Addition and subtraction drill sheet

Long-range goals can keep us from being frustrated by short-range failures.

Lesson 74

Concepts:
 Counting by fives, time equivalents, subtraction, money, addition, and multiplication

Objectives:
 1. The student shall be able to count out loud by fives to 60.

 2. The student shall be able to draw a line to match the given time equivalents.

 3. The student shall be able to write the missing minuend in a subtraction fact.

 4. The student shall be able to write the value of a given set of coins expressed in cents.

 5. The student shall be able to write the sum of three double-digit numbers when the ones' column has a double-digit answer.

 6. The student shall be able to write the difference of two four-digit numbers when borrowing from the tens' column.

 7. The student shall be able to write the product of the multiplication facts for zero, one, ten, and five.

Teaching Tips:
 1. Explain to the student(s) the meaning of the word "equivalents" in the directions for **Student Activity One** (equal or the same as). Have them say the word several times. They will enjoy telling everyone the big word they have learned.

Materials, Supplies, & Equipment:
 1. Flashcards for addition and multiplication facts

 2. Clock model

 3. Calendar

 4. Play money

 5. Number chart 0-99

Activities:

1. Drill subtraction facts using *Drill #4, Worksheet 35*.

2. Using *flashcards for addition facts*, drill sums 1–18 with the answers showing and covering one of the two addends.

3. Using *flashcards for multiplication facts*, drill 0's, 1's, and 10's without the answers showing and 5's with the answers showing. It is important for them to learn the facts in pairs every time (e.g., 4 x 5 = 20, 5 x 4 = 20).

4. Count out loud with the student(s) by fives to 60 from memory.

5. Using the *model clock* and a *calendar*, discuss the time equivalents. Ask the student(s) to guard against guessing. Allow them to count the days in a week, months in a year, weeks in a year, minutes in an hour or half hour, and seconds in a minute. They could add all the days in a year by adding each month together. The student(s) should be able to complete **Student Activity One** alone. Let them discover the answers for themselves.

6. Write a subtraction fact on the board with the minuend missing (e.g., __ – 7 = 5). When the minuend is missing, the student(s) will add the difference (5) and the subtrahend(7) just as they do when they check a subtraction problem. Do several examples for the student(s) to complete. They must work carefully when they do each problem in **Student Activity Two**.

7. Give the student(s) a combination of coins. Ask them to put into a group 1 quarter, 1 dime, 2 nickels, and 3 pennies. Then have them count the coins together (25, 35, 40, 45, 46, 47, 48). They may need to practice counting by tens from 25. Use the *number chart* to show how to count by tens starting at a number other than a multiple of ten. Have the student(s) complete **Student Activity Three** with your guidance.

8. The student(s) should be able to complete **Student Activity Four**, **Five**, and **Six** by themselves, following the directions carefully.

Worksheets:

1. *Worksheet 36* – Value of coins

2. *Worksheet 35* – Addition and subtraction drill sheet

If you have no goal, you will be sure to reach it every time.

Lesson 75

Concepts:
    Half dollar, time (5 minutes), subtraction, and addition

Objectives:
1. The student shall be able to recognize the half dollar both front and back and write the correct value of a given number of half dollars.

2. The student shall be able to write the correct time displayed on the face of a clock for given five minute increments.

3. The student shall be able to write the missing minuend in a subtraction fact.

4. The student shall be able to write the sum of three double-digit numbers when the ones' column has a double-digit answer.

5. The student shall be able to write the difference of two four-digit numbers when borrowing from the tens' column.

Teaching Tips:
1. Share the history of the half dollar with the student(s) when doing activity 3. The half dollar was first minted in 1794 with the figure of Liberty on the front and an eagle on the back. In 1948, Benjamin Franklin's picture appeared on the front of the half dollar. The Kennedy half dollar was issued in February of 1964. There was a special bicentennial half dollar during 1975 and 1976 with Kennedy on the front and Independence Hall on the back.

Materials, Supplies, & Equipment:
1. Flashcards for addition, subtraction, and multiplication facts

2. Real half dollar

3. Play money

4. Small clock model for student(s)

5. Clock model

Activities:

1. Have the student(s) take a clean sheet of paper on which to write the answers for their *addition* and *subtraction facts* using *flashcards* with sleeves over an addend and a minuend or subtrahend. Do as many sets as time permits in 5 minutes.

2. Using *flashcards for multiplication facts*, drill 0's, 1's, and 10's without the answers showing and 5's with the answers showing. It is important for them to learn the facts in pairs every time (e.g., 6 x 5 = 30, 5 x 6 = 30).

3. Show the student(s) a real half dollar. Allow them to hold it and feel the imprint as well as talk about the texture of the edge. Discuss the size, the man on the front (John F. Kennedy), the picture on the back (presidential seal), color, and value of the half dollar. Practice counting two, three, and four half dollars by 50's. Two half dollars equal one dollar bill. Discuss writing the two half dollars as $1.00. The decimal point separates the cents and dollars and is read with an "and." $1.50 is read "one dollar and fifty cents." Do **Student Activity One** with the student(s).

4. Give the student(s) *small clock models*. Write several 5 minute intervals on the board. Ask the student(s) which hand they need to set first (minute hand). Have them check their clock by the *clock model*. The student(s) should be able to complete **Student Activity Two** on their own.

5. Write several subtraction facts on the board with the minuend missing. Or you may want to use the *subtraction flashcards* with the sleeve over the minuends. Ask the student(s) what they do to find the missing minuend. The student(s) should be able to complete **Student Activity Three** by themselves.

6. **Student Activity Four** and **Five** should be completed by the student(s) independently. Remind the student(s) to check their answers in both activities.

*It is better to aim too high and fail than
to aim too low and make it.*

Lesson 76

Concepts:
Counting by twos, multiplication, half dollars, time (5 minutes), addition, subtraction, and word numbers

Objectives:

1. The student shall be able to count out loud by twos to 24.

2. The student shall be able to write the addition fact and sum that correspond to a given multiplication fact.

3. The student shall be able to write the correct value of a given number of half dollars.

4. The student shall be able to write the correct letter below a corresponding number that matches the answer to a multiplication fact.

5. The student shall be able to draw both hands on the face of a clock for given five minute increments.

6. The student shall be able to write the sum of three triple-digit numbers when the tens' column has a double-digit answer.

7. The student shall be able to write the difference of two four-digit numbers when borrowing from the tens' column.

8. The student shall be able to write the word number that corresponds to a given number.

Teaching Tips:

1. If the student(s) have difficulty counting by 50's in activity 6, use the *number charts 0–99* and *100–199* and point out the numbers used in counting by 50's to 200. See if they can continue to count by 50's to 1,000.

Materials, Supplies, & Equipment:

1. Flashcards for subtraction facts, multiplication facts, and word numbers

2. Play money

3. Clock model

4. Number chart 0–99 and 100–199

Activities:

1. Drill addition facts using *Drill #1, Worksheet 37.*

2. Using *flashcards for subtraction facts*, drill minuends 1–18 with the answers showing and covering the minuend or the subtrahend.

3. Using *flashcards for multiplication facts*, drill 0's, 1's, and 10's without the answers showing and 5's with the answers showing. It is important for them to learn the facts in pairs every time.

4. Count out loud with the student(s) by twos to 24.

5. Write the multiplication facts for twos (2 x 3, 2 x 8, etc.) in random order on the board. Discuss with the student(s) the meaning of 2 x 3 as being two 3's or 3 + 3 which equals 6, writing the addition fact and the sum beside the fact on the board. 2 x 8 is two 8's or 8 + 8 and equals 16. Follow the same thought process with the remainder of the multiplication facts for 2. Give the student(s) whatever guidance they need to be able to complete **Student Activity One** successfully.

6. Give the student(s) 4 *play money* half dollars. Have them count two, three, and four half dollars by 50's. Have the student(s) look at **Student Activity Two**. As they count the first two half dollars, have them write 50 and 100 in the two blanks. Then have them write the 100 as dollars and cents. For the three half dollars, have them write the numbers as they count 50, 100, and 150 and then write 150 as dollars and cents.

7. In **Student Activity Three**, have the students write the product of 5 x 5 after the equal sign. Find the number 25 in the boxes and write "Y" below it. Continue with the same procedure for the remainder of the activity.

8. Allow the student(s) to set the hands on the *clock model* at given 5 minute intervals. Emphasize the importance of setting the minute hand first so they know where to place the hour hand. The student(s) should be able to complete **Student Activity Four** by themselves.

9. The student(s) should be able to complete **Student Activity Five** and **Six** on their own.

10. Make the *word number flashcards*, for the multiples of ten and one hundred, available for spelling reference when the student(s) complete **Student Activity Seven**.

Worksheet:

1. *Worksheet 37* – Addition and subtraction drill sheet

Lesson 77

Concepts:
Counting by twos, time (5 minutes), equal and not equal, even and odd, multiplication readiness, addition, subtraction, and word problems

Objectives:
1. The student shall be able to count out loud by twos to 24.

2. The student shall be able to write the correct symbol (= or ≠) between the time displayed on the face of a clock and a given digital time.

3. The student shall be able to circle the word "even" or "odd" corresponding to a given number.

4. The student shall be able to write the number of objects in a given number of rows and the corresponding multiplication fact.

5. The student shall be able to write the sum of three triple-digit numbers when the tens' column has a double-digit answer.

6. The student shall be able to write the difference of two four-digit numbers when borrowing from the tens' column.

Teaching Tips:
1. When the student(s) write the subtraction problem in **Student Activity Six**, remind them to always write the larger number on the top. Also the name mentioned first in the question (How many more pages did Rod read then Rex?) will be the one that will be on the top.

Materials, Supplies, & Equipment:
1. Flashcards for addition and multiplication facts

2. Clock model

3. Number charts 0–99 and 100–199

Activities:

1. Drill subtraction facts using *Drill #2, Worksheet 37*.

2. Using *flashcards for addition facts*, drill sums 1–18 with the answers showing and covering one of the two addends.

3. Using *flashcards for multiplication facts*, drill 0's, 1's, and 10's without the answers showing and 5's with the answers showing. It is important for them to learn the facts in pairs every time (e.g., 8 x 5 = 40, 5 x 8 = 40).

4. Count out loud with the student(s) by twos to 24 from memory.

5. Have the student(s) write on a sheet of paper several 5 minute times that you display on the *clock model*. Discuss the meaning of the symbols = and ≠ with the student(s). They should be able to complete **Student Activity One** on their own once they have a clear understanding of the directions.

6. Point to several numbers on the *number charts 0–99* and *100–199* and have the student(s) tell if the numbers are even or odd. After the student(s) read the directions, they should be able to complete **Student Activity Two** by themselves.

7. On the board draw circles of 2 rows of 5 each and 5 rows of 2 each. Ask the student(s) to tell how many rows and how many in each row. Then have them express the 2 rows of 5 as a multiplication fact (2 x 5) and tell what the product equals (10). Do the same for 5 rows of 2 each. *Worksheet 38* will provide further practice for this concept. Complete **Student Activity Three** with the student(s).

8. The student(s) should be able to complete **Student Activity Four** and **Five** independently.

9. Ask the student(s) to tell the key word and if they add or subtract in the word problem for **Student Activity Six**. After they solve the problem by writing the fact vertically, check to see that the answers are labeled correctly.

Worksheets:

1. *Worksheet 38* – Multiplication by twos

2. *Worksheet 37* – Addition and subtraction drill sheet

Lesson 78

Concepts:
Counting by twos, multiplication, subtraction, word problems, even and odd, equal and not equal, and addition

Objectives:
1. The student shall be able to count out loud by twos to 24.

2. The student shall be able to draw a line to match pairs of multiplication facts.

3. The student shall be able to write the missing minuend or subtrahend in a subtraction fact.

4. The student shall be able to color the numbered shapes a given color corresponding to even and odd numbers.

5. The student shall be able to write the correct symbol (= or ≠) between a multiplication fact and a number.

6. The student shall be able to write the sum of three triple-digit numbers when the tens' column has a double-digit answer.

7. The student shall be able to write the difference of two four-digit numbers when borrowing from the tens' column.

Teaching Tips:
1. Award the student(s) who are consistently getting four smiley faces on their drill sheets in activity 1. You could allow them to skip the drill sheet for a week and control the stop watch during the drill. Set a time for those who are proficient to drill those who still need additional drill time.

Materials, Supplies, & Equipment:
1. Flashcards for multiplication and subtraction facts

Activities:

1. Drill addition facts using *Drill #3, Worksheet 37*.

2. Using *flashcards for multiplication facts*, drill 0's, 1's, and 10's without the answers showing and 5's and 2's with the answers showing. Be sure the student(s) repeat the facts in this manner: "2 x 5 = 10 and 5 x 2 = 10."

3. Count out loud with the student(s) by twos to 24.

4. Say several multiplication facts with the answers from the 0's, 1's, 5's, 10's, and 2's. Have the student(s) say the other pair back to you (e.g., you say "4 x 5 = 20" and they say "5 x 4 = 20"). The student(s) should be able to complete **Student Activity One** by themselves.

5. Drill the student(s) with several *subtraction facts flashcards* with the minuend covered. Discuss adding the difference and the subtrahend to find the minuend. Then drill several subtraction facts with the subtrahend covered. Discuss subtracting the difference from the minuend to find the subtrahend. The student(s) should be able to complete **Student Activity Two** on their own.

6. Ask the student(s) to find the key word (more than) and if they add or subtract to solve the word problems in **Student Activity Three**. The student(s) should be able to complete the activity alone.

7. After the student(s) read the directions for **Student Activity Four**, they should be able to complete the activity independently.

8. After discussing equal and not equal with the student(s), they should be able to complete **Student Activity Five** with no help.

9. The student(s) should be able to complete **Student Activity Six** and **Seven** independently.

Worksheet:

1. *Worksheet 37* – Addition and subtraction drill sheet

The world needs more warm hearts and fewer hot heads.

Lesson 79

Concepts:
>   Counting by twos, multiplication, equal and not equal, word numbers, subtraction, word sentences, addition, and word problems
>   *Definition*: The product is the answer in multiplication.

Objectives:
1. The student shall be able to count out loud by twos to 24.

2. The student shall be able to write the product of the multiplication facts for zero, one, ten, five, and two.

3. The student shall be able to write the correct symbol (= or ≠) between a word number and a number.

4. The student shall be able to write the missing minuend or subtrahend in a subtraction fact.

5. The student shall be able to rewrite an addition word sentence as a number sentence.

6. The student shall be able to write the sum of three triple-digit numbers when the ones' or tens' column has a double-digit answer.

7. The student shall be able to write the difference of two four-digit numbers when borrowing from the tens' column.

Teaching Tips:
1. Notice the directions for ***Student Activity One*** have changed. Discuss with the student(s) that the word "product" means the answer in multiplication. Suggest to the student(s) another way to think of 9 x 2 or similar facts. Think of the other pair, 2 x 9, as two 9's or 9 + 9 and therefore equal to 18.

Materials, Supplies, & Equipment:
1. Flashcards for addition and multiplication facts

2. Multiplication chart

Activities:

1. Drill subtraction facts using *Drill #4, Worksheet 37*.

2. Using *flashcards for addition facts*, drill sums 1–18 with the answers showing and covering one of the two addends.

3. Using *flashcards for multiplication facts*, drill 0's, 1's, and 10's without the answers showing and 5's and 2's with the answers showing. It is important for them to learn the facts in pairs every time (e.g., 2 x 8 = 16, 8 x 2 = 16).

4. Count out loud with the student(s) by twos to 24 from memory.

5. Allow the student(s) to use the *multiplication chart* to do the multiplication facts for 5 and 2 if necessary when completing **Student Activity One**.

6. The student(s) should be able to complete **Student Activity Two** on their own.

7. Point out to the student(s) that some of the problems in **Student Activity Three** have the minuend missing and some have the subtrahend missing. Discuss adding when the minuend is missing and subtracting when the subtrahend is missing (both begin with subtra). Do several examples on the board. Encourage the student(s) to stop and think before they do each problem in **Student Activity Three**.

8. Ask the student(s) if the word sentences in **Student Activity Four** indicate that they are to add or subtract. They should be able to complete the activity by themselves. Insist that they write "Eight added to seventy-one equals seventy-nine." as "71 + 8 = 79" and not "8 + 71 = 79."

9. The student(s) should be able to complete **Student Activity Five**, **Six**, and **Seven** on their own.

Worksheets:

1. *Worksheet 39* – Word numbers

2. *Worksheet 37* – Addition and subtraction drill sheet

Keep your temper; nobody wants it.

Lesson 80

Concepts:
Counting by twos, subtraction, multiplication, word sentences, word numbers, and addition

Objectives:
1. The student shall be able to count out loud by twos to 24.

2. The student shall be able to circle the greatest number of three given numbers.

3. The student shall be able to write the missing minuend or subtrahend in a subtraction fact.

4. The student shall be able to write the product of the multiplication facts for zero, one, ten, five, and two.

5. The student shall be able to rewrite a subtraction word sentence as a number sentence.

6. The student shall be able to write the sum of three triple-digit numbers when the ones' or tens' column has a double-digit answer.

Teaching Tips:
1. When doing the drill for multiplication in activity 3, try doing the facts for 5's and 2's without the answers showing but at a slower pace. This will given you some guidance as to how soon you feel they will be ready to do the drill on a daily basis without the answers showing.

Materials, Supplies, & Equipment:
1. Flashcards for addition, subtraction, and multiplication facts

2. Multiplication chart

Activities:

1. Administer **Test 8**.

2. Have the student(s) take a clean sheet of paper on which to write the answers for their *addition* and *subtraction facts* using *flashcards* with sleeves over an addend and a minuend or subtrahend. Do as many sets as time permits in 5 minutes.

3. Using *flashcards for multiplication facts*, drill 0's, 1's, and 10's without the answers showing. Drill the 5's and 2's with the answers showing.

4. Count out loud with the student(s) by twos to 24.

5. The student(s) should be able to complete **Student Activity One** by themselves.

6. Before the student(s) start **Student Activity Two**, remind them to add if the minuend is missing and to subtract if the subtrahend is missing.

7. Allow the student(s) to use the *multiplication chart* to do the multiplication facts for 5's and 2's if necessary when completing **Student Activity Three**. Discourage them from guessing.

8. Ask the student(s) if the word sentences in **Student Activity Four** indicate that they are to add or subtract. Discuss how they will write "Eight subtracted from forty-seven equals thirty-nine." as a number sentence ($47 - 8 = 39$). They should then be able to compete the activity by themselves.

9. The student(s) should be able to complete **Student Activity Five** and **Six** independently.

Yielding to uncontrolled anger causes a person to lose his own self respect and the esteem of others.

Lesson 81

Concepts:
Counting by twos, word sentences, word numbers, addition, sequence, subtraction, and multiplication

Objectives:
1. The student shall be able to count out loud by twos to 24.

2. The student shall be able to circle the least or smallest number of three given numbers.

3. The student shall be able to rewrite an addition word sentence as a number sentence.

4. The student shall be able to write the sum of three triple-digit numbers when the ones' or tens' column has a double-digit answer.

5. The student shall be able to place an "X" on the number that is incorrect in a sequence of numbers.

6. The student shall be able to write the difference of two four-digit numbers when borrowing from the tens' column.

7. The student shall be able to write the product of the multiplication facts for one, ten, five, and two.

Teaching Tips:
1. Before starting activity 6, have the student(s) tell all the words that are used in a word sentence to indicate that they are to add and all the words that are used in a word sentence to indicate that they are to subtract. Their goal will be to determine if the word sentence is addition or subtraction when the sentences appear at random in the same activity.

2. Once the student(s) have completed ***Student Activity Four***, have them write the correct numbers over the ones on which they have put "X's."

Materials, Supplies, & Equipment:
1. Flashcards for subtraction and multiplication facts

Activities:

1. Drill addition facts using *Drill #1, Worksheet 40*.

2. Using *flashcards for subtraction facts*, drill minuends 1–18 with the answers showing and covering the minuend or the subtrahend.

3. Using *flashcards for multiplication facts*, drill 0's, 1's, and 10's without the answers showing. Drill the 5's and 2's with the answers showing. Learning the facts in pairs every time is important.

4. Count out loud with the student(s) by twos to 24.

5. After discussing with the student(s) the meaning of the word "least" (smallest) in **Student Activity One,** they should be able to complete the activity by themselves.

6. Have the student(s) determine if the word sentences in **Student Activity Two** indicate that they are to add or subtract. Once they have completed the activity, discuss how each number sentence was written.

7. The student(s) should be able to complete **Student Activity Three** on their own.

8. Write a sequence of 12 even numbers over 400 on the board, having changed five of the numbers to be out of sequence. Have the student(s) select the numbers that are out of sequence and tell what the correct numbers should be. After discussing the sequence, help the student(s) find the first number that is out of sequence in **Student Activity Four**. Allow those who have understanding to continue on their own while you help those who need help.

9. The student(s) should be able to complete **Student Activity Five** and **Six** independently.

Worksheet:

1. *Worksheet 40* – Addition and subtraction drill sheet

Control your anger rather than letting it control you.

Lesson 82

Concepts:
Counting by twos, fractions, multiplication, addition, money, and sequence

Objectives:
1. The student shall be able to count out loud by twos to 24.

2. The student shall be able to write the fraction that represents the part of a whole that is shaded.

3. The student shall be able to write the product of the multiplication facts for five and two.

4. The student shall be able to write the sum of three triple-digit numbers when the answers for the ones' and tens' columns are double-digit.

5. The student shall be able to write the value of a given number of dimes and pennies.

6. The student shall be able to place an "X" on the number that is incorrect in a sequence of numbers.

Teaching Tips:
1. If the student(s) have mastered counting by twos in activity 4, have them count by twos starting at 1 instead of 2. Then have them count by twos starting at 241 and go to 279.

Materials, Supplies, & Equipment:
1. Flashcards for addition and multiplication facts

2. Fraction materials

3. Multiplication chart

4. Play money

Activities:

1. Drill subtraction facts using *Drill #2, Worksheet 40*.

2. Using *flashcards for addition facts*, drill sums 1–18 with the answers showing and covering one of the two addends.

3. Using *flashcards for multiplication facts*, drill 0's, 1's, and 10's without the answers showing. Drill the 5's and 2's with the answers showing.

4. Count out loud with the student(s) by twos to 24 from memory.

5. Use *fraction materials* to display several wholes divided into 2, 3, 4, … to 9 equal parts with one part shaded. Discuss with the student(s) the number of parts in which the whole is divided and how many of those parts are shaded. Ask the student(s) to tell what fractional part of the whole is shaded (1 out of 4 or $\frac{1}{4}$). Allow those who are capable to complete **Student Activity One** on their own. Give help to those who need it.

6. Have the student(s) complete **Student Activity Two** by themselves. Then have them use the *multiplication chart* to check any answers about which they were not sure. Do not allow them to guess. They must look up the answer if they do not have the fact memorized.

7. Write several sets of three triple-digit numbers on the board as vertical addition problems with carrying in both the ones' and the tens' places. Be sure that the student(s) show the carrying by placing the one above the tens' and the hundreds' places. As the student(s) complete **Student Activity Three,** check their first answers for accuracy.

8. Use *money* to remind the student(s) to count the dimes by tens and the pennies by ones before they complete **Student Activity Four**.

9. Discuss with the student(s) the sequence used in **Student Activity Five** (counting by threes with each number three more than the previous one). As soon as they have successfully located the first number out of sequence in the activity, allow them to complete the activity independently.

10. The student(s) should be able to complete **Student Activity Six** without assistance.

Worksheets:

1. *Worksheet 41* – Blank multiplication chart

2. *Worksheet 40* – Addition and subtraction drill sheet

Lesson 83

Concepts:
Counting by twos, money, greater than and less than, fractions, multiplication, word problems, and addition

Objectives:

1. The student shall be able to count out loud by twos to 24.

2. The student shall be able to write the value of a given number of nickels and pennies.

3. The student shall be able to write the correct symbol (< or >) between two coins.

4. The student shall be able to write two addition facts and two subtraction facts when given three numbers.

5. The student shall be able to write the fraction that represents the part of a whole that is shaded.

6. The student shall be able to write the product of the multiplication facts for zero, one, ten, five, and two.

7. The student shall be able to write the sum of three triple-digit numbers when the answers for the ones' and the tens' columns are double-digit.

Teaching Tips:

1. If the student(s) have difficulty completing the small multiplication tables in **_Student Activity Five_**, tell them to use their fingers to cover the two rows on which they are not working to enable them to concentrate on one row at a time.

Materials, Supplies, & Equipment:

1. Flashcards for subtraction and multiplication facts

2. Play money

3. Fraction materials

Activities:

1. Drill addition facts using *Drill #3, Worksheet 40*.

2. Using *flashcards for subtraction facts*, drill minuends 1–18 with the answers showing and covering the minuend or the subtrahend.

3. Using *flashcards for multiplication facts*, drill 0's, 1's, and 10's without the answers showing and 5's and 2's with the answers showing. Learning the facts in pairs every time is very important for them.

4. Count out loud with the student(s) by twos to 24.

5. Remind the student(s) to count the nickels by fives and the pennies by ones before they complete **Student Activity One**.

6. Review the value of each coin with the student(s). Then compare two coins and have them tell if one is greater than or less than the other. The student(s) should be able to complete **Student Activity Two** independently.

7. The student(s) should be able to complete **Student Activity Three** on their own.

8. Use *fraction materials* to display several wholes divided into 2-10 equal parts with one part shaded.Discuss with the student(s) into how many parts the whole is divided (the denominator or number that goes on the bottom of the fraction) and how many of those parts are shaded (the numerator or number that goes on the top of the fraction). Allow the student(s) to complete **Student Activity Four** by themselves. Give individual help if needed.

9. The student(s) should be able to complete **Student Activity Five**, **Six**, and **Seven** alone.

Worksheet:

1. *Worksheet 40* – Addition and subtraction drill sheet

Anytime you begin in anger, you will end in shame.

Lesson 84

Concepts:
Counting by twos, money, estimation, fractions, word sentences, word numbers, greater than and less than, addition, and word problems

Objectives:
1. The student shall be able to count out loud by twos to 24.

2. The student shall be able to write the number of coins needed to equal a given number of cents.

3. The student shall be able to write the correct number to which a given number is closer.

4. The student shall be able to draw lines to divide a whole into the necessary number of equal parts to color a given fractional part of that whole.

5. The student shall be able to rewrite a subtraction word sentence as a number sentence.

6. The student shall be able to write the correct symbol (< or >) between a given number of cents and a given number of coins.

7. The student shall be able to write the sum of three triple-digit numbers when the answers in the ones' and the tens' columns are double-digit.

Teaching Tips:
1. As a preview for shapes, ask the student(s) the names of the shapes used in **Student Activity Three**. See if they can recall the other shape studied in first grade (triangle). See how many of the solids they can recall from first grade (cube, cone, cylinder, and sphere).

Materials, Supplies, & Equipment:
1. Flashcards for addition and multiplication facts

2. Play money

3. Fraction materials

Activities:

1. Drill subtraction facts using *Drill #4, Worksheet 40*.

2. Using *flashcards for addition facts*, drill sums 1–18 with the answers showing and covering one of the two addends.

3. Using *flashcards for multiplication facts*, drill 0's, 1's, and 10's without the answers showing. Drill the 5's and 2's with the answers showing.

4. Count out loud with the student(s) by twos to 24.

5. Give the student(s) *play money*. Write several amounts of money in cents (less than a dollar) on the board. Have the student(s) select the coins they would need to equal that amount. There will be several combinations of coins as possible answers. Discuss the directions for **Student Activity One** with the student(s). Select the first set of coins needed to equal 38¢ with them. Continue to help them with each amount until you feel they are capable of finishing on their own.

6. Ask the student(s) if 34 is closer to 30 or 40, 52 closer to 50 or 60, and 88 closer to 80 or 90. Have them defend their answer (if the ones' digit is over 5, they choose the larger number and if the ones' digit is under 5, they choose the smaller number). Allow the student(s) to complete **Student Activity Two** by themselves.

7. Draw several shapes on the board that can be divided into 2–10 equal parts or use *fraction materials*. Ask the student(s) to come to the board and divide a shape into the necessary parts to shade a given fractional part. Encourage the student(s) to be careful to divide each shape into equal parts as they complete **Student Activity Three**.

8. After the student(s) have determined that the word sentences in **Student Activity Four** are subtraction, they should be able to write the number sentences alone.

9. When the student(s) begin **Student Activity Five**, have them write the value of the coins on their paper before they make the two comparisons.

10. The student(s) should be able to complete **Student Activity Six** and **Seven** independently.

Worksheets:

1. *Worksheet 42* – Multiplication

2. *Worksheet 40* – Addition and subtraction drill sheet

Lesson 85

Concepts:
Time equivalents, greater than and less than, money, fractions, addition, estimation, word sentences, and word numbers

Objectives:
1. The student shall be able to draw a line to match the given time equivalents.

2. The student shall be able to write the correct symbol (< or >) between a given number of cents and a given number of coins.

3. The student shall be able to draw lines to divide a whole into equal parts and shade a given fractional part of that whole.

4. The student shall be able to write the missing addend in an addition fact.

5. The student shall be able to write the correct number to which a given number is closer.

6. The student shall be able to rewrite an addition word sentence as a number sentence.

7. The student shall be able to write two addition and two subtraction facts when given three numbers.

Teaching Tips:
1. If the student(s) have difficulty with **Student Activity Five**, have them use the *number chart* to see to which multiple of ten the number is closer.

Materials, Supplies, & Equipment:
1. Flashcards for addition facts, subtraction facts, multiplication facts, and time equivalents

2. Play money

3. Fraction materials

4. Number chart 0–99

Activities:

1. Have the student(s) take a clean sheet of paper on which to write the answers for their ad*dition* and *subtraction facts* using *flashcards* with sleeves over an addend and a minuend or subtrahend. Do as many sets as time permits in 5 minutes.

2. Using *flashcards for multiplication facts*, drill 0's, 1's, and 10's without the answers showing. Drill the 5's and 2's with the answers showing.

3. Use *flashcards* to review the *time equivalents* with the student(s). Do not allow them to guess what the correct answer is when doing **Student Activity One**. Be willing to show them the answer using the *flashcards* if they do not know.

4. Have the student(s) find the value of several half dollar and penny combinations using *play money*. Tell them several given amounts and let them decide if the given amounts are greater than or less than the combinations. Encourage the student(s) to write the value of the combination in **Student Activity Two** on their paper before they determine which symbol to use.

5. With the aid of *fraction materials*, have the student(s) select the wholes that have been divided into 2, 3, 4, etc. parts. Then have them tell how many parts need to be shaded to equal a unit fraction (fraction with a 1 in the numerator). In **Student Activity Three,** encourage the student(s) to first divide the objects into the correct number of parts (denominator) and then shade one part (numerator).

6. Write "6 + __ = 11" and "__ + 8 = 13" on the board. Ask the student(s) to tell if they add or subtract to find the answer when the second addend is missing (6 + __ = 11). Then ask them if they add or subtract when the first addend is missing (__ + 8 = 13). Regardless which addend is missing in addition, the student(s) should subtract. They should be able to complete **Student Activity Four** by themselves.

7. Ask the student(s) if 38 is closer to 30 or 40, 56 closer to 50 or 60, and 72 closer to 70 or 80. Have them defend their answers. Allow the student(s) to complete **Student Activity Five** on their own.

8. Discuss with the student(s) whether the word sentences in **Student Activity Six** are addition or subtraction. They should be able to write the number sentences on their own.

9. The student(s) should be able to complete **Student Activity Seven** independently.

Lesson 86

Concepts:
Counting by threes, multiplication readiness, time equivalents, even and odd, addition, subtraction, word sentences, and word numbers

Objectives:
1. The student shall be able to count out loud by threes to 36.

2. The student shall be able to write a given number of threes as an addition problem, a multiplication problem, and the product.

3. The student shall be able to write the correct answers for given time equivalents.

4. The student shall be able to write the sum of two numbers and if the addends and sum are even or odd.

5. The student shall be able to write the missing minuend or subtrahend in a subtraction fact.

6. The student shall be able to write the sum of three four-digit numbers when the answers for the ones' and tens' columns are double-digit.

7. The student shall be able to rewrite a subtraction word sentence as a number sentence.

Teaching Tips:
1. When the student(s) are doing activity 5, give them *counting chips* to demonstrate the two 3's as addition (two groups of three each), as multiplication (two rows of three each), and as a product (count them). Do the same for the other groups of threes they discuss.

Materials, Supplies, & Equipment:
1. Flashcards for subtraction facts, multiplication facts, and time equivalents

2. Multiplication chart

3. Counting chips

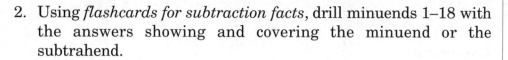

Activities:

1. Drill addition facts using *Drill #1, Worksheet 43*.

2. Using *flashcards for subtraction facts*, drill minuends 1–18 with the answers showing and covering the minuend or the subtrahend.

3. Using *flashcards for multiplication facts*, drill 5's and 2's with the answers showing. Notice that the drill of the multiplication facts for 0, 1, and 10 can now be omitted. Because there is a single rule for each set of facts, the student(s) should have mastered these facts by this time.

4. Count out loud with the student(s) by threes to 36.

5. Write "two 3's, three 3's, four 3's, etc." on the board. Ask the student(s) how to write two 3's as an addition problem (3 + 3). Then have them tell how to write two 3's as a multiplication problem (2 x 3). Now have them look at their *multiplication chart* for the answer to 2 x 3 if they do not already know it (3 + 3 should give them the answer). Follow the same procedure for three 3's, four 3's, etc. The student(s) should be able to complete **Student Activity One** with the help of the *multiplication chart*.

6. Drill the student(s) using the *time equivalent flashcards*. Test the student(s) on an individual basis with the *flashcards* to see what equivalents need the most review. Allow the student(s) to complete **Student Activity Two** on their own helping those who still do not know all of the correct equivalents.

7. Write several addition facts (both odd or both even) on the board. Discuss with the student(s) if the sum is odd or even when they add two odd numbers together and when they add two even numbers together (always even). The student(s) should be able to complete **Student Activity Three** by themselves after they write even or odd in the blanks for the first problem together.

8. Discuss with the student(s) whether they add or subtract when the minuend is missing (add) and when the subtrahend is missing (subtract). The student(s) should be able to complete **Student Activity Four** and **Five** alone.

9. The student(s) should be able to complete **Student Activity Six** and **Seven** independently after discussing whether the word sentences are addition or subtraction.

Worksheet:

1. *Worksheet 43* – Addition and subtraction drill sheet

Lesson 87

Concepts:
 Counting by threes, dollars, even and odd, addition, multiplication readiness, equal and not equal, time equivalents, and word problems

Objectives:
 1. The student shall be able to count out loud by threes to 36.

 2. The student shall be able to write the value of a given number of dollar bills.

 3. The student shall be able to write the sum of two numbers and if the addends and sum are even or odd.

 4. The student shall be able to draw a line to match corresponding number families.

 5. The student shall be able to write the correct symbol (= or ≠) between given time equivalents.

Teaching Tips:
 1. Pass around real *one, five, ten, and twenty dollar bills* for the student(s) to feel and examine during activity 5. Point out the texture of the paper. Notice that all the bills have the statement "IN GOD WE TRUST" printed on them. Show them the circle around a letter to the left of the picture on the front. This seal tells what Federal Reserve Bank issued the bill (written in the circle). The paper money is made by the Bureau of Engraving and Printing. They use special paper and ink which cannot be made or used by any unauthorized person or company. High-speed presses print sheets of 32 bills at a time. The sheets are then cut into stacks of individual bills.

Materials, Supplies, & Equipment:
 1. Flashcards for addition facts, multiplication facts, and time equivalents

 2. Play money

 3. Real one, five, ten, and twenty dollar bills

Activities:

1. Drill subtraction facts using *Drill #2, Worksheet 43*.

2. Using *flashcards for addition facts*, drill sums 1–18 with the answers showing and covering one of the two addends.

3. Using *flashcards for multiplication facts*, drill 5's and 2's with the answers showing.

4. Count out loud with the student(s) by threes to 36.

5. Give the student(s) a one dollar bill. Discuss with them the color, picture on the front (George Washington), the "1" in each corner on the front and back, and the word "ONE" on the back. Tell them that one dollar can be written as cents (100¢) or it can be written as a dollar and cents ($1.00). The decimal point is used to separate the dollar from the cents. The number on the left of the point means dollar and the numbers on the right of the point mean cents. $1.00 means they have one dollar and no cents. 99 is the most cents they can have since one more cent gives them 100 and that is $1.00. Give each student a five, ten, and twenty *play money* dollar bill. Discuss the color, picture on the front ($5 – Abraham Lincoln, $10 – Alexander Hamilton, $20 – Andrew Jackson), picture on the back ($5 – Lincoln Memorial, $10 – US Treasury building, $20 – The White House), and the number in each corner on the front and back. The date the bill was printed is to the lower right of the front picture. Have the student(s) find the value of each set of bills in ***Student Activity One*** together.

6. Write several addition facts (one addend odd and one addend even) on the board. Discuss with the student(s) if the sum is odd or even when they add an odd number to an even number. Discuss if the sum is odd or even when they add two odd numbers or two even numbers. The student(s) should be able to complete ***Student Activity Two*** on their own.

7. Ask the student(s) to write three 3's as an addition problem and as a multiplication problem on a sheet of paper. Then let them tell what to write on the board to use to check their answer. Do several groups of 3's in the same manner. The student(s) should be able to complete ***Student Activity Three*** by themselves.

8. Use the *time equivalent flashcards* to review. The student(s) should be able to complete ***Student Activity Four*** and ***Five*** independently.

Worksheet:

1. *Worksheet 43* Addition and subtraction drill sheet

Lesson 88

Concepts:
Counting by threes, place value, multiplication readiness, time (5 minutes), money, and addition

Objectives:
1. The student shall be able to count out loud by threes to 36.

2. The student shall be able to write the value of a given number of thousands, hundreds, tens, and ones as a sum.

3. The student shall be able to write the number of rows of a given number, the corresponding multiplication fact, and the product.

4. The student shall be able to draw both hands on the face of a clock according to the instructions given.

5. The student shall be able to write the value of a given number of five and ten dollar bills.

6. The student shall be able to write the missing addend in an addition fact.

7. The student shall be able to write the sum of three four-digit numbers when the answers for the ones' and the tens' columns are double-digit.

Teaching Tips:
1. When doing activity 7, discuss with the student(s) which hand they move if the time difference is an hour or multiples of an hour and which hand they move if the time difference is minutes. Ask how many numbers they move the minute hand for 10 minutes, 25 minutes, 40 minutes, etc.

Materials, Supplies, & Equipment:
1. Flashcards for subtraction and multiplication facts

2. Place value materials

3. Small clock model for student(s)

4. Clock model

5. Play money

Activities:

1. Drill addition facts using *Drill #3, Worksheet 43*.

2. Using *flashcards for subtraction facts*, drill minuends 1–18 with the answers showing and covering the minuend or the subtrahend.

3. Using *flashcards for multiplication facts*, drill 5's, 2's, and 3's with the answers showing. Be sure to do all of the 3's with their pairs (5 x 3 and 3 x 5) several times and then review the 5's and the 2's.

4. Count out loud with the student(s) by threes to 36.

5. "6 thousands + 8 hundreds + 3 tens + 7 ones = __ + __ + __ + __" should be written on the board. Have the student(s) tell the value of 6 thousands to write in the first blank, 8 hundreds to write in the second, 3 tens to write in the third, and 7 ones to write in the last blank. *Place value materials* should be helpful. Explain to the student(s) this is the expanded form (6,000 + 800 + 30 + 7) of a number. Put several problems similar to the one above on the board to be completed by the student(s). They should be able to complete ***Student Activity One*** by themselves.

6. On the board draw 4 rows of 3 squares each and beside it draw 3 rows of 4 squares each. Ask the student(s) to tell how many rows and how many in each row. Then have them express the 4 rows of 3 as a multiplication fact (4 x 3) and tell what the product equals (12). Do the same for 3 rows of 4 each. Have the student(s) complete ***Student Activity Two*** independently.

7. Give the student(s) a 5 minute time to set on their *small clock models*. Have them check their time by your *clock model*. Then tell them to set their clock for one hour later, three hours later, thirty minutes earlier, and two hours later. Each time let them check their clock by your *clock model*. They should be able to complete ***Student Activity Three*** with little help.

8. Give the student(s) five and ten *play money* dollar bills. Have them tell the value of 3 five dollar bills (counting by 5's), 6 ten dollar bills (counting by 10's), etc. Explain to the student(s) how to write the value using the dollar sign and the decimal. The student(s) should be able to complete ***Student Activity Four*** on their own. *Worksheet 44* will provide further practice in this area.

9. The student(s) should be able to complete ***Student Activity Five*** and ***Six*** alone.

Worksheets:

1. *Worksheet 44* – Money (bills)

2. *Worksheet 43* – Addition and subtraction drill sheet

Lesson 89

Concepts:
Counting by threes, fractions, multiplication readiness, place value, time (5 minutes), subtraction, and word problems

Definition: The denominator is the bottom number of a fraction and tells how many parts into which the whole is divided.

The numerator is the top number of a fraction and tells how many of the parts are being used.

Objectives:
1. The student shall be able to count out loud by threes to 36.

2. The student shall be able to draw a line to match a graphic representation of a fractional part of a whole to the given fraction.

3. The student shall be able to draw a line to match the pairs of multiplication facts.

4. The student shall be able to write the value of a given number of thousands, hundreds, tens, and ones as a sum.

5. The student shall be able to draw both hands on the face of a clock according to the instructions given.

6. The student shall be able to write the missing minuend or subtrahend in a subtraction fact.

Teaching Tips:
1. When drilling the multiplication facts for the 3's in activity 3, put special emphasis on 4 x 3, 6 x 3, 7 x 3, 8 x 3, and 9 x 3. These are the facts to which they have not been exposed. The remainder of the facts have been learned as a pair.

Materials, Supplies, & Equipment:
1. Flashcards for addition and multiplication facts

2. Fraction materials

3. Small clock model for student(s)

4. Clock model

Activities:

1. Drill subtraction facts using *Drill #4, Worksheet 43*.

2. Using *flashcards for addition facts*, drill sums 1–18 with the answers showing and covering one of the two addends.

3. Using *flashcards for multiplication facts*, drill 5's, 2's, and 3's with the answers showing. Be sure to do all of the 3's with their pairs several times and then review the 5's and the 2's.

4. Count out loud with the student(s) by threes to 36.

5. With *fraction materials*, have the student(s) tell what fractional part of different shapes are shaded. Use unit fractions. Discuss with the student(s) that the bottom number in a fraction tells how many parts into which the whole is divided and is called the denominator. The top number tells how many of the parts are being used and is called the numerator. The student(s) should be able to complete **Student Activity One** on their own.

6. Say several multiplication facts with the answers from the 3's and have the student(s) say the pair back to you (e.g., 6 x 3 = 18 and 3 x 6 = 18). The student(s) should then be able to complete **Student Activity Two** by themselves.

7. The student(s) should be able to complete **Student Activity Three** independently.

8. Using the *small clock models*, have the student(s) set their clocks for a given time. Then tell them to set their clocks for three hours later, 1 hour earlier, ¼ hour earlier, and 45 minutes later. Each time let them check their clocks by your *clock model*. The student(s) should be able to complete **Student Activity Four** alone.

9. The student(s) should be able to complete **Student Activity Five** by themselves.

10. Discuss with the student(s) the key word (fewer) and whether they should add or subtract the word problems in **Student Activity Six**. Allow them to complete the problems on their own. Check to see that they always put the larger number on top when they subtract.

Worksheet:

1. *Worksheet 43* – Addition and subtraction drill sheet

Lesson 90

Concepts:
Counting by threes, multiplication, time, addition, fractions, money, and word problems

Objectives:
1. The student shall be able to count out loud by threes to 36.

2. The student shall be able to write the product of the multiplication facts for zero, one, ten, five, two, and three.

3. The student shall be able to draw both hands on the face of the clock according to the instructions given.

4. The student shall be able to write the missing addend in an addition fact.

5. The student shall be able to write the correct symbol (= or ≠) between a unit fraction and a graphic representation of a fractional part of a whole.

6. The student shall be able to write the value of a given number of one, five, ten, and twenty dollar bills.

Teaching Tips:
1. When discussing fractions in activity 8, point out to the student(s) that the numerator of a fraction is read as a cardinal number which tells how many and the denominator of a fraction is read as an ordinal number which tells which one (e.g., ⅔ is read two-thirds – the two is cardinal and the thirds is ordinal).

Materials, Supplies, & Equipment:
1. Flashcards for addition, subtraction, and multiplication facts

2. Multiplication chart

3. Small clock model for student(s)

4. Fraction materials

5. Play money

Activities:

1. Administer **Test 9**.

2. Have the student(s) take a clean sheet of paper on which to write the answers for their *addition* and *subtraction facts* using *flashcards* with sleeves over an addend and a minuend or subtrahend. Do as many sets as time permits in 5 minutes.

3. Using *flashcards for multiplication facts*, drill 5's, 2's, and 3's with the answers showing. Place special emphasis on 4 x 3, 6 x 3, 7 x 3, 8 x 3, and 9 x 3.

4. Count out loud with the student(s) by threes to 36.

5. Encourage the student(s) to use the *multiplication chart* to write the correct products for any multiplication facts they have not mastered in **Student Activity One**. Do not allow them to guess.

6. Give the student(s) *small clock models* to set for given times when certain events happen in their lives. The hands drawn on the clock faces for **Student Activity Two** will vary. Allow the student(s) to individually determine the time they draw for each activity.

7. The student(s) should be able to complete **Student Activity Three** on their own.

8. Ask the student(s) to identify the fractional part shaded in various shapes from the *fraction materials*. Have the student(s) look at the shapes that have a fractional part shaded in **Student Activity Four**. They need to determine what part is shaded and then compare the fraction with the given fraction. Allow them to work independently.

9. Give the student(s) several *play money* bills in order to find the value of a given set. Ask the student(s) by what number they count the five, ten, and twenty dollar bills. They should be able to complete **Student Activity Five** and **Six** by themselves.

The best way to fight anger is to close your mouth.

Lesson 91

Concepts:
Counting by threes, subtraction regrouping, addition, multiplication, fractions, equal and not equal, and word problems

Objectives:

1. The student shall be able to count out loud by threes to 36.

2. The student shall be able to write the regrouping of one hundred to ten tens for borrowing in subtraction.

3. The student shall be able to write the missing addend, minuend, or subtrahend from an addition or subtraction fact.

4. The student shall be able to write the product of the multiplication facts for two and three.

5. The student shall be able to write the correct symbol (= or ≠) between a unit fraction and a graphic representation of a fractional part of a whole.

6. The student shall be able to write the sum of three triple-digit numbers when the answers for the ones' and the tens' columns are double-digit.

7. The student shall be able to write the difference of two triple-digit numbers when borrowing from the tens' column.

Teaching Tips:

1. When doing activity 8, give the student(s) *counting chips*. Tell them to take eight chips and divide them into two unequal piles. Ask them if they have one half of the chips in either pile. Tell them to separate the 8 chips into two equal piles (4 in each). Ask them if they have one half of the chips in each pile. To have one half, they must have two groups that are of equal size (4 each).

Materials, Supplies, & Equipment:

1. Flashcards for subtraction, multiplication, and addition facts

2. Place value materials

3. Multiplication chart

4. Fraction materials

5. Counting chips

Activities:

1. Drill addition facts using *Drill #1, Worksheet 45*.

2. Using *flashcards for subtraction facts*, drill minuends 1–18 with the answers showing and covering the minuend or the subtrahend.

3. Using *flashcards for multiplication facts*, drill 5's without the answers showing and 3's and 2's with the answers showing.

4. Count out loud with the student(s) by threes to 36.

5. Using *place value materials*, demonstrate for the student(s) how one place value square for one hundred can be regrouped to equal 10 tens. Discuss with them what happens if they have 5 hundreds and they take one hundred to regroup as 10 tens. How many hundreds are left (4)? 5 hundreds = 4 hundreds + 10 tens. Write on the board "8 hundreds = 7 hundreds + __ tens." Do this and other examples with the student(s). Look at **Student Activity One**. Give guidance to those who need it as the student(s) write the answers.

6. In random order, mix several *addition* and *subtraction flashcards* with sleeves. Call attention to the fact that one card may be addition and the next subtraction. Slowly show the cards allowing the student(s) to tell the missing addend, subtrahend, or minuend. Review rather they add or subtract in each instance (if an addend or subtrahend is missing you subtract and if a minuend is missing you add). Give help where needed as the student(s) complete **Student Activity Two**.

7. Encourage the student(s) to use the *multiplication chart,* instead of guessing, when they complete **Student Activity Three**.

8. Discuss with the student(s) that when working with fractional parts of a whole, the parts will be of equal size. Use *fraction materials* to demonstrate this. As the student(s) complete **Student Activity Four**, tell them to check to see that all parts of the whole are the same size.

9. The student(s) should be able to complete **Student Activity Five**, **Six**, and **Seven** independently.

Worksheet:

1. *Worksheet 45* – Addition and subtraction drill sheet

Lesson 92

Concepts:
Counting by threes, Roman numerals, money, subtraction regrouping, multiplication, and sequence

Objectives:

1. The student shall be able to count out loud by threes to 36.

2. The student shall be able to write the Roman numeral that corresponds to a given Arabic number.

3. The student shall be able to write the value of a given number of dollar bills and coins.

4. The student shall be able to write the regrouping of one hundred to ten tens for borrowing in subtraction.

5. The student shall be able to write the product of the multiplication facts for two and three.

6. The student shall be able to circle the next shape that would appear in a sequence of shapes.

Teaching Tips:

1. Discuss with the student(s) the origin of Roman numerals while going through activity 5. They were invented by the ancient Romans. They used 7 symbols to stand for numbers. They were used throughout Europe until the A.D. 1500's. Because of the difficulty to perform calculations other than addition and subtraction, people began to use Arabic numbers (our number system) at that time. It is not certain how the Arabic numbers originated but is believed that the 9 digits (1–9) originated with the Hindus in India during the 200's B.C. The zero was developed by the Hindus sometime after A.D. 600.

Materials, Supplies, & Equipment:

1. Flashcards for addition and multiplication facts

2. Play money

3. Place value materials

Activities:

1. Drill subtraction facts using *Drill #2, Worksheet 45*.

2. Using *flashcards for addition facts*, drill sums 1–18 with the answers showing and covering one of the two addends.

3. Using *flashcards for multiplication facts*, drill 5's without the answers showing and 3's and 2's with the answers showing.

4. Count out loud with the student(s) by threes to 36.

5. Roman numerals do not have a place value based on 10 as in Arabic numbers. But Roman numerals do follow certain rules which we will discuss in the next lesson but it is not necessary for the student(s) to learn them at this time. The student(s) will only be concerned with one through twenty in this lesson. If they learn how to write one through ten and then the multiples of ten, they will be able to write all of the Roman numerals they need to know. At this point they read a number by adding the numerals together recognizing that IV and IX have two numerals combined by subtraction for one value. Complete **Student Activity One** with the student(s) together.

6. Display several combinations of *play money* including different dollar bills and coins. Have the student(s) count the money together. The student(s) should be able to complete **Student Activity Two** with little help.

7. Display 2 hundreds + 5 tens using *place value materials*. Regroup 1 of the hundreds as 10 tens and add them to the 5 tens you already have. Ask the student(s) how many hundreds (1) and tens (15) they now have. Write on the board the equation "6 hundreds + 4 tens = 5 hundreds + __ tens." Have the student(s) tell the number of tens they have. Do several similar examples before the student(s) complete **Student Activity Three**.

8. The student(s) should be able to complete **Student Activity Four** independently.

9. When finding the next shape in **Student Activity Five**, remind the student(s) to find the first time the last shape appeared. The same shape will come after a given shape each time.

Worksheets:

1. *Worksheet 46* – Shape sequence

2. *Worksheet 45* – Addition and subtraction drill sheet

Lesson 93

Concepts:
Counting by threes, shapes, Roman numerals, multiplication, money, subtraction regrouping, and sequence

Objectives:
1. The student shall be able to count out loud by threes to 36.

2. The student shall be able to draw a line to match a shape to its name.

3. The student shall be able to write the Arabic number that corresponds to a given Roman numeral.

4. The student shall be able to write the product of the multiplication facts for zero, one, five, ten, two, and three.

5. The student shall be able to write the value of a given number of dollar bills and coins.

6. The student shall be able to write the regrouping of one hundred to ten tens for borrowing in subtraction.

7. The student shall be able to circle the next shape that would appear in a sequence of shapes.

Teaching Tips:
1. You may go over the rules for Roman numerals with the student(s) when doing activity 6, but they need not learn them. Notice that the I, X, C, and M are used up to three times and never over three times. When a numeral of smaller value is placed in front of a numeral of larger value, the smaller numeral is subtracted from the larger numeral (IV and IX). I can be used only in front of V and X, the X in front of L and C, and the C in front of D and M. You never subtract more than one numeral. The V, L, and D are never used more than once and never subtracted.

Materials, Supplies, & Equipment:
1. Flashcards for subtraction facts, multiplication facts, shapes, and Roman numerals

2. Play money

3. Place value materials

Activities:
1. Drill addition facts using *Drill #3, Worksheet 45*.

2. Using *flashcards for subtraction facts*, drill minuends 1–18 with the answers showing and covering the minuend or the subtrahend.

3. Using *flashcards for multiplication facts*, drill 5's without the answers showing and 3's and 2's with the answers showing.

4. Count out loud with the student(s) by threes to 36.

5. Have the student(s) name the seven basic *shapes* using *flashcards*. They should be able to complete **Student Activity One** with little help.

6. Using *flashcards* in random order, have the student(s) name the *Roman numerals* from one to ten. Combine the ten card with several of the other cards to represent some numerals between eleven and nineteen. The student(s) should be able to complete **Student Activity Two** on their own.

7. The student(s) should be able to complete **Student Activity Three** by themselves.

8. Give the student(s) *play money* including dollar bills. Ask them to find the bills and coins necessary to equal several given amounts of money. The student(s) should be able to complete **Student Activity Four** alone.

9. Display 4 hundreds + 7 tens using *place value materials*. Regroup 1 of the hundreds as 10 tens and add them to the 7 tens you already have. Ask the student(s) how many hundreds (3) and tens (17) they now have. Write on the board this equation: "3 hundreds + 5 tens = __ hundreds + 15 tens." Have the student(s) tell where the 15 tens can from and how many hundreds they have. Do several similar examples before the student(s) complete **Student Activity Five**.

10. Have the student(s) look at the first set of shapes in **Student Activity Six**. Ask them to tell how they determine what the next shape will be (the one that previously followed the last shape). Allow them to select the shape for the last two sets with no help.

Worksheet:
1. *Worksheet 45* – Addition and subtraction drill sheet

Lesson 94

Concepts:
Counting by threes, money, Roman numerals, sequence, subtraction, addition, shapes, and multiplication

Objectives:
1. The student shall be able to count out loud by threes to 36.

2. The student shall be able to put an "X" on the correct coins and bills to equal a given amount of money.

3. The student shall be able to write the Roman numeral that corresponds to a given Arabic number.

4. The student shall be able to circle the next shape that would appear in a sequence of shapes.

5. The student shall be able to write the missing addend, minuend, or subtrahend from an addition or subtraction fact.

6. The student shall be able to draw a line to match a given shape to its name.

7. The student shall be able to write the product of the multiplication facts for five and three.

Teaching Tips:
1. When doing activity 6, discuss with the student(s) where they have seen Roman numerals used in their every day lives (face of a clock, topics in outlines, name titles, record dates on monuments, public buildings, etc.). Help them write the present year using Roman numerals.

2. *Worksheet 47* gives additional practice for ***Student Activity One.***

Materials, Supplies, & Equipment:
1. Flashcards for addition facts, multiplication facts, Roman numerals, and shapes

2. Play money

Activities:

1. Drill subtraction facts using *Drill #4, Worksheet 45*.

2. Using *flashcards for addition facts*, drill sums 1–18 with the answers showing and covering one of the two addends.

3. Using *flashcards for multiplication facts*, drill 5's without the answers showing and 3's and 2's with the answers showing.

4. Count out loud with the student(s) by threes to 36.

5. Give the student(s) *play money* including various bills. Tell them several given amounts of money to count. Discuss the directions for **Student Activity One** with the student(s) before they begin the activity.

6. Display the *Roman numeral flashcards* on the board rail. Include the Roman numerals for the multiples of ten. Take special note of the way 40 and 90 are written (10 from 50 and 10 from 100). Say several numbers and have the student(s) choose the cards necessary to represent the numbers with Roman numerals. After discussing the answer given for the first problem in **Student Activity Two**, allow those who are capable to continue on their own. If help is needed, give assistance.

7. The student(s) should be able to complete **Student Activity Three** and **Four** independently.

8. Review the names of the *shapes* using *flashcards*. Discuss how many of the shapes the student(s) can find in the room. They should be able to complete **Student Activity Five** by themselves.

9. The student(s) should be able to complete **Student Activity Six** alone.

Worksheets:

1. *Worksheet 47* – Money

2. *Worksheet 45* – Addition and subtraction drill sheet

*You cannot perform today's duties well if
you are anxious about tomorrow.*

Lesson 95

Concepts:
Shapes, Roman numerals, addition, subtraction, money, and word problems

Objectives:

1. The student shall be able to write the name of a given shape.

2. The student shall be able to draw the line to match a Roman numeral to an Arabic number.

3. The student shall be able to write the missing addend, minuend, or subtrahend from an addition or subtraction fact.

4. The student shall be able to write the value needed on each bill and coin to equal a given amount of money.

Teaching Tips:

1. When drilling the multiplication facts for threes in activity 2, notice for enrichment that the sum of the digits in the answers add up to 3, 6, and 9 in that order and then begin to repeat 3, 6, and 9 (e.g., 4 x 3 = 12, 1 + 2 = 3; 5 x 3 = 15, 1 + 5 = 6; and 6 x 3 = 18, 1 + 8 = 9). Allow those student(s) who show interest to continue to 12 x 3 = 36. Beyond this point the pattern changes to 6, 9, 12, and repeats as before. At 21 x 3 = 63 it changes to 9, 12, and 15 and repeats as before. Ask if they have an idea what the next pattern would be (12, 15, 18).

Materials, Supplies, & Equipment:

1. Flashcards for addition facts, subtraction facts, multiplication facts, shapes, and Roman numerals

2. Play money

Activities:

1. Have the student(s) take a clean sheet of paper on which to write the answers for their *addition* and *subtraction facts* using *flashcards* with sleeves over an addend and a minuend or subtrahend. Do as many sets as time permits in 5 minutes.

2. Using *flashcards for multiplication facts*, drill 5's without the answers showing and 3's and 2's with the answers showing.

3. Show several names of *shapes* on *flashcards* and have the student(s) describe what the shapes look like. Then have the student(s) describe a shape and see if others can guess what shape they are describing. Display the *flashcard shape* names on the board rail for the student(s) to use as a spelling reference while they complete **Student Activity One**.

4. Tell the student(s) several numbers less than 100 and have them choose the *flashcards* necessary to represent that number using *Roman numerals*. Then write several Roman numerals on the board and have the student(s) tell what Arabic number corresponds to the Roman numeral. The student(s) should be able to complete **Student Activity Two** with little help.

5. The student(s) should be able to complete **Student Activity Three** by themselves.

6. Have the student(s) take a clean sheet of paper. Tell them to draw 5 rectangles and 7 circles in a row on their paper as you do it on the board. Write "$2.80" on the board. Ask the student(s) to draw the money needed to equal $2.80 on their paper by writing the numbers for the dollar bills in the four corners of the rectangles and writing the value of the coins in the center of each circle. For $2.80 they would need to put a 1 in each corner of two rectangles and write 50¢, 25¢, and 5¢ each in a circle. *Play money* may be a help here. Have the student(s) finish the first problem in **Student Activity Four** together and then complete the activity on their own.

7. After the student(s) read the first word problem in **Student Activity Five**, have them tell the key word (less . . . than) and if the key word tells them to add or subtract (subtract). Once the student(s) have completed both word problems check to see that the correct label has been used.

Do not worry about the future when you can do nothing about it.

Lesson 96

Concepts:
Counting by sixes, subtraction, multiplication readiness, Roman numerals, shapes, and word numbers

Objectives:
1. The student shall be able to count out loud by sixes to 72.

2. The student shall be able to write the difference of two triple-digit numbers when borrowing from the hundreds' column.

3. The student shall be able to write a given number of sixes as an addition problem, a multiplication problem, and the product.

4. The student shall be able to write the Roman numeral that corresponds to a given Arabic number.

5. The student shall be able to write a given letter on a given shape.

6. The student shall be able to circle the given hidden word numbers.

Teaching Tips:
1. Check with the student(s) on an individual basis as to how well they know the multiplication facts for the fives in activity 3. Set up individual practice times for the student(s) who need further help. Have a student drill a student, a teacher drill a student, or a volunteer drill a student using the *flashcards* without the answers showing.

Materials, Supplies, & Equipment:
1. Flashcards for subtraction facts, multiplication facts, Roman numerals, and shapes

2. Place value materials

3. Multiplication chart

Activities:

1. Drill addition facts using *Drill #1, Worksheet 48.*

2. Using *flashcards for subtraction facts*, drill minuends 1–18 with the answers showing and covering the minuend or the subtrahend.

3. Using *flashcards for multiplication facts*, drill 5's without the answers showing and 3's and 2's with the answers showing.

4. Count out loud with the student(s) by sixes to 72.

5. Write "605 – 372" as a vertical subtraction problem on the board. Ask the student(s) what 5 subtract 2 equals and write it in the answer under the ones' column. Then ask them if they can subtract 7 from 0. Tell them that they need to regroup 6 hundreds to equal 5 hundreds and 10 tens. *Place value materials* may help here. Draw the slanted line through the 6 and write "5" above the 6. Write "1" beside the 0 to make the 0 equal 10 tens (0 tens + 10 tens). Subtract the remainder of the problem. Do several subtraction problems similar to the one above with the 0 in the tens' place in the minuend. As the student(s) look at **Student Activity One**, point out that the first two problems have the regrouping done for them. Insist they show the regrouping on their paper as they do each problem.

6. Write "two 6's, three 6's, four 6's, etc." on the board. Ask the student(s) how to write two 6's as an addition and multiplication problem. Follow the same procedure for three 6's, four 6's, etc. Look on the *multiplication chart* for products they do not know. The student(s) should be able to complete **Student Activity Two** using the chart.

7. Display the *Roman numeral flashcards* on the board rail. Say several numbers less than 100 and have the students(s) choose the *flashcards* necessary to represent the numbers with Roman numerals. Give special attention to IV, IX, XL, and XC. The student(s) should be able to complete **Student Activity Three** with little help.

8. Discuss with the student(s) the characteristics of the 7 *shapes* using the *flashcards* (straight or curved sides, corners, square 90° corners). After the student(s) read the directions for **Student Activity Four**, have them point to the square. Look at the letter beside the name of the shape (S). Write it inside the square (S). Do the same for each of the following shapes.

9. Allow the student(s) to do **Student Activity Five** for fun. Do not spend more than five minutes on the activity or require the student(s) to find all of the word numbers.

Worksheet:

1. *Worksheet 48* – Addition and subtraction drill sheet

Lesson 97

Concepts:
> Counting by sixes, shapes, word problems, multiplication readiness, word sentences, word numbers, and subtraction

Objectives:
1. The student shall be able to count out loud by sixes to 72.

2. The student shall be able to color a given shape a given color.

3. The student shall be able to draw a line to match corresponding number families.

4. The student shall be able to rewrite a subtraction word sentence as a number sentence.

5. The student shall be able to write the difference of two triple-digit numbers when borrowing from the hundreds' column.

Teaching Tips:
1. The *Place Value Pockets* described in the Teaching Tips for lesson 7 could be used to demonstrate activity 9. Use craft sticks in the first row to represent the number in the minuend (408). Since 3 is to be subtracted from 8, take 3 of the sticks out of the pocket. Then ask if you can take 6 from the tens' column (no, there are no sticks). Borrow one stick from the hundreds' column and change it to how many tens (10 tens). Put the 10 tens into the tens' column. Now can they take 6 from the tens' column. Remove 6 sticks from the tens' column. Next take 1 from the hundreds' column. The top row is their answer.

Materials, Supplies, & Equipment:
1. Flashcards for addition facts, multiplication facts, and shapes

2. Multiplication chart

3. Place value materials

4. Place Value Pockets

224

Activities:

1. Drill subtraction facts using *Drill #2, Worksheet 48*.

2. Using *flashcards for addition facts*, drill sums 1–18 with the answers showing and covering one of the two addends.

3. Using *flashcards for multiplication facts*, drill 5's without the answers showing and 3's and 2's with the answers showing.

4. Count out loud with the student(s) by sixes to 72.

5. Show the student(s) two new *shapes* (pentagon and hexagon) using the *flashcards*. Count the sides and the corners of each. Discuss what the sides look like (straight lines, same length). The student(s) should be able to complete **Student Activity One** on their own.

6. After the student(s) have read the word problem in **Student Activity Two**, discuss the key word with them. Ask if they are to add or subtract and what the label should be.

7. Write "two 6's, three 6's, four 6's, etc." on the board. Ask the student(s) to tell the addition and multiplication problem that correspond to each. Then have them tell the product by using the *multiplication chart* to find the answers they do not know. The student(s) should be able to complete **Student Activity Three** alone.

8. Have the student(s) determine if the word sentences tell to add or subtract before they complete **Student Activity Four** independently.

9. Write "408 – 163" as a vertical subtraction problem on the board. Ask the student(s) what 8 subtract 3 equals and write it in the answer under the ones' column. Then ask them if they can subtract 6 from 0. Tell them that they need to regroup 4 hundreds to equal 3 hundreds and 10 tens. *Place value materials* may help here. Draw the slanted line through the 4 and write "3" above the 4. Write "1" beside the 0 to make the 0 equal 10 tens (0 tens + 10 tens). Subtract the remainder of the problem. Do several subtraction problems similar to the one above with the 0 in the tens' place in the minuend. As the student(s) look at **Student Activity Five**, point out that the first two problems have the regrouping done for them. Insist they show the regrouping on their paper as they do each problem.

Worksheet:

1. *Worksheet 48* – Addition and subtraction drill sheet

Lesson 98

Concepts:
Counting by sixes, bar graphs, addition, even and odd, subtraction, multiplication readiness, and shapes

Objectives:

1. The student shall be able to count out loud by sixes to 72.

2. The student shall be able to write the numbers represented on a bar graph.

3. The student shall be able to write the sum of two numbers and if the addends and sum are even or odd.

4. The student shall be able to write the difference of two triple-digit numbers when borrowing from the hundreds' column.

5. The student shall be able to write the number of objects in a given number of rows and the corresponding multiplication fact.

6. The student shall be able to write the name of a given shape.

Teaching Tips:

1. When doing activity 9, discuss with the student(s) the origin of the names pentagon, hexagon, and octagon by having the student(s) look the words up in the *dictionary*. Penta- is the Greek word for five, hexa- the Greek word for six, and octa- the Greek word for eight. The suffix -gon is the Greek word for angles. Therefore, a pentagon is a figure with five angles, a hexagon a figure with six angles, and an octagon a figure with eight angles. In our study, we will talk about a regular pentagon which means that all the angles will be the same size which dictates that the sides will be the same length.

Materials, Supplies, & Equipment:

1. Flashcards for subtraction facts, multiplication facts, and shapes

2. Counting chips

3. Dictionary

Activities:

1. Drill addition facts using *Drill #3, Worksheet 48.*

2. Using *flashcards for subtraction facts*, drill minuends 1–18 with the answers showing and covering the minuend or the subtrahend.

3. Using *flashcards for multiplication facts*, drill 5's without the answers showing and 3's, 2's, and 6's with the answers showing. Spend the major of the time in drilling 4 x 6, 6 x 6, 7 x 6, 8 x 6, and 9 x 6 with their pairs. They should know the other facts for 6's if you have always drilled the pairs.

4. Count out loud with the student(s) by sixes to 72.

5. Discuss with the student(s) what information is given on the bar graph in **Student Activity One** (number of persons in each family). Read each question with the student(s) but allow them to answer the questions individually.

6. Discuss what makes the sum of two even numbers even, two odd numbers even, and an even and an odd number to be odd with the aid of *counting chips*. The student(s) should be able to complete **Student Activity Two** on their own.

7. Write a three-digit subtraction problem with a 0 in the tens' place in the minuend on the board. Ask the student(s) to copy the problem on a sheet of paper and work it. Compare their answers. Hopefully they will all be the same. Then have them tell the correct way to find the difference. Answer any questions about mistakes that may have been made. The student(s) should be able to complete **Student Activity Three** with little help.

8. On the board draw 3 rows of circles 6 each and beside that 6 rows of 3 each. Ask the student(s) to tell how many rows and how many in each row. Then have them express the 3 rows of 6 as a multiplication fact (3 x 6) and tell what the product equals (18). Do the same for 6 rows of 3 each. *Worksheet 49* will provide further practice for this concept if needed. Work **Student Activity Four** together with the student(s).

9. Review the names of the *shapes* using *flashcards*. Discuss how the pentagon, hexagon, and octagon are alike and how they are different. The student(s) should be able to complete **Student Activity Five** by themselves.

Worksheets:

1. *Worksheet 49* – Multiplication of pairs

2. *Worksheet 48* – Addition and subtraction drill sheet

Lesson 99

Concepts:
> Counting by sixes, bar graphs, money, subtraction, multiplication, word sentences, word numbers, addition, even and odd, and shapes

Objectives:
1. The student shall be able to count out loud by sixes to 72.

2. The student shall be able to color a block for each given object to be represented on a bar graph.

3. The student shall be able to write the difference of two triple-digit numbers when borrowing from the hundreds' column.

4. The student shall be able to write the product of the multiplication facts for zero, one, ten, five, two, three, and six.

5. The student shall be able to rewrite an addition word sentence as a number sentence.

6. The student shall be able to write the sum of two numbers and if the addends and sum are even or odd.

7. The student shall be able to draw a line to match one half of a shape with the other half.

Teaching Tips:
1. Notice the directions for **Student Activity Two** have changed. Discuss with the student(s) what operation (add, subtract, or multiply) they do if they are told to find the difference. Review with them what the words "sum" and "product" tell them to do.

Materials, Supplies, & Equipment:
1. Flashcards for addition facts, multiplication facts, and shapes

2. Bar graph on posterboard or cut one out of the newspaper or print one from an online source

3. Multiplication chart

Activities:

1. Drill subtraction facts using *Drill #4, Worksheet 48*.

2. Using *flashcards for addition facts*, drill sums 1–18 with the answers showing and covering one of the two addends.

3. Using *flashcards for multiplication facts*, drill 5's without the answers showing and 3's, 2's, and 6's with the answers showing. Spend the majority of the time drilling 4 x 6, 6 x 6, 7 x 6, 8 x 6, and 9 x 6 with their pairs.

4. Count out loud with the student(s) by sixes to 72.

5. Display a simple *bar graph* for the student(s) to read (draw on board, *posterboard*, or large one from the *newspaper* or online sources). In **Student Activity One**, have the student(s) tell what the bar graph is about. Ask how many pennies are in the bank and have them draw the bar to represent 11 pennies. Continue with each coin in the same manner. Once they have completed the graph, ask them some questions about their graph (most coins, value of 8 nickels, least coins, etc.).

6. Write a three-digit subtraction problem with a 0 in the tens' place in the minuend on the board. Ask the student(s) to copy the problem on a sheet of paper and work it. Have the student(s) check their answer by adding. Work the problem on the board for those who made a mistake. The student(s) should be able to complete **Student Activity Two** with little help.

7. Allow the student(s) to use the *multiplication chart* to do the multiplication facts for 2's, 3's, and 6's if necessary when completing **Student Activity Three**.

8. Have the student(s) determine if the word sentences tell to add or subtract before they complete **Student Activity Four** and **Five** independently.

9. Cover one half of a *shape* on the *flashcards* and have the student(s) tell what shape it is. In **Student Activity Six**, have the student(s) name the first shape and then draw a line to the other half. Continue with each shape in the same manner.

Worksheet:

1. *Worksheet 48* – Addition and subtraction drill sheet

Lesson 100

Concepts:
Counting by sixes, addition, shapes, equal and not equal, subtraction, bar graphs, and multiplication

Objectives:
1. The student shall be able to count out loud by sixes to 72.

2. The student shall be able to write the sum of two four-digit numbers when the hundreds' column has a double-digit answer.

3. The student shall be able to write the correct symbol (= or ≠) between a shape and its name.

4. The student shall be able to write the difference of two triple-digit numbers when borrowing from the hundreds' column.

5. The student shall be able to draw a graph from the information given in a picture.

6. The student shall be able to write the product of the multiplication facts for zero, one, five, two, three, and six.

Teaching Tips:
1. If the student(s) have difficulty counting the sides of the pentagon, hexagon, and octagon in activity 6, have them make a mark with their pencil on each side of the polygon as they count its sides. Be sure they count one number for each mark on each side.

Materials, Supplies, & Equipment:
1. Flashcards for addition, subtraction, and multiplication facts

2. Place value materials

3. Multiplication chart

Activities:

1. Administer **Test 10**.

2. Have the student(s) take a clean sheet of paper on which to write the answers for their *addition* and *subtraction facts* using *flashcards* with sleeves over an addend and a minuend or subtrahend. Do as many sets as time permits in 5 minutes.

3. Using *flashcards for multiplication facts*, drill 5's without the answers showing and 3's, 2's, and 6's with the answers showing.

4. Count out loud with the student(s) by sixes to 72.

5. Do several four-digit addition problems with carrying only in the hundreds' column on the board. *Place value materials* could be a help here. Place the small box above the thousands' column in which to put the 1 that they carry. They should be able to complete **Student Activity One** with little help.

6. Have the student(s) describe a shape and then let the other student(s) tell what shape they are describing. The student(s) should be able to complete **Student Activity Two** alone once they understand the directions.

7. The student(s) should be able to complete **Student Activity Three** on their own.

8. As the student(s) look at **Student Activity Four**, ask them what their bar graph should tell them. Have them tell how many cows to put on their graph (count them in the picture). Follow the same procedure for the other animals.

9. The student(s) should be able to complete **Student Activity Five** with the help of the *multiplication chart* for the three and six multiplication facts.

Worksheet:

1. *Worksheet 50* – Bar graph

*Progress is the result of not being satisfied
to let well enough alone.*

Lesson 101

Concepts:
Counting by sixes, time (5 minutes), multiplication, subtraction, addition, and equal and not equal

Objectives:

1. The student shall be able to count out loud by sixes to 72.

2. The student shall be able to write the correct time displayed on the face of the clock for given 5 minute increments.

3. The student shall be able to write the product of the multiplication facts for zero, one, ten, five, two, three, and six.

4. The student shall be able to write the missing addend, minuend, or subtrahend from an addition or subtraction fact.

5. The student shall be able to write the difference of two triple-digit numbers when borrowing from the hundreds' column.

6. The student shall be able to write the sum of two four-digit numbers when the hundreds' column has a double-digit answer.

7. The student shall be able to write the correct symbol (= or ≠) between an addition fact and a subtraction fact.

Teaching Tips:

1. After completing **_Student Activity One_**, ask the student(s) to tell something they do at the time shown on each clock. If they should say sleep at 11:40 discuss with them the difference between 11:40 in the morning and 11:40 in the night (AM and PM). This will be taught in detail in the third grade so complete understanding is not necessary.

Materials, Supplies, & Equipment:

1. Flashcards for subtraction and multiplication facts

2. Clock model

3. Multiplication chart

Activities:

1. Drill addition facts using *Drill #1, Worksheet 51*.

2. Using *flashcards for subtraction facts*, drill minuends 1–18 with the answers showing and covering the minuend or the subtrahend.

3. Using *flashcards for multiplication facts*, drill 5's without the answers showing and 2's, 3's, and 6's with the answers showing.

4. Count out loud with the student(s) by sixes to 72.

5. Set the *model clock* for several 5 minute intervals and have the student(s) write the correct time on a sheet of paper. They should be able to complete **Student Activity One** by themselves.

6. Allow the student(s) to use the *multiplication chart* when needed for the 2, 3, and 6 multiplication facts in **Student Activity Two**.

7. Discuss with the student(s) subtracting to find a missing addend, adding to find a missing minuend, and subtracting to find the missing subtrahend. The student(s) should be able to complete **Student Activity Three** on their own.

8. The student(s) should be able to complete **Student Activity Four** and **Five** alone.

9. Remind the student(s) to write the sum or difference above each fact, if needed to be accurate, in completing **Student Activity Six**.

Worksheet:

1. *Worksheet 51* – Addition and subtraction drill sheet

The greatest of all faults is to say that you have none at all.

Lesson 102

Concepts:
Counting by sixes, place value, time, equal and not equal, multiplication, addition, and subtraction

Objectives:

1. The student shall be able to count out loud by sixes to 72.

2. The student shall be able to write the correct value of the digit in the thousands', hundreds', tens', and ones' places for a given number.

3. The student shall be able to write the correct symbol (= or ≠) between the time displayed on a clock face and the time displayed on a digital watch.

4. The student shall be able to write the missing addend, minuend, or subtrahend from an addition fact or a subtraction fact.

5. The student shall be able to write the product of the multiplication facts for zero, one, ten, five, two, three, and six.

6. The student shall be able to write the sum of two four-digit numbers when the hundreds' column has a double-digit answer.

7. The student shall be able to write the difference of two triple-digit numbers when borrowing from the hundreds' column.

Teaching Tips:

1. Notice that ***Student Activity Six*** says to check the answers. See that the student(s) actually draw a line under the answer and then add the answer and the subtrahend. The sum should equal the minuend.

Materials, Supplies, & Equipment:

1. Flashcards for addition and multiplication facts

2. Small clock model for student(s)

3. Clock model

4. Multiplication chart

Activities:

1. Drill subtraction facts using *Drill #2, Worksheet 51.*

2. Using *flashcards for addition facts*, drill sums 1–18 with the answers showing and covering one of the two addends.

3. Using *flashcards for multiplication facts*, drill 5's without the answers showing and 3's, 2's, and 6's with the answers showing.

4. Count out loud with the student(s) by sixes to 72.

5. Write several four-digit numbers on the board. Have the student(s) write the value of each digit in expanded form on a sheet of paper. Write the expanded form on the board to enable the student(s) to check their answers. They should be able to complete **Student Activity One** on their own.

6. Give the student(s) *small clock models*. Write several 5 minute intervals on the board. As the student(s) set their clocks, have them check their times by the *clock model*. When the student(s) start **Student Activity Two**, have them determine the time on the face of the clock and compare it with the time displayed on the digital watch.

7. The student(s) should be able to complete **Student Activity Three** by themselves.

8. Allow the student(s) to use the *multiplication chart* for the threes and sixes if necessary when doing **Student Activity Four**.

9. The student(s) should be able to complete **Student Activity Five** and **Six** independently.

Worksheet:

1. *Worksheet 51* – Addition and subtraction drill sheet

Satisfaction will not come from half heartedness.
Strive for the best that is in you.

Lesson 103

Concepts:
> Counting by sixes, fractions, place value, subtraction, time, multiplication, and addition

Objectives:
1. The student shall be able to count out loud by sixes to 72.

2. The student shall be able to write the fraction that represents the part of a whole that is shaded.

3. The student shall be able to write the difference of two triple-digit numbers when borrowing from the hundreds' column.

4. The student shall be able to draw both hands on the face of the clock for given five minute increments.

5. The student shall be able to write the product of the multiplication facts for two, three, and six.

6. The student shall be able to write the sum of two four-digit numbers when the hundreds' column has a double-digit answer.

Teaching Tips:

1. Suggest to the student(s) that when they are adding to check their difference in **Student Activity Three**, they should cover the minuend with a ruler or sheet of paper. This will prevent them from just copying the answer from above and force them to think through the sum.

Materials, Supplies, & Equipment:
1. Flashcards for subtraction and multiplication facts

2. Fraction materials

3. Small clock model for student(s)

4. Clock model

5. Multiplication chart

Activities:

1. Drill addition facts using *Drill #3, Worksheet 51*.

2. Using *flashcards for subtraction facts*, drill minuends 1–18 with the answers showing and covering the minuend or the subtrahend.

3. Using *flashcards for multiplication facts*, drill 5's without the answers showing and 2's, 3's, and 6's with the answers showing.

4. Count out loud with the student(s) by sixes to 72.

5. Write " ⅔ " on the board. Discuss with the student(s) the name of the top number (numerator) and the name of the bottom number (denominator). Remind them that the denominator tells them into how many part the whole is divided and the numerator tells them how many of the parts they are going to use or shade. Using *fraction materials*, display wholes divided into two to ten parts. Ask the student(s) into how many parts the first shape is divided. Write the number on the board as the denominator of a fraction. Take two parts away and ask them where to write the number of parts you are taking or using (in the numerator). Follow the same procedure for each of the wholes. Ask how many parts there are and how many of the parts are being used. In **Student Activity One**, have the student(s) go through the shapes together with your guidance. Additional practice is available on *Worksheet 52*.

6. The student(s) should be able to complete **Student Activity Two** and **Three** on their own.

7. Give the student(s) the *small clock models*. Ask them which hand they need to set first (minute hand). Write several 5 minute intervals on the board. Have the student(s) set their clock and use the *clock model* to check their times. Give individual help where needed. The student(s) should be able to complete **Student Activity Four** by themselves.

8. Encourage the student(s) to use the *multiplication chart* only when necessary as they complete **Student Activity Five**.

9. The student(s) should be able to complete **Student Activity Six** independently.

Worksheets:

1. *Worksheet 52* – Fractions

2. *Worksheet 51* – Addition and subtraction drill sheet

Lesson 104

Concepts:
  Counting by sixes, word problems, subtraction, fractions, multiplication, and addition

Objectives:
  1. The student shall be able to count out loud by sixes to 72.

  2. The student shall be able to write the answer to a multiplication word problem by writing the multiplication fact and the label.

  3. The student shall be able to write the difference of two triple-digit numbers when borrowing from the hundreds' column.

  4. The student shall be able to write the fraction that represents the part of a whole that is shaded.

  5. The student shall be able to write the product of the multiplication facts for zero, one, ten, five, two, three, and six.

  6. The student shall be able to write the sum of two four-digit numbers when the hundreds' column has a double-digit answer.

Teaching Tips:
  1. When doing ***Student Activity One***, encourage the student(s) not to count or add the flowers to arrive at an answer in the first word problem. It would be permissible for them to write "4 groups of 3's" on their paper to give them a clearer understanding as to why they would multiply. Remind them that multiplication is a short way to do addition and they want to learn the way that is the quickest.

Materials, Supplies, & Equipment:
  1. Flashcards for addition and multiplication facts

  2. Fraction materials

Activities:

1. Drill subtraction facts using *Drill #4, Worksheet 51.*

2. Using *flashcards for addition facts*, drill sums 1–18 with the answers showing and covering one of the two addends.

3. Using *flashcards for multiplication facts*, drill 5's without the answers showing and 3's, 2's, and 6's with the answers showing.

4. Count out loud with the student(s) by sixes to 72.

5. Read the first word problem in **Student Activity One** together with the student(s). Ask them to look at the picture and tell how many groups they have and how many are in each group (4 groups of 3's). Then ask them how they write 4 groups of 3's as a multiplication fact. Tell them to label their answer. Have the student(s) read the second word problem to themselves. Ask them to tell how many groups they have and how many in each group (5 groups of 6's). Tell them to write the multiplication fact and the label. Allow those who are capable to complete the third word problem on their own helping those who need it.

6. The student(s) should be able to complete **Student Activity Two** by themselves.

7. Draw several shapes on the board or use *fraction materials.* Divide each shape into two to ten parts. Ask into how many parts the first shape is divided. As you write the number in the bottom of a fraction, ask them to tell the name of the bottom number (denominator). Then ask them the name of the top number and what the top number tells them (numerator – how many parts are shaded or used). Have them tell what the top number should be. As the student(s) continue with the other shapes, have them tell what fractional part of the whole is shaded. Allow them to complete **Student Activity Three** alone giving help only where needed.

8. The student(s) should be able to complete **Student Activity Four** and **Five** independently.

Worksheet:

1. *Worksheet 51* – Addition and subtraction drill sheet

You should find ways to serve others not seek authority over them.

Lesson 105

Concepts:

> Counting by sixes, ratio, multiplication, subtraction, word problems, money, and fractions
> *Definition*: A ratio is the relationship or comparison of two numbers.

Objectives:

1. The student shall be able to count out loud by sixes to 72.

2. The student shall be able to write the comparison of two sets as a ratio.

3. The student shall be able to write the product of the multiplication facts for three and six.

4. The student shall be able to write the difference of two triple-digit numbers when borrowing from the hundreds' column.

5. The student shall be able to write the answer to a multiplication word problem by writing the multiplication fact and the label.

6. The student shall be able to circle the coins necessary to equal one dollar.

7. The student shall be able to write the fraction that represents the part of a whole that is shaded.

Teaching Tips:

1. The study of a ratio in activity 4, will be very elementary. The main emphasis is to enable the student(s) to write a ratio in the correct order. The student(s) will be exposed to writing a ratio in only one way at this point (2:4). The other two ways of writing a ratio (2 to 4 and ¾) will be dealt with at a later time.

Materials, Supplies, & Equipment:

1. Flashcards for addition, subtraction, and multiplication facts

2. Multiplication chart

3. Play money

240

Activities:

1. Have the student(s) take a clean sheet of paper on which to write the answers for their *addition* and *subtraction facts* using *flashcards* with sleeves over an addend and a minuend or subtrahend. Do as many sets as time permits in 5 minutes.

2. Using *flashcards for multiplication facts*, drill 5's without the answers showing and 3's, 2's, and 6's with the answers showing.

3. Count out loud with the student(s) by sixes to 72.

4. Discuss the word "ratio" with the student(s). Tell about situations in which two numbers may be compared (boys to girls in a family, dogs to cats in a family, desks to students, etc.). Draw three circles and four squares on the board. Ask the student(s) to compare the number of circles to the number of squares. Write the ratio as 3:4 (see Teaching Tips). Teach them to read a ratio "3 to 4." Stress to the student(s) that the numbers must be written in the same order as the ratio is given. If the number of circles is mentioned first, then the number of circles must be written first. Next compare the number of squares to the number of circles. Write the ratio as 4:3. Compare the number of circles to the number of circles and squares (3:7), number of squares to the number of circles and squares (4:7), the number of circles and squares to the number of circles (7:3), and the number of circle and squares to the number of squares (7:4). Complete **Student Activity One** together with the student(s).

5. The student(s) may need to use their *multiplication chart* to complete **Student Activity Two**.

6. The student(s) should be able to complete **Student Activity Three** on their own.

7. Have the student(s) read the first word problem in **Student Activity Four** to themselves. Ask them to tell how many groups there are and how many are in each group (6 groups of 2's). Then ask them to write the multiplication fact and label the answer. Allow them to complete the second word problem on their own giving help only where needed.

8. Give the student(s) *play money*. Have them choose the number of dimes, nickels, quarters, and half dollars they would need to equal a dollar. Discuss how many pennies they would need to equal a dollar. After the student(s) have circled the number of coins needed in **Student Activity Five**, be sure they write the number of coins they circled in the blank.

9. Review the numerator, the denominator, and what each tells the student(s) before they complete **Student Activity Six**.

Lesson 106

Concepts:
Counting by nines, ratio, money, word problems, multiplication, addition, and greater than and less than

Objectives:

1. The student shall be able to count out loud by nines to 108.

2. The student shall be able to write the comparison of two sets as a ratio.

3. The student shall be able to write the number of coins needed to equal one dollar.

4. The student shall be able to write the answer to a multiplication word problem by writing the multiplication fact and the label.

5. The student shall be able to write the given number of nines as an addition problem, a multiplication problem, and a product.

6. The student shall be able to write the sum of two four-digit numbers when the ones' and the hundreds' columns have double-digit answers.

7. The student shall be able to write two addition facts and two subtraction facts when given three numbers.

8. The student shall be able to write the correct symbol (< or >) between a subtraction fact and a number.

Teaching Tips:

1. When the student(s) are doing **Student Activity One**, compare the colon they use in telling time with the colon they use when writing a ratio. They are the same symbol but they are used in different ways. Discuss the fact that the diameter and radius of a circle are used when they want to find the distance around a circle. A formal definition of diameter and radius is not needed at this time.

Materials, Supplies, & Equipment:

1. Flashcards for subtraction and multiplication facts

2. Play money

3. Multiplication chart

Activities:

1. Drill addition facts using *Drill #1, Worksheet 53*.

2. Using *flashcards for subtraction facts*, drill minuends 1–18 with the answers showing and covering the minuend or the subtrahend.

3. Using *flashcards for multiplication facts*, drill 5's and 2's without the answers showing and 3's and 6's with the answers showing.

4. Count out loud with the student(s) by nines to 108.

5. Discuss how a ratio is a way to write the comparison of two numbers. Remind the student(s) that the order in which the ratio is given is the order in which it must be written. Display for the student(s) 6 dimes and 4 pennies. Ask them to tell the ratio of the number of dimes to the number of pennies, pennies to dimes, pennies and dimes to dimes, and pennies to pennies and dimes. Have the student(s) look at the first picture in **Student Activity One**. Ask them to point to the length and width of the rectangle and tell how long they are. Tell them to write what the ratio of the length to the width is. Discuss their answer. Continue the remainder of the activity in this manner.

6. Discuss the questions in **Student Activity Two** with the student(s). Use *play money* to discover the answers if necessary.

7. Allow the student(s) to complete **Student Activity Three** on their own when possible.

8. Write "two 9's, three 9's, four 9's, etc." on the board. Ask the student(s) how to write two 9's as an addition problem and as a multiplication problem. Now have them look on the *multiplication chart* for the answer to 2 x 9 if they do not already know it. Follow the same procedure for three 9's, four 9's, etc. The student(s) should be able to complete **Student Activity Four** with the help of the *multiplication chart*.

9. Write "1,205 + 2,958" on the board as an addition problem. Ask the student(s) to copy the problem on a sheet of paper and work it. Notice that both the ones' and the hundreds' columns have double-digit answers. Allow the student(s) to work the problem on their own and then discuss how they found the correct answer. After several more examples, the student(s) should be able to complete **Student Activity Five** alone.

10. The student(s) should be able to complete **Student Activity Six** and **Seven** independently.

Worksheet:

1. *Worksheet 53* – Addition and subtraction drill sheet

Lesson 107

Concepts:
Counting by nines, equations, addition, subtraction, greater than and less than, money, ratio, and multiplication

Objectives:
1. The student shall be able to count out loud by nines to 108.

2. The student shall be able to write the value of a variable in an addition equation.

3. The student shall be able to write the sum of two four-digit numbers when the ones' and the hundreds' columns have double-digit answers.

4. The student shall be able to write the difference of two four-digit numbers when borrowing from the hundreds' column.

5. The student shall be able to write the correct symbol (< or >) between a multiplication fact and a number.

6. The student shall be able to write the value of a set of coins.

7. The student shall be able to write the comparison of two sets as a ratio.

8. The student shall be able to draw a line to match corresponding number families.

Teaching Tips:
1. When doing activity 5, suggest to the student(s) they look at an equation as a balance scale. If the two sides are equal, the weights will be level with each other. If they take a given amount from one side what do they have to do to the other side to keep the two weights level (take the same amount away). The same is true with an equation. If they are going to subtract a given amount from one side, they must subtract the same given amount from the other side to keep the equation true.

Materials, Supplies, & Equipment:
1. Flashcards for addition and multiplication facts

2. Play money

3. Flannel board and materials

Activities:
1. Drill subtraction facts using *Drill #2, Worksheet 53*.

2. Using *flashcards for addition facts*, drill sums 1–18 with the answers showing and covering one of the two addends.

3. Using *flashcards for multiplication facts*, drill 5's and 2's without the answers showing and 3's and 6's with the answers showing.

4. Count out loud with the student(s) by nines to 108.

5. Write "5 + __ = 12" on the board. Have the student(s) tell the number that goes in the blank to make a true statement. Write "5 + n = 12" under the first equation. The unknown has been replaced with a letter called a variable and they are going to solve the equation for that unknown. Ask the student(s) what to do to find the missing number (subtract 5 from 12). What they do to one side of the equation they must also do to the other side of the equation. This is done in the manner shown above **Student Activity One**. Be sure to subtract 5 from both sides of the equation. 5 – 5 = 0 which can be marked out with a slanted line leaving "n" on the left hand side. 12 – 5 leaves 7 on the right hand side. The result is n = 7. Go over the three examples given above **Student Activity One** with the student(s) in the same manner. Then solve the given equations doing each step on the board as the student(s) do them on their paper.

6. The student(s) should be able to complete **Student Activity Two**, **Three**, and **Four** on their own.

7. Give the student(s) a variety of *play money*. Ask them to take 1 quarter, 2 dimes, and 1 nickel. Determine the value of the 4 coins. Then take 2 quarters, 3 nickels, and 2 pennies; 1 half dollar, 4 dimes, and 3 pennies; etc. and tell the value of each set of coins. The student(s) should be able to complete **Student Activity Five** by themselves.

8. Place 4 shapes or *cut outs* of one kind and 5 shapes of another kind on the *flannel board*. Ask the student(s) to tell the ratio of one set to the other in various orders and combinations. In **Student Activity Six**, read each sentence out loud and allow the student(s) to answer individually.

9. The student(s) should be able to complete **Student Activity Seven** independently.

Worksheets:
1. *Worksheet 54* – Solve equations

2. *Worksheet 53* – Addition and subtraction drill sheet

Lesson 108

Concepts:
Counting by nines, Roman numerals, subtraction, equations, multiplication, addition, money, and fractions

Objectives:

1. The student shall be able to count out loud by nines to 108.

2. The student shall be able to write the Roman numeral corresponding to a given Arabic number.

3. The student shall be able to write the difference of two four-digit numbers when borrowing from the hundreds' column.

4. The student shall be able to write the value of a variable in an addition equation.

5. The student shall be able to draw a line to match pairs of multiplication facts.

6. The student shall be able to write the sum of two four-digit numbers when the ones' and the hundreds' columns have double-digit answers.

7. The student shall be able to write the value of a given set of coins and bills.

8. The student shall be able to draw lines to divide a whole into the necessary number of equal parts to shade a given fractional part of that whole.

Teaching Tips:

1. Have the student(s) look in newspapers, books, or magazines at home to find places where Roman numerals are used as an addition to activity 5. They can make their own worksheet by cutting out and pasting these Roman numerals on a sheet of paper and writing the Arabic numbers beside the Roman numerals.

Materials, Supplies, & Equipment:

1. Flashcards for subtraction facts, multiplication facts, and Roman numerals

2. Play money

246

Activities:

1. Drill addition facts using *Drill #3, Worksheet 53*.

2. Using *flashcards for subtraction facts*, drill minuends 1–18 with the answers showing and covering the minuend or the subtrahend.

3. Using *flashcards for multiplication facts*, drill 5's and 2's without the answers showing and 3's and 6's with the answers showing.

4. Count out loud with the student(s) by nines to 108.

5. Review the value of each of the *Roman numeral* symbols using *flashcards*. Have the student(s) tell how to write one through ten with Roman numerals. Practice writing several Roman numerals from ten to one hundred. Give help to those who need it as the student(s) complete **Student Activity One**.

6. The student(s) should be able to complete **Student Activity Two** on their own.

7. Write several addition facts on the board replacing the second addend with the letter "n." Ask the student(s) how to find the value of "n." Remind them that what they do to one side of the equation, they must also do to the other side. Insist that they follow the steps on their paper that you follow on the board. Notice that in the first problem in **Student Activity Three**, the first step is done for them. They must do this step in each problem in the activity.

8. The student(s) should be able to complete **Student Activity Four** and **Five** by themselves.

9. Display several sets of coins and bills using *play money* and have the student(s) determine the value of each set. Review the bills and their value. They should be able to complete **Student Activity Six** alone.

10. Draw several different shapes on the board. Have the student(s) divide the shapes into equal parts. Shade the shapes to equal given fractions. Remind them the parts must be equal in size. Discuss the numerator, the denominator, and what they tell the student(s). Allow the student(s) to complete **Student Activity Seven** independently.

Worksheets:

1. *Worksheet 55* – Roman numerals

2. *Worksheet 53* – Addition and subtraction drill sheet

Lesson 109

Concepts:
Counting by nines, line graphs, subtraction, addition, solids, equations, estimation, fractions, Roman numerals, and multiplication

Objectives:

1. The student shall be able to count out loud by nines to 108.

2. The student shall be able to write the correct facts obtained from interpreting a line graph.

3. The student shall be able to write the difference of two four-digit numbers when borrowing from the hundreds' column.

4. The student shall be able to write the sum of two four-digit numbers when the ones' and the hundreds' columns have double-digit answers.

5. The student shall be able to draw a line to match a solid to its name.

6. The student shall be able to write the value of a variable in an addition equation.

7. The student shall be able to write the number to which a given number is closer.

8. The student shall be able to draw lines to divide a whole into the needed number of equal parts to shade a fractional part of the whole.

9. The student shall be able to write the Arabic number that corresponds to a given Roman numeral.

10. The student shall be able to write the number of rows of a given number and the corresponding multiplication fact.

Teaching Tips:

1. Draw the line graph needed for activity 3 before class.

2. Help the student(s) remember the cube and cone by associating the words "ice cube" and "ice cream cone" in activity 5.

Materials, Supplies, & Equipment:

1. Posterboard

2. Solid models

3. Number chart 0–99

4. Flashcards for Roman numerals

Activities:

1. Drill subtraction facts using *Drill #4, Worksheet 53*.

2. Count out loud with the student(s) by nines to 108.

3. Draw the line graph, located above **Student Activity One**, on the board or *posterboard*. Discuss with the student(s) the title of the graph, the numbers on the left hand side, and the numbers across the bottom of the graph. Point out to the student(s) how the point on the vertical line above Game 1 is across from the number 7. This tells them that in Game 1 Ken scored 7 points. Ask them to find the point on the vertical line above Game 2 and see what number is across from it. Discuss what the point tells them. Continue the same procedure with the other three points before the student(s) complete **Student Activity One** with your guidance.

4. The student(s) should be able to complete **Student Activity Two** and **Three** by themselves.

5. Show the student(s) *models* of the five *solids* in **Student Activity Four**. Allow them to handle them and look at them from all angles. Have them repeat the names of the solids after you and spell them. When the student(s) begin **Student Activity Four**, tell them to point to the cone and draw the line, then the cylinder, etc. Be sure they draw the lines correctly on this activity.

6. Write several addition facts on the board replacing the second addend with the letter "n." Ask the student(s) what they add or subtract from both sides of the equation. Insist that they put the steps on their paper as they complete **Student Activity Five**.

7. Allow the student(s) to use the *number chart* if necessary to complete **Student Activity Six**.

8. Let the student(s) complete **Student Activity Seven** on their own. Check to see that they divide the shapes into equal parts.

9. Review the value of each *Roman numeral* symbol using *flashcards*. Write several Roman numerals on the board and have the student(s) tell the corresponding Arabic numbers. The student(s) should be able to complete **Student Activity Eight** alone.

10. The student(s) should be able to complete **Student Activity Nine** independently.

Worksheet:

1. *Worksheet 53* – Addition and subtraction drill sheet

Lesson 110

Concepts:
Counting by nines, line graphs, addition, word problems, solids, fractions, and multiplication

Objectives:
1. The student shall be able to count out loud by nines to 108.

2. The student shall be able to write the correct facts obtained from interpreting a line graph.

3. The student shall be able to write the sum of two four-digit numbers when the ones' and the hundreds' columns have double-digit answers.

4. The student shall be able to write the name of a given solid.

5. The student shall be able to draw a line to match a fraction to the fractional part shaded on a shape.

6. The student shall be able to write the product of the multiplication facts for one, ten, five, two, three, six, and nine.

Teaching Tips:
1. For enrichment with activity 5, have the student(s) look for line graphs in *newspapers*, *magazines*, or other sources to bring to class. Make a bulletin board of the different examples. Discuss how the line graphs are alike and how they are different.

Materials, Supplies, & Equipment:
1. Flashcards for addition, subtraction, and multiplication facts

2. Solid models

3. Multiplication chart

4. Newspapers, magazines, or other sources

Activities:

1. Administer **Test 11**.

2. Have the student(s) take a clean sheet of paper on which to write the answers for their *addition* and *subtraction facts*. Use *flashcards* with sleeves over an addend and a minuend or subtrahend. Do as many sets as time permits in 5 minutes.

3. Using *flashcards for multiplication facts*, drill 5's and 2's without the answers showing and 3's, 6's, and 9's with the answers showing. Point out to the student(s) that the digits of the product in the 9 facts add to nine (e.g., 4 x 9 = 36; 3 + 6 = 9). When a number is taken times 9, the first digit in the answer will always be one less than that number (e.g., 4 x 9 = first digit is one less than 4 which is 3 and the second digit 6 because 3 + 6 = 9). Spend most of the drill time for the next four lessons on 4 x 9, 7 x 9, 8 x 9, 9 x 9, and their pairs.

4. Count out loud with the student(s) by nines to 108.

5. Have the student(s) look at the line graph in **Student Activity One**. Discuss the title of the graph, for what the numbers on the left side stand, and what the score for each test is. Read each question with the student(s) but allow them to answer individually.

6. The student(s) should be able to complete **Student Activity Two** by themselves.

7. Have the student(s) read the word problem in **Student Activity Three** to themselves. Discuss if they add or subtract and why. Allow them to solve the problem on their own.

8. Point to the *solid models* and have the student(s) name and spell them. Then say the name of a solid and have the student(s) point to the model you named. In **Student Activity Four**, have the student(s) point to the cube and write its name. Then do the same for the cone, cylinder, pyramid, and sphere.

9. Discuss the numerator and denominator of a fraction and what they tell the student(s). Remind them that the whole must be divided into equal parts in order to represent a fractional part. They should be able to complete **Student Activity Five** with little help.

10. Allow the student(s) to use the *multiplication chart* when necessary to complete **Student Activity Six**.

Lesson 111

Concepts:
> Counting by nines, line graphs, multiplication, fractions, equal and not equal, shapes, equations, subtraction, and word problems

Objectives:
1. The student shall be able to count out loud by nines to 108.

2. The student shall be able to draw the lines necessary to represent given information on a line graph.

3. The student shall be able to write the product of the multiplication facts for six and nine.

4. The student shall be able to write the correct symbol (= or ≠) between a fraction and a graphic representation of a fractional part of a whole.

5. The student shall be able to write an "X" on each corner of a shape and circle the "X" if the corner is a square corner.

6. The student shall be able to write the value of a variable in an addition equation.

7. The student shall be able to write the difference of two triple-digit numbers when borrowing from the hundreds' column.

Teaching Tips:
1. When doing activity 8, tell the student(s) that a sheet of paper has four square corners. They can check the squareness of a corner by laying the corner of a sheet of paper on top of the given corner to see if they are the same.

Materials, Supplies, & Equipment:
1. Flashcards for subtraction facts, multiplication facts, and shapes

2. Multiplication chart

Activities:

1. Drill addition facts using *Drill #1, Worksheet 56*.

2. Using *flashcards for subtraction facts*, drill minuends 1–18 with the answers showing and covering the minuend or the subtrahend.

3. Using *flashcards for multiplication facts*, drill 5's and 2's without the answers showing and 3's, 6's, and 9's with the answers showing.

4. Count out loud with the student(s) by nines to 108.

5. Duplicate the line graph in **Student Activity One** on the board before class time. Work on the board as you instruct the student(s). Ask how many days Pam was absent from school in September (1). Find September at the bottom of the graph. This is the first time the student(s) have been exposed to abbreviations for the months of the year. Follow the vertical line until it intersects the horizontal line that is across from 1. Put a dot at that intersection. Follow the same procedure for the remaining months. Once all of the dots are on the graph, have the student(s) connect the dots in consecutive order.

6. The student(s) will need to use their *multiplication chart* as they complete **Student Activity Two**.

7. Draw several shapes on the board. Divide some of them into equal parts and some into unequal parts. For each shape, have the student(s) tell into how many parts the whole is divided (denominator) and how many of those parts are shaded (numerator). Write the fraction beside the shape. Now have them tell if the given fraction represents the shaded area. The whole must be divided into equal parts if the fraction is to represent the shaded area. Have the student(s) follow the same procedure as you assist them in completing **Student Activity Three**.

8. Show the student(s) the *shape flashcards*. Discuss which shapes have corners and which do not. Discuss what makes a corner a square corner (90°). All squares and rectangles have square corners. Read the directions for **Student Activity Four** with the student(s). Have them place the "X's" on the corners. Then help them check for square corners and circle the "X's" on the square corners.

9. Write several addition facts on the board replacing the second addend with the letter "n." Ask the student(s) what they subtract from both sides of the equation. Insist that they put the steps on their paper as they complete **Student Activity Five**.

10. The student(s) should be able to complete **Student Activity Six** and **Seven** independently.

Worksheet:

1. *Worksheet 56* – Addition, subtraction, and multiplication drill sheet

Lesson 112

Concepts:

Counting by nines, fractions, addition, shapes, subtraction, line graph, multiplication, and word problems

Objectives:

1. The student shall be able to count out loud by nines to 108.

2. The student shall be able to draw a line to match a fraction to its word name.

3. The student shall be able to write the sum of two four-digit numbers when the tens' and hundreds' columns have double-digit answers.

4. The student shall be able to draw a line to match a shape to its name.

5. The student shall be able to write the difference of two four-digit numbers when borrowing from the hundreds' column.

6. The student shall be able to draw the lines necessary to represent given information on a line graph.

7. The student shall be able to write the product of the multiplication facts for three, six, and nine.

8. The student shall be able to write a word problem using the given information and solve it.

Teaching Tips:

1. Notice that in activity 1, the only multiplication facts that will be drilled on the drill sheet at the present are zero, one, and ten. Five will be added to the next drill sheet. You should begin to check the student(s) individually to see if they have mastered the fives. Plan additional practice using *flashcards* for those who would profit from it.

Materials, Supplies, & Equipment:

1. Flashcards for addition facts, multiplication facts, and shapes

2. Place value materials

254

Activities:

1. Drill multiplication facts using *Drill #2, Worksheet 56*.

2. Using *flashcards for addition facts*, drill sums 1–18 with the answers showing and covering an addend.

3. Using *flashcards for multiplication facts*, drill 5's and 2's without the answers showing and 3's, 6's, and 9's with the answers showing.

4. Count out loud with the student(s) by nines to 108.

5. Write several fractions on the board. Have the student(s) read and spell the name of each of the fractions. Again discuss that the numerator is a cardinal number and the denominator is an ordinal number. The student(s) should be able to complete **Student Activity One** on their own.

6. On the board, write several sets of two four-digit numbers as an addition problem with carrying in the tens' and the hundreds' columns. Work the first problem with the student(s) step by step. *Place value materials* may be a help here. Have them copy the remaining problems on a sheet of paper and work them individually before you work them on the board. The student(s) should be able to complete **Student Activity Two** by themselves.

7. Display the pictures of the shapes using *shape flashcards*. Have the student(s) name and spell each shape. Turn the *flashcards* over and have the student(s) describe each shape. They should be able to complete **Student Activity Three** alone.

8. The student(s) should be able to complete **Student Activity Four** and **Six** independently.

9. Duplicate the line graph in **Student Activity Five** on the board before class time. Work on the board as you instruct the student(s). Ask what the temperature was on Monday. Find Monday at the bottom of the graph. This is the first time the student(s) have been exposed to abbreviations for the days of the week. Follow the vertical line until it intersects the horizontal line that is across from 82°. Put a dot at that intersection. Allow the student(s) to do the remaining temperatures helping those who need individual attention. Remind them to connect the dots in consecutive order.

10. Have the student(s) write a word problem using the picture given in **Student Activity Seven**. They may write either an addition or a subtraction problem. Discuss some possibilities with the student(s).

Worksheet:

1. *Worksheet 56* – Addition, subtraction, and multiplication drill sheet

Lesson 113

Concepts:
> Counting by nines, fractions, equal and not equal, addition, even and odd, subtraction, shapes, multiplication, word sentences, and word numbers

Objectives:

1. The student shall be able to count out loud by nines to 108.

2. The student shall be able to write the correct symbol (= or ≠) between a fraction and a graphic representation of a fractional part of a whole.

3. The student shall be able to write the sum of two four-digit numbers when the tens' and hundreds' columns have double-digit answers.

4. The student shall be able to write the sum and circle the words "even" or "odd" as they correspond to addends and the sum.

5. The student shall be able to write the difference of two four-digit numbers when borrowing from the hundreds' column.

6. The student shall be able to write the name of a given shape.

7. The student shall be able to write the product of the multiplication facts for three, six, and nine.

8. The student shall be able to rewrite the word sentences as number sentences.

Teaching Tips:

1. You could use *fraction materials* when doing activity 5. Combine three-sixths and two-fourths to equal a whole. Remove two-sixths and ask the student(s) if you have removed two-fifths of the whole. Do other combinations that equal a whole with some being equally divided and some not equally divided.

Materials, Supplies, & Equipment:

1. Flashcards for subtraction facts, multiplication facts, and shapes

2. Number chart 0–99

3. Fraction materials

Activities:

1. Drill multiplication facts using *Drill #3, Worksheet 56*.

2. Using *flashcards for subtraction facts*, drill minuends 1–18 with the answers showing and covering a minuend or subtrahend.

3. Using *flashcards for multiplication facts*, drill 5's and 2's without the answers showing and 3's, 6's, and 9's with the answers showing.

4. Count out loud with the student(s) by nines to 108.

5. Draw several shapes on the board. Divide some of the shapes into equal parts and some into unequal parts. After shading parts of each of the wholes, remind the student(s) that a fraction represents the shaded area only if the whole is divided into equal parts. Have the student(s) tell into how many parts the whole is divided (denominator) and how many of those parts are shaded (numerator). Write the fraction beside the shape and have the student(s) tell if the fraction and the shape are equal or not equal. The student(s) should be able to complete **Student Activity One** with little help.

6. The student(s) should be able to complete **Student Activity Two**, **Four**, and **Six** on their own.

7. Review even numbers (those ending in 0, 2, 4, 6, and 8) and odd numbers (those ending in 1, 3, 5, 7, and 9) using the *number chart*. The student(s) should be able to complete **Student Activity Three** by themselves. The three statements at the end of this activity should be correctly answered by the student(s) without difficulty by this time.

8. Display the names from the *shape flashcards* on the board rail. Have the student(s) say the name, spell it, and describe the shape. The student(s) should be able to complete **Student Activity Five** alone.

9. Have the student(s) determine if the word sentences tell to add or subtract. They should be able to complete **Student Activity Seven** without further assistance.

Worksheet:

1. *Worksheet 56* – Addition, subtraction, and multiplication drill sheet

A good beginning is likely to bring about a good ending.

Lesson 114

Concepts:
Counting by nines, inches, multiplication, even and odd, solids, word numbers, word sentences, addition, and subtraction

Objectives:
1. The student shall be able to count out loud by nines to 108.

2. The student shall be able to measure the length of a given object in inches and label the answer.

3. The student shall be able to write the product of the multiplication facts for three, six, and nine.

4. The student shall be able to write a list of the given numbers that are even and the given numbers that are odd.

5. The student shall be able to draw a line to match a solid to its name.

6. The student shall be able to rewrite the word sentences as number sentences.

7. The student shall be able to write the sum of two four-digit numbers when the tens' and hundreds' columns have double-digit answers.

8. The student shall be able to write the difference of two four-digit numbers when borrowing from the hundreds' column.

Teaching Tips:
1. When doing *Student Activity Three*, have the student(s) draw a line through the individual numbers on the mile posts as they write them on the blank. This will prevent them from doing a number more than once or not doing a number at all.

2. *Worksheet 57* would be a help to those who may not have had much experience in measuring the length of a line.

Materials, Supplies, & Equipment:
1. Flashcards for addition facts, multiplication facts, and solids

2. 12-inch ruler

3. Multiplication chart

Activities:

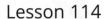

1. Drill subtraction facts using *Drill #4, Worksheet 56*.

2. Using *flashcards for addition facts*, drill sums 1–18 with the answers showing and covering one addend.

3. Using *flashcards for multiplication facts*, drill 5's and 2's without the answers showing and 3's, 6's, and 9's with the answers showing.

4. Count out loud with the student(s) by nines to 108.

5. Have the student(s) use their *12-inch ruler* with ½-inch increments to measure the objects in **Student Activity One**. Remind them to put the end of the object at zero on their ruler. Then read the length at the other end of the object and write the length on the blank. The second blank is for them to write the label "inches."

6. Encourage the student(s) to use the *multiplication chart* as little as possible when completing **Student Activity Two**. At the same time discourage them from guessing rather than learning the multiplication facts.

7. Discuss the directions for **Student Activity Three** with the student(s) before they complete the activity on their own.

8. Discuss with the student(s) different solids they can see in the room. Using *solid flashcards*, have them name and spell each solid. Read the names with the student(s) given in **Student Activity Four**. They should be able to complete the activity with little help.

9. The student(s) should be able to complete **Student Activity Five**, **Six**, and **Seven** on their own.

Worksheets:

1. *Worksheet 57* – Inches

2. *Worksheet 56* – Addition, subtraction, and multiplication drill sheet

You recognize easiest the faults in others
that are much like your own.

Lesson 115

Concepts:
 Counting by nines, place value, inches, addition, sequence, solids, multiplication, and subtraction

Objectives:
1. The student shall be able to count out loud by nines to 108.

2. The student shall be able to write the correct number when given the value of the digit in the thousands', hundreds', tens', and ones' places.

3. The student shall be able to measure the length of a given object in half inches and label the answer.

4. The student shall be able to write the sum of two four-digit numbers when the tens' and hundreds' columns have double-digit answers.

5. The student shall be able to write the next three numbers after a given sequence of numbers.

6. The student shall be able to write the name of a given solid.

7. The student shall be able to write the product of the multiplication facts for three, six, and nine.

8. The student shall be able to write the difference of two four-digit numbers when borrowing from the hundreds' column.

Teaching Tips:
1. When doing ***Student Activity Two***, have the student(s) take their *12-inch ruler* and compare it to the inch ruler in the activity. It is important for them to see that all *inch rulers* are alike. Have them compare the one-half inch marks on their ruler with the half inch marks on the ruler in the activity.

Materials, Supplies, & Equipment:
1. Flashcards for addition facts, subtraction facts, multiplication facts, and solids

2. Solid models

3. 12-inch ruler and yardstick

Activities:

1. Have the student(s) take a clean sheet of paper on which to write the answers for their *addition* and *subtraction facts* using *flashcards* with sleeves over an addend and a minuend or subtrahend. Do as many sets as time permits in 5 minutes.

2. Using *flashcards for multiplication facts*, drill 5's and 2's without the answers showing and 3's, 6's, and 9's with the answers showing.

3. Count out loud with the student(s) by nines to 108.

4. Write several numbers in expanded form (e.g., 5,000 + 300 + 20 + 7) on the board. Have the student(s) tell what numbers are represented. The student(s) should be able to complete **Student Activity One** on their own.

5. Discuss with the student(s) the equivalents of 12 inches in a foot, 3 feet in a yard, and 36 inches in a yard using a *12-inch ruler* and a *yardstick*. Have the student(s) look at the inch ruler in **Student Activity Two**. Point out the shorter marks on the ruler between two numbers. This mark is half way between two numbers and indicates one-half of an inch. Ask the student(s) how long the toothbrush is. Notice that it is longer than four inches but shorter than five inches. The length is $4\frac{1}{2}$ inches since it is half way between four and five. Tell them to write the length on the blank and label the answer. Discuss the length of the spoon with the student(s). After they write the answer and the label, they should be able to complete the remaining measurements by themselves.

6. The student(s) should be able to complete **Student Activity Three** independently.

7. Write "2 5 9 2 5 __ __ __" and "4 8 4 8 4 __ __ __" on the board. Have the student(s) tell the next three numbers to continue the sequence. They should be able to complete **Student Activity Four** alone.

8. Using the *solid models*, point to each solid and have the student(s) say and spell its name. Then have them describe each solid in their own words. Display the names from the *solid flashcards* on the board rail for a spelling reference as the student(s) complete **Student Activity Five**.

9. The student(s) should be able to complete **Student Activity Six** and **Seven** without assistance.

Lesson 116

Concepts:
 Multiplication, solids, sequence, addition, place value, inches, English linear equivalents, and word problems

Objectives:
 1. The student shall be able to write a given number of fours as an addition problem, a multiplication problem, and the product.

 2. The student shall be able to circle the picture that is different from the first solid given.

 3. The student shall be able to write the next three numbers after a given sequence of numbers.

 4. The student shall be able to write the sum of two four-digit numbers when the tens' and hundreds' columns have double-digit answers.

 5. The student shall be able to write the correct number when given the value of the digit in the thousands', hundreds', tens', and ones' places.

 6. The student shall be able to measure the length of a given object in half inches and label the answer.

 7. The student shall be able to write the equivalents between inches, feet, and yards.

 8. The student shall be able to write the answer to a multiplication word problem by writing the multiplication fact and the label.

Teaching Tips:
 1. If the student(s) have difficulty visualizing the word problem as a multiplication problem in *Student Activity Eight*, have them express it as an addition problem $(9 + 9 + 9 + 9 + 9 + 9 + 9)$ and then a multiplication problem.

Materials, Supplies, & Equipment:
 1. Flashcards for subtraction and multiplication facts

 2. Multiplication chart

 3. Solid models

 4. 12-inch ruler

 5. Yardstick

Activities:

1. Drill addition facts using *Drill #1, Worksheet 58*.

2. Using *flashcards for subtraction facts*, drill minuends 1–18 with the answers showing and covering the minuend or the subtrahend.

3. Using *flashcards for multiplication facts*, drill the 2's and 3's without the answers showing and the 6's and 9's with the answers showing.

4. Write "two 4's, three 4's, four 4's, etc." on the board. Ask the student(s) how to write two 4's as an addition problem and as a multiplication problem. They should know the answer (4 x 2). Follow the same procedure for three 4's, four 4's, etc. The student(s) should be able to complete **Student Activity One** with the help of the *multiplication chart*.

5. With *solid models*, review the names and spelling of the solids. Have the student(s) look at **Student Activity Two** and read the directions together. Ask them to name the first solid and point to the picture that is not a pyramid. Have the student(s) circle that picture. Discuss why the dunce hat is not a pyramid (the base is circular). Follow the same procedure with the other four solids.

6. Allow the student(s) to complete **Student Activity Three**, **Four**, and **Five** independently.

7. Have the student(s) put the zero on their *12-inch rulers* at the end of the first caterpillar in **Student Activity Six**. Notice that it is longer than two inches but shorter than three inches. Since it is half way in between two inches and three inches, the length is two and one-half inches. Ask the student(s) to tell how long the other caterpillars are. Be sure they label their answers. Before completing **Student Activity Seven**, discuss how many inches in a foot, inches in a yard, and feet in a yard using a *yardstick*.

8. Have the student(s) read the word problem in **Student Activity Eight** to themselves. Ask them to look at the picture and tell how many apples are there and how much each apple costs. Let them tell how they would write 7 apples at 9¢ each as a multiplication fact and have them write the fact on their paper. Notice there are no answer lines. The student(s) need to write the multiplication fact and label the answer in the blank space underneath.

Worksheet:

1. *Worksheet 58* – Addition, subtraction, and multiplication drill sheet

Lesson 117

Concepts:
> Counting by fours, months of the year, "Thirty Days Hath September," ordinal numbers, ratio, place value, word problems, inches, English linear equivalents, and multiplication

Objectives:

1. The student shall be able to count out loud by fours to 48.

2. The student shall be able to write the abbreviation for the months of the year when given in ordinal positions.

3. The student shall be able to write the comparison of two sets as a ratio.

4. The student shall be able to write the correct number when given the value of the digit in the thousands', hundreds', tens', and ones' places.

5. The student shall be able to write the answer to a multiplication word problem by writing the multiplication fact and the label.

6. The student shall be able to measure the length of a given object in half inches and label the answer.

7. The student shall be able to write the equivalents between inches, feet, and yards.

8. The student shall be able to draw a line to match corresponding number families.

Teaching Tips:

1. When doing activity 5, have the student(s) find some examples of the months of the year written in abbreviated form by looking in magazines, newspapers, or other sources at home. Have them paste them on a sheet of paper and write the month for each abbreviation.

Materials, Supplies, & Equipment:

1. Flashcards for addition facts, multiplication facts, and months of the year

2. Yardstick

Activities:

1. Drill multiplication facts using Dri*ll #2, Worksheet 58.*

2. Using *flashcards for addition facts*, drill sums 1–18 with the answers showing and covering an addend.

3. Using *flashcards for multiplication facts*, drill the 2's and 3's without the answers showing and the 6's and 9's with the answers showing.

4. Count out loud with the student(s) by fours to 48.

5. Recite "Thirty Days Hath September" with the student(s) (lesson 56). Discuss with them the abbreviations (a shortened form) for the months of the year using the *months of the year flashcards*. Note that there are no abbreviations for May, June, or July. All abbreviations end with a period. Have the student(s) spell the month and then its abbreviation. Number the months ordinally. The student(s) should be able to complete **Student Activity One** by themselves.

6. Draw 3 stars, 4 triangles, and 5 hearts on the board. Review with the student(s) the meaning of the word "ratio." On a sheet of paper, have them write the ratio of one set of the items on the board to another, in various orders. Remind them that the set named first must be written first. The student(s) should be able to complete **Student Activity Two** on their own.

7. The student(s) should be able to complete **Student Activity Three** independently.

8. Discuss with the student(s) whether the word problem in **Student Activity Four** is addition, subtraction, or multiplication. Allow them to complete the problem on their own. Check to see that they label their answer.

9. After discussing the equivalents for inches, feet, and yard with a *yardstick*, the student(s) should be able to complete **Student Activity Five** and **Seven** alone.

10. Ask the student(s) to write three 4's as an addition problem and as a multiplication problem on a sheet of paper. Then let them tell you what to write on the board for them to use to check their answer. Do several groups of 4's in the same manner. The student(s) should be able to complete **Student Activity Six** by themselves.

Worksheet:

1. *Worksheet 58* – Addition, subtraction, and multiplication drill sheet

Lesson 118

Concepts:
> Counting by fours, months of the year, "Thirty Days Hath September," line graphs, ratio, money, inches, multiplication, and word problems

Objectives:
1. The student shall be able to count out loud by fours to 48.

2. The student shall be able to spell the abbreviated form of the months of the year.

3. The student shall be able to write the correct facts obtained from interpreting a line graph.

4. The student shall be able to write the comparison of two sets as a ratio.

5. The student shall be able to write the cost of two given objects and the total value in dollars and cents.

6. The student shall be able to measure the length of a given line in half inches and write the length on the line.

7. The student shall be able to write the number of rows of a given number and the corresponding multiplication fact.

8. The student shall be able to write the answer to a multiplication word problem by writing the multiplication fact and the label.

Teaching Tips:
1. If the student(s) have difficulty understanding the word problem in **_Student Activity Six_**, have them draw 5 shirts and put 4 buttons on each shirt. Write the answer as an addition fact and then as a multiplication fact.

Materials, Supplies, & Equipment:
1. Flashcards for subtraction facts, multiplication facts, months of the year, and English linear equivalents

2. 12-inch ruler

Activities:

1. Drill multiplication facts using Drill #3, *Worksheet 58.*

2. Using *flashcards for subtraction facts*, drill minuends 1–18 with the answers showing and covering a minuend or subtrahend.

3. Using *flashcards for multiplication facts*, drill 2's and 3's without the answers showing and 6's, 9's, and 4's with the answers showing. Spend about three minutes drilling only 4 x 4, 7 x 4, 8 x 4, and their pairs. All other 4's should have been learned as a pair.

4. Count out loud with the student(s) by fours to 48.

5. Using the *months of the year flashcards*, have the student(s) spell the months that have abbreviated forms. Remember that all months of the year begin with a capital letter and the abbreviation ends with a period. Recite "Thirty Days Hath September."

6. After the student(s) have completed **Student Activity One** by themselves, discuss each of the questions with them.

7. Draw 4 circles, 6 hexagons, and 8 squares on the board. Discuss the meaning of the word "ratio " with the student(s). On a sheet of paper have the student(s) write several ratios of one set to two other sets (e.g., circles to hexagons and squares as 4:14). Then have them do several ratios of two sets to two other sets (e.g., circles and hexagons to circles and squares as 10:12). Allow the student(s) to complete **Student Activity Two** independently. Discuss their answers upon completion.

8. In **Student Activity Three**, complete the first problem with the student(s). Discuss how they write monetary values over one hundred cents as dollars and cents (there are always two digits after the decimal point). Then allow them to complete the last two problems on their own.

9. Review the equivalents for inches, feet, and yard using *English linear equivalent flashcards*. Instruct the student(s) to measure the first line in **Student Activity Four** by measuring with a *12-inch ruler* from point one to point two and writing the length on the line. Next measure from point two to point three and write the length on the line. Continue from point to point until they have measured from point six to point seven. Be sure the student(s) label their length in inches.

10. The student(s) should be able to complete **Student Activity Five** and **Six** alone.

Worksheet:

1. *Worksheet 58* – Addition, subtraction, and multiplication drill sheet

Lesson 119

Concepts:
> Counting by fours, months of the year, "Thirty Days Hath September," equations, line graphs, multiplication, ratio, money, and greater than and less than

Objectives:
1. The student shall be able to count out loud by fours to 48.

2. The student shall be able to spell the abbreviated form of the months of the year.

3. The student shall be able to write the value of a variable in an addition equation.

4. The student shall be able to write the correct facts obtained from interpreting a line graph.

5. The student shall be able to draw a line to match pairs of multiplication facts.

6. The student shall be able to write the comparison of two sets as a ratio.

7. The student shall be able to write the cost of a given number of fruits.

8. The student shall be able to write the correct symbol (< or >) between two sets of coins.

Teaching Tips:
1. Allow the student(s) to use the *multiplication chart* when needed while completing **Student Activity Five**.

Materials, Supplies, & Equipment:
1. Flashcards for addition and multiplication facts

2. Pencils, erasers, and note pads

3. Play money

4. Multiplication chart

Activities:

1. Drill subtraction facts using *Drill #4, Worksheet 58.*

2. Using *flashcards for addition facts*, drill sums 1–18 with the answers showing and covering one addend.

3. Using *flashcards for multiplication facts*, drill 2's and 3's without the answers showing and 6's, 9's, and 4's with the answers showing. Be sure the student(s) say the facts in pairs.

4. Count out loud with the student(s) by fours to 48.

5. Recite "Thirty days Hath September" with the student(s). Spell each of the abbreviations for the months of the year.

6. Write "__ + 8 = 12" on the board. Have the student(s) tell the number that goes in the blank to make a true statement. Write "n + 8 = 12" under the first equation. The unknown has been replaced with a letter called a variable. The student(s) are going to solve for that unknown. Ask the student(s) what to do to find the missing number (subtract 8 from 12). What they do to one side of the equation they must also do to the other side of the equation. Subtract 8 from both sides of the equation. Mark out 8 – 8 on the left hand side leaving "n." 12 – 8 leaves 4 on the right hand side. The result is n = 4. Do several similar equations with the student(s) before they attempt to complete **Student Activity One** on their own.

7. Allow the student(s) to complete **Student Activity Two** independently. Then discuss each question with them.

8. The student(s) should be able to complete **Student Activity Three** and **Four** by themselves.

9. Discuss with the student(s) what 7 pencils would cost at 10¢ each, 5 erasers at 8¢ each, and 2 note pads at 9¢ each. Encourage them to multiply to find the answer since that is much quicker than adding. Display the *pencils*, *erasers* and *note pads* for those who need them. This could be done on the board or by having the objects for the student(s) to see. The student(s) should be able to complete **Student Activity Five** alone.

10. Have the student(s) determine the value of each set of coins in **Student Activity Six** before they attempt to write the correct symbol. *Play money* may be a help for some student(s). Tell them to write the values on their paper if necessary to be accurate.

Worksheets:

1. *Worksheet 59* – Solve equations

2. *Worksheet 58* – Addition, subtraction, and multiplication drill sheet

Lesson 120

Concepts:
Counting by fours, centimeters, money, equations, multiplication, greater than and less than, addition, and subtraction

Objectives:

1. The student shall be able to count out loud by fours to 48.

2. The student shall be able to measure the length of a given object in centimeters and label the answer.

3. The student shall be able to write the cost of two given objects and the total value in dollars and cents.

4. The student shall be able to write the value of a variable in an addition equation.

5. The student shall be able to write the corresponding multiplication fact to make a pair.

6. The student shall be able to write the product of the multiplication facts for zero, one, ten, five, two, three, six, nine, and four.

7. The student shall be able to write the correct symbol (< or >) between an addition fact and a subtraction fact.

8. The student shall be able to write two addition and two subtraction facts when given three numbers and the sum or difference.

Teaching Tips:

1. After the student(s) have completed **Student Activity One**, have them take out their *centimeter ruler*. Tell them to compare their ruler with the one in the activity and then measure each of the objects. It is important for them to realize that all centimeter rulers will measure the same.

Materials, Supplies, & Equipment:

1. Flashcards for addition, subtraction, and multiplication facts

2. Centimeter ruler

3. Multiplication chart

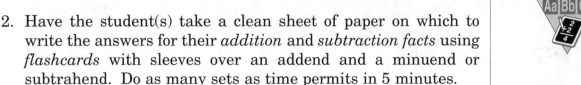

Activities:

1. Administer **Test 12**.

2. Have the student(s) take a clean sheet of paper on which to write the answers for their *addition* and *subtraction facts* using *flashcards* with sleeves over an addend and a minuend or subtrahend. Do as many sets as time permits in 5 minutes.

3. Using *flashcards for multiplication facts*, drill 2's and 3's without the answers showing and 6's, 9's, and 4's with the answers showing.

4. Count out loud with the student(s) by fours to 48.

5. Discuss with the student(s) that there are two different rulers that can be used to measure short lengths – the inch ruler and the *centimeter ruler*. Tell them the *centimeter ruler* is a metric measure while the inch ruler is the English measure. Explain that they use a *centimeter ruler* in the same way that they use an inch ruler. Ask the student(s) to tell the length of each object in **Student Activity One** and then have them write it on the blank and label their answer.

6. In **Student Activity Two**, complete the first problem with the student(s). Emphasize the importance of keeping the decimal points in a straight vertical line. Allow them to complete the last two problems on their own.

7. The student(s) should be able to complete **Student Activity Three** and **Four** by themselves.

8. The student(s) will need to use the *multiplication chart* for some facts when completing **Student Activity Five**.

9. Remind the student(s) to find each sum and difference before they determine the correct symbol to use in **Student Activity Six**. Have them write the sum and difference above the fact if necessary to be accurate.

10. Write three single-digit numbers on the board (e.g., 7, 6, and 3). Tell the student(s) a sum of two of them (13) and have them choose what the fact is (7 + 6). Then tell them a difference (3) and have them choose the fact (6 – 3). Do several other combinations with the student(s). Work the first problem in **Student Activity Seven** with the student(s). They should be able to complete the last two problems alone.

Lesson 121

Concepts:
 Counting by fours, fractions, centimeters, estimation, pictograph, multiplication, and equations

Objectives:
 1. The student shall be able to count out loud by fours to 48.

 2. The student shall be able to write the fraction that represents the number of objects colored in a given set.

 3. The student shall be able to measure the length of a given object in centimeters and label the answer.

 4. The student shall be able to write the correct number to which a given number over one hundred is closer.

 5. The student shall be able to write the correct facts obtained from interpreting a pictograph.

 6. The student shall be able to write the product of the multiplication facts for five, two, three, six, nine, and four.

 7. The student shall be able to write the value of a variable in an addition equation.

Teaching Tips:
 1. When doing activity 6, discuss with the student(s) the metric system which is used extensively throughout most of the world. Let them see the comparison of the *centimeter ruler* and the *meter stick*. See if the student(s) can think of anywhere the metric system is used in the United States (2 liter bottles, medicine measure, speedometers, wrenches for cars, distance on some highway signs, etc.).

Materials, Supplies, & Equipment:
 1. Flashcards for subtraction and multiplication facts

 2. Multiplication chart

 3. Centimeter ruler

 4. Meter stick

Activities:

1. Drill addition facts using *Drill #1, Worksheet 60.*

2. Using *flashcards for subtraction facts*, drill minuends 1–18 with the answers showing and covering the minuend or the subtrahend.

3. Using *flashcards for multiplication facts*, drill 2's and 3's without the answers showing and 6's, 9's, and 4's with the answers showing.

4. Count out loud with the student(s) by fours to 48.

5. Remind the student(s) that the denominator of a fraction tells them how many parts are in the whole or the set and that the numerator tells them how many of those parts they are using. On the board, draw six squares and shade five of them. Ask the student(s) what fractional part of the set is shaded. Do the same with several other sets of shapes. After the student(s) have completed the first problem in **Student Activity One**, check for correct answers. Then allow them to complete the remaining problems on their own.

6. The student(s) should be able to complete **Student Activity Two** alone.

7. Write "253" on the board. Ask if the number is closer to 250 or 260. If the digit in the ones place is less than 5, the smaller number is closer and if the digit is greater than 5, the larger number is closer. After doing several examples, the student(s) should be able to complete **Student Activity Three** independently.

8. Have the student(s) look at the pictograph in **Student Activity Four**. Be sure they see the key to know which symbol represents a boy and which represents a girl. Explain that the chart's purpose is to tell them how many children are in each family. The student(s) must consider families that have 0 boys or girls when answering the questions. Answer all the questions together with the student(s).

9. The student(s) should be able to complete **Student Activity Five** and **Six** with the help of the *multiplication chart*.

Worksheet:

1. *Worksheet 60* – Addition, subtraction, and multiplication drill sheet

The best things in life are not easy to come
by and hard to hold on to.

Lesson 122

Concepts:
Counting by fours, Roman numerals, fractions, estimation, centimeters, pictograph, and multiplication

Objectives:

1. The student shall be able to count out loud by fours to 48.

2. The student shall be able to write the Roman numeral that corresponds to the given Arabic number.

3. The student shall be able to write the fraction that represents the number of objects colored in a given set.

4. The student shall be able to write the correct number to which a given number over one hundred is closer.

5. The student shall be able to measure the length of a given object in centimeters and label the answer.

6. The student shall be able to write the correct facts obtained from interpreting a pictograph.

7. The student shall be able to write the product of the multiplication facts for three, six, nine, and four.

8. The student shall be able to write two addition facts and two subtraction facts when given three numbers and a sum or difference.

Teaching Tips:

1. When doing activity 8, have the student(s) look in newspapers, magazines, or other sources at home to find a pictograph. A pictograph is not as common as a bar graph or a line graph so do not put undo pressure on them to find one. Discuss the pictographs that are brought to class. Compare them with the ones the student(s) have been reading in class.

Materials, Supplies, & Equipment:

1. Flashcards for addition facts, multiplication facts, and Roman numerals

2. Multiplication chart

Activities:

1. Drill multiplication facts using *Drill #2, Worksheet 60*.

2. Using *flashcards for addition facts*, drill sums 1–18 with the answers showing and covering an addend.

3. Using *flashcards for multiplication facts*, drill 2's and 3's without the answers showing and 6's, 9's, and 4's with the answers showing.

4. Count out loud with the student(s) by fours to 48.

5. Review the value of each of the Roman numerals given in the boxes in **Student Activity One**. Discuss how 4 and 9 are formed. Let the student(s) choose the necessary *Roman numeral flashcards* to form several numbers from 100 to 1,000. Help them understand they must have a numeral for the value of each digit in the number. The hundreds' digit will start with C or D, the tens' digit with X or L, and the ones' digit with I or V. Allow the student(s) that are capable to complete **Student Activity One** alone. Be available to help, on an individual basis, student(s) who do not have a clear understanding.

6. On the board, draw eight hearts and shade five of them. Ask the student(s) what fractional part of the set is shaded. Do the same with several other sets of shapes. The student(s) should be able to complete **Student Activity Two** on their own.

7. The student(s) should be able to complete **Student Activity Three** and **Four** independently.

8. Discuss the pictograph in **Student Activity Five**. Point to the key and explain that each can symbol in the graph represents 5 cans. Discuss the meaning of the directions. With the student(s), find the number of cans collected by each person. Allow the student(s) to answer the last two questions by themselves.

9. The student(s) should be able to complete **Student Activity Six** with the help of the *multiplication chart*.

10. Write three single-digit numbers on the board. Tell the sum of two of them and have the student(s) tell what two you added. Then indicate the difference of two of the numbers and have the student(s) tell the two you subtracted. After doing several examples with the student(s), they should be able to complete **Student Activity Seven** without further help.

Worksheets:

1. *Worksheet 61* – Pictographs

2. *Worksheet 60* – Addition, subtraction, and multiplication drill sheet

Lesson 123

Concepts:

Counting by fours, addition, equations, centimeters, Roman numerals, fractions, multiplication, and word problems

Objectives:

1. The student shall be able to count out loud by fours to 48.

2. The student shall be able to write the sum of two four-digit numbers when the ones', tens', or hundreds' column has a double-digit answer.

3. The student shall be able to write the value of a variable in a subtraction equation.

4. The student shall be able to measure the length of a given line in centimeters and label the answer.

5. The student shall be able to write the Arabic number that corresponds to the given Roman numeral.

6. The student shall be able to shade a fractional part of a given set.

7. The student shall be able to write the product of the multiplication facts for three, six, nine, and four.

Teaching Tips:

1. For activity 6, show the student(s) how they can check each equation by substituting the answer for the variable. If the equation is true, the answer is correct. Example: In the equation $n - 4 = 6$, a solution of $n = 10$ is reached. Substitute 10 for "n" and they have $10 - 4 = 6$ which is a true statement. Therefore, their answer is correct.

Materials, Supplies, & Equipment:

1. Flashcards for subtraction and multiplication facts

2. Centimeter ruler

3. Flannel board and materials

4. Multiplication chart

Activities:

1. Drill multiplication facts using *Drill #3, Worksheet 60*.

2. Using *flashcards for subtraction facts*, drill minuends 1–18 with the answers showing and covering a minuend or subtrahend.

3. Using *flashcards for multiplication facts*, drill 2's and 3's without the answers showing and 6's, 9's, and 4's with the answers showing.

4. Count out loud with the student(s) by fours to 48.

5. On the board, write several sets of two four-digit numbers as addition problems with carrying in the ones', tens', or hundreds' column. Have the student(s) solve the problems on their own paper before you solve them on the board. They should complete **Student Activity One** alone.

6. Write "__ − 5 = 7" on the board. Have the student(s) tell the number that goes in the blank to make a true statement (equations are always true statements). Write "n − 5 = 7" under the first equation. Ask the student(s) how to find the missing number (add 5 to 7). Add 5 to both sides of the equation. Since -5 + 5 equals 0, draw a slanted line through each leaving "n" on the left hand side. The right hand side now equals 12 (7 + 5). Write "n = 12" as the solution. Go over the examples given above **Student Activity Two**. Solve the given equations step by step on the board as the student(s) do them on their paper.

7. As the student(s) use their *centimeter ruler* to measure the lines in **Student Activity Three**, remind them to put the zero on their ruler at the beginning of the line.

8. Write several Roman numerals from 100 to 999 on the board. Have the student(s) tell what Arabic number corresponds to each Roman numeral. Give help where needed as the student(s) complete **Student Activity Four**.

9. Place 6 *flannel objects* on the *flannel board*. Ask the student(s) how many of the objects would need to be removed to equal $\frac{5}{6}$ of them. Repeat the procedure with sets of 5, 7, and 8 objects, removing a fractional part of each. Complete the first problem in **Student Activity Five** with the student(s). Allow them to complete the remaining problems alone.

10. The student(s) should be able to complete **Student Activity Six** and **Seven** independently using the *multiplication chart* where needed.

Worksheets:

1. *Worksheet 62* – Centimeters

2. *Worksheet 60* – Addition, subtraction, and multiplication drill sheet

Lesson 124

Concepts:

Counting by fours, time, addition, equations, word problems, fractions, multiplication, word sentences, word numbers, and shapes

Objectives:

1. The student(s) shall be able to count out loud by fours to 48.

2. The student(s) shall be able to write the correct time displayed on the face of the clock.

3. The student(s) shall be able to write the sum of two four-digit numbers when the ones', tens', or hundreds' column has a double-digit answer.

4. The student(s) shall be able to write the value of a variable in a subtraction equation.

5. The student(s) shall be able to shade a fractional part of a given set.

6. The student(s) shall be able to write the product of the multiplication facts for three, six, nine, and four.

7. The student(s) shall be able to rewrite a word sentence as a number sentence.

8. The student(s) shall be able to draw a line to match similar shapes.

Teaching Tips:

1. If the student(s) have difficulty with the large numbers in ***Student Activity Four***, have them substitute smaller numbers to see if they add or subtract. Example: Fran's teacher asked her to read 5 pages in this nine weeks. She has read 3 pages. How many more pages must she read this nine weeks? If they subtract in this problem, then they also subtract when the numbers are larger.

Materials, Supplies, & Equipment:

1. Flashcards for addition facts, multiplication facts, and shapes

2. Small clock model for student(s)

3. Clock model

Activities:

1. Drill subtraction facts using *Drill #4, Worksheet 60*.

2. Using *flashcards for addition facts*, drill sums 1–18 with the answers showing and covering one addend.

3. Using *flashcards for multiplication facts*, drill 2's and 3's without the answers showing and 6's, 9's, and 4's with the answers showing. Be sure the student(s) say the facts in pairs.

4. Count out loud with the student(s) by fours to 48.

5. Give the student(s) a *small clock model*. Write several 5 minute intervals on the board. After the student(s) set their clocks for the individual times, have them check their work by the *clock model*. They should be able to complete **Student Activity One** by themselves.

6. The student(s) should be able to complete **Student Activity Two** on their own.

7. Write several horizontal subtraction facts on the board replacing the minuend with the letter "n." Ask the student(s) how to find the value of "n" (add the subtrahend to the difference). Remind them what they do to one side of the equation, they must also do to the other side. Insist that they follow the steps on their paper that you follow on the board. Notice in the first problem in **Student Activity Three** the first step is done for them. They must do this step in each problem in the activity.

8. The student(s) should be able to complete **Student Activity Four**, **Five**, and **Six** independently.

9. Have the student(s) read the first sentence in **Student Activity Seven** alone. Discuss if they are to add or subtract. Then have them write the number sentence. Follow this procedure for the remaining sentences.

10. Using the *shape flashcards*, have the student(s) identify and spell each shape. Explain that the shapes to be matched in **Student Activity Eight** are different sizes. When two shapes are the same shape but different sizes, they are called "similar" shapes. Have the student(s) find a triangle. Then ask them to find a second triangle either larger or smaller than the first one. Connect the two shapes with a line. Follow the same procedure for each of the shapes in the activity.

Worksheet:

1. *Worksheet 60* – Addition, subtraction, and multiplication drill sheet

279

Lesson 125

Concepts:
Counting by fours, fractions, equations, multiplication, time, addition, shapes, and word problems

Objectives:

1. The student shall be able to count out loud by fours to 48.

2. The student shall be able to circle sets equivalent to the denominator of a unit fraction, write the number of sets circled, and the fractional part of the given number.

3. The student shall be able to write the value of a variable in a subtraction equation.

4. The student shall be able to write the product of the multiplication facts for six, nine, and four.

5. The student shall be able to draw both hands on the face of the clock for given five minute increments.

6. The student shall be able to write the sum of two four-digit numbers when the ones', tens', or hundreds' column has a double-digit answer.

7. The student shall be able to draw a line to match a shape to its name.

8. The student shall be able to write a word problem using the given information.

Teaching Tips:

1. When doing the examples on the board in activity 4, you may have the student(s) divide each group into 2, 3, 4, etc. equal groups. Then the number in each group is the answer. The difficulty with this method is dividing a large group into equal parts but some student(s) may enjoy the added challenge.

Materials, Supplies, & Equipment:

1. Flashcards for addition facts, subtraction facts, multiplication facts, and shapes

2. Clock model

Activities:

1. Have the student(s) take a clean sheet of paper on which to write the answers for their *addition* and *subtraction facts* using *flashcards* with sleeves over an addend and a minuend or subtrahend. Do as many sets as time permits in 5 minutes.

2. Using *flashcards for multiplication facts*, drill 2's and 3's without the answers showing and 6's, 9's, and 4's with the answers showing.

3. Count out loud with the student(s) by fours to 48.

4. Draw 6 triangles on the board. Ask a student to draw circles around sets of 2's. Have the student(s) tell how many groups of 2's there are in 6 (3). ½ of 6 is 3. Draw 6 more triangles. Now have a student draw circles around sets of 3's. How many groups of 3's are there in 6 (2). ⅓ of 6 is 2. Draw 12 squares on the board. To find what ⅓ of 12 equals, have a student circle groups of 3's and tell how many groups of 3's they have (4). ⅓ of 12 = 4. Follow the same procedure to determine what ¼ of 12, ½ of 12, and ⅙ of 12 equals. Work step by step with the student(s) on each problem as they complete **Student Activity One**.

5. Have the student(s) solve the first equation in **Student Activity Two** alone. Then you solve the problem on the board so that the student(s) may check their answers. If they solved the equation correctly, allow them to solve the remaining equations on their own. If they did not solve the equation correctly, give individual help.

6. The student(s) should be able to complete **Student Activity Three** independently.

7. Remind the student(s) to draw the minute hand first in **Student Activity Four**. If there are less than 30 minutes, the hour hand will be closer to the given hour. If there are more than 30 minutes, the hour hand will be closer to the next hour. The *clock model* may be of help in explaining the placement of the clock hands. Give assistance where needed as the student(s) complete the activity.

8. The student(s) should be able to complete **Student Activity Five** without assistance.

9. Using *shape flashcards*, review the name and spelling of each shape. The student(s) should complete **Student Activity Six** alone.

10. Using the information given in **Student Activity Seven**, allow the student(s) to write either an addition or a subtraction word problem.

Lesson 126

Concepts:
> Counting by sevens, English weights, estimation, addition, subtraction, equal and not equal, shapes, time equivalents, fractions, and multiplication

Objectives:
1. The student shall be able to count out loud by sevens to 84.

2. The student shall be able to draw a line to match a given weight to a picture.

3. The student shall be able to write the sum of two four-digit numbers when the ones', tens', or hundreds' column has a double-digit answer.

4. The student shall be able to write the difference of two triple-digit numbers when borrowing from the tens' or the hundreds' column.

5. The student shall be able to write the correct symbol (= or ≠) between a shape and its name.

6. The student shall be able to write the time equivalents.

7. The student shall be able to circle sets equivalent to the denominator of a unit fraction, write the number of sets circled, and the fractional part of the given number.

8. The student shall be able to write a given number of sevens as an addition problem, a multiplication problem, and the product.

Teaching Tips:
1. If the student(s) have difficulty with **Student Activity One**, suggest that they begin by finding the lightest object and match it to the least weight. Continue in the same manner until they are matching the heaviest object with the largest weight.

Materials, Supplies, & Equipment:
1. Flashcards for subtraction facts, multiplication facts, and shapes

2. Clock model

3. Calendar

4. Multiplication chart

Activities:

1. Drill addition facts using *Drill #1, Worksheet 63*.

2. Using *flashcards for subtraction facts*, drill minuends 1–18 with the answers showing and covering the minuend or the subtrahend.

3. Using *flashcards for multiplication facts*, drill 2's and 3's without the answers showing and 6's, 9's, and 4's with the answers showing.

4. Count out loud with the student(s) by sevens to 84.

5. Discuss with the student(s) the standard unit of measure used in the United States for weight (ounces, pounds, and tons). Discuss the estimated weight, in ounces and pounds, of several objects in the room and make comparisons. Discuss objects that weigh about a ton (horse, cow, truck, etc.), Have the student(s) look at the pictures in **Student Activity One**. Discuss which object in the pictures weighs the most and which weighs the least. Allow the student(s) to draw the lines without individual help.

6. The student(s) should be able to complete **Student Activity Two** and **Three** independently.

7. Using the *shape flashcards*, have the student(s) identify and spell each shape. The student(s) should be able to complete **Student Activity Four** alone.

8. With the aid of the *clock model* and a *calendar*, discuss the time equivalents in **Student Activity Five**. The student(s) should be able to complete the equivalents on their own.

9. Draw 24 squares on the board. To find what ⅓ of 24 equals, have a student circle groups of 3's and tell how many groups of 3's they have (8). ⅓ of 24 = 8. Follow the same procedure to determine what ¼ of 24, ½ of 24, and ⅙ of 24 equals. After working the first problem in **Student Activity Six** with the student(s), allow them to complete the last two by themselves if possible.

10. Write "three 7's, four 7's, five 7's, etc." on the board. Ask the student(s) how to write three 7's as an addition problem and a multiplication problem. Now have them look at the *multiplication chart* for the answer to 3 x 7 if they do not know it (7 x 3). Follow the same procedure for four 7's, five 7's, etc. The student(s) should be able to complete **Student Activity Seven** with the help of the *multiplication chart*.

Worksheet:

1. Worksheet 63 – Addition, subtraction, and multiplication drill sheet

Lesson 127

Concepts:

Counting by sevens, pictographs, English weights, greater than and less than, equal to, multiplication, time equivalents, solids, fractions, equations, and number sequence

Objectives:

1. The student shall be able to count out loud by sevens to 84.

2. The student shall be able to draw the pictures necessary to represent given information on a pictograph.

3. The student shall be able to write the correct symbol (<, >, or =) between two pictures in respect to weight.

4. The student shall be able to draw a line to match pairs of multiplication facts.

5. The student shall be able to write the time equivalents.

6. The student shall be able to draw a line to match a solid to a corresponding picture.

7. The student shall be able to circle sets equivalent to the denominator of a unit fraction, write the number of sets circled, and the fractional part of the given number.

8. The student shall be able to write the value of a variable in an addition equation.

9. The student shall be able to write the next three numbers after a given sequence of numbers.

Teaching Tips:

1. For activity 6, you may want to use items other than flour and butter. Be sure that they weigh 5 pounds and 1 pound respectively.

Materials, Supplies, & Equipment:

1. Flashcards for addition and multiplication facts

2. Play money

3. 5 pound bag of flour and 1 pound of butter

4. Solid model

5. Counting chips

Activities:

1. Drill multiplication facts using *Drill #2, Worksheet 63*.

2. Using *flashcards for addition facts*, drill sums 1–18 with the answers showing and covering an addend.

3. Using *flashcards for multiplication facts*, drill 2's and 3's without the answers showing and 6's, 9's, and 4's with the answers showing.

4. Count out loud with the student(s) by seven to 84.

5. Have the student(s) look at the pictograph in **Student Activity One**. Using *play money*, let the student(s) determine how many nickels (a circle with 5¢ in the middle) they are going to draw for each of the boys. After they have drawn all the nickels, have them count the nickels by fives.

6. You will need a *5 pound bag of flour* and *1 pound of butter* for **Student Activity Two**. Allow the student(s) to compare the weight of the *flour* with items such as a shoe, a dictionary, and a chair. Then have them compare the weight of a *pound of butter* with items such as a sock, a pencil, and a book. Have them write their conclusions on their paper (greater than if the flour or butter is heavier, less than if they are lighter, and equal if they are about the same).

7. The student(s) should be able to complete **Student Activity Three** and **Four** on their own.

8. Name each solid and have the student(s) describe it. The *solid models* would be a help here. The student(s) should be able to complete **Student Activity Five** by themselves.

9. Give each student 16 *counting chips*. Write "¼ of 16 = __" on the board. Have the student(s) put the 16 counting chips into sets of 4's and count to see how many sets they have. Then ask them what ¼ of 16 equals. Do the same with ½ of 16 and ⅛ of 16. The student(s) should be able to complete **Student Activity Six** without further help.

10. The student(s) should be able to complete **Student Activity Seven** and **Eight** alone.

Worksheets:

1. *Worksheet 64* – Fractions

2. *Worksheet 63* – Addition, subtraction, and multiplication drill sheet

Lesson 128

Concepts:
> Counting by sevens, place value, number sequence, solids, word problems, equations, pictographs, multiplication, and subtraction

Objectives:
1. The student shall be able to count out loud by sevens to 84.

2. The student shall be able to write the place value of a digit in a given four-digit number.

3. The student shall be able to write the next three numbers after a given sequence of numbers.

4. The student shall be able to write the name of a given solid.

5. The student shall be able to write the value of a variable in an addition equation.

6. The student shall be able to draw the pictures necessary to represent given information on a pictograph.

7. The student shall be able to write the product of the multiplication facts for six, nine, four, and seven.

8. The student shall be able to write the difference of two triple-digit numbers when borrowing from the tens' or the hundreds' column.

Teaching Tips:
1. Notice that the multiplication facts for 6's are to be drilled without the answers showing in activity 3. Check the student(s) individually to see if they have mastered the 6's. If not, additional drill time needs to be arranged.

Materials, Supplies, & Equipment:
1. Flashcards for subtraction facts, multiplication facts, and solids

2. Solid models

Activities:

1. Drill multiplication facts using *Drill #3, Worksheet 63*.

2. Using *flashcards for subtraction facts*, drill minuends 1–18 with the answers showing and covering a minuend or subtrahend.

3. Using *flashcards for multiplication facts*, drill 2's, 3's, and 6's without the answers showing and 9's, 4's, and 7's with the answers showing.

4. Count out loud with the student(s) by sevens to 84.

5. Write several 4-digit numbers on the board. As you point to the digits in random order, have the student(s) tell the place the digit holds. Then name a place value and have the student(s) tell what digit is in that place. The student(s) should be able to complete **Student Activity One** on their own.

6. Allow the student(s) to complete **Student Activity Two** with as little help as possible.

7. As you point to each of the *solid models*, have the student(s) name and spell them. Display the *solid flashcards* on the board rail for spelling reference as the student(s) complete **Student Activity Three**.

8. After the student(s) have read the word problem in **Student Activity Four**, ask them if they are to add, subtract, or multiply. Allow them to draw pictures if necessary to visualize their answer.

9. The student(s) should be able to complete **Student Activity Five**, **Seven**, and **Eight** by themselves.

10. Have the student(s) tell how many points each football represents in **Student Activity Six**. Allow the student(s) to find the total points Matt scored together. They should be able to determine the number of points the other boys scored alone.

Worksheet:

1. *Worksheet 63* – Addition, subtraction, and multiplication drill sheet

It is not necessary to boast about what others see you do.

Lesson 129

Concepts:

Counting by sevens, inches, addition, place value, subtraction, ratio, multiplication, equations, and word problems

Objectives:

1. The student shall be able to count out loud by sevens to 84.

2. The student shall be able to measure the length of a given line in quarter inches and label the answer.

3. The student shall be able to write the sum of two four-digit numbers when the ones', tens', or hundreds' column has double-digit answers.

4. The student shall be able to write the place value of a digit in a given four-digit number.

5. The student shall be able to write the difference of two triple-digit numbers when borrowing from the tens' or hundreds' column.

6. The student shall be able to write the comparison of two sets as a ratio.

7. The student shall be able to write the product of the multiplication facts for nine, four, and seven.

8. The student shall be able to write the value of a variable in an addition equation.

Teaching Tips:

1. After the student(s) have completed activity 5, have them take their *12-inch ruler* and compare the ¼-inch marks with the ruler in *Student Activity One*. It is important for them to be able to see the ¼-inch marks on their ruler.

Materials, Supplies, & Equipment:

1. Flashcards for addition and multiplication facts

2. 12-inch ruler

3. Pencils, pens, and erasers

Activities:

1. Drill subtraction facts using *Drill #4, Worksheet 63*.

2. Using *flashcards for addition facts*, drill sums 1–18 with the answers showing and covering one addend.

3. Using *flashcards for multiplication facts*, drill 2's, 3's, and 6's without the answers showing and 9's, 4's, and 7's with the answers showing. Be sure the student(s) say the facts in pairs.

4. Count out loud with the student(s) by sevens to 84.

5. Have the student(s) look at the *inch ruler* in **Student Activity One**. Ask them into how many parts one inch would be divided if they wanted to measure ¼ of an inch (4). Point out that each inch is divided into four equal parts. Instruct them to look at the first line and write its length and label on the blank. Discuss their answer. Point out that the inches is always the number just past and not the number to which the line is closer. After the student(s) write their answers for the remaining problems, discuss their solutions.

6. The student(s) should be able to complete **Student Activity Two**, **Three**, and **Four** by themselves.

7. Discuss a ratio as a way to write the comparison of two numbers. Remind the student(s) that the order in which the ratio is given is the order in which it must be written. Display for the student(s) 6 *pencils*, 5 *pens*, and 4 *erasers*. Ask them to tell the ratio of the number of pencils to the number of pens, pens to erasers, pens and pencils to erasers, and erasers to pens and pencils. The student(s) should be able to complete **Student Activity Five** with little help.

8. The student(s) should be able to complete **Student Activity Six** and **Seven** independently.

9. Have the student(s) tell if the word problems in **Student Activity Eight** are addition, subtraction, or multiplication and why. Then allow them to complete the problems on their own. Check for correct labels to their answers.

Worksheet:

1. *Worksheet 63* – Addition, subtraction, and multiplication drill sheet

Lesson 130

Concepts:
   Counting by sevens, days of the week, ordinal numbers, subtraction, addition, inches, ratio, multiplication, and word problems

Objectives:
1. The student shall be able to count out loud by sevens to 84.

2. The student shall be able to write the abbreviation for the days of the week when given in ordinal positions.

3. The student shall be able to write the difference of two triple-digit numbers when borrowing from the tens' or the hundreds' column.

4. The student shall be able to write the correct letter that corresponds to the sum of the addition problem.

5. The student shall be able to measure the length of a given line in quarter inches and label the answer.

6. The student shall be able to write the comparison of two sets as a ratio.

7. The student shall be able to write the product of the multiplication facts for three, six, nine, four, and seven.

Teaching Tips:
1. If you do **Test 30** before lesson 130, discuss with the student(s) the abbreviations for the days of the week on the line graph in **Test 30**. After reading each of the days with the student(s), tell them that they will have a further discussion about the abbreviations during class time.

Materials, Supplies, & Equipment:
1. Flashcards for addition facts, subtraction facts, multiplication facts, and days of the week

2. 12-inch ruler

3. Markers, rulers, and books

290

Activities:

1. Administer **Test 13**.

2. Have the student(s) take a clean sheet of paper on which to write the answers for their *addition* and *subtraction facts* using *flashcards* with sleeves over an addend and a minuend or subtrahend. Do as many sets as time permits in 5 minutes.

3. Using *flashcards for multiplication facts*, drill 2's, 3's, and 6's without the answers showing and 9's, 4's, and 7's with the answers showing.

4. Count out loud with the student(s) by sevens to 84.

5. Discuss the abbreviations (a shortened form) for the days of the week using the *days of the week flashcards*. All abbreviations end with a period. Have the student(s) spell the days and then their abbreviations. The student(s) should be able to complete **Student Activity One** by themselves.

6. The student(s) should be able to complete **Student Activity Two** independently.

7. To begin **Student Activity Three**, tell the student(s) to find the sum of the first problem. The letter that corresponds to the sum should be written on the blank underneath the problem. Follow the same procedure for each problem.

8. Have the student(s) take out their *12-inch ruler*. Ask them into how many parts each inch is divided. Have them point to the 2½-inch mark, 4¼-inch mark, 3¾-inch mark, etc. After they have written the measurements for each of the lines in **Student Activity Four**, discuss their results.

9. Ask the student(s) to describe a ratio. Remind them that the order in which the ratio is given is the order in which it must be written. Display for the student(s) 3 *felt tip markers*, 2 *rulers*, and 5 *books*. Have the student(s) tell the ratio of markers to rulers and books, of rulers to markers and books, of rulers and books to markers and books, etc. Give help where needed as the student(s) complete **Student Activity Five**.

10. The student(s) should be able to complete **Student Activity Six** on their own.

11. After the student(s) determine if they are to add, subtract, or multiply in **Student Activity Seven**, remind them to write the fact needed to solve the problem and label their answer.

Lesson 131

Concepts:
Counting by sevens, addition (horizontal to vertical), money, inches, word problems, equations, area, subtraction, and multiplication

Definition: Area is the number of square units necessary to cover a given surface.

Objectives:
1. The student shall be able to count out loud by sevens to 84.

2. The student shall be able to rewrite vertically two horizontal three- or four-digit numbers and write the sum.

3. The student shall be able to measure the length of a given line in quarter inches and label the answer.

4. The student shall be able to write the value of a variable in a subtraction equation.

5. The student shall be able to write the number of square centimeters in a given area.

6. The student shall be able to write the difference of two triple-digit numbers when borrowing from the tens' or the hundreds' column.

7. The student shall be able to write the product of the multiplication facts for three, six, nine, four, and seven.

Teaching Tips:
1. When discussing the area for diagram A in **Student Activity Five,** ask the student(s) how many rows of squares there are and how many squares are in each row. See if they recognize that, since there are 2 rows of 3 squares each, they can find the area by multiplying 2 x 3 instead of counting the squares.

Materials, Supplies, & Equipment:
1. Flashcards for subtraction and multiplication facts

2. 12-inch ruler

Activities:

1. Drill addition facts using *Drill #1, Worksheet 65*.

2. Using *flashcards for subtraction facts*, drill minuends 1–18 with the answers showing and covering the minuend or the subtrahend.

3. Using *flashcards for multiplication facts*, drill 2's, 3's, and 6's without the answers showing and 9's, 4's, and 7's with the answers showing.

4. Count out loud with the student(s) by sevens to 84.

5. Write "$32.58 + $7. 24" on the board as a horizontal addition problem. Show the student(s) how to write the problem as a vertical addition problem by keeping the decimals in a straight vertical line. Solve the problem with the student(s) putting the decimals in the same vertical line. Have them read the answer. Write several similar problems on the board and have the student(s) copy them on their paper. Allow them to solve the problems alone before you solve them on the board. If the student(s) have a wrong answer, give them individual help. They should be able to complete **Student Activity One** on their own.

6. As the student(s) begin to measure the lines in **Student Activity Two**, remind them to put the zero on the *12-inch ruler* at the beginning of the line. The number of inches is always the last number the line past and not the number closer to the line. Give individual help to the student(s) who have difficulty.

7. The student(s) should be able to complete **Student Activity Three** with little help. Check that they label their answer.

8. Ask the student(s) if they should add or subtract to find the solution to the first equation in **Student Activity Four**. Remind them that if they add 7 to 9 on the right side of the equation, they must add 7 to the left side also. Make sure they write the steps as they solve the remaining equations.

9. Discuss with the student(s) the meaning of area. Tell them how area is used in finding the quantity of carpet needed to cover a floor. Area is measured in square units. Have the student(s) look at diagram A in **Student Activity Five**. By counting the squares in A, they can find the number of square centimeters in the area. Have the student(s) find the area of B, C, and D together.

10. The student(s) should be able to complete **Student Activity Six** and **Seven** independently.

Worksheet:

1. *Worksheet 65* – Addition, subtraction, and multiplication drill sheet

Lesson 132

Concepts:

Counting by sevens, days of the week, money, subtraction (horizontal to vertical), area, addition, inches, equations, multiplication, and optical illusion

Objectives:

1. The student shall be able to count out loud by sevens to 84.

2. The student shall be able to say and spell the days of the week and their abbreviations.

3. The student shall be able to rewrite vertically two horizontal three- or four-digit numbers and write the difference.

4. The student shall be able to write the number of square centimeters in a given area.

5. The student shall be able to write the sum of two four-digit numbers when the ones', tens', and hundreds' columns have double-digit answers.

6. The student shall be able to measure the length of the given line and write the length on the line.

7. The student shall be able to write the value of a variable in a subtraction equation.

8. The student shall be able to write the product of the multiplication facts for six, nine, four, and seven.

9. The student shall be able to circle the lines that are equal in length to a given line by observation.

Teaching Tips:

1. When doing activity 10, discuss with the student(s) some optical illusions that they see in everyday life (looking down a railroad track, fence poles, telephone poles, long buildings, etc.). Have the student(s) test some of the suggestions and report on their findings.

Materials, Supplies, & Equipment:

1. Flashcards for addition facts, multiplication facts, and days of the week

2. 12-inch ruler

Activities:

1. Drill multiplication facts using *Drill #2, Worksheet 65*.

2. Using *flashcards for addition facts*, drill sums 1–18 with the answers showing and covering an addend.

3. Using *flashcards for multiplication facts*, drill 2's, 3's, and 6's without the answers showing and 9's, 4's, and 7's with the answers showing.

4. Count out loud with the student(s) by sevens to 84.

5. Have the student(s) say and spell the days of the week and their abbreviations. *Days of the week flashcards* may be a help.

6. Write "$83.57 – $31.82, $67.95 – $1.48, and $50.34 – $0.27" on the board as horizontal subtraction problems. Have the student(s) copy the problems vertically on their paper. Show them that the decimal points must always be in a straight vertical line before they can subtract. The decimal must be put in the answer in the same vertical line. Allow the student(s) to solve the problems alone before you solve them on the board. They should be able to complete **Student Activity One** on their own.

7. Discuss with the student(s) the meaning of area. Remind them that area is measured in square units. Have the student(s) look at the diagrams in **Student Activity Two**. Discuss how each square represents one square unit (centimeters). They should be able to count the squares alone.

8. The student(s) should be able to complete **Student Activity Three**, **Five**, and **Six** independently.

9. Have the student(s) take their *12-inch ruler* and look at **Student Activity Four**. Tell them to place the zero on their *ruler* at point 1 and measure the line to point 2. Write the length on the line. Then place the zero on their *ruler* at point 2 and measure the line to point 3. Write the length on the line. Continue in the same manner until they put the zero at point 7 and measure to point 8.

10. Ask the student(s) to look at the lines in **Student Activity Seven**. Have them point to line AB and circle the lines that they think are about the same length as line AB. Then have them measure the lines with a *12-inch ruler* to see if they were correct. Discuss how your eyes can deceive you by giving you a false impression. This is called an optical illusion.

Worksheets:

1. *Worksheet 66* – Adding money

2. *Worksheet 65* – Addition, subtraction, and multiplication drill sheet

Lesson 133

Concepts:
  Counting by sevens, estimation, inches, pictographs, subtraction, addition, area, multiplication, and equations

Objectives:

  1. The student shall be able to count out loud by sevens to 84.

  2. The student shall be able to measure a line to the nearest whole inch and label the answer.

  3. The student shall be able to write the correct facts obtained from interpreting a pictograph.

  4. The student shall be able to write the difference of two triple-digit numbers when borrowing from the tens' or the hundreds' column.

  5. The student shall be able to write the sum of two four-digit numbers when the ones', tens', or hundreds' column has a double-digit answer.

  6. The student shall be able to shade the number of squares needed to represent a given area.

  7. The student shall be able to write the product of the multiplication facts for three, six, nine, four, and seven.

  8. The student shall be able to write the value of a variable in a subtraction equation.

  9. The student shall be able to write two addition facts and two subtraction facts when given three numbers and a sum or difference.

Teaching Tips:

  1. When doing activity 8, use *posterboard* to make 6 squares, eight centimeters on a side, to represent one centimeter squares. Put a *magnetic strip* on the back of each. On the board, allow the student(s) to arrange the 6 squares in different positions to equal an area of 6 square centimeters.

Materials, Supplies, & Equipment:

  1. Flashcards for subtraction and multiplication facts

  2. 12-inch ruler

  3. Posterboard and magnetic strips

Activities:

1. Drill multiplication facts using *Drill #3, Worksheet 65*.

2. Using *flashcards for subtraction facts*, drill minuends 1–18 with the answers showing and covering a minuend or subtrahend.

3. Using *flashcards for multiplication facts*, drill 2's, 3's, and 6's without the answers showing and 9's, 4's, and 7's with the answers showing.

4. Count out loud with the student(s) by sevens to 84.

5. Explain to the student(s) that they are going to measure the lines in **Student Activity One** and estimate their length (determine "about" how long each line is) to the nearest whole inch. After they put the zero of their *12-inch ruler* at the end of the line, they should determine to what number the other end of the line is closer. Have the student(s) write the number and label the answer.

6. Ask how many students each symbol represents in **Student Activity Two**. After the student(s) have completed the activity, discuss their answers together.

7. The student(s) should be able to complete **Student Activity Three** and **Four** independently.

8. Discuss with the student(s) how an area of 6 square centimeters is made of 6 squares measuring one centimeter on a side. Ask them how many squares they would shade to have an area of 6 square centimeters. Explain that there are many different ways this could be done, but all shaded squares must be touching. Suggest they be creative in shading the squares in **Student Activity Five**.

9. The student(s) should be able to complete **Student Activity Six** and **Seven** by themselves.

10. Draw a triangle on the board and write a single-digit number at each vertex. Tell the student(s) the sum of two of the numbers. Have them choose what two you added and the resulting addition fact. Then tell them a difference of two of the numbers and have them choose the two numbers you subtracted and the fact. Complete the first set of combinations in **Student Activity Eight** together with the student(s). Allow them to complete the remaining ones on their own.

Worksheet:

1. *Worksheet 65* – Addition, subtraction, and multiplication drill sheet

Lesson 134

Concepts:
Counting by sevens, fractions, English weight equivalents, greater than and less than, pictographs, estimation, inches, multiplication, and word problems

Objectives:
1. The student shall be able to count out loud by sevens to 84.

2. The student shall be able to circle sets equivalent to the denominator of a fraction, in each set shade the number equivalent to the numerator, and write the fractional part of the given number.

3. The student shall be able to write the symbol (< or >) between two given English weights.

4. The student shall be able to write the correct facts obtained from interpreting a pictograph.

5. The student shall be able to measure a line to the nearer whole inch and label the answer.

6. The student shall be able to write the product of the multiplication facts for nine and seven.

7. The student shall be able to write two addition facts and two subtraction facts when given three numbers and a sum or difference.

Teaching Tips:
1. When the student(s) start **Student Activity Seven**, ask them what the word "decrease" tells them to do. They should be familiar with its use in changing word sentences to number sentences. Have them name other words that denote the need to subtract (less, take away, subtracted from, minus, etc.).

Materials, Supplies, & Equipment:
1. Flashcards for addition and multiplication facts

2. Counting chips

3. 12-inch ruler

Activities:

1. Drill subtraction facts using *Drill #4, Worksheet 65*.

2. Using *flashcards for addition facts*, drill sums 1–18 with the answers showing and covering one addend.

3. Using *flashcards for multiplication facts*, drill the 2's, 3's, and 6's without the answers showing and the 9's, 4's, and 7's with the answers showing. Be sure the student(s) say the facts in pairs.

4. Count out loud with the student(s) by sevens to 84.

5. Give each student 16 *counting chips*. Write "¾ of 16 = __" on the board. Explain to the student(s) that they are going to find the answer to ¾ of 16. Have them put the 16 *counting chips* into sets of 4's (4 sets). Then have them separate 3 from each set to form a new set. Count this set (12). ¾ of 16 = 12. Remind them that the denominator tells them how many are to be in each set and the numerator tells them how many to use in each set. Have the student(s) look at **Student Activity One**. Ask them how many boats they want in each set they circle in the first problem (4) and why (the denominator tells them to divide into sets of 4). Then ask them why they are to shade 3 in each circled set (the numerator tells them to use 3 from each set). Now count the shaded boats to see what ¾ of 8 equals. Continue to do the next two problems in the same manner.

6. Discuss with the student(s) how much the weight of one ounce, one pound, and one ton is. In the following comparisons ask the student(s) which would be greater: 10 pounds of potatoes or 10 ounces of potatoes, 4 tons of rock or 4 pounds of rock, 8 ounces of meat or 8 pounds of meat, etc. Allow the student(s) to complete **Student Activity Two** on their own.

7. After the student(s) tell what each foot print symbol represents (2 blocks traveled), they should be able to complete **Student Activity Three** by themselves.

8. Remind the student(s) they are going to estimate how long the lines in **Student Activity Four** are by determining to what number the end of the line is closer on their *12-inch ruler*. Give individual help to the student(s) as they complete the measurements.

9. The student(s) should be able to complete **Student Activity Five** and **Seven** alone.

10. After doing several examples similar to **Student Activity Six**, have the student(s) complete the problems independently.

Worksheet:

1. *Worksheet 65* – Addition, subtraction, and multiplication drill sheet

Lesson 135

Concepts:
    Counting by sevens, time equivalents, fractions, word problems, perimeter, addition, subtraction, and multiplication
    Definition: The distance around a shape is the perimeter.

Objectives:
1. The student shall be able to count out loud by sevens to 84.

2. The student shall be able to write the time equivalents.

3. The student shall be able to circle sets equivalent to the denominator of a fraction, in each set shade the number equivalent to the numerator, and write the fractional part of the given number.

4. The student shall be able to write addition and subtraction word problems using the given information.

5. The student shall be able to write the answers when finding the perimeter of a given shape.

6. The student shall be able to write the sum of two four-digit numbers when the ones', tens', and hundreds' columns have double-digit answers.

7. The student shall be able to write the difference of two triple-digit numbers when borrowing from the tens' and hundreds' columns.

8. The student shall be able to write the product of the multiplication facts for six, nine, four, and seven.

Teaching Tips:
1. When doing activity 7, the student(s) could find other perimeters. For example, let them find the distance around (perimeter) their wrist. Place a piece of *string* around the wrist and measure the length of the *string* on a *12-inch ruler*.

Materials, Supplies, & Equipment:
1. Flashcards for addition, subtraction, and multiplication facts

2. Clock model and calendar

3. Counting chips

4. String and 12-inch ruler

Activities:

1. Have the student(s) take a clean sheet of paper on which to write the answers for their *addition* and *subtraction facts* using *flashcards* with sleeves over an addend and a minuend or subtrahend.

2. Using *flashcards for multiplication facts*, drill 2's, 3's, and 6's without the answers showing and 9's, 4's, and 7's with the answers showing.

3. Count out loud with the student(s) by sevens to 84.

4. Using a *clock model* and *calendar*, review the time equivalents. The student(s) should be able to complete **Student Activity One** alone.

5. Give the student(s) 12 *counting chips*. Write "⅔ of 12 = __" on the board. Explain to the student(s) that they are going to find the answer to ⅔ of 12. Have them put the 12 *counting chips* into sets of 6's (2 sets). Then have them separate 2 from each set to form a new set. Count this set (4). ⅔ of 12 = 4. Remind them that the denominator tells how many are to be in each set and the numerator tells how many to use in each set. Solve the first problem in **Student Activity Two** with the student(s). Then allow them to complete the remaining problems on their own.

6. When the student(s) are doing **Student Activity Three**, have them use a different operation (+ or -) for each word problem.

7. Discuss with the student(s) the meaning of the word "perimeter." Draw a triangle on the board. Write a length on each side. Ask the student(s) if they would add, subtract, or multiply to find the distance around the triangle. Explain that distance is labeled in inches, feet, etc. or units are used if no label is given. The student(s) should be able to complete **Student Activity Four** without further help.

8. The student(s) should be able to complete **Student Activity Five** and **Seven** independently.

9. On the board, write several three-digit subtraction problems with borrowing in both the tens' and the hundreds' columns. Have the student(s) follow along as you solve the first problem. Then have them copy the second problem on their paper and solve it along with you as you solve it on the board. Ask them to solve the third problem by themselves before you solve it on the board. Check on the progress of the student(s) individually as they complete **Student Activity Six**.

Worksheet:

1. *Worksheet 67 – Fractions*

Lesson 136

Concepts:
Counting by eights, multiplication, fractions, word sentences, word numbers, subtraction, perimeter, addition, and word problems

Objectives:
1. The student shall be able to count out loud by eights to 96.

2. The student shall be able to write a given number of eights as an addition problem, a multiplication problem, and the product.

3. The student shall be able to circle sets equivalent to the denominator of a fraction, in each set shade the number equivalent to the numerator, and write the fractional part of the given number.

4. The student shall be able to rewrite a word sentence as a number sentence.

5. The student shall be able to write the difference of two triple-digit numbers when borrowing from the tens' and hundreds' columns.

6. The student shall be able to write the sum when finding the perimeter of a given shape.

7. The student shall be able to write the sum of two four-digit numbers when the ones', tens', and hundreds' columns have double-digit answers.

8. The student shall be able to write addition and subtraction word problems using the given information.

Teaching Tips:
1. Encourage the student(s) to find the answers in **Student Activity Five** by adding mentally if possible. Allow them to write the numbers as a vertical addition problem only when necessary or to check their answers.

Materials, Supplies, & Equipment:
1. Flashcards for subtraction and multiplication facts

2. Counting chips

Activities:

1. Drill addition facts using *Drill #1, Worksheet 68.*

2. Using *flashcards for subtraction facts*, drill minuends 1–18 with the answers showing and covering the minuend or the subtrahend.

3. Using *flashcards for multiplication facts*, drill 2's, 3's, and 6's without the answers showing and 9's, 4's, and 7's with the answers showing.

4. Count out loud with the student(s) by eights to 96.

5. Have the student(s) look at **Student Activity One** and together give the answers orally to the first problem. Then have them write the answers in the blanks. Allow them to complete the remaining problems independently. Give individual help where needed.

6. Ask the student(s) why they are circling sets of 3's in the first problem in **Student Activity Two** (denominator tells how many are in each set). Then ask them why they are shading 2 in each set (numerator tells how many in each set is to be used). Allow the student(s) to complete the problems on their own giving help where needed. *Counting chips* may be a help here.

7. Have the student(s) read each sentence in **Student Activity Three** and tell if it is an addition or a subtraction sentence. Then let them write the number sentences by themselves.

8. On the board, write several three-digit subtraction problems when borrowing from the tens' and the hundreds' columns. Have the student(s) copy the problems on their paper and solve them. Ask them to tell how to solve the problems on the board. Encourage them to ask questions in any area that they do not understand. The student(s) should be able to complete **Student Activity Four** with little further help.

9. After asking the student(s) to define perimeter, they should be able to complete **Student Activity Five** and **Six** alone.

10. Have the student(s) write one addition and one subtraction word problem for **Student Activity Seven**.

Worksheet:

1. *Worksheet 68* – Addition, subtraction, and multiplication drill sheet

Lesson 137

Concepts:
Counting by eights, symmetry, sequence, greater than and less than, equal to, multiplication, perimeter, centimeters, subtraction, time equivalents, word sentences, and word numbers

Definition: A line on which a shape can be folded so that the two parts match is the line of symmetry.

Objectives:
1. The student shall be able to count out loud by eights to 96.

2. The student shall be able to circle the shapes that have a line of symmetry drawn.

3. The student shall be able to number a given set of events in the order of their occurrence.

4. The student shall be able to write the symbol (<, >, or =) between a multiplication fact and a number.

5. The student shall be able to write the measure of the sides of a shape in centimeters and the sum of the sides to find the perimeter.

6. The student shall be able to write the difference of two triple-digit numbers when borrowing from the tens' and the hundreds' columns.

7. The student shall be able to write the time equivalents.

8. The student shall be able to rewrite a word sentence as a number sentence.

Teaching Tips:
1. In **Student Activity One**, have the student(s) determine where the line of symmetry should be drawn for the shapes that they could not circle. Some student(s) might see the relevance of symmetry to folding paper airplanes.

Materials, Supplies, & Equipment:
1. Flashcards for addition and multiplication facts

2. Triangle, square, and hexagon cut from 8 1/2 x 11 plain paper for each student

3. Centimeter ruler

Activities:

1. Drill multiplication facts using *Drill #2, Worksheet 68*.

2. Using *flashcards for addition facts*, drill sums 1–18 with the answers showing and covering an addend.

3. Using *flashcards for multiplication facts*, drill 2's, 3's, and 6's without the answers showing and 9's, 4's, and 7's with the answers showing.

4. Count out loud with the student(s) by eights to 96.

5. Give the student(s) an equilateral *triangle*, a *square*, and a *hexagon* cut from *8 1/2 x 11 plain paper*. Ask the student(s) to fold the shapes so that the two parts, into which the fold divides the shape, match one another. Using a large similar shape, demonstrate where the fold should be. The fold is called a line of symmetry. If there is a line of symmetry, the line will cut the shape into two parts of equal size and shape. Have the student(s) repeat the word "symmetry" several times. Tell them that the shape is symmetrical if there is at least one line of symmetry. Encourage the student(s) to find more than one line of symmetry for each shape. When the student(s) begin **Student Activity One**, discuss each shape individually with them.

6. Tell the student(s) to read the first three events in **Student Activity Two**. Let them choose which happened first, second, and third. Have them write "1" by the one they chose as first, "2" by the one they chose as second, and "3" by the one they chose as third. Now have them read them in the correct order. After they have numbered the second set of events in the correct order, discuss the results together.

7. For **Student Activity Three**, briefly review the concepts of greater than, less than, and equal. The student(s) need to determine what the multiplication fact equals and then decide if the product is greater than, less than, or equal to the number. Check the student(s) first two answers before you allow them to continue on their own.

8. Have the student(s) measure each side of the shapes in **Student Activity Four** with a *centimeter ruler*. Write the length by the sides. Ask the student(s) to tell the meaning of the word "perimeter." Then have them mentally find the perimeter of each shape before writing the answer.

9. The student(s) should be able to complete **Student Activity Five, Six,** and **Seven** independently.

Worksheet:

1. *Worksheet 68* – Addition, subtraction, and multiplication drill sheet

Lesson 138

Concepts:
> Counting by eights, ratio, symmetry, multiplication, perimeter, sequence, fractions, greater than and less than, equal to, and subtraction

Objectives:
1. The student shall be able to count out loud by eights to 96.

2. The student shall be able to write the comparison of two sets as a ratio.

3. The student shall be able to circle the shapes that have a line of symmetry drawn.

4. The student shall be able to write the product of the multiplication facts for three, six, nine, four, seven, and eight.

5. The student shall be able to write the sum when finding the perimeter of a given shape.

6. The student shall be able to number a given set of events in the order of their occurrence.

7. The student shall be able to write a fraction that represents a part of the whole and the correct symbol (<, >, or =) that goes between each pair of fractions.

8. The student shall be able to write the difference of two triple-digit numbers when borrowing from the tens' and the hundreds' columns.

Teaching Tips:
1. When doing activity 6, show the student(s) another way to check for a line of symmetry. Have them place the edge of the shape they have folded against a *mirror*. If the fold is on the line of symmetry, the reflection on the *mirror* and the half held to the *mirror* will look the same as the unfolded shape.

Materials, Supplies, & Equipment:
1. Flashcards for subtraction and multiplication facts

2. Rectangle, circle, and octagon cut from 8 1/2 x 11 plain paper for each student

3. Multiplication chart

4. Mirror

Activities:

1. Drill multiplication facts using *Drill #3, Worksheet 68*.

2. Using *flashcards for subtraction facts*, drill minuends 1–18 with the answers showing and covering a minuend or subtrahend.

3. Using *flashcards for multiplication facts*, drill 2's, 3's, 6's, and 9's without the answers showing and 4's, 7's, and 8's with the answers showing. The only multiplication fact for eight the student(s) should not be familiar with is 8 x 8. All the other facts should have been learned as pairs.

4. Count out loud with the student(s) by eights to 96.

5. Have the student(s) write ratios on their paper as you give them examples orally. Check their answers. Ask the student(s) to write the first two answers in **Student Activity One** as they determine the ratios together. Allow them to find the remaining ratios on their own.

6. Give the student(s) a *rectangle*, a *circle,* and an *octagon* cut from *8 1/2 x 11 plain paper*. Ask the student(s) to fold the shapes so that the two parts, into which the fold divides the shapes, match one another. Using a large similar shape, demonstrate where the fold should be. The fold is called a line of symmetry. The line of symmetry cuts the shape into two parts of equal size and shape. The shape is symmetrical if there is at least one line of symmetry. Encourage the student(s) to find more than one line of symmetry for each shape. Ask how many lines of symmetry they can find for a circle. After the student(s) complete **Student Activity Two**, discuss each shape with them.

7. The student(s) should be able to complete **Student Activity Three** independently. Allow them to use the *multiplication chart* only if necessary.

8. Discuss the meaning of perimeter and identify the abbreviation "ft." as indicating feet and "in." as indicating inches. Allow the student(s) to complete **Student Activity Four** by themselves.

9. Be sure the student(s) read all three events in each set before they attempt to number them in the correct order in **Student Activity Five**.

10. After the student(s) have written the fraction for each part shaded in **Student Activity Six**, they should look at the shapes to help them determine which symbol to write between the fractions.

11. The student(s) should be able to complete **Student Activity Seven** alone.

Worksheet:

1. *Worksheet 68* – Addition, subtraction, and multiplication drill sheet

Lesson 139

Concepts:
> Counting by eights, sequence, solids, time, addition, symmetry ratio, equations, and multiplication

Objectives:

1. The student shall be able to count out loud by eights to 96.

2. The student shall be able to circle the next picture that would appear in a sequence of pictures.

3. The student shall be able to draw a line to match a solid to its name.

4. The student shall be able to write the correct time displayed on the face of a clock for given five minute increments.

5. The student shall be able to write the sum of two four-digit numbers when the ones', tens', and hundreds' columns have double-digit answers.

6. The student shall be able to draw a line of symmetry for given shapes.

7. The student shall be able to write the comparison of two sets as a ratio.

8. The student shall be able to write the value of the variable in an addition or subtraction equation.

9. The student shall be able to write the product of the multiplications facts for six, nine, four, seven, and eight.

Teaching Tips:
1. In activity 6, have the student(s) name some ordinary objects they have seen that would represent each of the solids.

Materials, Supplies, & Equipment:
1. Flashcards for addition and multiplication facts

2. Solid models

3. Multiplication chart

Activities:

1. Drill subtraction facts using *Drill #4, Worksheet 68*.

2. Using *flashcards for addition facts*, drill sums 1–18 with the answers showing and covering one addend.

3. Using *flashcards for multiplication facts*, drill the 2's, 3's, 6's, and 9's without the answers showing and the 4's, 7's, and 8's with the answers showing. Be sure the student(s) say the facts in pairs.

4. Count out loud with the student(s) by eights to 96.

5. Tell the student(s) to look at **Student Activity One**. Have them name the first five pictures. Then have them name the last picture (top), find a previous top, and tell what picture came after that top (yo-yo). That is the picture that should appear next in the sequence. Ask them what picture they should circle as the next picture in the sequence. If they are able to complete this problem with little difficulty, allow them to complete the activity on their own.

6. Have the student(s) name the solids that each object represents in **Student Activity Two**. *Solid models* may help here. They should be able to draw the lines to the solids' names without further help.

7. The student(s) should be able to complete **Student Activity Three** and **Four** independently.

8. Discuss with the student(s) the meaning of the line of symmetry. After they have drawn their lines of symmetry in **Student Activity Five**, have them fold their paper to see that the two halves lay on top of each other.

9. Allow the student(s) to complete **Student Activity Six**, **Seven**, and **Eight** by themselves. A *multiplication chart* may be needed.

Worksheets:

1. *Worksheet 69* – Line of symmetry

2. *Worksheet 68* – Addition, subtraction, and multiplication drill sheet

It is not fair to inflict on others our bad moods.

Lesson 140

Concepts:
>Counting by eights, equations, sequence, addition, subtraction, symmetry, solids, and multiplication

Objectives:
1. The student shall be able to count out loud by eights to 96.

2. The student shall be able to number a given set of events in the order of their occurrence.

3. The student shall be able to write the value of the variable in an addition or subtraction equation.

4. The student shall be able to circle the next picture that would appear in a sequence of pictures.

5. The student shall be able to write the sum of two four-digit numbers when the ones', tens', and hundreds' columns have double-digit answers.

6. The student shall be able to write the difference of two triple-digit numbers when borrowing from the tens' and the hundreds' columns.

7. The student shall be able to draw a line of symmetry for given shapes.

8. The student shall be able to write the name of the given solids.

9. The student shall be able to write the product of the multiplication facts for three and eight.

Teaching Tips:
1. When doing activity 5, have the student(s) write three events that tell a story on a sheet of paper. Then have them read their events in the wrong order. Allow the other student(s) to determine in which order the events should be read.

Materials, Supplies, & Equipment:
1. Flashcards for addition facts, subtraction facts, multiplication facts, and solids

2. Solid models

Activities:

1. Administer **Test 14**.

2. Have the student(s) take a clean sheet of paper on which to write the answers for their *addition* and *subtraction facts* using *flashcards* with sleeves over an addend and a minuend or subtrahend.

3. Using *flashcards for multiplication facts*, drill 2's, 3's, 6's, and 9's without the answers showing and 4's, 7's, and 8's with the answers showing.

4. Count out loud with the student(s) by eights to 96.

5. When the student(s) begin **Student Activity One**, have them determine what must happen first. Then ask if they give a birthday gift or go to the party first. Allow them to number the events by themselves. They should be able to number the second set of events without further help.

6. Before the student(s) start **Student Activity Two**, ask them to tell if they are going to add or subtract on both sides of each equation. As they are solving the equations, be sure they are putting the proper steps on their paper.

7. The student(s) should complete **Student Activity Three**, **Four**, and **Five** independently.

8. Discuss with the student(s) how many lines of symmetry each object in **Student Activity Six** could have. Allow them to draw the lines alone.

9. Using the *solid models*, have the student(s) name and spell each solid. Display the *solid flashcards* with the names showing on the board rail. Use it as a spelling reference when the student(s) complete **Student Activity Seven**.

10. The student(s) should be able to complete **Student Activity Eight** on their own.

Worksheet:

1. *Worksheet 70* – Multiplication word problems

The brave man always does his best without
seeking the honor of men.

Lesson 141

Concepts:
    Counting by eights, subtraction, area, English liquid equivalents, greater than and less than, equal to, bar graphs, time, time equivalents, equations, and word problems

Objectives:
1. The student shall be able to count out loud by eights to 96.

2. The student shall be able to write the difference of two triple-digit numbers when the ones' and tens' digits in the minuend are zeros.

3. The student shall be able to draw a shape of a given area.

4. The student shall be able to write the symbol (<, >, or =) between two units of English liquid measure.

5. The student shall be able to write the correct facts obtained from interpreting a bar graph.

6. The student shall be able to draw a line to match the time displayed on the face of a clock to a digital clock and write the time equivalents.

7. The student shall be able to write the value of the variable in an addition or subtraction equation.

Teaching Tips:
1. In ***Student Activity One***, notice that the first two problems have the borrowing done for the student(s). Make sure that the student(s) mark the borrowing on their paper to prevent careless errors. You could use the *Place Value Pockets* to visually demonstrate the borrowing in these problems.

Materials, Supplies, & Equipment:
1. Flashcards for subtraction facts, multiplication facts, and time equivalents

2. English liquid measure containers

3. Place Value Pockets

Activities:

1. Drill addition facts using *Drill #1, Worksheet 71*.

2. Using *flashcards for subtraction facts*, drill minuends 1–18 with the answers showing and covering the minuend or the subtrahend.

3. Using *flashcards for multiplication facts*, drill 2's, 3's, 6's, and 9's without the answers showing and 4's, 7's, and 8's with the answers showing.

4. Count out loud with the student(s) by eights to 96.

5. Write "700 – 256" as a vertical subtraction problem on the board. Ask the student(s) if they can take 6 away from 0. They need to borrow 1 ten from the tens' place. Since there is a 0 in the tens' place, they will need to borrow 1 from 70 tens (7 hundreds equal 70 tens). This will leave 69 in the place of the 70. Mark out the 70 and write 69 above it (the 7 becomes a 6 and the 0 becomes a 9). The 1 ten that they borrowed becomes 10 ones. They now can subtract 6 from 10, 5 from 9, and 2 from 6 to give an answer of 444. Solve several subtraction problems with zeros in the ones' and the tens' places in the minuend before the student(s) complete **Student Activity One**.

6. Have the student(s) look at **Student Activity Two**. Ask them how many squares they need to equal 4 square centimeters, 7 square centimeters, etc. The student(s) should be able to draw the shapes on their own.

7. Using *English liquid measure containers*, discuss the relative size of each in relationship to each other. Fill the gallon container with water. Demonstrate how many ounces in a cup, cups in a pint, pints in a quart, and quarts in a gallon with the water. Allow the student(s) to complete **Student Activity Three** together with your guidance.

8. Discuss with the student(s) the bar graph in **Student Activity Four**. The student(s) should be able to answer the questions by themselves.

9. Review the time equivalents. The *time equivalent flashcards* would be a help here. The student(s) should then be able to complete **Student Activity Five** without further help.

10. The student(s) should be able to complete **Student Activity Six** and **Seven** alone.

Worksheet:

1. *Worksheet 71* – Addition, subtraction, and multiplication drill sheet

Lesson 142

Concepts:
Counting by eights, shapes, temperature, English liquid equivalents, greater than and less than, equal to, inches, line graphs, area, and subtraction

Objectives:
1. The student should be able to count out loud by eights to 96.

2. The student should be able to draw given shapes on a geosheet.

3. The student should be able to write the correct temperature displayed on the thermometer.

4. The student should be able to write the correct symbol (<, >, or =) between two English liquid measures.

5. The student should be able to draw a line a given length with a 12-inch ruler.

6. The student should be able to write the correct facts obtained from interpreting a line graph.

7. The student should be able to draw a shape of a given area.

8. The student should be able to write the difference of two triple-digit numbers when the ones' and the tens' digits in the minuend are zeros.

Teaching Tips:
1. During activity 6, discuss with the student(s) how a thermometer, like the one in this activity, is made. The thermometer may be used to measure the temperature in or outside the house. It has a glass bulb filled with mercury. The mercury expands as it gets warm and contracts as it gets cold. If the thermometer is going to be used where the temperature goes below the freezing point of mercury (-38°), alcohol is used instead.

Materials, Supplies, & Equipment:
1. Flashcards for addition and multiplication facts

2. Fahrenheit thermometer

3. English liquid measure containers

4. 12-inch ruler

Activities:

1. Drill multiplication facts using *Drill #2, Worksheet 71*.

2. Using *flashcards for addition facts*, drill sums 1–18 with the answers showing and covering an addend.

3. Using *flashcards for multiplication facts*, drill 2's, 3's, 6's, and 9's without the answers showing and 4's, 7's, and 8's with the answers showing.

4. Count out loud with the student(s) by eights to 96.

5. Give the student(s) a copy of *Worksheet 72*. Write the names of the seven shapes on the board. Have the student(s) draw the shapes on the worksheet using the bold dots as a guide for each shape. Then have the student(s) write the name of each shape in the corresponding drawing.

6. Give the student(s) a *Fahrenheit thermometer* to examine. Discuss the value of each line between the multiples of ten (2). Then say the value of each line by counting by twos. When the student(s) read the thermometer, have them start counting by twos at the last multiple of ten the temperature passed (e.g., if the temperature is 48⁰, begin counting at 40⁰ by twos). Have the student(s) read the first two thermometers in **Student Activity One** together. Help those who need it. Allow those that are able to read the remaining thermometers on their own.

7. Discuss the English liquid equivalents given in **Student Activity Two**. *English liquid measure containers* would be a help here. Have the student(s) compare different quantities of each measure and determine if a <, >, or = sign should go between them. You may need to give the student(s) guidance as they determine which symbol to write for the problems in **Student Activity Two**.

8. Review with the student(s) the ¼, ½, and ¾ marks on a *12-inch ruler*. Remind them to put the zero on the ruler at the point in **Student Activity Three**.

9. The student(s) should be able to complete **Student Activity Four**, **Five**, and **Six** independently.

Worksheets:

1. *Worksheet 72* – Shapes

2. *Worksheet 71* – Addition, subtraction, and multiplication drill sheet

Lesson 143

Concepts:
Counting by eights, shapes, pictograph, English liquid equivalents, addition, greater than and less than, equal to, time equivalents, inches, multiplication, temperature, and subtraction

Objectives:
1. The student shall be able to count out loud by eights to 96.

2. The student shall be able to draw given shapes on a geosheet.

3. The student shall be able to write the correct facts obtained from interpreting a pictograph.

4. The student shall be able to circle the correct English liquid measure that corresponds to a given sentence and write the equivalents.

5. The student shall be able to write the sum of three four-digit numbers when the tens' and hundreds' columns have double-digits for answers.

6. The student shall be able to write the correct symbol (<, >, or =) between time equivalents.

7. The student shall be able to draw a line a given length with a 12-inch ruler.

8. The student shall be able to write the correct temperature displayed on the thermometer.

9. The student shall be able to write the difference of two triple-digit numbers when the ones' and tens' digits in the minuend are zeros.

Teaching Tips:
1. If a *thermometer model* is not available, make one. On *posterboard*, write a vertical scale for a thermometer. Put a horizontal slit beside the top and bottom of the scale. Run a strip of *paper* (top half white and bottom half red) through the slit.

Materials, Supplies, & Equipment:
1. Flashcards for subtraction facts, multiplication facts, and time equivalents

2. English liquid measure containers

3. Thermometer model

4. Posterboard and 8 1/2 x 11 plain paper

Activities:

1. Drill multiplication facts using *Drill #3, Worksheet 71*.

2. Using *flashcards for subtraction facts*, drill minuends 1–18 with the answers showing and covering a minuend or subtrahend.

3. Using *flashcards for multiplication facts*, drill 2's, 3's, 6's, and 9's without the answers showing and 4's, 7's, and 8's with the answers showing.

4. Count out loud with the student(s) by eights to 96.

5. Give the student(s) a copy of *Worksheet 73*. Write the names of the seven shapes on the board. Have the student(s) draw and label each of the shapes on the worksheet.

6. Discuss the pictograph in **Student Activity One**. The student(s) should be able to answer the questions on their own.

7. Compare the various quantities of the *English liquid measure containers*. Discuss how each container is used. Talk about the answers for each of the questions in **Student Activity Two** with the student(s). Help them fill in the correct equivalents where needed.

8. The student(s) should be able to complete **Student Activity Three** by themselves.

9. Review the equivalents for time with the help of the *time equivalent flashcards*. Write "1 hour __ 40 minutes" on the board. Have the student(s) tell how many minutes are in an hour. Write 60 minutes above 1 hour. Now have the student(s) compare 60 minutes and 40 minutes with <, >, and = symbols. Do several examples on the board. Follow the same procedure for **Student Activity Four**.

10. After reviewing the ¼, ½, and ¾-inch marks on the *12-inch ruler*, the student(s) should be able to complete **Student Activity Five**, **Six**, and **Eight** independently.

11. Ask the student(s) what kind of liquid is used in most thermometers. Discuss the value of each mark on the scale. Using a *thermometer model*, have the student(s) read several settings. They should be able to complete **Student Activity Seven** without further help.

Worksheets:

1. *Worksheet 73* – Shapes

2. *Worksheet 71* – Addition, subtraction, and multiplication drill sheet

Lesson 144

Concepts:
Counting by eights, Roman numerals, centimeters, perimeter, greater than and less than, equal to, English liquid equivalents, addition, grid, time, and temperature

Objectives:

1. The student shall be able to count out loud by eights to 96.

2. The student shall be able to write the Roman numeral that corresponds to a given Arabic number.

3. Using a centimeter ruler to measure, the student shall be able to write the length of the given sides of a shape and its perimeter.

4. The student shall be able to write the correct symbol (<, >, or =) between English liquid equivalents.

5. The student shall be able to write the sum of three four-digit numbers when the tens' and hundreds' columns have double digits for answers.

6. The student shall be able to place a dot at given grid intersections and draw lines to connect the dots in consecutive order.

7. The student shall be able to write the correct time displayed on the face of a clock.

8. The student shall be able to write the correct temperature displayed on a thermometer and the answers to given questions pertaining to that temperature.

Teaching Tips:

1. After the student(s) have found the perimeter of the shapes in **_Student Activity Two_**, ask how many of them found the perimeter of the equilateral triangle by multiplying by three instead of adding.

Materials, Supplies, & Equipment:

1. Flashcards for addition facts, multiplication facts, Roman numerals, and English liquid equivalents

2. Centimeter ruler

3. Thermometer model

Activities:

1. Drill subtraction facts using *Drill #4, Worksheet 71*.

2. Using *flashcards for addition facts*, drill sums 1–18 with the answers showing and covering one addend.

3. Using *flashcards for multiplication facts*, drill the 2's, 3's, 6's, and 9's without the answers showing and the 4's, 7's, and 8's with the answers showing. Be sure the student(s) say the facts in pairs.

4. Count out loud with the student(s) by eights to 96.

5. Review the value of each symbol on the *Roman numeral flashcards*. Write several numbers from 100–999 on the board. Have the student(s) tell what Roman numeral corresponds to each Arabic number. Encourage them to do each digit individually (e.g., 368: 300 is CCC, 60 is LX, and 8 is VIII – CCCLXVIII). The student(s) should be able to complete **Student Activity One** on their own.

6. Have the student(s) measure the sides of the shapes in **Student Activity Two** with a *centimeter ruler* and write the length on the line by the side. Then have them find the perimeter of each shape.

7. Review the *English liquid equivalents* with *flashcards*. Write "1 quart ___ 1 pint" on the board. Have the student(s) tell how many pints in a quart. Write 2 pints above 1 quart. Now have them compare 2 pints and 1 pint with <, >, or = symbols. Do several examples on the board. Follow the same procedure for **Student Activity Three**.

8. The student(s) should be able to complete **Student Activity Four** and **Six** on their own.

9. Before math class draw a grid on the board like the one in **Student Activity Five**. Write several locations on the board (e.g., A4, B3, C6, D2, E5, etc.). Tell the student(s) to find the letter and move up the grid until they are across from the number. At this intersection they are to make a dot. Once all dots are made, connect them in order. As the student(s) begin **Student Activity Five**, guide them in locating the first three dots. From that point on, assist the student(s) who need individual help.

10. Display several temperatures for the student(s) to read on a *thermometer model*. After they have written the temperature displayed in **Student Activity Seven**, discuss the answers to the questions together.

Worksheet:

1. *Worksheet 71* – Addition, subtraction, and multiplication drill sheet

Lesson 145

Concepts:
   Counting by eights, estimation, subtraction, money, Roman numerals, temperature, grid, multiplication, and fractions

Objectives:

1. The student shall be able to count out loud by eights to 96.

2. The student shall be able to write the correct number to which a given number is closer.

3. The student shall be able to write the difference of two triple-digit numbers when the ones' and tens' digits in the minuend are zeros and expressed in dollars and cents.

4. The student shall be able to write the correct Arabic number corresponding to a given Roman numeral.

5. The student shall be able to make a mark on a thermometer for a given temperature and color the liquid red.

6. The student shall be able to place a dot at given grid intersections and draw lines to connect the dots in consecutive order.

7. The student shall be able to write the product of the multiplication facts for six, nine, and eight.

8. The student shall be able to write the product of a fractional part of a number from a graphic illustration.

Teaching Tips:

1. Discuss with the student(s) the freezing point and boiling point of water on the thermometer in activity 7. Ice will form outside when it is 32°. Ask the student(s) if it would be possible for it to get so hot outside that water would boil.

Materials, Supplies, & Equipment:

1. Flashcards for addition facts, subtraction facts, multiplication facts, and Roman numerals

2. Number chart 100–199

3. Thermometer model

Activities:

1. Have the student(s) take a clean sheet of paper on which to write the answers for their *addition* and *subtraction facts* using *flashcards* with sleeves over an addend and a minuend or subtrahend.

2. Using *flashcards for multiplication facts*, drill 2's, 3's, 6's, and 9's without the answers showing and 4's, 7's, and 8's with the answers showing.

3. Count out loud with the student(s) by eights to 96.

4. Discuss with the student(s) what number is half way between 100 and 200 (150). Remind them that if the number is less than 150, it will be closer to 100. If the number is greater than 150, it will be closer to 200. Point to several numbers on the *number chart 100–199* and have the student(s) tell if the number is closer to 100 or 200. The student(s) should be able to complete **Student Activity One** on their own.

5. Write several subtraction problems (minuend whole dollars) on the board. Have the student(s) solve the problems on their paper. Give individual help to those who arrived at an incorrect answer. The student(s) should be able to complete **Student Activity Two** alone.

6. Review the symbols used on *Roman numeral flashcards*. Remind the student(s) that the hundreds always begin with C or D, the tens with X or L, and the ones with I or V. Write "CMXCIX" on the board. To understand how to read Roman numerals, have the student(s) begin at C and go over until they come to an X or L (CM). What does CM equal (900). Then start at X and go over until they come to an I or V (XC). What does XC equal (90). Then start at I and go to the end (IX). What does IX equal (9). The number is 900 + 90 + 9 or 999. Give individual help where needed as the student(s) complete **Student Activity Three**.

7. Allow the student(s) to set the *thermometer model* at various temperatures. They should be able to complete **Student Activity Four** and **Six** without further help.

8. The student(s) may need your guidance as they locate each dot in **Student Activity Five**.

9. Have the student(s) look at **Student Activity Seven**. In the first problem, ask them how many hearts are in each group (3) and how many hearts in each group are shaded (2). If you have three parts and are using two of them, they represent what fraction (⅔)? Write ⅔ in the first blank. How many hearts are there altogether (12)? Write 12 in the second blank. ⅔ of 12 equals the number of shaded hearts (8). Follow the same procedure with the student(s) for each of the remaining problems.

Lesson 146

Concepts:
Volume, subtraction, money, estimation, word problems, fractions, addition, and multiplication
Definition: The space a box will hold or fill is volume.

Objectives:

1. The student shall be able to write the number of cubic units in a given set.

2. The student shall be able to write the difference of two triple-digit numbers when borrowing from the tens' and hundreds' columns.

3. The student shall be able to write the correct number to which a given number is closer.

4. The student shall be able to write the product of a fractional part of a number from a graphic illustration.

5. The student shall be able to write the sum of three four-digit numbers when the tens' and the hundreds' columns have double-digit answers.

6. The student shall be able to write the product of the multiplication facts for four, seven, and eight.

Teaching Tips:

1. To make a *cube* for activity 4, trace the pattern given in *Worksheet 75*. You may want to have the student(s) each make one to use to fill the space in the shoe box.

Materials, Supplies, & Equipment:

1. Flashcards for subtraction and multiplication facts

2. Cube

3. Shoe box

4. Number chart 0–99

Activities:

1. Drill addition facts using *Drill #1, Worksheet 74.*

2. Using *flashcards for subtraction facts*, drill minuends 1–18 with the answers showing and covering the minuend or the subtrahend.

3. Using *flashcards for multiplication facts*, drill 2's, 3's, 6's, 9's, and 4's without the answers and 7's and 8's with the answers.

4. Hold up a *cube* for the student(s) to examine. Explain that a cube is used to measure volume. Discuss with the student(s) the meaning of volume. To find the volume have the student(s) count how many cubes are in a row and how many rows it takes to cover the bottom of a *shoe box*. Then count how many layers it takes to fill the box. Extra space the cubes cannot fit into will make the answer an estimation or an approximate volume. Ask them to suggest a label for volume (cubic units). In **Student Activity One**, continue the same procedure to guide the student(s) in finding the volume of each set of cubes.

5. Write "$5.03 – $2.57" on the board as a vertical subtraction problem. Solve the problem step by step by asking the student(s) leading questions to enable them to tell you what to write. Write several similar problems on the board and have the student(s) copy and solve the problems on their own paper before you have them tell you what to write on the board. Allow the student(s) to complete **Student Activity Two** on their own giving individual help if needed.

6. Write "478" on the board. Have the student(s) pretend that the *number chart 0–99* is for 400 to 499. Ask the student(s) what number is half way between 400 and 500. Then ask them if 478 (pointing to 78 on the number chart) is closer to 400 or 500. Do several other numbers between 200 and 999. The student(s) should be able to complete **Student Activity Three** alone.

7. The student(s) should be able to complete **Student Activity Four, Six**, and **Seven** independently.

8. Have the student(s) look at **Student Activity Five**. In the first problem, ask them how many diamonds are in each group (3) and how many diamonds in each group are shaded (2). If there are three parts and only two are used, they represent what fraction (⅔)? Write ⅔ in the first blank. How many diamonds are there altogether (15)? Write 15 in the second blank. ⅔ of 15 equals the number of shaded diamonds (10). Follow the same procedure with the student(s) for each of the remaining problems.

Worksheets:

1. *Worksheet 75* – Cube pattern

2. *Worksheet 74* – Addition, subtraction, and multiplication drill sheet

Lesson 147

Concepts:

Sequence, volume, greater than and less than, equal to, equations, subtraction, money, fractions, addition, multiplication, and word problems

Objectives:

1. The student shall be able to number a given set of events in the order of their occurrence.

2. The student shall be able to write the correct symbol (<, >, or =) between two sets of cubes.

3. The student shall be able to write the value of the variable in an addition or subtraction equation.

4. The student shall be able to write the difference of two triple-digit numbers when borrowing from the tens' and hundreds' columns.

5. The student shall be able to write the product of a fractional part of a number from a graphic illustration.

6. The student shall be able to write the sum of three four-digit numbers when the tens' and the hundreds' columns have double-digit answers.

7. The student shall be able to write the product of the multiplication facts three, four, and six.

Teaching Tips:

1. If you have sufficient *cubes* to use in activity 5, demonstrate several sets similar to **Student Activity Two** for the student(s) to determine the correct symbol needed. Let a student form two sets and another student determine what symbol would go between the sets.

Materials, Supplies, & Equipment:

1. Flashcards for addition and multiplication facts

2. Cubes

Activities:

1. Drill multiplication facts using *Drill #2, Worksheet 74.*

2. Using *flashcards for addition facts*, drill sums 1–18 with the answers showing and covering an addend.

3. Using *flashcards for multiplication facts*, drill 2's, 3's, 6's, 9's, and 4's without the answers showing and 7's and 8's with the answers showing.

4. Have the student(s) read the three events in **Student Activity One** by themselves. Ask them to determine which event came first, second, and third. Number the events in that order. Then have a student(s) read the events in the correct order.

5. In **Student Activity Two**, have the student(s) count the number of cubes in each set. Then allow them to determine independently which symbol would be correct.

6. Review with the student(s) when they are to add the same number to both sides of an equation and when they are to subtract the same number from both sides of an equation. They should be able to complete **Student Activity Three** alone.

7. Have the student(s) subtract several problems similar to those in **Student Activity Four** (two triple-digit numbers borrowing from the tens' and the hundreds' columns). They should then be able to complete the subtraction problems without further help.

8. Draw 24 circles on the board. Circle sets of 8 and shade 3 in each set. Ask the student(s) to tell the fraction problem that is represented by the circles. The number in each set is the denominator and the number shaded in each set is the numerator. The problem becomes ⅜ of 24 (total number of circles) equals 9 (total of circles shaded). Allow the student(s) to complete **Student Activity Five** independently, giving help if needed.

9. The student(s) should be able to complete **Student Activity Six**, **Seven**, and **Eight** on their own.

Worksheet:

1. *Worksheet 74* – Addition, subtraction, and multiplication drill sheet

You are not free if you are a slave to your feelings.

Lesson 148

Concepts:
 Word sentences, word numbers, sequence, word problems, volume, greater than and less than, equal to, equations, addition, and multiplication

Objectives:
 1. The student shall be able to rewrite a word sentence as a number sentence.

 2. The student shall be able to number a given set of events in the order of their occurrence.

 3. The student shall be able to write addition and subtraction word problems using the given information.

 4. The student shall be able to write the correct symbol (<, >, or =) between two sets of cubes.

 5. The student shall be able to write the value of the variable in an addition or subtraction equation.

 6. The student shall be able to write the sum of three four-digit numbers when the tens' and the hundreds' columns have double-digit answers.

 7. The student shall be able to write the product of the multiplication facts for four, six, and seven.

Teaching Tips:
 1. Before doing activity 6, let the student(s) make up events or situations for writing a word problem. Have them do it for addition and subtraction. Then have the student(s) solve their word problems.

Materials, Supplies, & Equipment:
 1. Flashcards for subtraction and multiplication facts

Activities:

1. Drill multiplication facts using *Drill #3, Worksheet 74.*

2. Using *flashcards for subtraction facts*, drill minuends 1–18 with the answers showing and covering a minuend or subtrahend.

3. Using *flashcards for multiplication facts*, drill 2's, 3's, 6's, 9's, and 4's without the answers showing and 7's and 8's with the answers showing.

4. Once the student(s) determine if the word sentence is addition or subtraction, they should be able to complete **Student Activity One** alone.

5. The student(s) should be able to complete **Student Activity Two** by themselves.

6. Ask the student(s) to write one addition and one subtraction problem for **Student Activity Three**.

7. The student(s) should be able to complete **Student Activity Four**, **Five**, **Six**, and **Seven** independently.

Worksheet:

1. *Worksheet 74* – Addition, subtraction, and multiplication drill sheet

True courage is doing your duty despite fear.

Lesson 149

Concepts:
> Fractions, sequence, Roman numerals, word sentences, word numbers, symmetry, multiplication, and subtraction

Objectives:
1. The student shall be able to shade a fractional part of a given set.

2. The student shall be able to number a given set of events in the order of their occurrence.

3. The student shall be able to write the Roman numeral that corresponds to the given Arabic number.

4. The student shall be able to rewrite a word sentence as a number sentence.

5. The student shall be able to draw a line of symmetry for given shapes.

6. The student shall be able to write the product of the multiplication facts six, seven, and eight.

7. The student shall be able to write the difference of two triple-digit numbers when borrowing from the tens' and the hundreds' columns.

Teaching Tips:
1. While doing activity 8, have the student(s) look around the room to find symmetrical shapes. Ask them how many lines of symmetry the shape has and where such lines are located. Encourage them to look for symmetrical shapes and locate a line of symmetry in other places they may go (car, store, etc.).

Materials, Supplies, & Equipment:
1. Flashcards for addition facts, multiplication facts, and Roman numerals

2. Flannel board

3. Flannel board materials

Activities:

1. Drill subtraction facts using *Drill #4, Worksheet 74*.

2. Using *flashcards for addition facts*, drill sums 1–18 with the answers showing and covering one addend.

3. Using *flashcards for multiplication facts*, drill the 2's, 3's, 6's, 9's, and 4's without the answers showing and the 7's and 8's with the answers showing. Be sure the student(s) say the facts in pairs.

4. Draw 10 triangles on the board. You might want to use *flannel board materials* for fractional parts here. Have a student come to the board and shade ⅘ of the triangles (circle sets of 5 each and shade four of the five). Draw 12 kites on the board. Have a student shade ⅔ of the kites. Do more examples if needed. Complete the first problem in **Student Activity One** together. Allow the student(s) to shade the remaining fractional parts by themselves.

5. The student(s) should be able to number the events in **Student Activity Two** on their own. Then have them read the events in the correct order.

6. Review the symbols for *Roman numerals* using *flashcards*. Write several numbers from 100–999 on the board and have the student(s) tell what the corresponding Roman numerals would be. Encourage them to determine the Roman numeral(s) used for each place value. Allow the student(s) to write the Roman numerals in **Student Activity Three** alone, giving help if needed.

7. The student(s) should be able to complete **Student Activity Four** independently.

8. Discuss with the student(s) the meaning of the line of symmetry. Draw a symmetrical shape on the board and talk about the line(s) of symmetry on the shape. Encourage them to fold their paper to see that one side of the shape lays on top of the other side once they have drawn their line of symmetry in **Student Activity Five**.

9. The student(s) should be able to complete **Student Activity Six** and **Seven** without assistance.

Worksheet:

1. *Worksheet 74* – Addition, subtraction, and multiplication drill sheet

Lesson 150

Concepts:

Grid, Roman numerals, fractions, subtraction, symmetry, ratio, addition, and multiplication

Objectives:

1. The student shall be able to write the point of intersection on a given grid and draw lines to connect the dots in consecutive order.

2. The student shall be able to write the Arabic number that corresponds to a given Roman numeral.

3. The student shall be able to shade a fractional part of a given set.

4. The student shall be able to write the difference of two triple-digit numbers when borrowing from the tens' and the hundreds' columns.

5. The student shall be able to draw a line of symmetry for given objects.

6. The student shall be able to write the comparison of two sets as a ratio.

7. The student shall be able to write the sum of three four-digit numbers when the tens' and the hundreds' columns have double-digit answers.

8. The student shall be able to write the product of the multiplication facts for three, seven, and eight.

Teaching Tips:

1. When doing activity 5, have the student(s) determine what Roman numerals they would use to write the present year. Then let each of them determine what Roman numerals they would use to write the year they were born and the year you were born.

Materials, Supplies, & Equipment:

1. Flashcards for addition facts, subtraction facts, multiplication facts, and Roman numerals

2. Flannel board

3. Flannel board materials

4. Construction paper shapes

1. Administer **Test 15**.

2. Have the student(s) take a clean sheet of paper on which to write the answers for their *addition* and *subtraction facts* using *flashcards* with sleeves over an addend and a minuend or subtrahend.

3. Using *flashcards for multiplication facts*, drill 2's, 3's, 6's, 9's, and 4's without answers showing and 7's and 8's with answers showing.

4. Before class, draw a grid on the board similar to the one in **Student Activity One**. Point to several intersections on the grid and have the student(s) tell the coordinates of the points. Be sure that they tell the letter coordinate first and then the number coordinate. Learning to do the letter first will prevent them from having to unlearn the process at a higher level of math. Help the student(s) locate the first point in the activity and determine what coordinates to write. They will need your help as they write the remaining coordinates.

5. After reviewing the *Roman numeral flashcards* with the student(s), remind them that the hundreds' will begin with C or D, the tens' with X and L, and the ones' with I or V. Write several Roman numerals on the board and have the student(s) tell the corresponding Arabic numbers. They should complete **Student Activity Two** by themselves.

6. Draw 10 squares and 12 stars on the board. You might want to use *flannel board materials* for fractional parts. Have a student come to the board and shade ⅖ of the squares (circle sets of 5 and shade 2) and ⅚ of 12 stars. Complete the first problem in **Student Activity Three** together. Allow the student(s) to shade the remaining fractional parts by themselves.

7. The student(s) should be able to complete **Student Activity Four** on their own.

8. Ask the student(s) to describe a line of symmetry. Give them several *shapes* cut out of *construction paper* to fold on a line of symmetry. Discuss how many lines of symmetry the different shapes have. Allow the student(s) to complete **Student Activity Five** alone.

9. Discuss with the student(s) the meaning of the word "ratio." Have them compare the number of males to the number of females in the room, females to males, and males to both females and males. The student(s) should be able to complete **Student Activity Six** without further help.

10. The student(s) should be able to complete **Student Activity Seven** and **Eight** independently.

Lesson 151

Concepts:
> Time equivalents, English weight equivalents, solids, addition, subtraction, time, grid, ratio, and multiplication

Objectives:
1. The student shall be able to write the answers for given time and weight equivalents.

2. The student shall be able to write the names of given solids.

3. The student shall be able to write the sum of three four-digit numbers when the ones', tens', and hundreds' columns have double-digit answers.

4. The student shall be able to write the difference of two triple-digit numbers when borrowing from the tens' and hundreds' columns.

5. The student shall be able to write the correct time displayed on the face of a clock for given 5 minute increments.

6. The student shall be able to write the point of intersection from a given grid and draw lines to connect the dots in consecutive order.

7. The student shall be able to write the comparison of two sets as a ratio.

8. The student shall be able to write the product of the multiplication facts for four and nine.

Teaching Tips:
1. In connection with activity 7, give the student(s) a sheet of graph paper and have them create a picture by drawing lines that connect intersections. Show them how to write the numbers 0–6 vertically on the left hand side and the letters across the bottom. Then have them name the coordinates at each point where their lines meet an intersection.

Materials, Supplies, & Equipment:
1. Flashcards for subtraction facts, multiplication facts, time equivalents, English weight equivalents, and solids

2. Solid models

Activities:

1. Drill addition facts using *Drill #1, Worksheet 76.*

2. Using *flashcards for subtraction facts*, drill minuends 1–18 with the answers showing and covering the minuend or the subtrahend.

3. Using *flashcards for multiplication facts*, drill 2's, 3's, 6's, 9's, and 4's without the answers showing and 7's and 8's with the answers showing.

4. Using the *time* and *English weight equivalent flashcards*, have the student(s) review the equivalents. Encourage the student(s) not to guess as they complete **Student Activity One**. Those who do not know the answers should look them up on the flashcards.

5. Have the student(s) name and spell the solids as you point to each of the *solid models*. Leave the *solid flashcards* with the names showing on display to aid in spelling as the student(s) complete **Student Activity Two**.

6. The student(s) should be able to complete **Student Activity Three**, **Four**, and **Five** independently.

7. Before class, draw a grid on the board similar to the one in **Student Activity Six**. Point to several intersections on the grid and have the student(s) tell the coordinates of the points. Be sure that they tell the letter coordinate first and then the number coordinate. Help the student(s) locate the first point in the activity and determine what coordinates to write. They may need your help as they write the remaining coordinates.

8. The student(s) should be able to complete **Student Activity Seven** and **Eight** by themselves.

Worksheet:

1. *Worksheet 76* – Addition, subtraction, and multiplication drill sheet

*Freedom is not an opportunity to do as you please but
the liberty to do what you should.*

Lesson 152

Concepts:
Sequence, time, multiplication, time equivalents, English weight equivalents, English linear equivalents, English liquid equivalents, addition, subtraction, and word problems

Objectives:
1. The student shall be able to circle the next shape that would appear in a sequence of shapes.

2. The student shall be able to draw both hands on the face of the clock for given five minute increments.

3. The student shall be able to write the product of the multiplication facts for nine, four, seven, and eight.

4. The student shall be able to write the answers for equivalents of a given time, English weights, English linear measure, and English liquid measure.

5. The student shall be able to write the sum of three four-digit numbers when the ones', tens', and hundreds' columns have double-digit answers.

6. The student shall be able to write the difference of two triple-digit numbers when borrowing from the tens' and hundreds' columns.

Teaching Tips:
1. Some student(s) may profit from one-on-one drill work with the *equivalent flashcards* used in activity 7. Allow two student(s) to work together. Work with just one set of cards at a time until all are mastered. Then the student(s) may mix them up.

Materials, Supplies, & Equipment:
1. Flashcards for addition facts, multiplication facts, time equivalents, English weight equivalents, English linear equivalents, and English liquid equivalents

2. Flannel board

3. Flannel board materials

4. Small clock model for student(s)

5. Clock model

Activities:

1. Drill multiplication facts using *Drill #2, Worksheet 76.*

2. Using *flashcards for addition facts*, drill sums 1–18 with the answers showing and covering an addend.

3. Using *flashcards for multiplication facts*, drill 2's, 3's, 6's, 9's, and 4's without the answers showing and 7's, and 8's with the answers showing.

4. Display a *circle, triangle, square, circle,* and *triangle* in a row on the *flannel board* or board. Have the student(s) tell the shape that would come next in the sequence. Remind them to find the last place a triangle was used and see what comes after it. Do several combinations of shapes with the student(s). They should be able to complete **Student Activity One** by themselves.

5. Give the student(s) a *small clock model*. Ask them which hand they should set first. Tell them several five minute intervals for which to set their clocks. Set the *clock model* for them to use in checking their settings. The student(s) should be able to complete **Student Activity Two** on their own.

6. The student(s) should be able to complete **Student Activity Three** independently.

7. Review *time equivalents, English weight equivalents, English linear equivalents,* and *English liquid equivalents* with *flashcards*. Extra time may need to be spent on the English liquid equivalents. Allow the student(s) to look at the answers if they cannot answer all of the equivalents in **Student Activity Four** correctly.

8. The student(s) should be able to complete **Student Activity Five** and **Six** alone.

9. After the student(s) have read the word problem in **Student Activity Seven** to themselves, discuss if they are to add, subtract, or multiply and why. Encourage those who have difficulty to visualize the problem. They should then be able to solve the problem without further help.

Worksheet:

1. *Worksheet 76* – Addition, subtraction, and multiplication drill sheet

The books you read are as important as the company you keep.
They both influence your character.

335

Lesson 153

Concepts:
Temperature, solids, word problems, dozen, time, area, greater than and less than, equal to, subtraction, and multiplication

Objectives:

1. The student shall be able to write the correct temperature displayed on the thermometer.

2. The student shall be able to draw a line to match a large solid to a similar small solid.

3. The student shall be able to draw both hands on the face of a clock according to the given information.

4. The student shall be able to write the number of square inches in a given area.

5. The student shall be able to write the correct symbol (<, >, or =) between two given areas.

6. The student shall be able to write the difference of two triple-digit numbers when borrowing from the tens' and hundreds' columns.

7. The student shall be able to write the product of the multiplication facts for seven and eight.

Teaching Tips:

1. During activity 3, check the student(s) on an individual basis to see what multiplication facts they have not mastered. The last five lessons will have the drill done without the answers showing. The student(s) should have a working knowledge of the multiplication facts at the end of second grade.

Materials, Supplies, & Equipment:

1. Flashcards for subtraction and multiplication facts

2. Thermometer model

3. Small clock model for student(s)

4. Clock model

Activities:

1. Drill multiplication facts using *Drill #3, Worksheet 76*.

2. Using *flashcards for subtraction facts*, drill minuends 1–18 with the answers showing and covering a minuend or subtrahend.

3. Using *flashcards for multiplication facts*, drill 2's, 3's, 6's, 9's, and 4's without the answers showing and 7's and 8's with the answers showing.

4. Count by twos with the student(s) on the thermometer scale. Show several temperatures on the *thermometer model* for the student(s) to determine the degrees shown. Note the thermometers in **Student Activity One** are circular. After doing the first one together, the student(s) should be able to read the remaining thermometers by themselves.

5. Describe several solids for the student(s) and have them spell the names. They should be able to complete **Student Activity Two** on their own.

6. Discuss with the student(s) how many are in a dozen before the student(s) read the word problem in **Student Activity Three**. After they have determined if the word problem is addition, subtraction, or multiplication, they should be able to solve it without further help.

7. Discuss with the student(s) the time different events occur throughout the day. Allow them to set the *small clock models* for each time. Let the student(s) check their settings by the *clock model*. They should be able to complete **Student Activity Four** alone.

8. Have the student(s) find the area of each shape in **Student Activity Five** by counting the square units and writing their answers in the blanks. Then have them compare the two areas to determine the correct symbol to be placed between these areas.

9. The student(s) should be able to complete **Student Activity Six** and **Seven** independently.

Worksheets:

1. *Worksheet 77* – Area

2. *Worksheet 76* – Addition, subtraction, and multiplication drill sheet

No matter what your lot in life is, build something on it.

Lesson 154

Concepts:
   Solids, addition, temperature, perimeter, subtraction, multiplication, and word problems

Objectives:
1. The student shall be able to write a given letter beside the corresponding solid.

2. The student shall be able to write the sum of four double-digit numbers when the ones' column has a double-digit answer.

3. The student shall be able to mark the thermometer for a given temperature and draw a red pointer.

4. The student shall be able to write the perimeter of a given shape.

5. The student shall be able to write the difference of two triple-digit numbers when borrowing from the tens' and the hundreds' columns.

6. The student shall be able to write the product of the multiplication facts for eight and nine.

Teaching Tips:
1. When doing **Student Activity Three**, ask the student(s) to name some activity they would enjoy doing at each of the temperatures given. Some examples are: ice skating 12°, sledding 28°, football 60°, hiking 74°, baseball 82°, and swimming 96°.

Materials, Supplies, & Equipment:
1. Flashcards for addition and multiplication facts

2. Thermometer model

Activities:

1. Drill subtraction facts using *Drill #4, Worksheet 76.*

2. Using *flashcards for addition facts*, drill sums 1–18 with the answers showing and covering one addend.

3. Using *flashcards for multiplication facts*, drill the 2's, 3's, 6's, 9's, and 4's without the answers showing and the 7's and 8's with the answers showing. Be sure the student(s) say the facts in pairs.

4. Have the student(s) look at **Student Activity One**. Read the first sentence to them. Ask them to point to the objects that have the shape of a cube. Then write a B on the line beside the objects. Follow the same procedure for each of the remaining sentences.

5. The student(s) should be able to complete **Student Activity Two** on their own.

6. Have the student(s) count by twos using the *thermometer model* scale. Write several temperatures on the board and have the student(s) set the *thermometer model* for the correct temperatures. They should be able to complete **Student Activity Three** by themselves.

7. Discuss with the student(s) the meaning of the word "perimeter" and the abbreviation for centimeter (cm). Ask them the long (addition) and the short (multiplication) way of finding the perimeter of the shapes in **Student Activity Four**.

8. The student(s) should be able to complete **Student Activity Five, Six,** and **Seven** independently.

Worksheet:

1. *Worksheet 76* – Addition, subtraction, and multiplication drill sheet

If you build walls instead of bridges,
you will have a lonely life.

Lesson 155

Concepts:
 Temperature, line graphs, subtraction, volume, addition, time equivalents, English weight equivalents, English liquid equivalents, and English linear equivalents

Objectives:
1. The student shall be able to write the correct temperature displayed on the thermometer.

2. The student shall be able to draw the lines necessary to represent given information on a line graph.

3. The student shall be able to write the difference of two triple-digit numbers when borrowing from the tens' and hundreds' columns.

4. The student shall be able to write the number of cubic units in a given set.

5. The student shall be able to write the sum of four double-digit numbers when the ones' column has a double-digit answer.

6. The student shall be able to draw a line to match the equivalents of a given time, English weight, English liquid measure, and English linear measure.

Teaching Tips:
1. The next five lessons will not have answers showing for Activity 2. Although a thorough review will be given in third grade, use *Worksheet 78* as a guide to determine those student(s) who could use further drill practice during the summer months.

Materials, Supplies, & Equipment:
1. Flashcards for addition facts, subtraction facts, multiplication facts, time equivalents, English weight equivalents, English liquid equivalents, and English linear equivalents

2. Thermometer model

340

Activities:

1. Have the student(s) take a clean sheet of paper on which to write the answers for their *addition* and *subtraction facts* using *flashcards* with sleeves over an addend and a minuend or subtrahend.

2. Using *flashcards for multiplication facts*, drill 2's, 3's, 6's, 9's, and 4's without the answers showing and 7's and 8's with the answers showing.

3. Display several temperatures on the *thermometer model*. Have the student(s) write the temperatures on a sheet of paper. Then allow the student(s) to set the *thermometer model* for several temperatures. The student(s) should be able to complete **Student Activity One** on their own.

4. Have the student(s) tell the correct temperature on the first thermometer in **Student Activity One**. Then have them look at the line graph in **Student Activity Two** and place a dot on the intersection above 1st and across from 34°. Guide the student(s) as they place the remaining dots on the line graph. Be sure they connect the dots in consecutive order.

5. The student(s) should be able to compete **Student Activity Three** by themselves.

6. Discuss with the student(s) the meaning of the word "volume." Count each of the cubes with the student(s) in **Student Activity Four**.

7. The student(s) should be able to compete **Student Activity Five** independently.

8. Review *time equivalents*, *English weight equivalents*, *English liquid equivalents*, and *English linear equivalents* using *flashcards*. Allow the student(s) to complete **Student Activity Six** giving help where needed.

Worksheet:

1. *Worksheet 78 – Multiplication*

If we are not careful
of the truth we have heard, it will slip away

Lesson 156

Concepts:
> Grid, equations, subtraction, multiplication, addition, bar graphs, solids, and Roman numerals

Objectives:
1. The student shall be able to write the letter that is at the given point of intersection on a grid.

2. The student shall be able to write the value of the variable in an addition or subtraction equation.

3. The student shall be able to write the difference of two four-digit numbers when borrowing from the tens' and hundreds' columns.

4. The student shall be able to write the product of the multiplication facts for six, seven, eight, and nine.

5. The student shall be able to write the sum of four double-digit numbers when the ones' column has a double-digit answer.

6. The student shall be able to draw the bars necessary to represent given information on a bar graph.

7. The student shall be able to draw a line to match a Roman numeral to its corresponding Arabic number.

Teaching Tips:
1. For **Student Activity Six**, use the *solid models* to review the names of each of the solids. Or you may describe a solid, have the student(s) tell its name and spell it, and then show them the corresponding *solid model*.

Materials, Supplies, & Equipment:
1. Flashcards for subtraction facts, multiplication facts, and Roman numerals

2. Solid models

Activities:

1. Drill addition facts using *Drill #1, Worksheet 79*.

2. Using *flashcards for subtraction facts*, drill minuends 1–18 with the answers showing and covering the minuend or the subtrahend.

3. Using *flashcards for multiplication facts*, drill 2's, 3's, 6's, 9's, 4's, 7's, and 8's without the answers showing.

4. Ask the student(s) to find the location of the point C5 in **Student Activity One**. Have them write the letter that is at that point on the line beside C5. Next have them locate the point A1 and write the letter that is at that point on the line beside A1. Once they have found the location of all of the points, have them read the two words.

5. Write an addition and a subtraction equation on the board. Have the student(s) copy the equations on a sheet of paper and solve them. Check to see that the student(s) are using the correct steps on their papers after the equations are solved on the board. The student(s) should be able to complete **Student Activity Two** without much help.

6. The student(s) should be able to complete **Student Activity Three**, **Four**, and **Five** independently.

7. Allow the student(s) to draw the bar graph in **Student Activity Six** alone. Give individual help when needed.

8. Using the *Roman numeral flashcards*, review the symbols. Then allow the student(s) to tell what Roman numerals would be needed for several corresponding Arabic numbers over 100. The student(s) should be able to complete **Student Activity Seven** with little help.

Worksheet:

1. *Worksheet 79* – Addition, subtraction, and multiplication drill sheet

Your character is seen in what you do when no one sees you.

Lesson 157

Concepts:
Pictograph, addition, subtraction, sequence, grid, Roman numerals, time equivalents, English weight equivalents, English linear equivalents, English liquid equivalents, and multiplication

Objectives:
1. The student shall be able to draw the pictures necessary to represent given information on a pictograph.

2. The student shall be able to write the sum of four double-digit numbers when the ones' column has a double-digit answer.

3. The student shall be able to write the difference of two four-digit numbers when borrowing from the tens' and hundreds' columns.

4. The student shall be able to number a given set of events in the order of their occurrence.

5. The student shall be able to write the point of intersection on a given grid and draw lines to connect the dots in consecutive order.

6. The student shall be able to write the Arabic number that corresponds to a given Roman numeral.

7. The student shall be able to write the answers for equivalents of a given time, English weight, English liquid measure, and English linear measure.

8. The student shall be able to write the product of the multiplication facts for three, four, and five.

Teaching Tips:
1. For additional work as found in activity 6, the student(s) might enjoy creating their own picture on a grid (*graph paper* would be best). Tell them to write the alphabet across the bottom and numbers, beginning with 1, up the left side. Once their picture is drawn, have them write the location of each point on their picture.

Materials, Supplies, & Equipment:

1. Flashcards for addition facts, multiplication facts, Roman numerals, time equivalents, English weight equivalents, English liquid equivalents, and English linear equivalents.

2. Posterboard grid

3. Graph paper (half sheet per student)

344

Activities:

1. Drill multiplication facts using *Drill #2, Worksheet 79.*

2. Using *flashcards for addition facts*, drill sums 1–18 with the answers showing and covering an addend.

3. Using *flashcards for multiplication facts*, drill 2's, 3's, 6's, 9's, 4's, 7's, and 8's without the answers showing.

4. Discuss with the student(s) the value of the bone in the pictograph in **Student Activity One**. Then have them tell the number of bones that would be needed for each of the dogs to represent their weight. Allow the student(s) to draw the bones by themselves.

5. Notice in **Student Activity Four**, the first event is marked for the student(s). They should be able to complete **Student Activity Two**, **Three**, and **Four** independently.

6. Before class begins, have a grid on the board or on *posterboard*. Point to several intersections and have the student(s) tell the location of the points. Complete the first three points in **Student Activity Five** with the student(s). Then allow them to locate the remaining points on their own.

7. Using the *Roman numeral flashcards*, have the student(s) tell the value of each symbol. Write several Roman numerals over 100 on the board. Let the student(s) tell the corresponding Arabic number. They should be able to complete **Student Activity Six** with little help.

8. Review the *equivalents* with *flashcards*. The student(s) should be able to complete **Student Activity Seven** alone.

9. The student(s) should be able to complete **Student Activity Eight** without assistance.

Worksheet:

1. *Worksheet 79* – Addition, subtraction, and multiplication drill sheet

Being careful of choices is what builds good character.

Lesson 158

Concepts:
>Fractions, multiplication, addition, sequence, time equivalents, English linear equivalents, English weight equivalents, English liquid equivalents, subtraction, and word problems

Objectives:
1. The student shall be able to write the number equivalent to one-half of a number.

2. The student shall be able to write the missing multiplier in a multiplication fact.

3. The student shall be able to write the sum of four double-digit numbers when the tens' column has a double-digit answer.

4. The student shall be able to number a given set of events in the order of their occurrence.

5. The student shall be able to write the answers for equivalents of a given time, English weight, English liquid measure, and English linear measure.

6. The student shall be able to write the difference of two four-digit numbers when borrowing from the tens' and hundreds' columns.

Teaching Tips:
1. When doing Activity 7, allow the student(s) to ask the equivalents with you or another student giving the answer. For enrichment, have the student(s) identify the equivalent as time, English linear measure, English liquid measure, or English weight.

Materials, Supplies, & Equipment:
1. Flashcards for subtraction and multiplication facts

Activities:

1. Drill multiplication facts using *Drill #3, Worksheet 79.*

2. Using *flashcards for subtraction facts*, drill minuends 1–18 with the answers showing and covering a minuend or subtrahend.

3. Using *flashcards for multiplication facts*, drill 2's, 3's, 6's, 9's, 4's, 7's, and 8's without the answers showing.

4. Review all the even numbered doubles in the addition facts (e.g., 4 + 4, 6 + 6, 8 + 8, etc.). Discuss with the student(s) that if 4 + 4 = 8, then what is ½ of 8. Or what do they have if they divide 8 into two equal parts. Have the student(s) find ½ of all the even numbers to 20. They should be able to complete **Student Activity One** with little help.

5. Cover the multiplier on the *multiplication flashcards* with the answers showing. Have the student(s) tell what they would take times 4 to equal 24 (4 x __ = 24). Or 4 times what equals 24. Do several flashcards until they get the thinking process in mind. Complete the first column with the student(s) in **Student Activity Two**. Allow those who are capable to continue on their own.

6. Notice the first event is marked for the student(s) in **Student Activity Four**. The student(s) should be able to complete **Student Activity Three** and **Four** alone.

7. When reviewing the equivalents, have the student(s) identify what is equal to 12 inches (1 foot), what is equal to 24 hours (1 day), etc. Do all of **Student Activity Five** with the student(s) orally before they write the answers on the blanks.

8. The student(s) should be able to complete **Student Activity Six** independently.

9. Have the student(s) read the word problems in **Student Activity Seven** to themselves. Discuss if they should add, subtract, or multiply and why. Allow them to solve the problems on their own.

Worksheet:

1. *Worksheet 79* – Addition, subtraction, and multiplication drill sheet

Reputation is how our friends see us:
character is how God sees us.

Lesson 159

Concepts:
  Map reading, fractions, multiplication, temperature, addition, and word problems

Objectives:
  1. The student shall be able to write the distance from one town to another by interpreting a given map.

  2. The student shall be able to write the number equivalent to one-half of a number.

  3. The student shall be able to write the missing multiplier in a multiplication fact.

  4. The student shall be able to write the answer to questions pertaining to a given temperature.

  5. The student shall be able to write the sum of four double-digit numbers when the ones' and the tens' columns have double digits for their sum.

Teaching Tips:
  1. When doing Activity 5, discuss with the student(s) why they cannot take ½ of an odd number. Demonstrate with *counting chips* what happens when they try to divide the odd number of chips into two equal sets. The reason even numbers are named such is because they can be divided into two even (same number in each) sets.

Materials, Supplies, & Equipment:
  1. Flashcards for addition and multiplication facts

  2. Thermometer model

  3. Counting chips

Activities:

1. Drill subtraction facts using *Drill #4, Worksheet 79*.

2. Using *flashcards for addition facts*, drill sums 1–18 with the answers showing and covering one addend.

3. Using *flashcards for multiplication facts*, drill the 2's, 3's, 6's, 9's, 4's, 7's, and 8's without the answers showing.

4. Have the student(s) look at the map in **Student Activity One**. Discuss the distance between different cities. Ask what route they would take to travel from one city to another. What is the longest route and what is the shortest route. The student(s) should be able to complete **Student Activity One** on their own.

5. Review the even numbered doubles in the addition facts. Discuss with the student(s) what ½ of an even number would equal. You may want to use some numbers over 20 for those who are capable (e.g., any multiple of 10). The student(s) should be able to complete **Student Activity Two** by themselves.

6. Cover the multiplier on the *multiplication flashcards* with the answers showing. Have the student(s) tell what number they would take times 6 to equal 48 (6 x __ = 48). Or 6 times what equals 48. Do several flashcards until they get the thinking process in mind. Allow those who are capable to complete **Student Activity Three** without assistance.

7. Allow the student(s) to set the *thermometer model* for several given temperatures. After the student(s) have written the temperature displayed on the thermometer in **Student Activity Four**, discuss with them the questions relating to that temperature.

8. The student(s) should be able to complete **Student Activity Five** and **Six** independently.

Worksheets:

1. *Worksheet 80* – Map reading

2. *Worksheet 79* – Addition, subtraction, and multiplication drill sheet

Take care of your character, and your reputation will take care of itself.

Lesson 160

Concepts:
Fractions, time equivalents, English weight equivalents, English linear equivalents, English liquid equivalents, temperature, subtraction, map reading, and word problems

Objectives:
1. The student shall be able to write the number equivalent to one-half of a number.

2. The student shall be able to write the answers for equivalents of a given time, English weight, English liquid measure, and English linear measure.

3. The student shall be able to make a mark on a thermometer for a given temperature and color the liquid red.

4. The student shall be able to write the difference of two four-digit numbers when borrowing from the tens' and hundreds' columns.

5. The student shall be able to write the answers to questions about the distance from one town to another by interpreting a given map.

6. The student shall be able to write addition and subtraction word problems using given information.

Teaching Tips:
1. After the student(s) complete **Student Activity Six**, allow them to read their word problems and tell how they solved them. Then have the student(s) make up some multiplication word problems using the same given information. Discuss the word problems and what the solutions should be.

Materials, Supplies, & Equipment:
1. Flashcards for addition, subtraction, and multiplication facts

2. Thermometer model

Activities:

1. Have the student(s) take a clean sheet of paper on which to write the answers for their *addition* and *subtraction facts* using *flashcards* with sleeves over an addend and a minuend or subtrahend.

2. Using *flashcards for multiplication facts*, drill 2's, 3's, 6's, 9's, 4's, 7's, and 8's without the answers showing.

3. Discuss with the student(s) how to find ½ of an even number up to 20. Do several examples with them on the board. The student(s) should be able to complete **Student Activity One** by themselves.

4. Review the equivalents by asking the student(s) to tell what 3 feet equal (1 yard), 2 cups equal (1 pint), 60 minutes equal (1 hour), etc. Do all of **Student Activity Two** with the student(s) orally before they write the answers in the blanks.

5. Allow the student(s) to set the *thermometer model* for several temperatures. They should be able to complete **Student Activity Three** on their own.

6. The student(s) should be able to complete **Student Activity Four** independently.

7. Have the student(s) look at the map in **Student Activity Five**. Discuss the distance between different towns. Compare the distance from Show Low to Snow Flake with the distance from Show Low to Sunrise. Find the closest city to Strawberry. Ask several other questions. After the student(s) have answered the questions about the map, discuss their answers.

8. The student(s) should be able to complete **Student Activity Six** without assistance.

9. Administer **Test 16**. This test should be administered the day after you complete lesson 160.

*A few good friends are better than
a good many friends.*

Answer Key

① Count each set. Write the number.

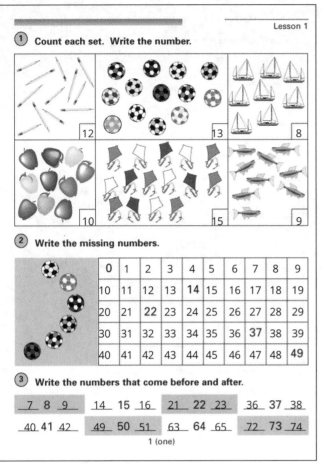

12

13

8

10

15

9

② Write the missing numbers.

0	1	2	3	4	5	6	7	8	9
10	11	12	13	**14**	15	16	17	18	19
20	21	**22**	23	24	25	26	27	28	29
30	31	32	33	34	35	36	**37**	38	39
40	41	42	43	44	45	46	47	48	**49**

③ Write the numbers that come before and after.

_7_ 8 _9_   _14_ 15 _16_   _21_ 22 _23_   36 37 _38_

_40_ 41 _42_   _49_ 50 _51_   63 64 _65_   _72_ 73 _74_

1 (one)

④ Write the letters on the blanks.

W E L C O M E   B A C K

second _E_	seventh _E_	fourth _C_	first _W_
sixth _M_	third _L_	fifth _O_	eighth _B_
tenth _C_	ninth _A_	eleventh _K_	

⑤

3	4		6	7
9			2	
	1	4		8	3
5	0			9	
8		7	2		1
	6	0		2	5

Across
1. The number before 35
2. 68 - 1=
3. The number after 13
5. 82 + 1=
6. The number after 49
8. 73 - 1=
10. The number before 61
11. 24 + 1=

Down
1. 38 + 1=
2. The number after 61
3. 11 - 1=
5. 90 - 1=
6. The number after 57
8. 69 + 1=
9. The number before 16

⑥ Circle the larger numbers.

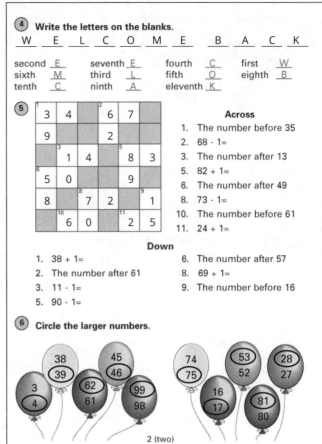

2 (two)

---

① Connect the dots.

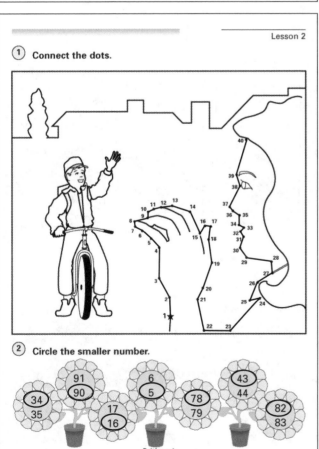

② Circle the smaller number.

3 (three)

③ Write the missing numbers.

50	51	52	53	54	55	56	57	58	59
60	61	62	**63**	64	65	66	67	68	69
70	71	72	73	74	75	76	**77**	78	79
80	81	82	83	84	**85**	86	87	88	89
90	91	92	93	94	95	96	97	98	**99**

④ Write the numbers that come before and after.

_6_ 7 _8_   _12_ 13 _14_   _20_ 21 _22_   79 80 _81_

_45_ 46 _47_   _58_ 59 _60_   _67_ 68 _69_   _91_ 92 _93_

⑤ Match the ordinal numbers.

first	3rd
second	5th
third	2nd
fourth	1st
fifth	4th

sixth	7th
seventh	10th
eighth	6th
ninth	8th
tenth	9th

⑥ Count each set. Write the number.

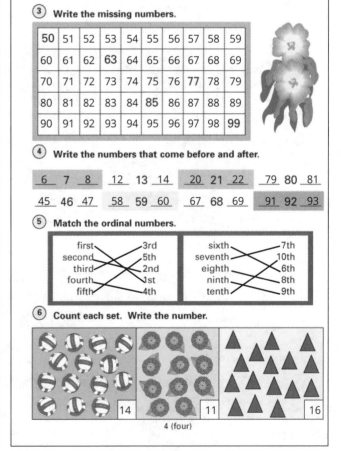

14

11

16

4 (four)

1 Make a tally mark for each object.

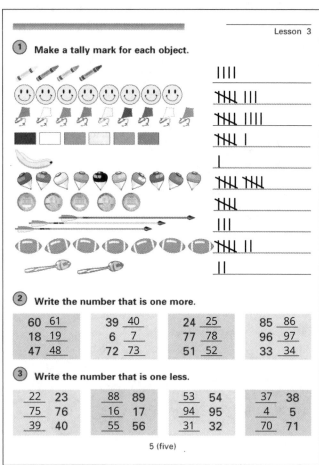

2 Write the number that is one more.

60 _61_	39 _40_	24 _25_	85 _86_
18 _19_	6 _7_	77 _78_	96 _97_
47 _48_	72 _73_	51 _52_	33 _34_

3 Write the number that is one less.

_22_ 23	_88_ 89	_53_ 54	_37_ 38
_75_ 76	_16_ 17	_94_ 95	_4_ 5
_39_ 40	_55_ 56	_31_ 32	_70_ 71

5 (five)

---

4 Write the letters on the blanks.

B E   K I N D   T O
O N E   A N O T H E R

seventeenth	E	ninth	O	sixth	D
fourth	I	fifth	N	tenth	N
twelfth	A	eleventh	E	third	K
first	B	second	E	sixteenth	H
fourteenth	O	eighteenth	R	thirteenth	N
eighth	O	fifteenth	T	seventh	T

5 Circle 17 stars.   Circle 12 octagons.   Circle 18 cones.

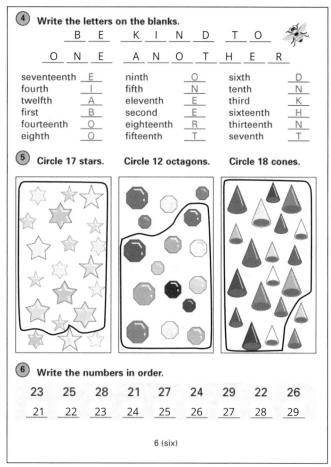

6 Write the numbers in order.

23 25 28 21 27 24 29 22 26
_21_ _22_ _23_ _24_ _25_ _26_ _27_ _28_ _29_

6 (six)

---

1 Make tally marks for each number.

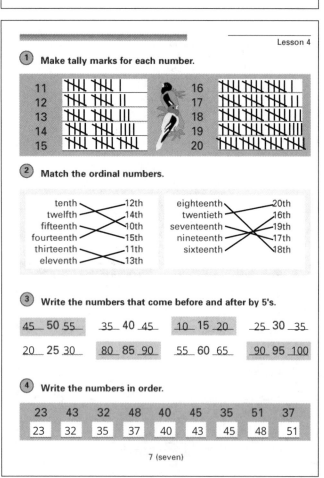

2 Match the ordinal numbers.

tenth	12th
twelfth	14th
fifteenth	10th
fourteenth	15th
thirteenth	11th
eleventh	13th

eighteenth	20th
twentieth	16th
seventeenth	19th
nineteenth	17th
sixteenth	18th

3 Write the numbers that come before and after by 5's.

_45_ 50 _55_   _35_ 40 _45_   _10_ 15 _20_   _25_ 30 _35_

_20_ 25 _30_   _80_ 85 _90_   _55_ 60 _65_   _90_ 95 _100_

4 Write the numbers in order.

23 43 32 48 40 45 35 51 37
_23_ _32_ _35_ _37_ _40_ _43_ _45_ _48_ _51_

7 (seven)

---

5 Circle 13 dimes.   Circle 15 oranges.   Circle 10 cars.

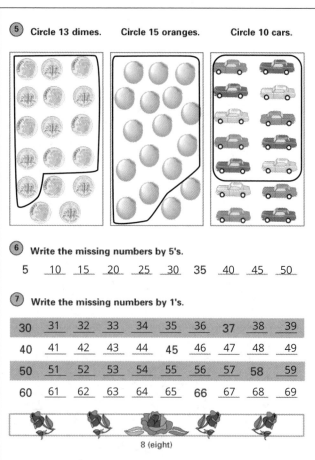

6 Write the missing numbers by 5's.

5 _10_ _15_ _20_ _25_ _30_ 35 _40_ _45_ _50_

7 Write the missing numbers by 1's.

30	_31_	_32_	_33_	_34_	_35_	_36_	37	_38_	_39_
40	_41_	_42_	_43_	_44_	45	_46_	_47_	_48_	_49_
50	_51_	_52_	_53_	_54_	_55_	_56_	_57_	_58_	_59_
60	_61_	_62_	_63_	_64_	_65_	66	_67_	_68_	_69_

8 (eight)

356

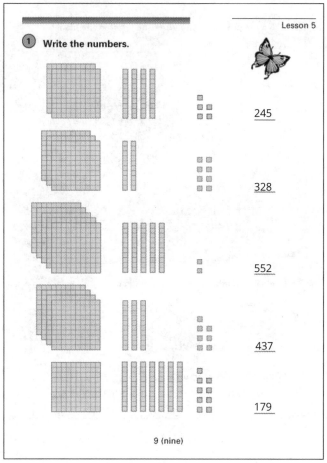

1 Write the numbers.

245

328

552

437

179

9 (nine)

---

2 Match the tally marks to the numbers.

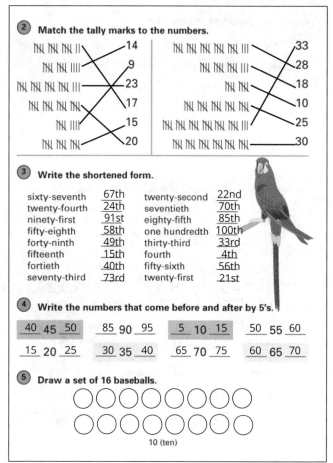

14
9
23
17
15
20

33
28
18
10
25
30

3 Write the shortened form.

sixty-seventh	67th	twenty-second	22nd
twenty-fourth	24th	seventieth	70th
ninety-first	91st	eighty-fifth	85th
fifty-eighth	58th	one hundredth	100th
forty-ninth	49th	thirty-third	33rd
fifteenth	15th	fourth	4th
fortieth	40th	fifty-sixth	56th
seventy-third	73rd	twenty-first	21st

4 Write the numbers that come before and after by 5's.

40 45 50   85 90 95   5 10 15   50 55 60

15 20 25   30 35 40   65 70 75   60 65 70

5 Draw a set of 16 baseballs.

◯◯◯◯◯◯◯◯
◯◯◯◯◯◯◯◯

10 (ten)

---

1 Write the numbers.

3 hundreds = 300	8 tens = 80	5 ones = 5
7 hundreds = 700	7 tens = 70	6 ones = 6
6 hundreds = 600	1 ten = 10	3 ones = 3
9 hundreds = 900	5 tens = 50	8 ones = 8
4 hundreds = 400	4 tens = 40	1 one = 1
1 hundred = 100	6 tens = 60	2 ones = 2
8 hundreds = 800	2 tens = 20	4 ones = 4
2 hundreds = 200	9 tens = 90	7 ones = 7
5 hundreds = 500	3 tens = 30	9 ones = 9

2 Circle the number that is the greatest in each color group.

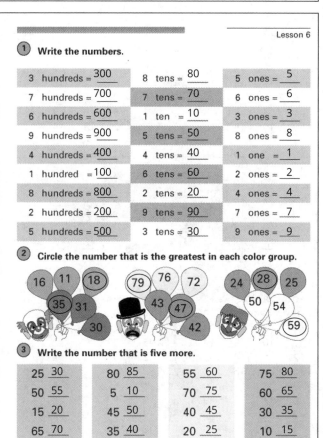

16 11 18 79 76 72 24 28 25
35 31 43 47 50 54
30 42 59

3 Write the number that is five more.

25 30	80 85	55 60	75 80
50 55	5 10	70 75	60 65
15 20	45 50	40 45	30 35
65 70	35 40	20 25	10 15

11 (eleven)

---

4 Write the number that is five less.

65 70	40 45	80 85	55 60
50 55	85 90	45 50	35 40
75 80	70 75	60 65	90 95

5 Write the numbers.

ⅢⅠⅠ 7		ⅢⅢⅢⅢⅠⅠ 22
ⅢⅢⅠⅠⅠ 13		ⅢⅢⅠⅠ 12
ⅢⅢⅢⅠⅠⅠⅠ 19		ⅢⅢⅢⅢⅢⅠ 26
ⅢⅢⅢⅠ 16		ⅢⅢⅢⅢⅢⅠ 31
ⅢⅢⅢⅢⅠ 21		ⅢⅢⅢⅢⅠⅠⅠⅠ 24

6 Write the numbers in order.

40	20	45	10	30	35	15	25	5
5	10	15	20	25	30	35	40	45

35	19	27	16	40	23	42	31	54
16	19	23	27	31	35	40	42	54

7 Write the missing numbers by 1's.

70	71	72	73	74	75	76	77	78	79
80	81	82	83	84	85	86	87	88	89
90	91	92	93	94	95	96	97	98	99

12 (twelve)

① Write the numbers.

4 hundreds + 5 tens + 3 ones = __400__ + __50__ + __3__ = __453__
6 hundreds + 2 tens + 1 one = __600__ + __20__ + __1__ = __621__
7 hundreds + 9 tens + 8 ones = __700__ + __90__ + __8__ = __798__
2 hundreds + 6 tens + 4 ones = __200__ + __60__ + __4__ = __264__
9 hundreds + 3 tens + 6 ones = __900__ + __30__ + __6__ = __936__
5 hundreds + 7 tens + 2 ones = __500__ + __70__ + __2__ = __572__
1 hundred   + 8 tens + 0 ones = __100__ + __80__ + __0__ = __180__
3 hundreds + 0 tens + 7 ones = __300__ + __00__ + __7__ = __307__

② Write the tally marks for each number.

12 𝍷𝍷𝍷𝍷𝍸 𝍷𝍷
24 𝍷𝍷𝍷𝍷𝍸 𝍷𝍷𝍷𝍷𝍸 𝍷𝍷𝍷𝍷𝍸 𝍷𝍷𝍷𝍷
27 𝍷𝍷𝍷𝍷𝍸 𝍷𝍷𝍷𝍷𝍸 𝍷𝍷𝍷𝍷𝍸 𝍷𝍷𝍷𝍷𝍸 𝍷𝍷
15 𝍷𝍷𝍷𝍷𝍸 𝍷𝍷𝍷𝍷𝍸 𝍷𝍷𝍷𝍷𝍸
8   𝍷𝍷𝍷𝍷𝍸 𝍷𝍷𝍷
31 𝍷𝍷𝍷𝍷𝍸 𝍷𝍷𝍷𝍷𝍸 𝍷𝍷𝍷𝍷𝍸 𝍷𝍷𝍷𝍷𝍸 𝍷𝍷𝍷𝍷𝍸 𝍷𝍷𝍷𝍷𝍸 𝍷

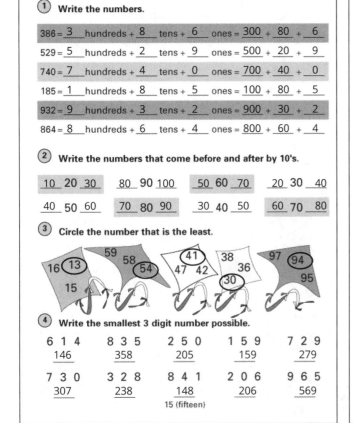

③ Write the numbers that come before and after by 10's.

| 30 | 40 | 50 | 10 | 20 | 30 | 50 | 60 | 70 | 70 | 80 | 90 |
| 60 | 70 | 80 | 20 | 30 | 40 | 0 | 10 | 20 | 40 | 50 | 60 |

13 (thirteen)

---

④ Solve the problems and write the letter in the blanks.

G O O D   F R I E N D S
0 1 2 3   4 5 6 7 8 9 10

A R E   L I K E   G O L D
11 12 13   14 15 16 17   18 19 20 21

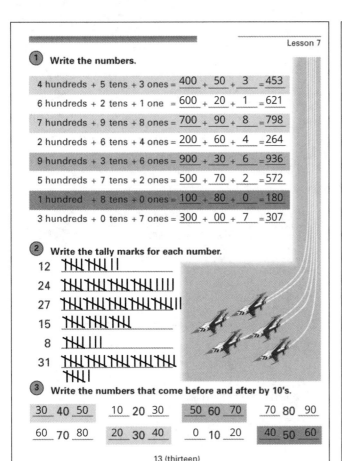

N
3+5= 8

E
7+6=13

K
8+8=16

I
4+2= 6

G
9+9=18

D
2+7= 9

O
9+10=19

L
5+9=14

E
3+4= 7

D
2+1= 3

G
0+0= 0

S
6+4=10

R
7+5=12

D
10+11=21

I
8+7=15

O
1+1= 2

F
2+2= 4

L
10+10=20

A
3+8= 11

O
1+0= 1

R
2+3= 5

E
8+9=17

⑤ Circle the number that is the greatest.

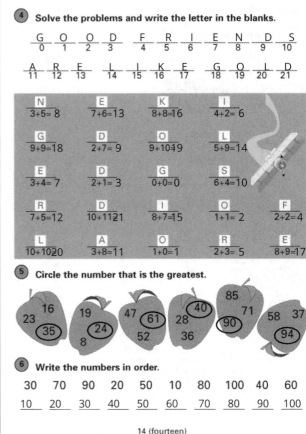

| 16 (35) 23 | 19 (24) 8 | 47 (61) 52 | (40) 28 | 85 90 71 | 58 37 (94) |

⑥ Write the numbers in order.

30 70 90 20 50 10 80 100 40 60

10 20 30 40 50 60 70 80 90 100

14 (fourteen)

---

① Write the numbers.

386 = __3__ hundreds + __8__ tens + __6__ ones = __300__ + __80__ + __6__
529 = __5__ hundreds + __2__ tens + __9__ ones = __500__ + __20__ + __9__
740 = __7__ hundreds + __4__ tens + __0__ ones = __700__ + __40__ + __0__
185 = __1__ hundreds + __8__ tens + __5__ ones = __100__ + __80__ + __5__
932 = __9__ hundreds + __3__ tens + __2__ ones = __900__ + __30__ + __2__
864 = __8__ hundreds + __6__ tens + __4__ ones = __800__ + __60__ + __4__

② Write the numbers that come before and after by 10's.

| 10 | 20 | 30 | 80 | 90 | 100 | 50 | 60 | 70 | 20 | 30 | 40 |
| 40 | 50 | 60 | 70 | 80 | 90 | 30 | 40 | 50 | 60 | 70 | 80 |

③ Circle the number that is the least.

16 (13) 15   59 58 (54)   (41) 47 42   38 36 (30)   97 (94) 95

④ Write the smallest 3 digit number possible.

6 1 4 __146__   8 3 5 __358__   2 5 0 __205__   1 5 9 __159__   7 2 9 __279__

7 3 0 __307__   3 2 8 __238__   8 4 1 __148__   2 0 6 __206__   9 6 5 __569__

15 (fifteen)

---

⑤ Add.

6	9	6	7	7	9	5	3	9	3
+7	+8	+2	+6	+7	+0	+5	+1	+7	+6
13	17	8	13	14	9	10	4	16	9
4	7	5	9	3	6	3	8	6	7
+4	+8	+8	+6	+0	+1	+9	+5	+8	+9
8	15	13	15	3	7	12	13	14	16
2	8	6	4	7	8	5	6	9	3
+9	+6	+9	+5	+5	+4	+7	+0	+5	+2
11	14	15	9	12	12	12	6	14	5
6	3	8					5	8	4
+3	+4	+3					+0	+7	+6
9	7	11					5	15	10
5	9	4					2	7	8
+9	+2	+7					+8	+2	+2
14	11	11					10	9	10
7	2	8					4	9	4
+3	+6	+8					+8	+3	+1
10	8	16					12	12	5
8	3	2	9	4	4	5	8	6	7
+9	+7	+7	+4	+3	+9	+4	+1	+6	+0
17	10	9	13	7	13	9	9	12	7
2	1	2	0	1	2	1	1	2	2
+1	+1	+5	+0	+2	+3	+4	+3	+4	+0
3	2	7	0	3	5	5	4	6	2
0	7	3	9	5	9	6	8	3	6
+4	+4	+8	+1	+6	+9	+4	+0	+5	+5
4	11	11	10	11	18	10	8	8	11

16 (sixteen)

1 Write the numbers.

500 + 60 + 4 = __564__   100 + 40 + 6 = __146__
800 + 30 + 7 = __837__   300 + 10 + 0 = __310__
200 + 90 + 1 = __291__   900 + 70 + 3 = __973__
400 + 50 + 9 = __459__   600 + 20 + 8 = __628__
700 + 00 + 2 = __702__   500 + 80 + 5 = __585__

2 Write the number that is 10 more.

90 __100__   10 __20__   70 __80__   40 __50__
30 __40__   50 __60__   20 __30__   60 __70__

3 Write the number that is 10 less.

__10__ 20   __40__ 50   __80__ 90   __30__ 40
__50__ 60   __60__ 70   __20__ 30   __70__ 80

4 Circle the number that is the least.

91 57 (14)   (28) 42 95   76 (39) 53   (57) 85 70   61 44 (36)   85 62 (38)

5 Write the missing numbers by 10's.

__10__ __20__ 30 __40__ __50__ __60__ 70 80 90 __100__

17 (seventeen)

---

6 Write the problems vertically. Add.

36 + 42 =	51 + 27 =	78 + 21 =
36 +42 —— 78	51 +27 —— 78	78 +21 —— 99
13 + 45 =	**60 + 29 =**	**4 + 13 =**
13 +45 —— 58	60 +29 —— 89	4 +13 —— 17
18 + 40 =	**7 + 22 =**	**36 + 1 =**
18 + 40 —— 58	7 + 22 —— 29	36 + 1 —— 37
54 + 15 =	**14 + 82 =**	**23 + 74 =**
54 + 15 —— 69	14 + 82 —— 96	23 + 74 —— 97
31 + 4 =	**42 + 26 =**	**12 + 52 =**
31 + 4 —— 35	42 + 26 —— 68	12 + 52 —— 64
25 + 31 =		**27 + 40 =**
25 + 31 —— 56		27 + 40 —— 67

18 (eighteen)

---

1 Write the letters on the blanks.   13 pts.

A	L	W	A	Y	S		D	O

R	I	G	H	T

fourth __A__   fifth __Y__   ninth __R__
twelfth __H__   tenth __I__   eleventh __G__
sixth __S__   eighth __O__   second __L__
thirteenth __T__   first __A__   seventh __D__
third __W__

2 Write the missing numbers.   90 pts. for this exercise

0	1	2	3	4	5	6	7	8	9
10	11	12	13	14	15	16	17	18	19
20	21	22	23	24	25	26	27	28	29
30	31	32	33	34	35	36	37	38	39
40	41	42	43	44	45	46	47	48	49
50	51	52	53	54	55	56	57	58	59
60	61	62	63	64	65	66	67	68	69
70	71	72	73	74	75	76	77	78	79
80	81	82	83	84	85	86	87	88	89
90	91	92	93	94	95	96	97	98	99

19 (nineteen)

---

3 Write the numbers that come before and after by 1's.   20 pts.

__42__ 43 __44__   __63__ 64 __65__   __11__ 12 __13__   95 96 __97__
85 86 __87__   __6__ 7 __8__   __23__ 24 __25__
__27__ 28 __29__   __58__ 59 __60__   __30__ 31 __32__

4 Write the missing numbers by 5's.   8 pts.

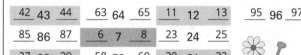

55

5 10 15 20 25 **30** 35 40 45 50

5 Write the numbers.   8 pts.

||||| ||||| |||| __14__	||||| ||||| ||||| ||||| ||| __23__
||||| || __7__	||||| ||||| ||||| |||| __19__
||||| ||||| |||||	__16__	||||| ||| __8__
||||| ||||| __10__	||||| ||||| ||||| ||||| ||||| __25__

6 Circle the larger number.   5 pts.

36 (87)   15 (21)   (42) 9   (73) 65   (98) 80

7 Circle the smaller number.   5 pts.

(44) 50   60 (30)   25 (12)   (76) 84   (59) 95

20 (twenty)

359

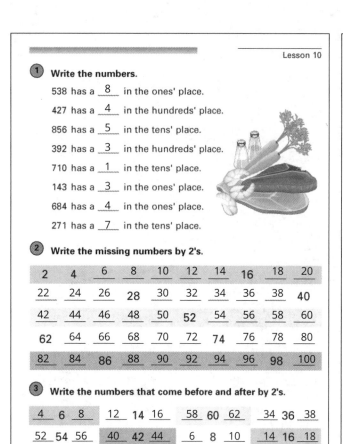

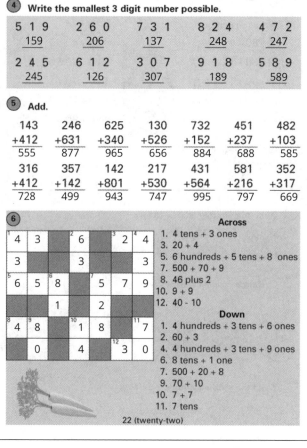

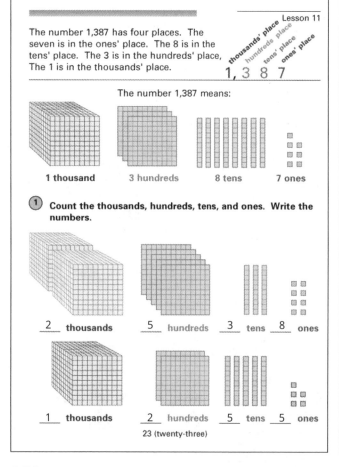

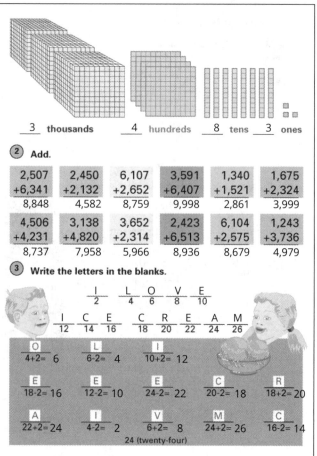

Lesson 10

1 Write the numbers.

538 has a __8__ in the ones' place.

427 has a __4__ in the hundreds' place.

856 has a __5__ in the tens' place.

392 has a __3__ in the hundreds' place.

710 has a __1__ in the tens' place.

143 has a __3__ in the ones' place.

684 has a __4__ in the ones' place.

271 has a __7__ in the tens' place.

2 Write the missing numbers by 2's.

2	4	6	8	10	12	14	16	18	20
22	24	26	28	30	32	34	36	38	40
42	44	46	48	50	52	54	56	58	60
62	64	66	68	70	72	74	76	78	80
82	84	86	88	90	92	94	96	98	100

3 Write the numbers that come before and after by 2's.

4 __6__ 8   12 __14__ 16   __58__ 60 __62__   34 36 __38__

52 54 __56__   __40__ 42 __44__   __6__ 8 __10__   __14__ 16 __18__

21 (twenty-one)

---

4 Write the smallest 3 digit number possible.

5 1 9	2 6 0	7 3 1	8 2 4	4 7 2
159	206	137	248	247

2 4 5	6 1 2	3 0 7	9 1 8	5 8 9
245	126	307	189	589

5 Add.

143	246	625	130	732	451	482
+412	+631	+340	+526	+152	+237	+103
555	877	965	656	884	688	585

316	357	142	217	431	581	352
+412	+142	+801	+530	+564	+216	+317
728	499	943	747	995	797	669

6

Across
1. 4 tens + 3 ones
3. 20 + 4
5. 6 hundreds + 5 tens + 8 ones
7. 500 + 70 + 9
8. 46 plus 2
10. 9 + 9
12. 40 - 10

Down
1. 4 hundreds + 3 tens + 6 ones
2. 60 + 3
4. 4 hundreds + 3 tens + 9 ones
6. 8 tens + 1 one
7. 500 + 20 + 8
9. 70 + 10
10. 7 + 7
11. 7 tens

22 (twenty-two)

Lesson 11

The number 1,387 has four places. The seven is in the ones' place. The 8 is in the tens' place. The 3 is in the hundreds' place. The 1 is in the thousands' place.

thousands' place
hundreds' place
tens' place
ones' place

1, 3 8 7

The number 1,387 means:

1 thousand   **3 hundreds**   **8 tens**   **7 ones**

1 Count the thousands, hundreds, tens, and ones. Write the numbers.

__2__ thousands   __5__ hundreds   __3__ tens   __8__ ones

__1__ thousands   __2__ hundreds   __5__ tens   __5__ ones

23 (twenty-three)

__3__ thousands   __4__ hundreds   __8__ tens   __3__ ones

2 Add.

2,507	2,450	6,107	3,591	1,340	1,675
+6,341	+2,132	+2,652	+6,407	+1,521	+2,324
8,848	4,582	8,759	9,998	2,861	3,999

4,506	3,138	3,652	2,423	6,104	1,243
+4,231	+4,820	+2,314	+6,513	+2,575	+3,736
8,737	7,958	5,966	8,936	8,679	4,979

3 Write the letters in the blanks.

I L O V E
2 4 6 8 10

I C E C R E A M
12 14 16 18 20 22 24 26

O	L	I
4+2= 6	6-2= 4	10+2= 12

E	E	E	C	R
18-2= 16	12-2= 10	24-2= 22	20-2= 18	18+2= 20

A	I	V	M	C
22+2= 24	4-2= 2	6+2= 8	24+2= 26	16-2= 14

24 (twenty-four)

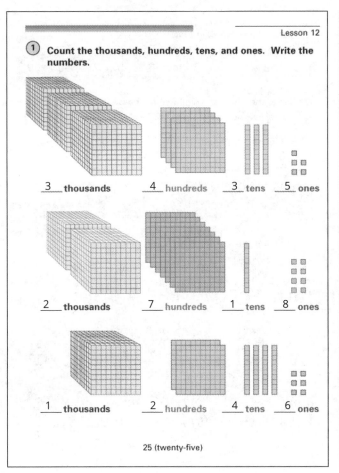

Lesson 12

① Count the thousands, hundreds, tens, and ones. Write the numbers.

__3__ thousands __4__ hundreds __3__ tens __5__ ones

__2__ thousands __7__ hundreds __1__ tens __8__ ones

__1__ thousands __2__ hundreds __4__ tens __6__ ones

25 (twenty-five)

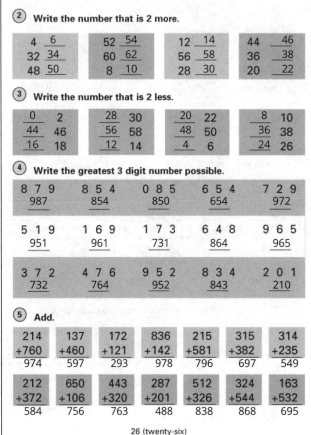

② Write the number that is 2 more.

4 __6__	52 __54__	12 __14__	44 __46__
32 __34__	60 __62__	56 __58__	36 __38__
48 __50__	8 __10__	28 __30__	20 __22__

③ Write the number that is 2 less.

__0__ 2	__28__ 30	__20__ 22	__8__ 10
__44__ 46	__56__ 58	__48__ 50	__36__ 38
__16__ 18	__12__ 14	__4__ 6	__24__ 26

④ Write the greatest 3 digit number possible.

8 7 9	8 5 4	0 8 5	6 5 4	7 2 9
987	854	850	654	972

5 1 9	1 6 9	1 7 3	6 4 8	9 6 5
951	961	731	864	965

3 7 2	4 7 6	9 5 2	8 3 4	2 0 1
732	764	952	843	210

⑤ Add.

214	137	172	836	215	315	314
+760	+460	+121	+142	+581	+382	+235
974	597	293	978	796	697	549

212	650	443	287	512	324	163
+372	+106	+320	+201	+326	+544	+532
584	756	763	488	838	868	695

26 (twenty-six)

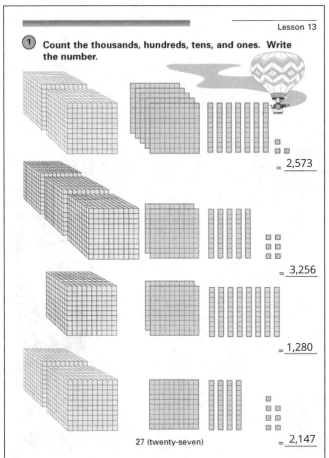

Lesson 13

① Count the thousands, hundreds, tens, and ones. Write the number.

= __2,573__

= __3,256__

= __1,280__

= __2,147__

27 (twenty-seven)

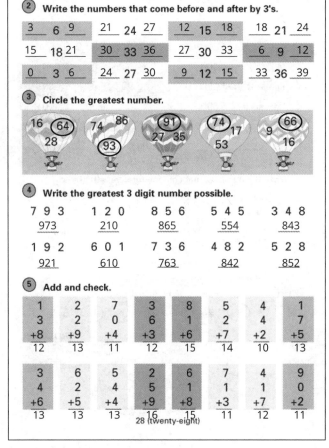

② Write the numbers that come before and after by 3's.

__3__ 6 __9__	21 24 __27__	__12__ 15 __18__	__18__ 21 __24__
__15__ 18 __21__	__30__ 33 __36__	__27__ 30 __33__	__6__ 9 __12__
__0__ 3 __6__	__24__ 27 __30__	__9__ 12 __15__	__33__ 36 __39__

③ Circle the greatest number.

16 ⑥④ 28 74 86 ⑨③ ⑨① 27 35 ⑦④ 17 53 9 ⑥⑥ 16

④ Write the greatest 3 digit number possible.

7 9 3	1 2 0	8 5 6	5 4 5	3 4 8
973	210	865	554	843

1 9 2	6 0 1	7 3 6	4 8 2	5 2 8
921	610	763	842	852

⑤ Add and check.

1	2	7	3	8	5	4	1
3	2	0	6	1	2	4	7
+8	+9	+4	+3	+6	+7	+2	+5
12	13	11	12	15	14	10	13

3	6	5	2	6	7	4	9
4	2	4	5	1	1	1	0
+6	+5	+4	+9	+8	+3	+7	+2
13	13	13	16	15	11	12	11

28 (twenty-eight)

① Write the numbers.

6 thousands = 6,000   1 thousand = 1,000

4 thousands = 4,000   5 thousands = 5,000

7 thousands = 7,000   9 thousands = 9,000

8 thousands = 8,000   2 thousands = 2,000

3 thousands = 3,000

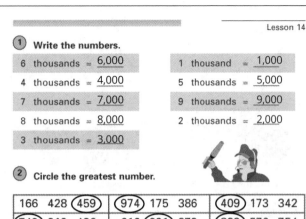

② Circle the greatest number.

166	428	(459)	(974)	175	386	(409)	173	342
(749)	319	436	616	(991)	273	(829)	576	754
542	(735)	286	(691)	664	284	538	860	(947)

③ Write the missing numbers by 3's.

3   6   9   12   15   18   21   24   27   30

④ Write the numbers that come before and after by 3's.

3   6   9   12   15   18   21   24   27   9   12   15

18   21   24   24   27   30   0   3   6   30   33   36

27   30   33   6   9   12   33   36   39   15   18   21

29 (twenty-nine)

---

⑤ Write the numbers in order.

37   50   13   21   46   34   18   59   25   42

13   18   21   25   34   37   42   46   50   59

⑥ Write the smallest 4 digit number possible.

8 1 3 2	7 2 9 4	3 6 5 0	4 8 6 0	5 7 2 6
1,238	2,479	3,056	4,068	2,567
6 4 3 7	6 2 5 4	9 6 8 1	3 9 5 7	4 7 5 1
3,467	2,456	1,689	3,579	1,457
3 9 8 6	9 4 7 3	6 2 1 3	8 6 2 3	6 1 2 5
3,689	3,479	1,236	2,368	1,256

⑦ Add and check.

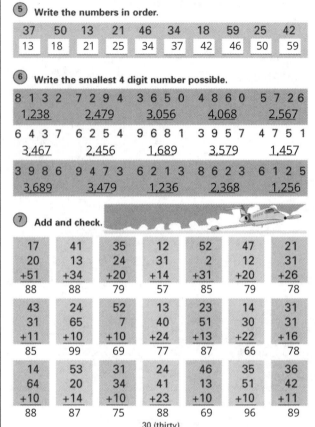

17	41	35	12	52	47	21
20	13	24	31	2	12	31
+51	+34	+20	+14	+31	+20	+26
88	88	79	57	85	79	78

43	24	52	13	23	14	31
31	65	7	40	51	30	31
+11	+10	+10	+24	+13	+22	+16
85	99	69	77	87	66	78

14	53	31	24	46	35	36
64	20	34	41	13	51	42
+10	+14	+10	+23	+10	+10	+11
88	87	75	88	69	96	89

30 (thirty)

---

① Write the numbers.

5 thousands = 5,000   2 thousands = 2,000

4 thousands = 4,000   7 thousands = 7,000

1 thousand = 1,000   3 thousands = 3,000

6 thousands = 6,000   8 thousands = 8,000

9 thousands = 9,000

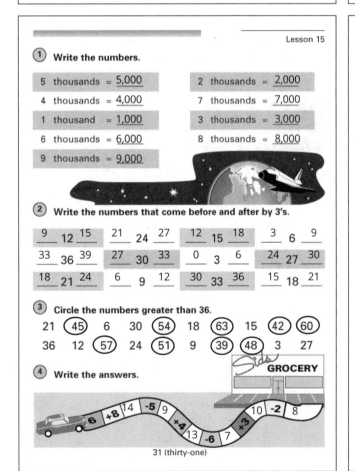

② Write the numbers that come before and after by 3's.

9   12   15   21   24   27   12   15   18   3   6   9

33   36   39   27   30   33   0   3   6   24   27   30

18   21   24   6   9   12   30   33   36   15   18   21

③ Circle the numbers greater than 36.

21   (45)   6   30   (54)   18   (63)   15   (42)   (60)

36   12   (57)   24   (51)   9   (39)   (48)   3   27

④ Write the answers.

GROCERY

6 +8 14 -5 9   10 -2 8
+4 13 -6 7 +3

31 (thirty-one)

---

⑤ Write the numbers in order.

15   9   24   3   21   12   27   0   18   6

0   3   6   9   12   15   18   21   24   27

⑥ Add.

430	417	605	241	835	123	360
+251	+312	+241	+345	+102	+642	+337
681	729	846	586	937	765	697

414	216	432	152	565	231	254
+523	+103	+412	+320	+114	+564	+601
937	319	844	472	679	795	855

⑦ Write the missing numbers.

100	101	102	103	104	105	106	107	108	109
110	111	112	113	114	115	116	117	118	119
120	121	122	**123**	124	125	126	127	128	129
130	131	132	133	134	135	136	137	138	139
140	141	142	143	144	145	**146**	147	148	149
150	151	152	153	154	155	156	157	158	159
160	161	162	163	**164**	165	166	167	168	169
170	171	172	173	174	175	176	177	178	179
180	181	182	183	184	185	186	187	**188**	189
190	191	**192**	193	194	195	196	197	198	199

32 (thirty-two)

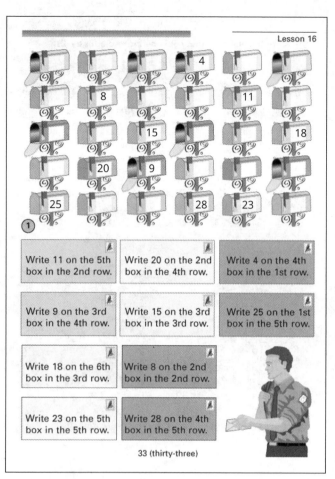

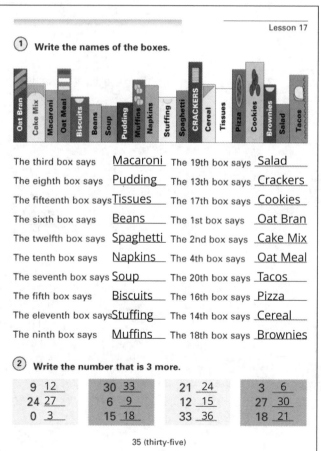

①

Write 11 on the 5th box in the 2nd row.

Write 20 on the 2nd box in the 4th row.

Write 4 on the 4th box in the 1st row.

Write 9 on the 3rd box in the 4th row.

Write 15 on the 3rd box in the 3rd row.

Write 25 on the 1st box in the 5th row.

Write 18 on the 6th box in the 3rd row.

Write 8 on the 2nd box in the 2nd row.

Write 23 on the 5th box in the 5th row.

Write 28 on the 4th box in the 5th row.

33 (thirty-three)

---

② Write the numbers that come before and after by 3's.

| 12 | _15_ | _18_ | 24 | 27 | _30_ | _3_ | 6 | _9_ | _27_ | 30 | _33_ |

| 30 | _33_ | 36 | _6_ | 9 | _12_ | 21 | _24_ | 27 | _18_ | 21 | _24_ |

| 0 | _3_ | 6 | _15_ | 18 | _21_ | 33 | _36_ | 39 | _9_ | 12 | _15_ |

③ Circle the numbers greater than 126.

65 (158) 48 94 (193) 113 (146) (200) (185) 82

(132) 87 (174) 120 71 59 (161) (216) (129) 106

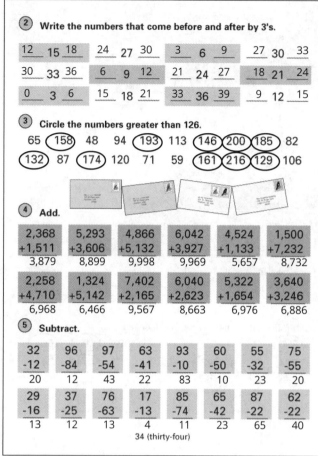

④ Add.

2,368	5,293	4,866	6,042	4,524	1,500
+1,511	+3,606	+5,132	+3,927	+1,133	+7,232
3,879	8,899	9,998	9,969	5,657	8,732

2,258	1,324	7,402	6,040	5,322	3,640
+4,710	+5,142	+2,165	+2,623	+1,654	+3,246
6,968	6,466	9,567	8,663	6,976	6,886

⑤ Subtract.

32	96	97	63	93	60	55	75
-12	-84	-54	-41	-10	-50	-32	-55
20	12	43	22	83	10	23	20

29	37	76	17	85	65	87	62
-16	-25	-63	-13	-74	-42	-22	-22
13	12	13	4	11	23	65	40

34 (thirty-four)

---

① Write the names of the boxes.

The third box says __Macaroni__   The 19th box says __Salad__

The eighth box says __Pudding__   The 13th box says __Crackers__

The fifteenth box says __Tissues__   The 17th box says __Cookies__

The sixth box says __Beans__   The 1st box says __Oat Bran__

The twelfth box says __Spaghetti__   The 2nd box says __Cake Mix__

The tenth box says __Napkins__   The 4th box says __Oat Meal__

The seventh box says __Soup__   The 20th box says __Tacos__

The fifth box says __Biscuits__   The 16th box says __Pizza__

The eleventh box says __Stuffing__   The 14th box says __Cereal__

The ninth box says __Muffins__   The 18th box says __Brownies__

② Write the number that is 3 more.

9	_12_		30	_33_		21	_24_		3	_6_
24	_27_		6	_9_		12	_15_		27	_30_
0	_3_		15	_18_		33	_36_		18	_21_

35 (thirty-five)

---

③ Write the number that is 3 less.

_24_	27		_15_	18		0	3		_21_	24
_9_	12		_3_	6		_30_	33		_27_	30
18	21		_33_	36		12	15		_6_	9

④ Write the missing numbers by 1's.

246	_247_	_248_	_249_	_250_	251	_252_	_253_
673	_674_	_675_	_676_	677	_678_	_679_	_680_
301	_302_	_303_	_304_	_305_	_306_	307	_308_
525	_526_	_527_	528	_529_	_530_	_531_	532

⑤ Write the missing numbers by 3's.

3   _6_   _9_   _12_   _15_   _18_   _21_   _24_   _27_   _30_

⑥ Subtract.

16	12	17	10	14	15	11	13
- 9	- 8	- 9	- 5	- 7	- 9	- 3	- 6
7	4	8	5	7	6	8	7

12	14	17	11	15	13	18	16
- 5	- 8	- 8	- 4	- 7	- 4	- 9	- 8
7	6	9	7	8	9	9	8

49	48	78	95	67	83	57	78
-17	-23	-62	-45	-17	-52	-24	-27
32	25	16	50	50	31	33	51

63	93	55			65	96	89
-51	-30	-13			-34	-24	-45
12	63	42		36 (thirty-six)	31	72	44

363

① Write the correct time.

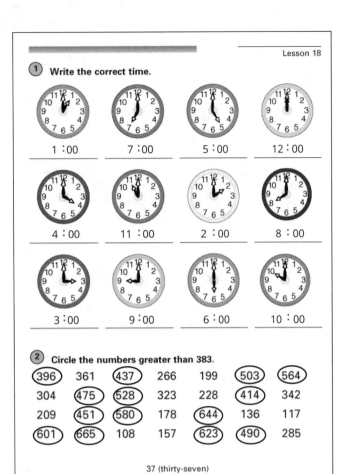

1 : 00   7 : 00   5 : 00   12 : 00

4 : 00   11 : 00   2 : 00   8 : 00

3 : 00   9 : 00   6 : 00   10 : 00

② Circle the numbers greater than 383.

(396)	361	(437)	266	199	(503)	(564)
304	(475)	(528)	323	228	(414)	342
209	(451)	(580)	178	(644)	136	117
(601)	(665)	108	157	(623)	(490)	285

37 (thirty-seven)

---

③ Write the numbers that come before and after by 6's.

30 36 42   6 12 18   18 24 30   66 72 78

54 60 66   36 42 48   0 6 12   24 30 36

12 18 24   42 48 54   60 66 72   48 54 60

④ Add and check.

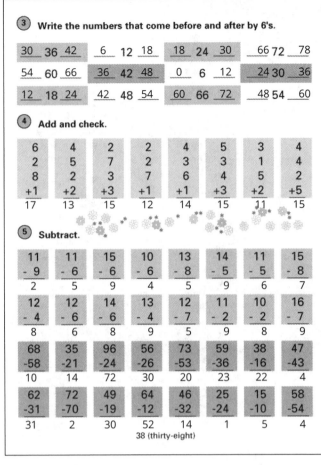

6	4	2	2	4	5	3	4
2	5	7	2	3	3	1	4
8	2	3	7	6	4	5	2
+1	+2	+3	+1	+1	+3	+2	+5
17	13	15	12	14	15	11	15

⑤ Subtract.

11	11	15	10	13	14	11	15
- 9	- 6	- 6	- 6	- 8	- 5	- 5	- 8
2	5	9	4	5	9	6	7

12	12	14	13	12	11	10	16
- 4	- 6	- 6	- 4	- 7	- 2	- 2	- 7
8	6	8	9	5	9	8	9

68	35	96	56	73	59	38	47
-58	-21	-24	-26	-53	-36	-16	-43
10	14	72	30	20	23	22	4

62	72	49	64	46	25	15	58
-31	-70	-19	-12	-32	-24	-10	-54
31	2	30	52	14	1	5	4

38 (thirty-eight)

---

① Write the correct time.

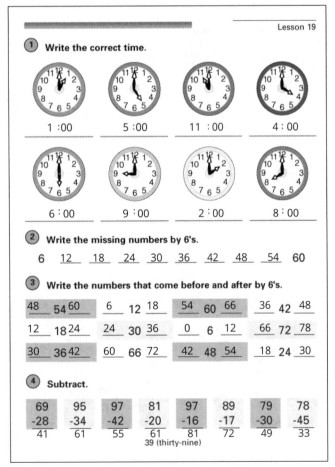

1 : 00   5 : 00   11 : 00   4 : 00

6 : 00   9 : 00   2 : 00   8 : 00

② Write the missing numbers by 6's.

6 12 18 24 30 36 42 48 54 60

③ Write the numbers that come before and after by 6's.

48 54 60   6 12 18   54 60 66   36 42 48

12 18 24   24 30 36   0 6 12   66 72 78

30 36 42   60 66 72   42 48 54   18 24 30

④ Subtract.

69	95	97	81	97	89	79	78
-28	-34	-42	-20	-16	-17	-30	-45
41	61	55	61	81	72	49	33

39 (thirty-nine)

---

⑤ Add and check.

3 + 5 + 7 + 1 =

3
5
7
+ 1
16

6 + 1 + 5 + 4 =

6
1
5
+ 4
16

4 + 2 + 8 + 3 =

4
2
8
+ 3
17

7 + 4 + 2 + 4 =

7
4
2
+ 4
17

7 + 5 + 3 + 4 =

7
5
3
+ 4
19

2 + 9 + 5 + 1 =

2
9
5
+ 1
17

3 + 6 + 4 + 2 =

3
6
4
+ 2
15

3 + 4 + 7 + 2 =

3
4
7
+ 2
16

40 (forty)

1 Write the numbers. 8 pts.

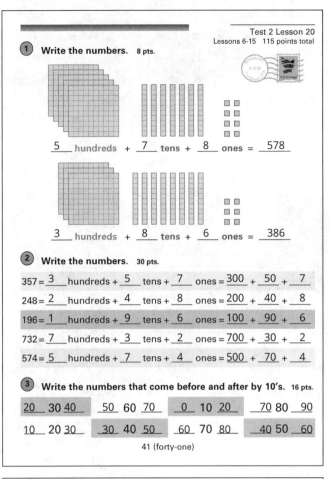

5 hundreds + 7 tens + 8 ones = 578

3 hundreds + 8 tens + 6 ones = 386

2 Write the numbers. 30 pts.

357 = 3 hundreds + 5 tens + 7 ones = 300 + 50 + 7
248 = 2 hundreds + 4 tens + 8 ones = 200 + 40 + 8
196 = 1 hundreds + 9 tens + 6 ones = 100 + 90 + 6
732 = 7 hundreds + 3 tens + 2 ones = 700 + 30 + 2
574 = 5 hundreds + 7 tens + 4 ones = 500 + 70 + 4

3 Write the numbers that come before and after by 10's. 16 pts.

20 30 40   50 60 70   0 10 20   70 80 90
10 20 30   30 40 50   60 70 80   40 50 60

41 (forty-one)

4 Circle the numbers larger than the first number in each row.

14	13	5	(19)	10	(24)	(16)	2	7	(21)
35	(43)	(37)	26	(46)	(45)	23	(40)	32	29
56	(57)	48	(63)	51	(70)	(59)	45	(66)	55
82	(84)	(92)	75	81	(87)	79	(95)	72	(90)

19 pts.

5 Write the missing numbers by 2's. 12 pts.

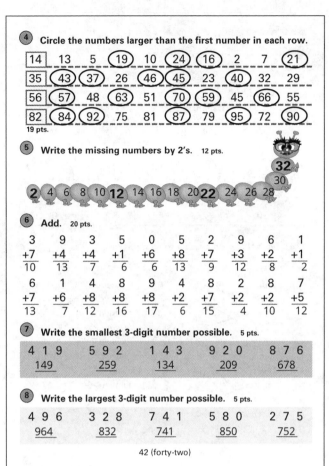

32
30

2 4 6 8 10 12 14 16 18 20 22 24 26 28

6 Add. 20 pts.

3	9	3	5	0	5	2	9	6	1
+7	+4	+4	+1	+6	+8	+7	+3	+2	+1
10	13	7	6	6	13	9	12	8	2

6	1	4	8	9	4	8	2	8	7
+7	+6	+8	+8	+8	+2	+7	+2	+2	+5
13	7	12	16	17	6	15	4	10	12

7 Write the smallest 3-digit number possible. 5 pts.

| 4 1 9 | 5 9 2 | 1 4 3 | 9 2 0 | 8 7 6 |
| 149 | 259 | 134 | 209 | 678 |

8 Write the largest 3-digit number possible. 5 pts.

| 4 9 6 | 3 2 8 | 7 4 1 | 5 8 0 | 2 7 5 |
| 964 | 832 | 741 | 850 | 752 |

42 (forty-two)

1 Write the correct time.

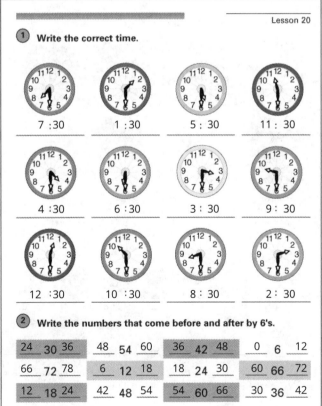

7 :30   1 :30   5 : 30   11 : 30

4 :30   6 :30   9 : 30

12 :30   10 :30   8 : 30   2 : 30

2 Write the numbers that come before and after by 6's.

24 30 36   48 54 60   36 42 48   0 6 12
66 72 78   6 12 18   18 24 30   60 66 72
12 18 24   42 48 54   54 60 66   30 36 42

43 (forty-three)

3 Write the numbers in order.

| 30 | 6 | 48 | 18 | 60 | 36 | 12 | 54 | 42 | 24 |
| 6 | 12 | 18 | 24 | 30 | 36 | 42 | 48 | 54 | 60 |

4 Subtract.

9	4	13	5	12	7	17	8	14	10
-9	-3	-6	-3	-9	-5	-9	-4	-8	-2
0	1	7	2	3	2	8	4	6	8

6	9	14	8	13	7	12	6	16	10
-0	-4	-7	-5	-5	-7	-8	-2	-8	-4
6	5	7	3	8	0	4	4	8	6

8	11	5	4	18	9	6	13	2	11
-2	-8	-4	-4	-9	-5	-4	-7	-2	-3
6	3	1	0	9	4	2	6	0	8

12	3	15	10	8	7	11	5	14	9
-6	-3	-8	-6	-8	-6	-4	-1	-6	-3
6	0	7	4	0	1	7	4	8	6

10	6	11	11	3	14	9	8	16	5
-5	-5	-9	-7	-1	-9	-7	-3	-9	-5
5	1	2	4	2	5	2	5	7	0

8	17	9	7	13	8	10	14	4	12
-1	-8	-2	-4	-8	-7	-8	-5	-2	-5
7	9	7	3	5	1	2	9	2	7

10	11	15	11	6	12	3	13	9	7
-1	-5	-7	-6	-3	-3	-2	-4	-8	-2
9	6	8	5	3	9	1	9	1	5

13	8	12	5		6	9	15	7
-9	-6	-4	-2		-1	-1	-9	-0
4	2	8	3		5	8	6	7

44 (forty-four)

365

1 Write the correct time.

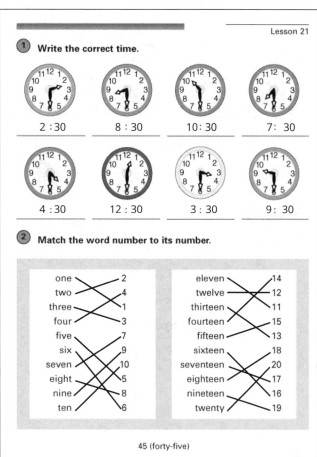

2 : 30   8 : 30   10 : 30   7 : 30

4 : 30   12 : 30   3 : 30   9 : 30

2 Match the word number to its number.

one — 2	eleven — 14
two — 4	twelve — 12
three — 1	thirteen — 11
four — 3	fourteen — 15
five — 7	fifteen — 13
six — 9	sixteen — 18
seven — 10	seventeen — 20
eight — 5	eighteen — 17
nine — 8	nineteen — 16
ten — 6	twenty — 19

45 (forty-five)

---

3 Write the numbers that come before and after by 6's.

12 18 24   36 42 48   6 12 18   18 24 30

60 66 72   0 6 12   48 54 60   54 60 66

30 36 42   66 72 78   24 30 36   42 48 54

4 Subtract.

369	278	753	896	457	976	489
- 165	- 158	- 650	- 785	- 441	- 374	- 356
204	120	103	111	16	602	133

387	965	789	497	865	985	869
- 264	- 421	- 349	- 112	- 312	- 723	- 132
123	544	440	385	553	262	737

5 Amy has 32 crayons. Joyce gave her 26 more. How many crayons did Amy have altogether?

```
  32
+ 26
  58  crayons
```

Sam gave Joe 16 marbles to add to the 53 he already had. How many marbles did Joe have altogether?

```
  53
+ 16
  69  marbles
```

There were 32 girls and 25 boys on the bus for a roller skating party. How many children were on the bus altogether?

```
  32
+ 25
  57  children
```

46 (forty-six)

---

1 Add.

59	26	42	45	48	15	27	37
+28	+18	+49	+38	+19	+26	+43	+27
87	44	91	83	67	41	70	64

68	28	39	17	73	43	56	29
+18	+62	+46	+55	+19	+27	+36	+54
86	90	85	72	92	70	92	83

56	28	37	15	19	51	37	18
+14	+25	+19	+65	+73	+29	+48	+14
70	53	56	80	92	80	85	32

2 Match the clock to its time.

5:30   10:30

1:30   2:30

3:30   8:30

11:30   6:30

47 (forty-seven)

---

3 Write the number that is 6 more.

48 54	36 42	18 24	6 12
60 66	12 18	42 48	30 36
24 30	72 78	66 72	54 60

4 Write the number that is 6 less.

18 24	30 36	48 54	0 6
60 66	54 60	6 12	36 42
42 48	12 18	24 30	66 72

5 Write the numbers.

fourteen 14	sixteen 16	eleven 11
seven 7	one 1	five 5
eighteen 18	fifteen 15	nineteen 19
twelve 12	three 3	eight 8

6 Subtract.

516	947	285	693	878	458	873
- 113	- 646	- 155	- 570	- 670	- 327	- 841
403	301	130	123	208	131	32

897	692	586	569	939	746	867
- 135	- 252	- 424	- 362	- 134	- 121	- 402
762	440	162	207	805	625	465

7 Jimmy practiced his trumpet for 45 minutes on Tuesday and 30 minutes on Thursday. How many minutes did he practice his trumpet altogether?

```
  45
+ 30
  75  minutes
```

48 (forty-eight)

1 Write the correct time.

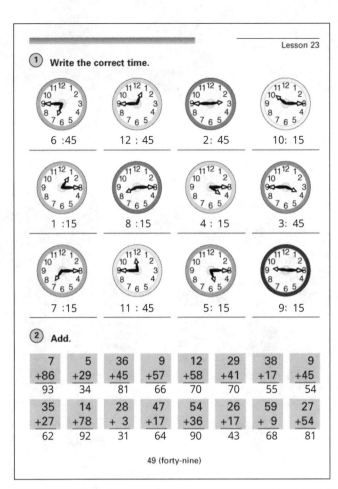

6 :45   12 : 45   2: 45   10: 15

1 :15   8 :15   4 : 15   3: 45

7 :15   11 : 45   5: 15   9: 15

2 Add.

7	5	36	9	12	29	38	9
+86	+29	+45	+57	+58	+41	+17	+45
93	34	81	66	70	70	55	54

35	14	28	47	54	26	59	27
+27	+78	+ 3	+17	+36	+17	+ 9	+54
62	92	31	64	90	43	68	81

49 (forty-nine)

3 Subtract.

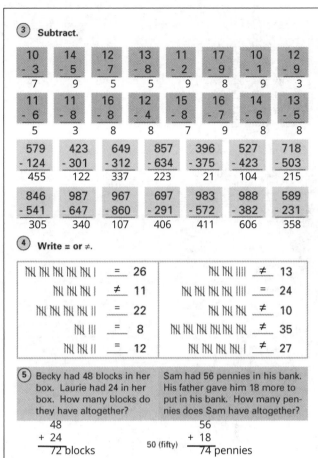

10	14	12	13	11	17	10	12
- 3	- 5	- 7	- 8	- 2	- 9	- 1	- 9
7	9	5	5	9	8	9	3

11	11	16	12	15	16	14	13
- 6	- 8	- 8	- 4	- 8	- 7	- 6	- 5
5	3	8	8	7	9	8	8

579	423	649	857	396	527	718
- 124	- 301	- 312	- 634	- 375	- 423	- 503
455	122	337	223	21	104	215

846	987	967	697	983	988	589
- 541	- 647	- 860	- 291	- 572	- 382	- 231
305	340	107	406	411	606	358

4 Write = or ≠.

‖‖‖‖‖	= 26		‖‖‖‖	≠ 13
‖‖‖	≠ 11		‖‖‖‖	= 24
‖‖‖‖	= 22		‖‖‖	≠ 10
‖‖	= 8		‖‖‖‖‖‖	≠ 35
‖‖	= 12		‖‖‖‖	≠ 27

5

Becky had 48 blocks in her box. Laurie had 24 in her box. How many blocks do they have altogether?

48
+ 24
72 blocks

Sam had 56 pennies in his bank. His father gave him 18 more to put in his bank. How many pennies does Sam have altogether?

56
+ 18
74 pennies

50 (fifty)

---

1 Match the word number to its number.

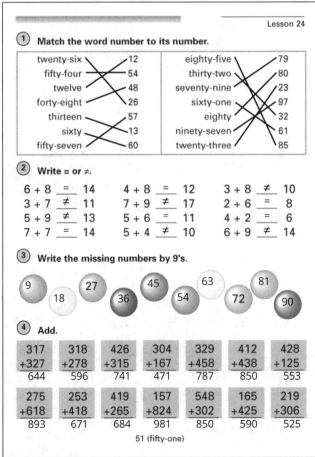

twenty-six	12
fifty-four	54
twelve	48
forty-eight	26
thirteen	57
sixty	13
fifty-seven	60

eighty-five	79
thirty-two	80
seventy-nine	23
sixty-one	97
eighty	32
ninety-seven	61
twenty-three	85

2 Write = or ≠.

6 + 8 = 14   4 + 8 = 12   3 + 8 ≠ 10
3 + 7 ≠ 11   7 + 9 ≠ 17   2 + 6 = 8
5 + 9 ≠ 13   5 + 6 = 11   4 + 2 = 6
7 + 7 = 14   5 + 4 ≠ 10   6 + 9 ≠ 14

3 Write the missing numbers by 9's.

9   18   27   36   45   54   63   72   81   90

4 Add.

317	318	426	304	329	412	428
+327	+278	+315	+167	+458	+438	+125
644	596	741	471	787	850	553

275	253	419	157	548	165	219
+618	+418	+265	+824	+302	+425	+306
893	671	684	981	850	590	525

51 (fifty-one)

5 Write the correct time.

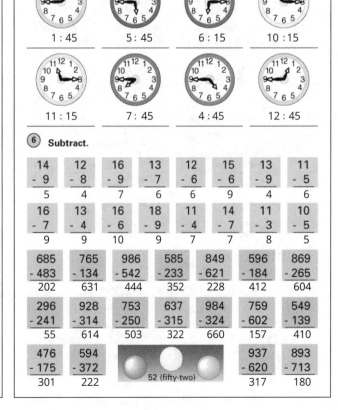

1 : 45   5 : 45   6 : 15   10 :15

11 : 15   7 : 45   4 :45   12 : 45

6 Subtract.

14	12	16	13	12	15	13	11
- 9	- 8	- 9	- 7	- 6	- 6	- 9	- 5
5	4	7	6	6	9	4	6

16	13	16	18	11	14	11	10
- 7	- 4	- 6	- 9	- 4	- 7	- 3	- 5
9	9	10	9	7	7	8	5

685	765	986	585	849	596	869
- 483	- 134	- 542	- 233	- 621	- 184	- 265
202	631	444	352	228	412	604

296	928	753	637	984	759	549
- 241	- 314	- 250	- 315	- 324	- 602	- 139
55	614	503	322	660	157	410

476	594			937	893
- 175	- 372			- 620	- 713
301	222			317	180

52 (fifty-two)

367

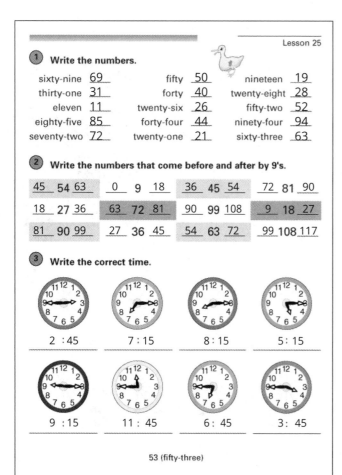

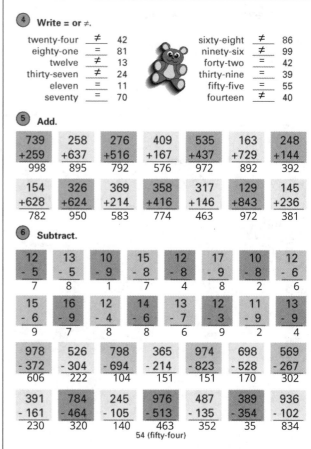

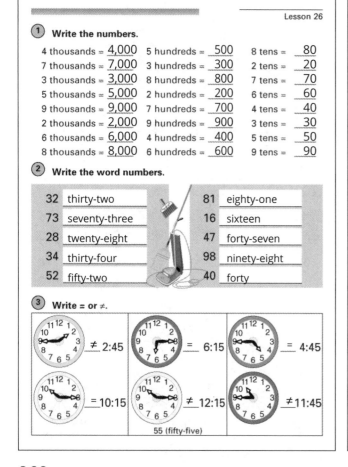

Lesson 25

1 Write the numbers.

sixty-nine	69	fifty	50	nineteen	19
thirty-one	31	forty	40	twenty-eight	28
eleven	11	twenty-six	26	fifty-two	52
eighty-five	85	forty-four	44	ninety-four	94
seventy-two	72	twenty-one	21	sixty-three	63

2 Write the numbers that come before and after by 9's.

45 __54__ 63   0 __9__ 18   36 __45__ 54   72 __81__ 90

18 __27__ 36   63 __72__ 81   90 __99__ 108   9 __18__ 27

81 __90__ 99   27 __36__ 45   54 __63__ 72   99 108 __117__

3 Write the correct time.

2 : 45   7 : 15   8 : 15   5 : 15

9 : 15   11 : 45   6 : 45   3 : 45

53 (fifty-three)

---

4 Write = or ≠.

twenty-four	≠	42	sixty-eight	≠	86
eighty-one	=	81	ninety-six	≠	99
twelve	≠	13	forty-two	=	42
thirty-seven	≠	24	thirty-nine	=	39
eleven	=	11	fifty-five	=	55
seventy	=	70	fourteen	≠	40

5 Add.

739	258	276	409	535	163	248
+259	+637	+516	+167	+437	+729	+144
998	895	792	576	972	892	392

154	326	369	358	317	129	145
+628	+624	+214	+416	+146	+843	+236
782	950	583	774	463	972	381

6 Subtract.

12	13	10	15	12	17	10	12
- 5	- 5	- 9	- 8	- 8	- 9	- 8	- 6
7	8	1	7	4	8	2	6

15	16	12	14	13	12	11	13
- 6	- 9	- 4	- 6	- 7	- 3	- 9	- 9
9	7	8	8	6	9	2	4

978	526	798	365	974	698	569
- 372	- 304	- 694	- 214	- 823	- 528	- 267
606	222	104	151	151	170	302

391	784	245	976	487	389	936
- 161	- 464	- 105	- 513	- 135	- 354	- 102
230	320	140	463	352	35	834

54 (fifty-four)

Lesson 26

1 Write the numbers.

4 thousands = 4,000	5 hundreds = 500	8 tens = 80
7 thousands = 7,000	3 hundreds = 300	2 tens = 20
3 thousands = 3,000	8 hundreds = 800	7 tens = 70
5 thousands = 5,000	2 hundreds = 200	6 tens = 60
9 thousands = 9,000	7 hundreds = 700	4 tens = 40
2 thousands = 2,000	9 hundreds = 900	3 tens = 30
6 thousands = 6,000	4 hundreds = 400	5 tens = 50
8 thousands = 8,000	6 hundreds = 600	9 tens = 90

2 Write the word numbers.

32	thirty-two	81	eighty-one
73	seventy-three	16	sixteen
28	twenty-eight	47	forty-seven
34	thirty-four	98	ninety-eight
52	fifty-two	40	forty

3 Write = or ≠.

≠ 2:45   = 6:15   = 4:45

= 10:15   ≠ 12:15   ≠ 11:45

55 (fifty-five)

---

4 Write the numbers that come before and after by 9's.

54 __63__ 72   90 __99__ 108   0 __9__ 18   36 __45__ 54

9 __18__ 27   27 __36__ 45   72 __81__ 90   45 __54__ 63

63 __72__ 81   81 __90__ 99   18 __27__ 36   99 108 __117__

5 Add.

1,362	2,407	3,716	6,028	4,514	3,529
+8,219	+2,313	+3,127	+3,413	+4,139	+4,301
9,581	4,720	6,843	9,441	8,653	7,830

4,327	1,256	3,103	2,318	5,017	6,215
+2,168	+5,309	+5,469	+4,079	+2,915	+2,569
6,495	6,565	8,572	6,397	7,932	8,784

6 Subtract.

10	11	12	13	14	18	10	15
- 2	- 4	- 9	- 4	- 5	- 9	- 5	- 7
8	7	3	9	9	9	5	8

16	13	10	15	12	11	14	11
- 8	- 6	- 3	- 9	- 7	- 5	- 7	- 2
8	7	7	6	5	6	7	9

9,879	6,549	8,389	8,654	3,161	9,389
-3,578	-3,139	-1,146	-2,404	-2,051	-7,379
6,301	3,410	7,243	6,250	1,110	2,010

8,634	7,965	9,786	8,278	2,996	9,548
-3,202	-3,512	-1,480	-4,254	-1,686	-2,505
5,432	4,453	8,306	4,024	1,310	7,043

56 (fifty-six)

368

1 Write the numbers.

3 thousands + 6 hundreds + 8 tens + 4 ones
= 3,000 + 600 + 80 + 4

4 thousands + 1 hundred + 2 tens + 7 ones
= 4,000 + 100 + 20 + 7

8 thousands + 4 hundreds + 5 tens + 2 ones
= 8,000 + 400 + 50 + 2

5 thousands + 3 hundreds + 7 tens + 6 ones
= 5,000 + 300 + 70 + 6

2 thousands + 9 hundreds + 4 tens + 3 ones
= 2,000 + 900 + 40 + 3

2 Write the number that is 9 more.

18	27	36	45	63	72	9	18
45	54	0	9	27	36	54	63
81	90	72	81	90	99	99	108

3 Write the number that is 9 less.

36	45	72	81	27	36	54	63
63	72	0	9	90	99	9	18
18	27	99	108	45	54	81	90

4 There were 23 bees in a hive. 18 more joined them. How many bees are in the hive?

26 blackbirds were on the fence. 8 more joined them. How many blackbirds are now on the fence?

```
  23
+ 18
  41 bees
```
57 (fifty-seven)
```
  26
+  8
  34 blackbirds
```

---

5 Write the correct time.

5 :15   3 : 00   4: 30   1: 45

8 :30   6 : 45   7 : 45   10: 15

6 Add.

2,672	2,567	2,649	4,643	2,357	4,586
+5,318	+3,127	+7,031	+4,128	+1,624	+1,309
7,990	5,694	9,680	8,771	3,981	5,895

1,458	2,935	4,239	8,328	3,714	1,536
+8,208	+6,047	+5,418	+1,524	+2,069	+7,437
9,666	8,982	9,657	9,852	5,783	8,973

7 Subtract.

58 (fifty-eight)

---

1 Write the numbers.

1 thousand + 2 hundreds + 3 tens + 1 one
= 1,000 + 200 + 30 + 1

6 thousands + 7 hundreds + 9 tens + 8 ones
= 6,000 + 700 + 90 + 8

9 thousands + 5 hundreds + 6 tens + 5 ones
= 9,000 + 500 + 60 + 5

7 thousands + 8 hundreds + 1 ten + 9 ones
= 7,000 + 800 + 10 + 9

3 thousands + 4 hundreds + 0 tens + 3 ones
= 3,000 + 400 + 00 + 3

2 Write the correct time.

2 :45   10 : 30   9 : 15   1: 00

3 Write = or ≠.

first	≠	2nd		third	=	3rd
seventeenth	=	17th		fourteenth	≠	4th
sixth	=	6th		second	≠	3rd
twelfth	≠	11th		ninth	=	9th
fifteenth	=	15th		eleventh	=	11th
tenth	≠	9th		eighth	=	8th

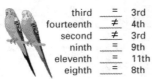

59 (fifty-nine)

---

4 Circle the number that is least.

(34) 36 39 | 81 84 (80) | (52) 56 57 | 93 (91) 99

5 Add and check.

57	16	32	15	11	16	34	33
12	41	16	62	52	23	24	12
+13	+38	+39	+14	+14	+44	+15	+16
82	95	87	91	77	83	73	61

25	24	12	21	41	14	13	22
22	11	43	17	13	12	23	12
+13	+28	+26	+35	+29	+37	+47	+27
60	63	81	73	83	63	83	61

6 Subtract.

5,679	5,896	2,789	9,876	4,579	4,896
-5,273	-1,834	-1,439	-1,236	-3,468	-1,705
406	4,062	1,350	8,640	1,111	3,191

5,396	8,743	5,974	8,173	3,986	9,482
-2,071	-1,203	-3,612	-4,152	-1,254	-5,462
3,325	7,540	2,362	4,021	2,732	4,020

7 The Boys Scouts Troop had 36 boys. 8 more joined the troop for a camp out. How many boys went on the camp out?

```
  36
+  8
  44 boys
```
60 (sixty)

1 Write the names of the books.

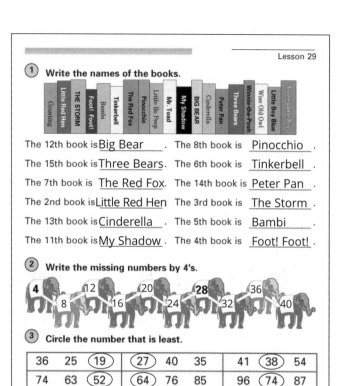

The 12th book is **Big Bear**. The 8th book is **Pinocchio**.

The 15th book is **Three Bears**. The 6th book is **Tinkerbell**.

The 7th book is **The Red Fox**. The 14th book is **Peter Pan**.

The 2nd book is **Little Red Hen**. The 3rd book is **The Storm**.

The 13th book is **Cinderella**. The 5th book is **Bambi**.

The 11th book is **My Shadow**. The 4th book is **Foot! Foot!**.

2 Write the missing numbers by 4's.

4 8 12 16 20 24 **28** 32 36 40

3 Circle the number that is least.

36	25	(19)	(27)	40	35	41	(38)	54
74	63	(52)	(64)	76	85	96	(74)	87
(13)	57	31	46	62	(29)	54	(38)	75

4 James had 37 baseball cards. Mike gave him 16 more. How many baseball cards does James now have?

37
+ 16
53 baseball cards

61 (sixty-one)

---

5 Write the numbers.

243	244	245	246	247	248	249
576	577	578	579	580	581	582
385	386	387	388	389	390	391
462	463	464	465	466	467	468
824	825	826	827	828	829	830
657	658	659	660	661	662	663

6 Add and check.

28	44	37	14	32	23	13	23
11	13	11	20	22	34	32	26
+33	+16	+38	+17	+29	+25	+27	+34
72	73	86	51	83	82	72	83

30	26	12	12	15	20	13	33
12	40	34	55	21	47	14	35
+49	+27	+48	+17	+59	+15	+66	+28
91	93	94	84	95	82	93	96

7 Subtract.

12	13	10	14	17	16	11	10
- 5	- 6	- 8	- 9	- 8	- 4	- 7	- 1
7	7	2	5	9	12	4	9

3,678	7,942	8,726	5,964	9,468	5,964
-3,528	-3,511	-5,701	-4,723	-3,267	-1,234
150	4,431	3,025	1,241	6,201	4,730

62 (sixty-two)

Test 3 Lesson 30
Lessons 16-25 80 points total

1 Write the correct time. 8 pts.

4 : 00   8 : 15   1 : 45   10: 30

7 : 30   2 : 45   9 : 00   11 : 15

2 Write the numbers. 12 pts.

twenty-four	24	fourteen	14	thirty-seven	37
twelve	12	eleven	11	seventy-one	71
fifty	50	forty-three	43	fifty-two	52
ninety-one	91	eighty-five	85	sixty-five	65

3 Write the numbers that come before and after by 3's. 16 pts.

9 12 15   21 24 27   0 3 6   15 18 21

24 27 30   3 6 9   18 21 24   6 9 12

4 Write = or ≠. 9 pts.

7 + 8 = 15   7 + 3 ≠ 10   6 + 5 ≠ 10
3 + 9 ≠ 13   7 + 2 = 9   4 + 1 = 5
3 + 3 ≠ 7   2 + 5 ≠ 6   1 + 7 = 8

63 (sixty-three)

---

5 Write the missing numbers by 6's. 9 pts.

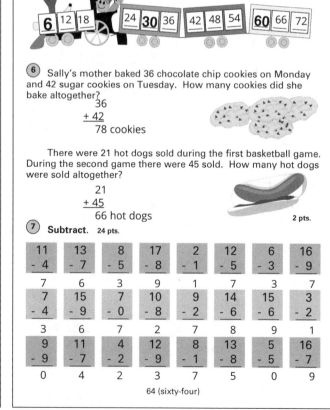

6 12 18 **24** **30** 36 **42** 48 54 **60** 66 72

6 Sally's mother baked 36 chocolate chip cookies on Monday and 42 sugar cookies on Tuesday. How many cookies did she bake altogether?

36
+ 42
78 cookies

There were 21 hot dogs sold during the first basketball game. During the second game there were 45 sold. How many hot dogs were sold altogether?

21
+ 45
66 hot dogs

2 pts.

7 Subtract. 24 pts.

11	13	8	17	2	12	6	16
- 4	- 7	- 5	- 8	- 1	- 5	- 3	- 9
7	6	3	9	1	7	3	7

7	15	7	10	9	14	15	3
- 4	- 9	- 0	- 8	- 2	- 6	- 6	- 2
3	6	7	2	7	8	9	1

9	11	4	12	8	13	5	16
- 9	- 7	- 2	- 9	- 1	- 8	- 5	- 7
0	4	2	3	7	5	0	9

64 (sixty-four)

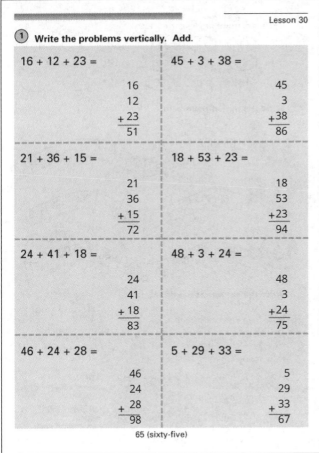

1 Write the problems vertically. Add.

16 + 12 + 23 =

```
  16
  12
+ 23
----
  51
```

45 + 3 + 38 =

```
  45
   3
+ 38
----
  86
```

21 + 36 + 15 =

```
  21
  36
+ 15
----
  72
```

18 + 53 + 23 =

```
  18
  53
+ 23
----
  94
```

24 + 41 + 18 =

```
  24
  41
+ 18
----
  83
```

48 + 3 + 24 =

```
  48
   3
+ 24
----
  75
```

46 + 24 + 28 =

```
  46
  24
+ 28
----
  98
```

5 + 29 + 33 =

```
   5
  29
+ 33
----
  67
```

65 (sixty-five)

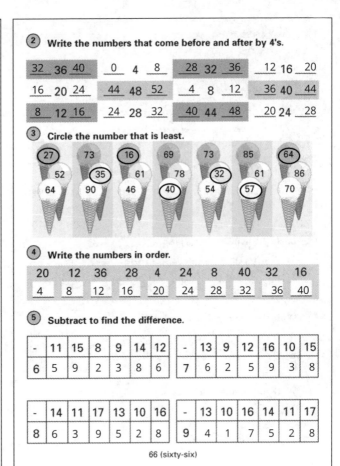

2 Write the numbers that come before and after by 4's.

32	36	40		0	4	8		28	32	36		12	16	20
16	20	24		44	48	52		4	8	12		36	40	44
8	12	16		24	28	32		40	44	48		20	24	28

3 Circle the number that is least.

Least circled: 27, 16, 40, 32, 57, 64

4 Write the numbers in order.

20 12 36 28 4 24 8 40 32 16

4 8 12 16 20 24 28 32 36 40

5 Subtract to find the difference.

-	11	15	8	9	14	12
6	5	9	2	3	8	6

-	13	9	12	16	10	15
7	6	2	5	9	3	8

-	14	11	17	13	10	16
8	6	3	9	5	2	8

-	13	10	16	14	11	17
9	4	1	7	5	2	8

66 (sixty-six)

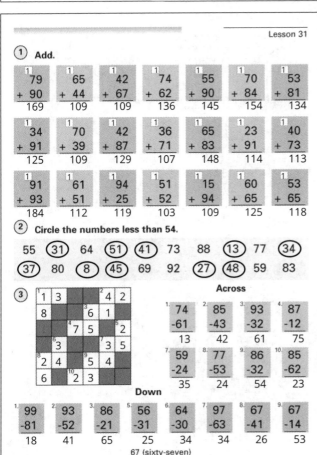

1 Add.

```
  79      65      42      74      55      70      53
+ 90    + 44    + 67    + 62    + 90    + 84    + 81
-----   -----   -----   -----   -----   -----   -----
 169     109     109     136     145     154     134

  34      70      42      36      65      23      40
+ 91    + 39    + 87    + 71    + 83    + 91    + 73
-----   -----   -----   -----   -----   -----   -----
 125     109     129     107     148     114     113

  91      61      94      51      15      60      53
+ 93    + 51    + 25    + 52    + 94    + 65    + 65
-----   -----   -----   -----   -----   -----   -----
 184     112     119     103     109     125     118
```

2 Circle the numbers less than 54.

55 (31) 64 (51) (41) 73 88 (13) 77 (34)
(37) 80 (8) (45) 69 92 (27) (48) 59 83

3

Across

```
  74      85      93      87
- 61    - 43    - 32    - 12
-----   -----   -----   -----
  13      42      61      75

  59      77      86      85
- 24    - 53    - 32    - 62
-----   -----   -----   -----
  35      24      54      23
```

Down

```
  99      93      86      56      64      97      67      67
- 81    - 52    - 21    - 31    - 30    - 63    - 41    - 14
-----   -----   -----   -----   -----   -----   -----   -----
  18      41      65      25      34      34      26      53
```

67 (sixty-seven)

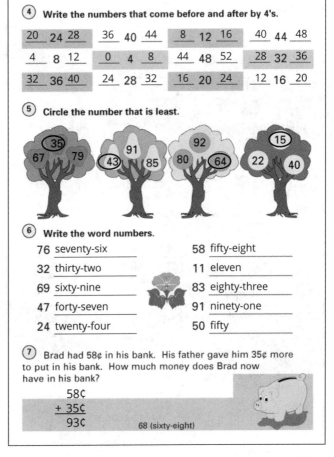

4 Write the numbers that come before and after by 4's.

20	24	28		36	40	44		8	12	16		40	44	48
4	8	12		0	4	8		44	48	52		28	32	36
32	36	40		24	28	32		16	20	24		12	16	20

5 Circle the number that is least.

Least circled: 35, 43, 64, 15

6 Write the word numbers.

76	seventy-six	58	fifty-eight
32	thirty-two	11	eleven
69	sixty-nine	83	eighty-three
47	forty-seven	91	ninety-one
24	twenty-four	50	fifty

7 Brad had 58¢ in his bank. His father gave him 35¢ more to put in his bank. How much money does Brad now have in his bank?

```
  58¢
+ 35¢
-----
  93¢
```

68 (sixty-eight)

371

1 Add.

21	62	71	92	73	83	94
+ 91	+ 42	+ 52	+ 43	+ 61	+ 53	+ 73
112	104	123	135	134	136	167

66	78	64	85	73	91	82
+ 82	+ 40	+ 91	+ 42	+ 85	+ 56	+ 67
148	118	155	127	158	147	149

92	83	85	82	47	93	83
+ 65	+ 96	+ 33	+ 71	+ 91	+ 32	+ 20
157	179	118	153	138	125	103

2 Circle the number that is least.

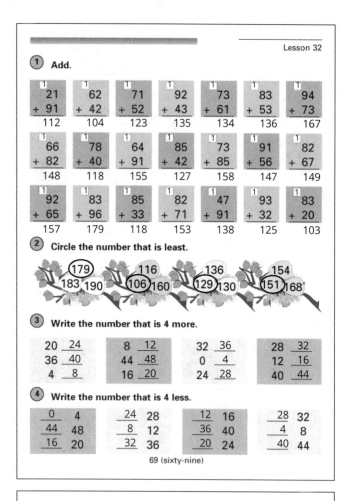

(179) 183 190   (106) 116 160   (129) 136 130   (151) 154 168

3 Write the number that is 4 more.

20 _24_	8 _12_	32 _36_	28 _32_
36 _40_	44 _48_	0 _4_	12 _16_
4 _8_	16 _20_	24 _28_	40 _44_

4 Write the number that is 4 less.

_0_ 4	_24_ 28	_12_ 16	_28_ 32
_44_ 48	_8_ 12	_36_ 40	_4_ 8
_16_ 20	_32_ 36	_20_ 24	_40_ 44

69 (sixty-nine)

---

5 Circle the numbers less than 128.

137 (111) (79) 133 156 (117) 161
172 (98) 151 (101) 148 164 (125)
(90) 169 129 (86) 142 (105) (127)

6 Write the missing numbers.

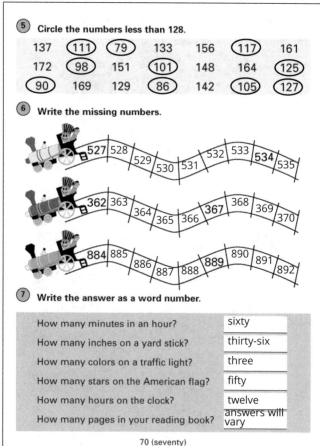

527 528 529 530 531 532 533 **534** 535

362 363 364 365 366 **367** 368 369 370

884 885 886 887 888 **889** 890 891 892

7 Write the answer as a word number.

How many minutes in an hour?	sixty
How many inches on a yard stick?	thirty-six
How many colors on a traffic light?	three
How many stars on the American flag?	fifty
How many hours on the clock?	twelve
How many pages in your reading book?	answers will vary

70 (seventy)

---

1 Add.

695	151	674	570	531	148	357
+223	+760	+174	+198	+293	+371	+491
918	911	848	768	824	519	848

244	261	371	551	230	594	260
+485	+672	+234	+288	+586	+191	+654
729	933	605	839	816	785	914

352	486	333	425	461	243	297
+452	+383	+572	+384	+265	+463	+382
804	869	905	809	726	706	679

2 Circle the numbers less than 376.

381 (205) 490 (314) 509 (167) 452
(238) 398 403 (153) (260) 516 (339)
474 (182) 486 (291) (367) (374) (276)

3 When going to her grandparents, Mary's family drove 335 miles on Monday and 258 miles on Tuesday. How far did they drive the two days?

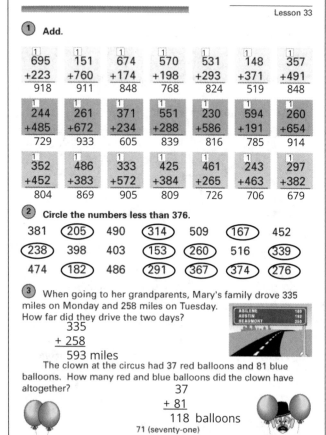

335
+ 258
593 miles

The clown at the circus had 37 red balloons and 81 blue balloons. How many red and blue balloons did the clown have altogether?

37
+ 81
118 balloons

71 (seventy-one)

---

4 Write the correct letters.

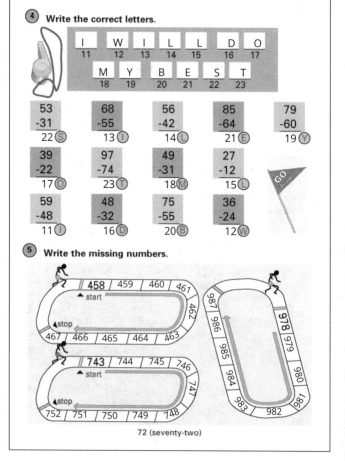

I	W	I	L	L	D	O
11	12	13	14	15	16	17

M	Y	B	E	S	T
18	19	20	21	22	23

53	68	56	85	79
-31	-55	-42	-64	-60
22 (S)	13 (I)	14 (L)	21 (E)	19 (Y)

39	97	49	27
-22	-74	-31	-12
17 (O)	23 (T)	18 (M)	15 (L)

59	48	75	36
-48	-32	-55	-24
11 (I)	16 (D)	20 (B)	12 (W)

5 Write the missing numbers.

458 459 460 461 462 463 464 465 466 467
987 986 985 984 983 982 981 980 979 978
743 744 745 746 747 748 749 750 751 752

72 (seventy-two)

① Write the next 3 numbers.

37	38	39	40	41	42
153	154	155	156	157	158
280	281	282	283	284	285
425	426	427	428	429	430
768	769	770	771	772	773

② Write the missing numbers.

$4 + 3 = 7$ $- 2 = 5$ $+ 5 = 10$ $+ 6 = 16$ $- 7 = 9$
$7 + 6 = 13$ $- 4 = 9$ $+ 3 = 12$ $- 5 = 7$ $+ 8 = 15$
$5 + 9 = 14$ $- 6 = 8$ $+ 7 = 15$ $- 8 = 7$ $+ 4 = 11$
$2 + 8 = 10$ $- 5 = 5$ $+ 6 = 11$ $- 7 = 4$ $+ 9 = 13$
$6 + 5 = 11$ $- 8 = 3$ $+ 9 = 12$ $- 4 = 8$ $+ 5 = 13$
$8 + 4 = 12$ $- 7 = 5$ $+ 8 = 13$ $- 9 = 4$ $+ 6 = 10$

③ Write the missing numbers by 8's.

8 16 24 32 40 48 56 64 72 80

④ Add to write the numbers in the boxes.

4	5	9
3	2	5
7	7	14

7	1	8
2	5	7
9	6	15

6	2	8
1	7	8
7	9	16

73 (seventy-three)

⑤ Add.

560	388	174	615	591	287	394
+346	+291	+583	+194	+230	+352	+175
906	679	757	809	821	639	569
271	581	352	690	781	271	463
+596	+221	+390	+247	+162	+477	+256
867	802	742	937	943	748	719
194	296	284	370	492	183	561
+312	+253	+674	+468	+167	+435	+168
506	549	958	838	659	618	729

⑥ 38 boys and 23 girls took part in the field day activities. How many children were there?

38
+ 23
61 children

Smith's Bakery baked 183 cookies on Friday and 145 on Saturday. The bakery baked how many cookies the two days?

183
+ 145
328 cookies

The gasoline station sold 336 gallons of gas on Wednesday and 257 gallons on Thursday. How many gallons did the station sell in the two days?

336
+ 257
593 gallons

74 (seventy-four)

① Write the next three numbers.

56	58	60	62	64	66
422	424	426	428	430	432
780	782	784	786	788	790
264	266	268	270	272	274
648	650	652	654	656	658

② Write the numbers that come before and after by 8's.

24 32 40   72 80 88   48 56 64   0 8 16
8 16 24   40 48 56   64 72 80   88 96 104
80 88 96   16 24 32   32 40 48   56 64 72

③ Subtract.

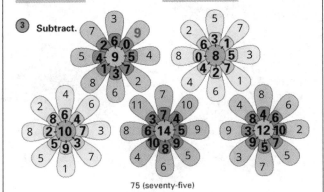

75 (seventy-five)

④ Add.

194	253	461	542	186	146	472
+695	+681	+494	+384	+543	+170	+231
889	934	955	926	729	316	703
572	247	692	351	465	387	234
+247	+391	+285	+276	+370	+582	+382
819	638	977	627	835	969	616
158	174	540	635	691	354	561
+251	+350	+267	+294	+127	+461	+188
409	524	807	929	818	815	749

⑤ Write the numbers in order.

24 56 16 72 40 8 64 48 32 80

8 16 24 32 40 48 56 64 72 80

⑥ Mother bought bread for 46¢ and milk for 92¢. How much did mother pay for the groceries?

46¢
+ 92¢
138¢

There were 146 books in the first grade library and 183 in the second grade library. How many books are in the two libraries?

146
+ 183
329 books

Brent had 43 pennies in a box and 35 pennies in a bag. How many pennies did he have?

43
+ 35
78 pennies

76 (seventy-six)

(1) Write the numbers.

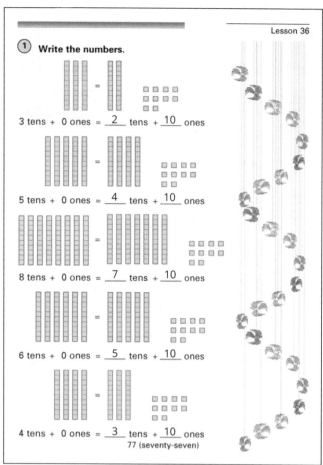

3 tens + 0 ones = __2__ tens + __10__ ones

5 tens + 0 ones = __4__ tens + __10__ ones

8 tens + 0 ones = __7__ tens + __10__ ones

6 tens + 0 ones = __5__ tens + __10__ ones

4 tens + 0 ones = __3__ tens + __10__ ones

77 (seventy-seven)

---

(2) Write the numbers that come before and after by 8's.

16	24	32		40	48	56		80	88	96		24	32	40
0	8	16		64	72	80		8	16	24		56	64	72
48	56	64		32	40	48		88	96	104		72	80	88

(3) Write the next three numbers.

81	84	87	90	93	96
324	327	330	333	336	339
512	515	518	521	524	527
803	806	809	812	815	818
430	433	436	439	442	445

(4) The numbers on the right of each ladder are to be added to or subtracted from the bottom number.

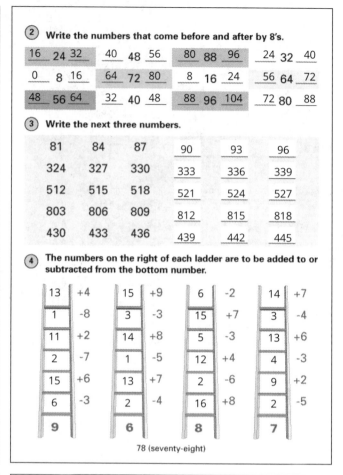

78 (seventy-eight)

---

(1) Write the numbers.

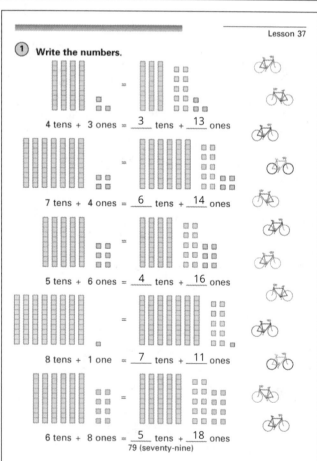

4 tens + 3 ones = __3__ tens + __13__ ones

7 tens + 4 ones = __6__ tens + __14__ ones

5 tens + 6 ones = __4__ tens + __16__ ones

8 tens + 1 one = __7__ tens + __11__ ones

6 tens + 8 ones = __5__ tens + __18__ ones

79 (seventy-nine)

---

(2) Write the number that is 8 more.

40 48	24 32	72 80	16 24
8 16	56 64	48 56	64 72

(3) Write the number that is 8 less.

0 8	88 96	64 72	24 32
72 80	16 24	8 16	80 88

(4) Add.

1,458 +5,291	3,635 +4,271	1,382 +6,593	5,160 +2,397	2,394 +4,164	2,123 +2,496
6,749	7,906	7,975	7,557	6,558	4,619
7,692 +2,195	7,585 +1,360	4,278 +1,150	3,125 +3,184	3,182 +2,736	4,160 +3,264
9,887	8,945	5,428	6,309	5,918	7,424

(5) Write the numbers.

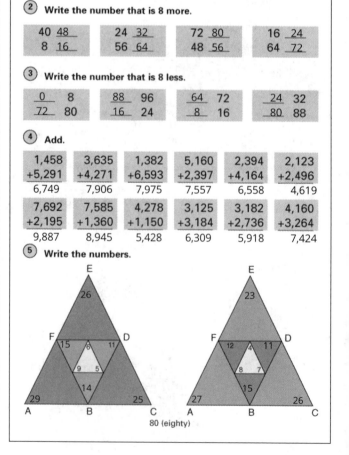

80 (eighty)

374

① Draw both hands on the clock.

5:00 10:00 2:00 8:00

4:00 11:00 6:00 1:00

② Write the numbers.

3 tens + 0 ones = 2 tens + __10__ ones

7 tens + 0 ones = 6 tens + __10__ ones

5 tens + 0 ones = 4 tens + __10__ ones

2 tens + 0 ones = 1 ten + __10__ ones

6 tens + 0 ones = 5 tens + __10__ ones

8 tens + 0 ones = 7 tens + __10__ ones

4 tens + 0 ones = 3 tens + __10__ ones

③ Write = or ≠.

6 + 4 _=_ 5 + 5	2 + 7 _=_ 4 + 5	6 + 9 _≠_ 8 + 8
5 + 7 _≠_ 3 + 8	8 + 6 _=_ 5 + 9	7 + 6 _≠_ 6 + 9

81 (eighty-one)

---

④ Add.

4,240	6,192	3,651	3,684	4,297	5,274
+2,682	+3,185	+5,164	+4,285	+1,051	+1,434
6,922	9,377	8,815	7,969	5,348	6,708

5,194	4,136	3,470	8,492	3,382	3,695
+2,632	+3,281	+2,365	+1,423	+3,157	+3,041
7,826	7,417	5,835	9,915	6,539	6,736

1,361	5,482	7,294	6,521	7,163	5,380
+7,248	+3,071	+1,271	+2,375	+2,375	+3,429
8,609	8,553	8,565	8,896	9,538	8,809

⑤ Write the missing numbers by 7's.

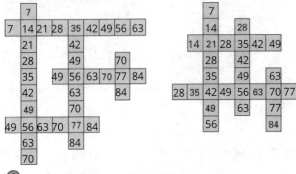

⑥ Write the missing numbers by 1's.

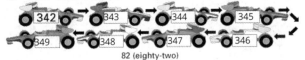

342 343 344 345
349 348 347 346

82 (eighty-two)

---

① Write the numbers.

8 thousand + 2 hundreds + 9 tens + 4 ones
= __8,000__ + __200__ + __90__ + __4__

3 thousands + 5 hundreds + 4 tens + 1 one
= __3,000__ + __500__ + __40__ + __1__

7 thousands + 8 hundreds + 6 tens + 6 ones
= __7,000__ + __800__ + __60__ + __6__

2 thousands + 7 hundreds + 5 ten + 5 ones
= __2,000__ + __700__ + __50__ + __5__

6 thousands + 4 hundreds + 2 tens + 8 ones
= __6,000__ + __400__ + __20__ + __8__

9 thousands + 1 hundred + 7 tens + 3 ones
= __9,000__ + __100__ + __70__ + __3__

② Draw both hands on the clocks.

9:30 2:30 12:30 3:30

10:30 1:30 4:30 7:30

83 (eighty-three)

---

③ Add.

5,052	6,128	4,376	6,367	3,187	4,042
+3,651	+2,291	+2,143	+1,350	+5,452	+3,873
8,703	8,419	6,519	7,717	8,639	7,915

3,579	2,742	3,196	5,434	1,253	2,173
+6,270	+4,195	+4,630	+4,471	+7,680	+7,582
9,849	6,937	7,826	9,905	8,933	9,755

④ Write the numbers.

3 tens + 6 ones = 2 tens + __16__ ones

5 tens + 9 ones = 4 tens + __19__ ones

8 tens + 1 one = 7 tens + __11__ ones

4 tens + 3 ones = 3 tens + __13__ ones

7 tens + 8 ones = 6 tens + __18__ ones

⑤ Write the missing numbers by 7's.

7 14 21 28 35 42 49 56 63 70 77 84

⑥ Write = or ≠.

7 + 4 _=_ 5 + 6	5 + 9 _≠_ 6 + 7	8 + 2 _=_ 3 + 7
7 + 5 _=_ 6 + 6	6 + 4 _≠_ 7 + 2	3 + 9 _=_ 8 + 4
4 + 8 _=_ 9 + 3	7 + 7 _≠_ 8 + 5	5 + 6 _≠_ 8 + 4

84 (eighty-four)

---

① **Circle the number that is greatest.**   6 pts.

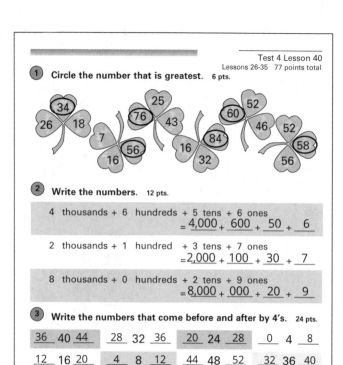

② **Write the numbers.**   12 pts.

4 thousands + 6 hundreds + 5 tens + 6 ones
= 4,000 + 600 + 50 + 6

2 thousands + 1 hundred + 3 tens + 7 ones
= 2,000 + 100 + 30 + 7

8 thousands + 0 hundreds + 2 tens + 9 ones
= 8,000 + 000 + 20 + 9

③ **Write the numbers that come before and after by 4's.**   24 pts.

36 40 44   28 32 36   20 24 28   0 4 8

12 16 20   4 8 12   44 48 52   32 36 40

24 28 32   40 44 48   8 12 16   16 20 24

④ **Add.**   7 pts.

718	147	439	366	525	309	249
+276	+335	+127	+417	+355	+342	+127
994	482	566	783	880	651	376

85 (eighty-five)

---

⑤ **Write the missing numbers by 9's.**   7 pts.

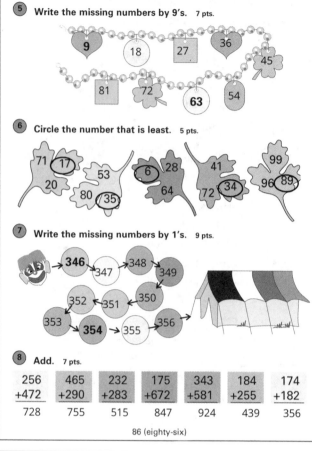

9   18   27   36   45

81   72   63   54

⑥ **Circle the number that is least.**   5 pts.

71 17   53   6 28   41   99
20   80 35   64   72 34   96 89

⑦ **Write the missing numbers by 1's.**   9 pts.

346   347   348   349
352   351   350
353   354   355   356

⑧ **Add.**   7 pts.

256	465	232	175	343	184	174
+472	+290	+283	+672	+581	+255	+182
728	755	515	847	924	439	356

86 (eighty-six)

Lesson 40

① **Write the numbers.**

3,782 = 3 thousands + 7 hundreds + 8 tens + 2 ones
6,539 = 6 thousands + 5 hundreds + 3 tens + 9 ones
5,246 = 5 thousands + 2 hundreds + 4 tens + 6 ones
9,654 = 9 thousands + 6 hundreds + 5 tens + 4 ones
7,308 = 7 thousands + 3 hundreds + 0 tens + 8 ones
2,813 = 2 thousands + 8 hundreds + 1 tens + 3 ones

② **Write the answer as a word number.**

1.
34
+15
49

2.
25
+32
57

3.
7
+ 4
11

4.
20
+40
60

5.
20
+ 1
21

6.
11
+21
32

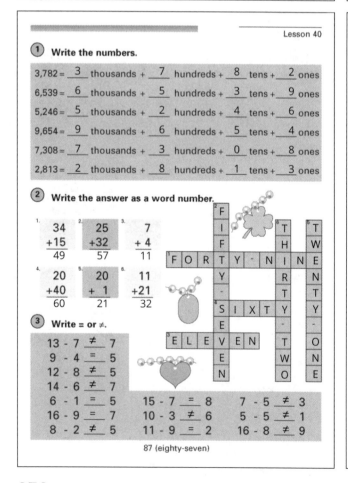

Crossword:
F I F T Y - N I N E
F O R T Y - N I N E
S I X T Y
E L E V E N
T H I R T Y - T W O
T W E N T Y - O N E

③ **Write = or ≠.**

13 - 7 ≠ 7
9 - 4 = 5
12 - 8 ≠ 5
14 - 6 ≠ 7
6 - 1 = 5   15 - 7 = 8   7 - 5 ≠ 3
16 - 9 = 7   10 - 3 ≠ 6   5 - 5 ≠ 1
8 - 2 ≠ 5   11 - 9 = 2   16 - 8 ≠ 9

87 (eighty-seven)

---

④ **Draw both hands on the clocks.**

6:45   10:15   1:15   11:45

2:45   8:15   12:15   4:45

⑤ **Write the numbers that come before and after by 7's.**

42 49 56   0 7 14   28 35 42   70 77 84

21 28 35   35 42 49   77 84 91   7 14 21

56 63 70   63 70 77   14 21 28   49 56 63

⑥ **Write the numbers.**

5 tens + 3 ones = 4 tens + 13 ones
2 tens + 9 ones = 1 tens + 19 ones
8 tens + 5 ones = 7 tens + 15 ones
4 tens + 1 one = 3 tens + 11 ones
7 tens + 6 ones = 6 tens + 16 ones
6 tens + 4 ones = 5 tens + 14 ones

88 (eighty-eight)

376

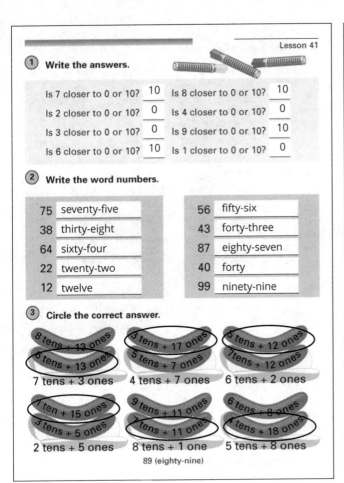

Lesson 41

1 Write the answers.

Is 7 closer to 0 or 10?	10	Is 8 closer to 0 or 10?	10
Is 2 closer to 0 or 10?	0	Is 4 closer to 0 or 10?	0
Is 3 closer to 0 or 10?	0	Is 9 closer to 0 or 10?	10
Is 6 closer to 0 or 10?	10	Is 1 closer to 0 or 10?	0

2 Write the word numbers.

75	seventy-five		56	fifty-six
38	thirty-eight		43	forty-three
64	sixty-four		87	eighty-seven
22	twenty-two		40	forty
12	twelve		99	ninety-nine

3 Circle the correct answer.

8 tens + 13 ones / 6 tens + 13 ones / *7 tens + 3 ones*

3 tens + 17 ones / 5 tens + 7 ones / *4 tens + 7 ones*

5 tens + 12 ones / 7 tens + 12 ones / *6 tens + 2 ones*

1 ten + 15 ones / 3 tens + 5 ones / *2 tens + 5 ones*

9 tens + 11 ones / 7 tens + 11 ones / *8 tens + 1 one*

6 tens + 8 ones / 7 tens + 18 ones / *5 tens + 8 ones*

89 (eighty-nine)

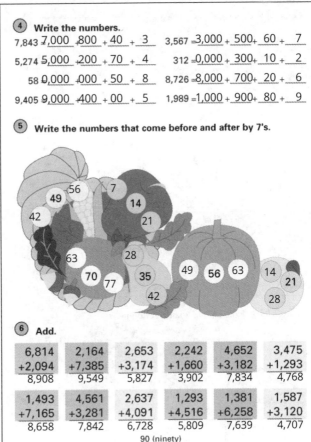

4 Write the numbers.

7,843 = 7,000 + 800 + 40 + 3   3,567 = 3,000 + 500 + 60 + 7

5,274 = 5,000 + 200 + 70 + 4   312 = 0,000 + 300 + 10 + 2

58 = 0,000 + 000 + 50 + 8   8,726 = 8,000 + 700 + 20 + 6

9,405 = 9,000 + 400 + 00 + 5   1,989 = 1,000 + 900 + 80 + 9

5 Write the numbers that come before and after by 7's.

(56) (7)
(49)   (14)
(42)   (21)
(63)   (28)
(70) (35)   (49) (56) (63)   (14)
(77)   (42)   (21)
                                  (28)

6 Add.

6,814	2,164	2,653	2,242	4,652	3,475
+2,094	+7,385	+3,174	+1,660	+3,182	+1,293
8,908	9,549	5,827	3,902	7,834	4,768

1,493	4,561	2,637	1,293	1,381	1,587
+7,165	+3,281	+4,091	+4,516	+6,258	+3,120
8,658	7,842	6,728	5,809	7,639	4,707

90 (ninety)

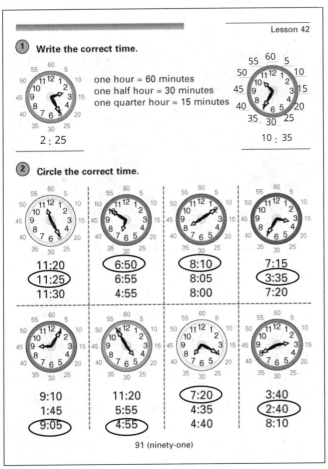

Lesson 42

1 Write the correct time.

one hour = 60 minutes
one half hour = 30 minutes
one quarter hour = 15 minutes

2 : 25   10 : 35

2 Circle the correct time.

11:20	6:50	8:10	7:15
11:25	6:55	8:05	**3:35**
11:30	4:55	8:00	7:20

9:10	11:20	**7:20**	3:40
1:45	5:55	4:35	**2:40**
9:05	**4:55**	4:40	8:10

91 (ninety-one)

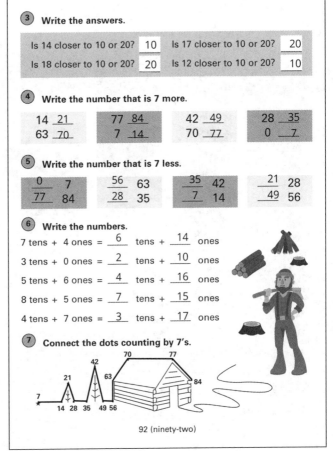

3 Write the answers.

Is 14 closer to 10 or 20?	10	Is 17 closer to 10 or 20?	20
Is 18 closer to 10 or 20?	20	Is 12 closer to 10 or 20?	10

4 Write the number that is 7 more.

14 __21__   77 __84__   42 __49__   28 __35__
63 __70__   7 __14__   70 __77__   0 __7__

5 Write the number that is 7 less.

__0__ 7   __56__ 63   __35__ 42   __21__ 28
__77__ 84   __28__ 35   __7__ 14   __49__ 56

6 Write the numbers.

7 tens + 4 ones = __6__ tens + __14__ ones

3 tens + 0 ones = __2__ tens + __10__ ones

5 tens + 6 ones = __4__ tens + __16__ ones

8 tens + 5 ones = __7__ tens + __15__ ones

4 tens + 7 ones = __3__ tens + __17__ ones

7 Connect the dots counting by 7's.

92 (ninety-two)

377

① Write the correct time.

8 : 35   3 : 20   1 : 40   11 : 05

4 :10   10 : 00   6 : 25   5 : 50

7 : 45   2 : 30   12 : 45   9 : 55

② Write 2 addition and 2 subtraction facts.

6 1 7	3 5 2	4 5 9	13 7 6
6 + 1 = 7	3 + 2 = 5	4 + 5 = 9	7 + 6 = 13
1 + 6 = 7	2 + 3 = 5	5 + 4 = 9	6 + 7 = 13
7 - 1 = 6	5 - 2 = 3	9 - 5 = 4	13 - 6 = 7
7 - 6 = 1	5 - 3 = 2	9 - 4 = 5	13 - 7 = 6

93 (ninety-three)

---

③ Write the next three numbers.

9	8	7	6	5	4
65	64	63	62	61	60
121	120	119	118	117	116
357	356	355	354	353	352

④ Write the answers.

Is 26 closer to 20 or 30?	30	Is 27 closer to 20 or 30?	30
Is 21 closer to 20 or 30?	20	Is 23 closer to 20 or 30?	20
Is 24 closer to 20 or 30?	20	Is 22 closer to 20 or 30?	20
Is 28 closer to 20 or 30?	30	Is 29 closer to 20 or 30?	30

⑤ Write the numbers.

46 = __4__ tens + __6__ ones = 3 tens + __16__ ones

74 = __7__ tens + __4__ ones = 6 tens + __14__ ones

32 = __3__ tens + __2__ ones = 2 tens + __12__ ones

58 = __5__ tens + __8__ ones = 4 tens + __18__ ones

17 = __1__ tens + __7__ ones = 0 tens + __17__ ones

⑥ Seth had 133 building blocks. Beth gave him 48 more. Seth now has how many building blocks?

   133
+   48
   181 building blocks 94 (ninety-four)

---

① Write < or > and read the sentence.

5 < 9	34 > 31	78 < 80	104 < 114
148 > 143	175 > 171	265 > 256	289 < 298
421 > 412	683 > 516	716 > 594	398 < 408

② Write the correct time.

8 : 05   12 : 40   6 : 55   10 : 35

11 : 20   4 : 25   9 : 10   3 : 50

③ Write the numbers.

38 = __3__ tens + __8__ ones = __2__ tens + 18 ones

75 = __7__ tens + __5__ ones = __6__ tens + 15 ones

42 = __4__ tens + __2__ ones = __3__ tens + 12 ones

83 = __8__ tens + __3__ ones = __7__ tens + 13 ones

96 = __9__ tens + __6__ ones = __8__ tens + 16 ones

54 = __5__ tens + __4__ ones = __4__ tens + 14 ones

95 (ninety-five)

---

④ Write the answers.

Is 64 closer to 60 or 70?	60	Is 69 closer to 60 or 70?	70
Is 62 closer to 60 or 70?	60	Is 63 closer to 60 or 70?	60
Is 68 closer to 60 or 70?	70	Is 67 closer to 60 or 70?	70
Is 61 closer to 60 or 70?	60	Is 66 closer to 60 or 70?	70

⑤ Write 2 addition and 2 subtraction facts.

7 4 11	6 14 8	5 9 14	3 8 5
7 + 4 = 11	6 + 8 = 14	5 + 9 = 14	3 + 5 = 8
4 + 7 = 11	8 + 6 = 14	9 + 5 = 14	5 + 3 = 8
11 - 4 = 7	14 - 8 = 6	14 - 9 = 5	8 - 5 = 3
11 - 7 = 4	14 - 6 = 8	14 - 5 = 9	8 - 3 = 5

⑥ Write the next three numbers.

10	8	6	4	2	0
18	16	14	12	10	8
34	32	30	28	26	24
56	54	52	50	48	46

⑦ Josh has 74¢ in pennies in his piggy bank. Susie gave him 8 more pennies. Josh now has how many pennies in his piggy bank?

   74
+   8
   82 pennies 96 (ninety-six)

378

① **Write 2 addition and 2 subtraction facts.**

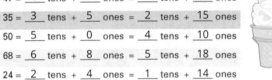

3 _7_ 10
3 + 7 = 10
7 + 3 = 10
10 - 7 = 3
10 - 3 = 7

4 _2_ 6
4 + 2 = 6
2 + 4 = 6
6 - 2 = 4
6 - 4 = 2

8 _9_ 17
8 + 9 = 17
9 + 8 = 17
17 - 9 = 8
17 - 8 = 9

7 _9_ 2
7 + 2 = 9
2 + 7 = 9
9 - 2 = 7
9 - 7 = 2

5 _6_ 11
5 + 6 = 11
6 + 5 = 11
11 - 6 = 5
11 - 5 = 6

3 _12_ 9
3 + 9 = 12
9 + 3 = 12
12 - 9 = 3
12 - 3 = 9

② **Write < or >.**

4 + 6 < 11	7 + 7 > 13	8 + 9 > 16
5 + 4 < 10	2 + 4 > 5	4 + 5 > 8
9 + 5 > 13	7 + 6 < 14	6 + 3 < 10
3 + 4 < 8	3 + 8 < 12	2 + 5 < 8

③ **Write the numbers.**

93 = 9 tens + 3 ones = 8 tens + 13 ones
47 = 4 tens + 7 ones = 3 tens + 17 ones
35 = 3 tens + 5 ones = 2 tens + 15 ones
50 = 5 tens + 0 ones = 4 tens + 10 ones
68 = 6 tens + 8 ones = 5 tens + 18 ones
24 = 2 tens + 4 ones = 1 tens + 14 ones

97 (ninety-seven)

---

④ **Write the correct time.**

7:55   3:05   10:20   6:40

4:35   12:25   1:10   9:50

⑤ **Write the next three numbers.**

15	12	9	6	3	0
27	24	21	18	15	12
60	57	54	51	48	45
81	78	75	72	69	66
121	118	115	112	109	106

⑥ The zookeeper counted 38 monkeys in the cages at the zoo. He had 13 more to join them. How many monkeys are now in the cages at the zoo?

38
+ 13
51 monkeys

98 (ninety-eight)

---

① **Circle the estimated time.**

Johnny is eating dinner.	2:30	(5:30)	9:00
Sally is walking to school.	(8:00)	10:15	2:45
The grocery store is closing.	2:15	4:00	(9:30)
Bob is going to bed.	4:00	(8:30)	12:00
Ann is reading at school.	(9:15)	6:30	5:15
Jim is playing after school.	11:00	2:15	(4:30)

② **Write < or >.**

12 < 9 + 4	16 > 6 + 9	12 < 4 + 9
11 < 5 + 7	12 > 4 + 7	7 < 5 + 3
11 > 5 + 5	17 > 7 + 9	10 > 8 + 1
15 > 8 + 6	10 < 5 + 6	13 > 6 + 6

③ **Write the numbers.**

73 = 6 tens + 13 ones   37 = 2 tens + 17 ones
25 = 1 ten + 15 ones   54 = 4 tens + 14 ones
48 = 3 tens + 18 ones   19 = 0 tens + 19 ones
62 = 5 tens + 12 ones   86 = 7 tens + 16 ones

④ Jill counted 44 roses and 38 pansies blooming in her flower garden. How many roses and pansies were blooming in all?

44
+ 38
82 roses and pansies

99 (ninety-nine)

---

⑤ **Match the clock to the time.**

10:05
7:25
1:35
4:30
11:10
5:20
2:15

⑥

How many miles is it from Roy's house to Jack's house? 76 miles
How many miles is it from Chuck's apartment to Ken's house? 25 miles
Jack went to Ken's house after visiting with Chuck. How many miles did he travel? 63 miles

38
+ 25
63 miles

100 (one hundred)

① Add to find the sum.

471	268	158	539	258	796	369
+489	+662	+757	+193	+276	+187	+195
960	930	915	732	534	983	564

248	529	645	427	695	394	187
+588	+289	+266	+399	+149	+277	+693
836	818	911	826	844	671	880

396	284	269	573	378	478	497
+314	+139	+352	+367	+545	+274	+165
710	423	621	940	923	752	662

② Write the correct time.

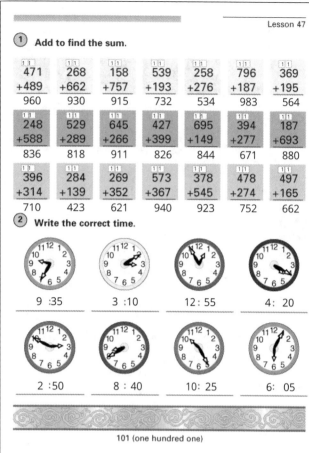

9 :35   3 :10   12 : 55   4: 20

2 :50   8 : 40   10: 25   6: 05

101 (one hundred one)

③ Write the numbers.

73 = __6__ tens + 13 ones   27 = __1__ tens + 17 ones

72 = __6__ tens + 12 ones   51 = __4__ tens + 11 ones

85 = __7__ tens + 15 ones   96 = __8__ tens + 16 ones

64 = __5__ tens + 14 ones   38 = __2__ tens + 18 ones

④ Match the estimated time to the event.

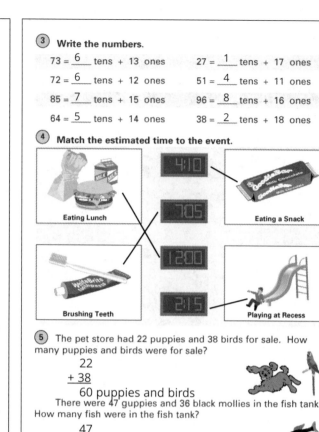

Eating Lunch — 4:10 — Eating a Snack
— 7:05 —
Brushing Teeth — 12:00 — 2:15 — Playing at Recess

⑤

The pet store had 22 puppies and 38 birds for sale. How many puppies and birds were for sale?

```
   22
 + 38
   60 puppies and birds
```

There were 47 guppies and 36 black mollies in the fish tank. How many fish were in the fish tank?

```
   47
 + 36
   83 fish
```

102 (one hundred two)

---

① Draw the minute hand on the clock.

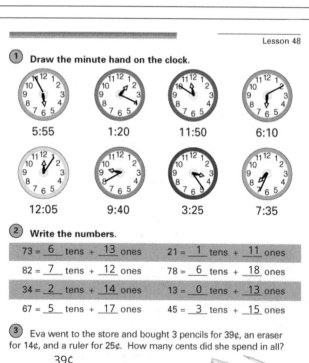

5:55   1:20   11:50   6:10

12:05   9:40   3:25   7:35

② Write the numbers.

73 = __6__ tens + __13__ ones	21 = __1__ tens + __11__ ones
82 = __7__ tens + __12__ ones	78 = __6__ tens + __18__ ones
34 = __2__ tens + __14__ ones	13 = __0__ tens + __13__ ones
67 = __5__ tens + __17__ ones	45 = __3__ tens + __15__ ones

③

Eva went to the store and bought 3 pencils for 39¢, an eraser for 14¢, and a ruler for 25¢. How many cents did she spend in all?

```
   39¢
   14¢
 + 25¢
   78¢
```

Jan came to Karen's house to play at 2 o'clock. She went home at 5 o'clock. How many hours was she at Karen's house?

```
   5
 - 2
   3 hours
```

103 (one hundred three)

④ Add to find the sum.

195	783	249	138	267	393	172
+118	+127	+263	+394	+343	+458	+698
313	910	512	532	610	851	870

564	195	371	128	649	484	167
+288	+596	+259	+498	+297	+467	+267
852	791	630	626	946	951	434

⑤ Write the answers.

If it is about 2:00, about what time will it be 4 hours from now? __6:00__

If it is 10:15 and Ron got up about 6 hours ago, about what time did Ron get up? __4:15__

Barb went to work about 2 hours ago. It is now 9:30. About what time did Barb go to work? __7:30__

⑥ Subtract.

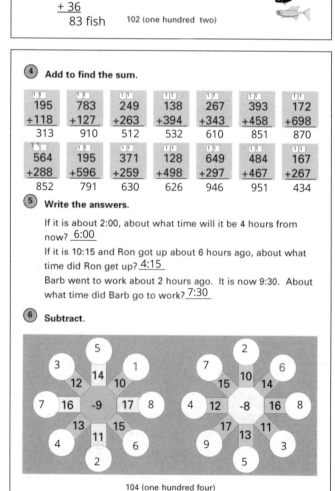

104 (one hundred four)

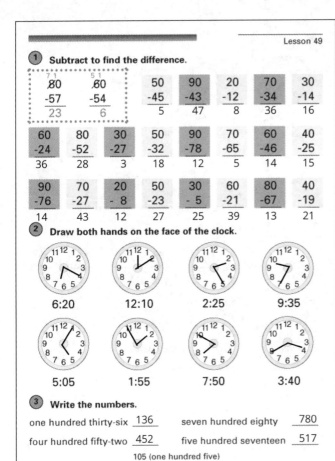

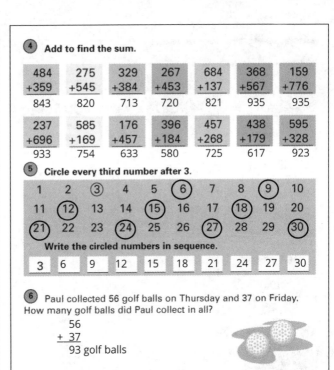

Lesson 49

1. Subtract to find the difference.

80 −57 = 23	60 −54 = 6	50 −45 = 5	90 −43 = 47	20 −12 = 8	70 −34 = 36	30 −14 = 16
60 −24 = 36	80 −52 = 28	30 −27 = 3	50 −32 = 18	90 −78 = 12	70 −65 = 5	60 −46 = 14	40 −25 = 15
90 −76 = 14	70 −27 = 43	20 − 8 = 12	50 −23 = 27	30 − 5 = 25	60 −21 = 39	80 −67 = 13	40 −19 = 21

2. Draw both hands on the face of the clock.

6:20   12:10   2:25   9:35

5:05   1:55   7:50   3:40

3. Write the numbers.

one hundred thirty-six __136__   seven hundred eighty __780__

four hundred fifty-two __452__   five hundred seventeen __517__

105 (one hundred five)

---

4. Add to find the sum.

484 +359	275 +545	329 +384	267 +453	684 +137	368 +567	159 +776
843	820	713	720	821	935	935
237 +696	585 +169	176 +457	396 +184	457 +268	438 +179	595 +328
933	754	633	580	725	617	923

5. Circle every third number after 3.

1 2 ③ 4 5 ⑥ 7 8 ⑨ 10
11 ⑫ 13 14 ⑮ 16 17 ⑱ 19 20
㉑ 22 23 ㉔ 25 26 ㉗ 28 29 ㉚

Write the circled numbers in sequence.

| 3 | 6 | 9 | 12 | 15 | 18 | 21 | 24 | 27 | 30 |

6. Paul collected 56 golf balls on Thursday and 37 on Friday. How many golf balls did Paul collect in all?

56
+ 37
93 golf balls

David made $234 the first week painting and $286 the second week. How much money did David make in all?

$234
+ $286
$520

106 (one hundred six)

Test 5 Lesson 50
Lessons 36-45 86 points total

1. Write the numbers that come before and after by 8's. 8 pts.

8 16 24 __ 32 40 48 __ 56 64 72 __ 80 88 96

2. Write the numbers. 15 pts.

37 = __3__ tens + __7__ ones = 2 tens + __17__ ones
64 = __6__ tens + __4__ ones = 5 tens + __14__ ones
25 = __2__ tens + __5__ ones = 1 ten + __15__ ones
83 = __8__ tens + __3__ ones = 7 tens + __13__ ones
56 = __5__ tens + __6__ ones = 4 tens + __16__ ones

3. Write the numbers. 9 pts.

forty-six	46	ninety	90	thirty-six	36
twenty-three	23	fourteen	14	eighty-nine	89
sixty-two	62	fifty-one	51	sixty-five	65

4. Write the answers. 8 pts.

Is 42 closer to 40 or 50?	40	Is 44 closer to 40 or 50?	40
Is 47 closer to 40 or 50?	50	Is 46 closer to 40 or 50?	50
Ia 49 closer to 40 or 50?	50	Is 48 closer to 40 or 50?	50
Is 41 closer to 40 or 50?	40	Is 43 closer to 40 or 50?	40

107 (one hundred seven)

---

5. Add to find the sum. 14 pts.

197 +454	279 +168	385 +146	469 +159	465 +268	488 +497	563 +289
651	447	531	628	733	985	852
748 +192	479 +384	258 +293	294 +637	189 +581	377 +239	529 +196
940	863	551	931	770	616	725

6. Write the missing numbers by 7's. 7 pts.

7 14 21 28 35 42 49 56 63

7. Write the numbers. 24 pts.

4,683 = __4__ thousands + __6__ hundreds + __8__ tens + __3__ ones
4,000 + 600 + 80 + 3

7,352 = __7__ thousands + __3__ hundreds + __5__ tens + __2__ ones
7,000 + 300 + 50 + 2

8,916 = __8__ thousands + __9__ hundreds + __1__ tens + __6__ ones
8,000 + 900 + 10 + 6

8. Kerry read 34 pages on Wednesday and 58 on Thursday. How many pages did Kerry read in all? 1 pt.

34
+ 58
92 pages

108 (one hundred eight)

① Add to find the sum.

276 + 258 =	138 + 598 =	358 + 264 =
276 + 258 534	138 + 598 736	358 + 264 622
187 + 227 =	694+ 137 =	146+ 199 =
187 + 227 414	694 + 137 831	146 + 199 345
196 + 654 =	395 + 78 =	275 + 97 =
196 + 654 850	395 + 78 473	275 + 97 372

② Circle every fourth number after 4.

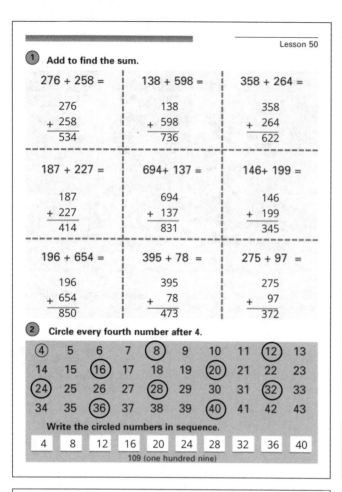

Write the circled numbers in sequence.

| 4 | 8 | 12 | 16 | 20 | 24 | 28 | 32 | 36 | 40 |

109 (one hundred nine)

③ Write the correct time.

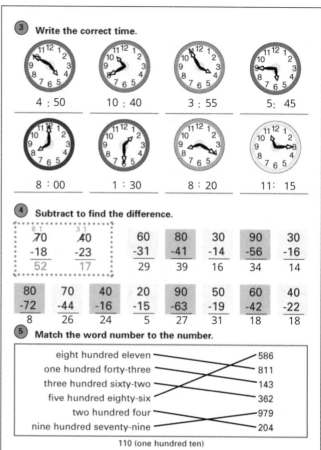

4 : 50   10 : 40   3 : 55   5: 45

8 : 00   1 : 30   8 : 20   11: 15

④ Subtract to find the difference.

⁶ ¹ 70 -18 52	³ ¹ 40 -23 17	60 -31 29	80 -41 39	30 -14 16	90 -56 34	30 -16 14
80 -72 8	70 -44 26	40 -16 24	20 -15 5	90 -63 27	50 -19 31	60 -42 18	40 -22 18

⑤ Match the word number to the number.

eight hundred eleven — 586
one hundred forty-three — 811
three hundred sixty-two — 143
five hundred eighty-six — 362
two hundred four — 979
nine hundred seventy-nine — 204

110 (one hundred ten)

① Write as a number sentence.

Three plus eight equals eleven. 3 + 8 = 11

Fifty-four and thirty-nine is ninety-three. 54 + 39 = 93

The sum of twenty-two and sixteen is thirty-eight. 22 + 16 = 38

Fifteen and twenty more equals thirty-five. 15 + 20 = 35

Forty-one increased by five equals forty-six. 41 + 5 = 46

Twelve added to five is seventeen. 5 + 12 = 17

② Write = or ≠.

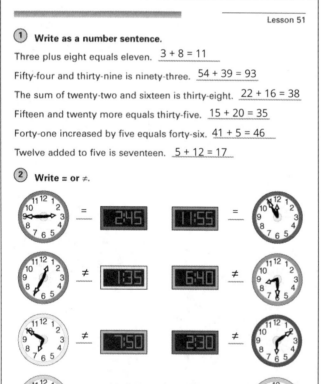

111 (one hundred eleven)

③ Add to find the sum.

615 +295 910	178 +584 762	449 +269 718	158 +479 637	563 +198 761	496 +427 923	379 +135 514
298 +565 863	154 +768 922	486 +335 821	562 +289 851	289 +678 967	353 +397 750	197 +656 853

④ Write the word numbers.

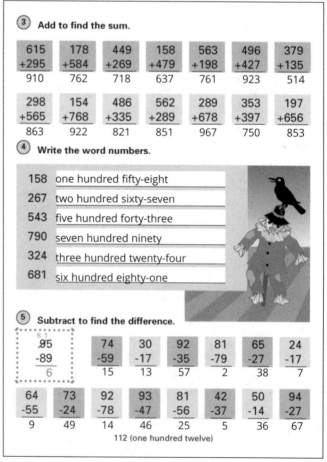

158	one hundred fifty-eight
267	two hundred sixty-seven
543	five hundred forty-three
790	seven hundred ninety
324	three hundred twenty-four
681	six hundred eighty-one

⑤ Subtract to find the difference.

⁸ ¹ 95 -89 6	74 -59 15	30 -17 13	92 -35 57	81 -79 2	65 -27 38	24 -17 7
64 -55 9	73 -24 49	92 -78 14	93 -47 46	81 -56 25	42 -37 5	50 -14 36	94 -27 67

112 (one hundred twelve)

382

1 Write the numbers.

6,431 = 6,000 + 400 + 30 + 1   7,543 = 7,000 + 500 + 40 + 3

5,729 = 5,000 + 700 + 20 + 9   2,378 = 2,000 + 300 + 70 + 8

8,105 = 8,000 + 100 + 00 + 5   1,682 = 1,000 + 600 + 80 + 2

3,264 = 3,000 + 200 + 60 + 4   4,816 = 4,000 + 800 + 10 + 6

2 Write the letters in the blanks.

D	O		T	H	E	
H	A	R	D	E	S	T
T	H	I	N	G	S		F	I	R	S	T

17th G	9th D	12th T	7th A
6th H	16th N	19th F	13th I
23rd T	3rd O	2nd O	20th I
1st D	18th S	15th L	4th H
10th E	5th E	8th R	14th H
22nd S	11th S	21st R	

3 Add to find the sum.

377	351	274	289	688	179	482
+ 85	+389	+396	+174	+ 36	+146	+399
462	740	670	463	724	325	881

638	158	596	497	348	594	139
+279	+392	+ 29	+186	+575	+138	+286
917	550	625	683	923	732	425

113 (one hundred thirteen)

---

4 Write as a number sentence.

Thirty-six and forty-nine equals eighty-five.   36 + 49 = 85

Fifty plus twenty-three is seventy-three.   50 + 23 = 73

Eleven increased by one is twelve.   11 + 1 = 12

The sum of thirty-four and two is thirty-six.   34 + 2 = 36

Fourteen added to sixteen equals thirty.   16 + 14 = 30

Twenty-three added to seven is thirty.   7 + 23 = 30

5 Write = or ≠.

3 = 12 - 9	9 = 16 - 7	5 = 13 - 8
7 ≠ 14 - 6	5 = 10 - 5	9 ≠ 17 - 9
5 ≠ 11 - 7	6 = 11 - 5	6 = 12 - 6
8 ≠ 12 - 3	7 ≠ 10 - 2	4 = 13 - 9

6 Subtract to find the difference.

60	91	42	53	75	82	50	30
-23	-73	-34	- 8	-26	-45	-45	-25
37	18	8	45	49	37	5	5

90	72	84	43	61	50	96	58
-66	-46	-26	-29	- 5	-38	-59	-29
24	26	58	14	56	12	37	29

37	64	73	90	61	72	86	70
-19	-58	- 5	-32	-47	-69	-47	-39
18	6	68	58	14	3	39	31

114 (one hundred fourteen)

---

1 Color the shapes.

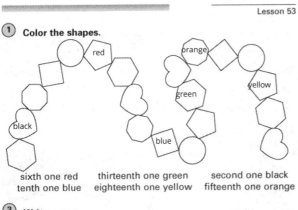

sixth one red   thirteenth one green   second one black
tenth one blue   eighteenth one yellow   fifteenth one orange

2 Write = or ≠.

5,000 + 600 + 40 + 3 = 5,643	3,000 + 400 + 10 + 8 = 3,418
2,000 + 300 + 70 + 5 ≠ 2,735	8,000 + 000 + 60 + 2 ≠ 8,602
7,000 + 800 + 20 + 9 = 7,829	6,000 + 500 + 30 + 0 = 6,530
4,000 + 100 + 90 + 6 = 4,196	9,000 + 700 + 80 + 4 ≠ 9,847

3 Add.

3,092	5,178	3,249	4,167	4,056	7,283
+4,238	+4,154	+6,078	+4,389	+2,489	+1,567
7,330	9,332	9,327	8,556	6,545	8,850

6,297	2,173	5,089	1,358	5,254	3,136
+1,457	+4,469	+3,727	+5,368	+2,659	+2,684
7,754	6,642	8,816	6,726	7,913	5,820

115 (one hundred fifteen)

---

4 Write as a number sentence.

Fifty-seven added to eighteen equals seventy-five.   18 + 57 = 75

Thirty-two added to twelve is forty-four.   12 + 32 = 44

Twenty-five added to twenty-one is forty-six.   21 + 25 = 46

Sixty-eight added to thirteen equals eighty-one.   13 + 68 = 81

Fourteen added to sixteen is thirty.   16 + 14 = 30

5 Subtract to find the difference.

60	91	34	73	55	91	83	80
-31	-62	-26	-15	-17	-25	-57	-25
29	29	8	58	38	66	26	55

42	84	71	62	90	82	63	47
-13	-17	-34	-14	-46	-37	- 8	-19
29	67	37	48	44	45	55	28

6

4		2,9	5	6
3	0	4		8
8		1	6	3
		9	2	8
6	0		5	
7		7	2	

Across

2. 468 + 488
4. three hundred four
6. 7 more than 56
7. 900 + 20 + 8
9. Is 64 closer to 60 or 70?
11. 78, 76, 74, ___

Down

1. 143 + 295
3. 600 + 80 + 3
5. four hundred nineteen
6. 83 - 15
8. 2 hundred + 5 tens + 7 ones
9. 64, 65, 66, ___

116 (one hundred sixteen)

383

Calendar

JANUARY	FEBRUARY	MARCH	APRIL
MAY	JUNE	JULY	AUGUST
SEPTEMBER	OCTOBER	NOVEMBER	DECEMBER

① **Circle the correct number.**

Which date is on a Monday in November?

3 (29) 14

July 4th is on what day?

Monday Thursday (Sunday)

What date is the second Wednesday in April?

(14) 26 7

The fourth of December is what day?

(Saturday) Tuesday Friday

What date is on a Sunday in February?

9 31 (21)

117 (one hundred seventeen)

② **Write the numbers.**

1,000 + 700 + 30 + 0 = 1,730	2,000 + 100 + 40 + 4 = 2,144
5,000 + 400 + 60 + 6 = 5,466	7,000 + 600 + 20 + 9 = 7,629
8,000 + 200 + 10 + 3 = 8,213	4,000 + 800 + 50 + 7 = 4,857
6,000 + 500 + 80 + 5 = 6,585	3,000 + 100 + 70 + 8 = 3,178

③ **Add to find the sum.**

2,626	2,594	2,448	4,478	4,373	4,592
+7,285	+3,197	+1,367	+5,198	+3,589	+2,039
9,911	5,791	3,815	9,676	7,962	6,631

1,365	3,089	3,287	569	1,645	4,779
+7,269	+5,156	+6,623	+5,347	+8,298	+4,072
8,634	8,245	9,910	5,916	9,943	8,851

④ **Write as a number sentence.**

Forty-two plus twenty is sixty-two. 42 + 20 = 62

The sum of sixteen and eighteen equals thirty-four. 16 + 18 = 34

Thirty-eight added to ten equals forty-eight. 10 + 38 = 48

Fifty-three increased by nine is sixty-two. 53 + 9 = 62

Five and two is seven. 5 + 2 = 7

⑤ **Subtract to find the difference.**

68	94	53	72	86	91	56	48
-39	-27	-26	-19	-29	-48	-47	-29
29	67	27	53	57	43	9	19

118 (one hundred eighteen)

① **Write the missing even numbers.**

2	4	6	8	10	12	14	16	18	20
22	24	26	28	30	32	34	36	38	40
42	44	46	48	50	52	54	56	58	60

② **Number the months of the year in the correct order.**

6	June	12	December	3	March
2	February	1	January	8	August
7	July	5	May	10	October
11	November	9	September	4	April

③ **Subtract to find the difference.**

91	77	40	51	92	70	75	66
-73	-58	-29	- 4	-85	-48	-29	-37
18	19	11	47	7	22	46	29

80	84	62	83	90	72	45	64
-41	-69	-38	-29	-15	-18	-16	-28
39	15	24	54	75	54	29	36

61	54	87	91	96	90	77	53
-29	-18	- 9	-46	-28	-86	-59	-37
32	36	78	45	68	4	18	16

119 (one hundred nineteen)

④ **Write as a number sentence.**

Seventy-three increased by twelve equals eighty-five. 73 + 12 = 85

Twenty-nine and five equals thirty-four. 29 + 5 = 34

The sum of thirty-two and forty-six is seventy-eight. 32 + 46 = 78

Fifty-one plus twenty is seventy-one. 51 + 20 = 71

Sixty-seven added to thirty-two equals ninety-nine. 32 + 67 = 99

⑤ **Circle the greatest number.**

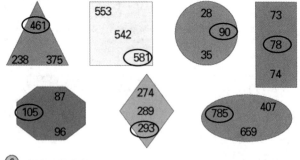

⑥ **Add to find the sum.**

8,189	2,664	1,531	1,095	2,587	1,048
+1,431	+3,198	+3,179	+8,386	+1,068	+7,369
9,620	5,862	4,710	9,481	3,655	8,417

4,362	1,188	2,496	5,177	2,398	2,453
+5,349	+6,596	+7,126	+4,165	+5,454	+2,079
9,711	7,784	9,622	9,342	7,852	4,532

120 (one hundred twenty)

384

1 Write the answers in the blanks. answers may vary

Circle groups of 2's
_3_ groups of 2's
2 + 2 + 2 = _6_
3 x _2_ = 6

Circle groups of 3's
_2_ groups of 3's
3 + 3 = _6_
2 x _3_ = 6

Circle groups of 2's
_5_ groups of 2's
2 + 2 + 2 + 2 + 2 = _10_
5 x _2_ = 10

Circle groups of 5's
_2_ groups of 5's
5 + 5 = _10_
2 x _5_ = 10

Circle groups of 2's
_6_ groups of 2's
2+2+2+2+2+2= _12_
6 x _2_ = 12

Circle groups of 6's
_2_ groups of 6's
6 + 6 = _12_
2 x _6_ = 12

Circle groups of 3's
_4_ groups of 3's
3 + 3 + 3 + 3 = _12_
4 x _3_ = 12

Circle groups of 4's
_3_ groups of 4's
4 + 4 + 4 = _12_
3 x _4_ = 12

121 (one hundred twenty-one)

---

2 Write the missing odd numbers.

1	3	_5_	_7_	_9_	_11_	_13_	15	_17_	_19_
_21_	_23_	25	_27_	_29_	_31_	_33_	_35_	_37_	39
_41_	_43_	_45_	_47_	_49_	51	_53_	_55_	_57_	_59_

3 Write the months of the year in order.

March September February December
May January August October
July November April June

1. _January_ 2. _February_ 3. _March_
4. _April_ 5. _May_ 6. _June_
7. _July_ 8. _August_ 9. _September_
10. _October_ 11. _November_ 12. _December_

4 Circle the smallest number.

(54) 67 91
273 280 (249)
356 219 (152)
175 (99) 268
900 (371) 465

122 (one hundred twenty-two)

---

1 Write the numbers in the correct blanks.

5 9	16 11	28 25	34 37
_9_ > _5_	_16_ > _11_	_28_ > _25_	_37_ > _34_

6 8	18 19	24 23	32 31
_6_ < _8_	_18_ < _19_	_23_ < _24_	_31_ < _32_

2 Write the multiplication facts.

3 + 3 + 3 + 3 = 12	4 x 3 = 12
2 + 2 +2 + 2 + 2 + 2 = 12	6 x 2 = 12
4 + 4 + 4 + 4 + 4 = 20	5 x 4 = 20
1 + 1 + 1 + 1 + 1 + 1 = 6	6 x 1 = 6
6 + 6 + 6 = 18	3 x 6 = 18
8 + 8 = 16	2 x 8 = 16
5 + 5 + 5 + 5 + 5 = 25	5 x 5 = 25
7 + 7 + 7 + 7 = 28	4 x 7 = 28

3 Add to find the sum.

637	757	509	473	461	236	563
+219	+152	+106	+175	+252	+480	+219
856	909	615	648	713	716	782

123 (one hundred twenty-three)

194	562	124	528	607	512	315
+575	+185	+807	+414	+384	+308	+468
769	747	931	942	991	820	783

4 Write 2 addition and 2 subtraction facts.

9 / 7 16
7 + 9 = 16
9 + 7 = 16
16 - 9 = 7
16 - 7 = 9

9 / 13 4
4 + 9 = 13
9 + 4 = 13
13 - 9 = 4
13 - 4 = 9

12 / 8 4
8 + 4 = 12
4 + 8 = 12
12 - 4 = 8
12 - 8 = 4

7 / 13 6
7 + 6 = 13
6 + 7 = 13
13 - 6 = 7
13 - 7 = 6

9 / 10 1
9 + 1 = 10
1 + 9 = 10
10 - 1 = 9
10 - 9 = 1

11 / 6 5
6 + 5 = 11
5 + 6 = 11
11 - 5 = 6
11 - 6 = 5

5 Subtract to find the difference.

31	73	90	26	82	51	50	60
-29	-19	-84	-18	-15	-42	-18	-25
2	54	6	8	67	9	32	35

92	64	63	78	41	40	95	84
-46	-16	-44	-59	-26	-16	- 7	-59
46	48	19	19	15	24	88	25

124 (one hundred twenty-four)

385

1 Circle the animals that are about 12 inches tall.

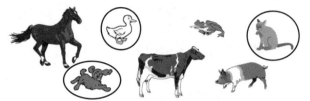

2 Write the numbers.

4 groups of 2's	2 groups of 4's	3 groups of 5's
four 2's	two 4's	three 5's
2 + 2 + 2 + 2 = 8	4 + 4 = 8	5 + 5 + 5 = 15
4 x 2 = 8	2 x 4 = 8	3 x 5 = 15

3 groups of 2's	2 groups of 3's	5 groups of 3's
three 2's	two 3's	five 3's
2 + 2 + 2 = 6	3 + 3 = 6	3 + 3 + 3 + 3 + 3 = 15
3 x 2 = 6	2 x 3 = 6	5 x 3 = 15

3 Add to find the sum.

711	530	659	188	218	493	586
+ 39	+285	+204	+471	+275	+396	+321
750	815	863	659	493	889	907

344	482	457	190	135	206	239
+209	+293	+451	+132	+427	+668	+531
553	775	908	322	562	874	770

125 (one hundred twenty-five)

4 Write the numbers in the correct blanks.

56 78	35 42	61 93	86 74
78 > 56	42 > 35	61 < 93	86 > 74

125 136	117 142	161 188	174 190
125 < 136	117 < 142	188 > 161	190 > 174

5 Write 2 addition facts and 2 subtraction facts.

5 8 3
5 + 3 = 8
3 + 5 = 8
8 - 3 = 5
8 - 5 = 3

4 11 7
4 + 7 = 11
7 + 4 = 11
11 - 7 = 4
11 - 4 = 7

13 5 8
5 + 8 = 13
8 + 5 = 13
13 - 8 = 5
13 - 5 = 8

6 14 8
6 + 8 = 14
8 + 6 = 14
14 - 8 = 6
14 - 6 = 8

6 2 8
6 + 2 = 8
2 + 6 = 8
8 - 2 = 6
8 - 6 = 2

15 8 7
8 + 7 = 15
7 + 8 = 15
15 - 7 = 8
15 - 8 = 7

6 Subtract to find the difference.

40	94	86	51	75	60	43	55
-34	-16	-27	-28	-26	-28	-15	-37
6	78	59	23	49	32	28	18

87	36	61	74	63	92	52	24
-69	-19	-34	-68	-57	-57	-35	-19
18	17	27	6	6	35	17	5

126 (one hundred twenty-six)

---

1 Write 2 addition facts and 2 subtraction facts.

7 9 16
7 + 9 = 16
9 + 7 = 16
16 - 9 = 7
16 - 7 = 9

14 5 9
5 + 9 = 14
9 + 5 = 14
14 - 9 = 5
14 - 5 = 9

3 10 7
3 + 7 = 10
7 + 3 = 10
10 - 7 = 3
10 - 3 = 7

4 12 8
4 + 8 = 12
8 + 4 = 12
12 - 8 = 4
12 - 4 = 8

11 9 2
2 + 9 = 11
9 + 2 = 11
11 - 9 = 2
11 - 2 = 9

13 7 6
7 + 6 = 13
6 + 7 = 13
13 - 6 = 7
13 - 7 = 6

2 Write the multiplication facts.

four 6's	six 4's	three 7's	seven 3's
4 x 6 = 24	6 x 4 = 24	3 x 7 = 21	7 x 3 = 21
two 9's	nine 2's	five 8's	eight 5's
2 x 9 = 18	9 x 2 = 18	5 x 8 = 40	8 x 5 = 40
five 3's	three 5's	seven 6's	six 7's
5 x 3 = 15	3 x 5 = 15	7 x 6 = 42	6 x 7 = 42

127 (one hundred twenty-seven)

3 Add to find the sum.

185	190	342	317	207	329	534
+244	+374	+629	+568	+457	+215	+173
429	564	971	885	664	544	707

816	125	340	862	309	275	576
+175	+529	+369	+ 75	+186	+660	+243
991	654	709	937	495	935	819

4 Draw 3 objects that are about 36 inches tall.

answers will vary

5 Write the numbers in the correct blanks.

24 36	89 85	127 151	143 168
24 < 36	85 < 89	151 > 127	143 < 168

243 265	289 291	367 333	316 408
243 < 265	291 > 289	367 > 333	408 > 316

128 (one hundred twenty-eight)

1 Write the correct time.   8 pts.

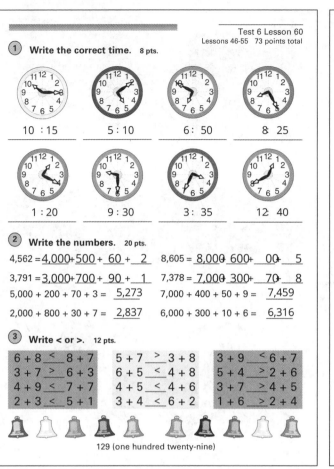

10 : 15   5 : 10   6 : 50   8 : 25

1 : 20   9 : 30   3 : 35   12 : 40

2 Write the numbers.   20 pts.

4,562 = 4,000 + 500 + 60 + 2   8,605 = 8,000 + 600 + 00 + 5

3,791 = 3,000 + 700 + 90 + 1   7,378 = 7,000 + 300 + 70 + 8

5,000 + 200 + 70 + 3 = 5,273   7,000 + 400 + 50 + 9 = 7,459

2,000 + 800 + 30 + 7 = 2,837   6,000 + 300 + 10 + 6 = 6,316

3 Write < or >.   12 pts.

6 + 8 < 8 + 7	5 + 7 > 3 + 8	3 + 9 < 6 + 7
3 + 7 > 6 + 3	6 + 5 < 4 + 8	5 + 4 > 2 + 6
4 + 9 < 7 + 7	4 + 5 < 4 + 6	3 + 7 > 4 + 5
2 + 3 < 5 + 1	3 + 4 < 6 + 2	1 + 6 > 2 + 4

129 (one hundred twenty-nine)

---

4 Subtract to find the difference.   16 pts.

41	80	52	84	81	74	95	66
-36	-26	-34	-35	-73	-69	-88	-28
5	54	18	49	8	5	7	38

62	68	93	74	51	90	73	84
-57	-29	-15	-38	-29	-42	-24	-58
5	39	78	36	22	48	49	26

5 Circle every third number after 2.   10 pts.

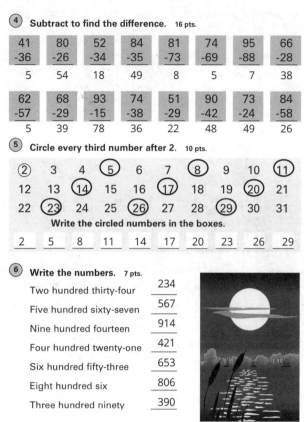

② 3 4 ⑤ 6 7 ⑧ 9 10 ⑪
12 13 ⑭ 15 16 ⑰ 18 19 ⑳ 21
22 ㉓ 24 25 ㉖ 27 28 ㉙ 30 31

Write the circled numbers in the boxes.

2   5   8   11   14   17   20   23   26   29

6 Write the numbers.   7 pts.

Two hundred thirty-four ___234___

Five hundred sixty-seven ___567___

Nine hundred fourteen ___914___

Four hundred twenty-one ___421___

Six hundred fifty-three ___653___

Eight hundred six ___806___

Three hundred ninety ___390___

130 (one hundred thirty)

Lesson 60

1 Write as a number sentence.

The difference between sixteen and nine is seven. _16 - 9 = 7_

Twenty-five take away four equals twenty-one. _25 - 4 = 21_

Forty-three less twelve equals thirty-one. _43 - 12 = 31_

Fourteen subtracted from sixty-eight is fifty-four. _68 - 14 = 54_

Eighty-one minus twenty-nine is fifty-two. _81 - 29 = 52_

Fifty-four decreased by ten is forty-four. _54 - 10 = 44_

2 Write the numbers.

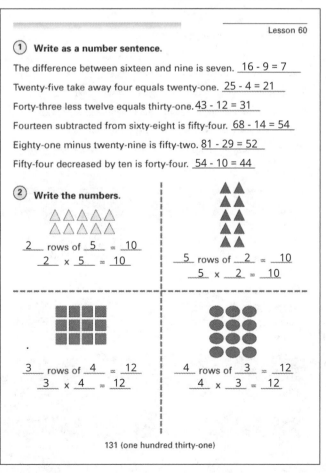

_2_ rows of _5_ = _10_
_2_ x _5_ = _10_

_5_ rows of _2_ = _10_
_5_ x _2_ = _10_

_3_ rows of _4_ = _12_
_3_ x _4_ = _12_

_4_ rows of _3_ = _12_
_4_ x _3_ = _12_

131 (one hundred thirty-one)

---

3 Match the number families.

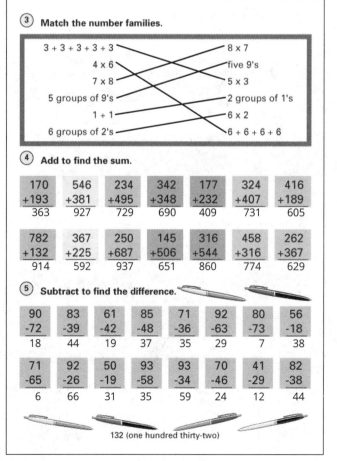

3 + 3 + 3 + 3 + 3 — 8 x 7
4 x 6 — five 9's
7 x 8 — 5 x 3
5 groups of 9's — 2 groups of 1's
1 + 1 — 6 x 2
6 groups of 2's — 6 + 6 + 6 + 6

4 Add to find the sum.

170	546	234	342	177	324	416
+193	+381	+495	+348	+232	+407	+189
363	927	729	690	409	731	605

782	367	250	145	316	458	262
+132	+225	+687	+506	+544	+316	+367
914	592	937	651	860	774	629

5 Subtract to find the difference.

90	83	61	85	71	92	80	56
-72	-39	-42	-48	-36	-63	-73	-18
18	44	19	37	35	29	7	38

71	92	50	93	93	70	41	82
-65	-26	-19	-58	-34	-46	-29	-38
6	66	31	35	59	24	12	44

132 (one hundred thirty-two)

387

1. Write the numbers.

4 + _5_ = 9   9 + _8_ = 17   8 + _8_ = 16
4 + _8_ = 12   6 + _4_ = 10   9 + _4_ = 13
2 + _8_ = 10   4 + _3_ = 7   3 + _5_ = 8
9 + _2_ = 11   5 + _3_ = 8   7 + _8_ = 15

2. Multiply.

1	0	4	6	1	3	1	0	1
x 2	x 8	x 1	x 0	x 0	x 1	x 9	x 5	x 6
2	0	4	0	0	3	9	0	6

1	4	5	0	0	1	0	8	1
x 7	x 0	x 1	x 0	x 9	x 1	x 3	x 1	x 4
7	0	5	0	0	1	0	8	4

3. Write as a number sentence.

Thirty-one subtracted from eighty is forty-nine. _80 - 31 = 49_

Sixty-five subtracted from ninety equals twenty-five. _90 - 65 = 25_

Twenty-eight subtracted from seventy-eight equals fifty. _78 - 28 = 50_

Forty-three subtracted from fifty-six is thirteen. _56 - 43 = 13_

Twelve subtracted from eighty is sixty-eight. _80 - 12 = 68_

Seven subtracted from fifteen equals eight. _15 - 7 = 8_

4. Larry ran 458 yards and Lisa ran 123 yards. How many yards did they both run?

```
  458
+ 123
  581 yards
```

133 (one hundred thirty-three)

---

5. Add to find the sum.

192	407	314	325	453	638	197
+683	+416	+516	+394	+270	+149	+361
875	823	830	719	723	787	558

249	167	281	469	532	105	253
+512	+482	+150	+123	+287	+765	+691
761	649	431	592	819	870	944

6. Subtract to find the difference.

431	870	461	657	982	893	148
- 123	- 215	- 327	- 138	- 614	- 626	- 29
308	655	134	519	368	267	119

796	684	572	890	970	784	585
- 548	- 359	- 438	- 471	- 347	- 25	- 239
248	325	134	419	623	759	346

7. Write the numbers.

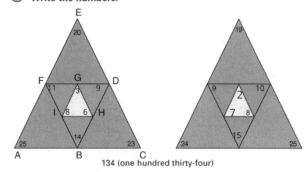

134 (one hundred thirty-four)

---

1. Write the correct time.

1 :25   9 : 05   7: 20   4: 55

10 :10   12 : 50   2 : 40   5: 35

2. Write the numbers.

7 + _2_ = 9   6 + _7_ = 13   5 + _5_ = 10
8 + _9_ = 17   7 + _5_ = 12   3 + _7_ = 10
5 + _2_ = 7   9 + _6_ = 15   8 + _4_ = 12
3 + _6_ = 9   4 + _9_ = 13   6 + _8_ = 14

3. Match the pairs.

5 x 8 = 40   6 x 7 = 42   3 x 9 = 27   4 x 6 = 24

9 x 3 = 27   8 x 5 = 40   7 x 6 = 42   6 x 4 = 24

4. Lee gathered 35 eggs from the hen house. Sue gathered 28 eggs. How many eggs did they both gather from the hen house?

```
  35
+ 28
  63 eggs
```

135 (one hundred thirty-five)

---

5. Write as a number sentence.

Fifty-four minus twenty-six is twenty-eight. _54 - 26 = 28_

Sixty-five less fourteen equals fifty-one. _65 - 14 = 51_

The difference between forty-one and thirty-one is ten. _41 - 31 = 10_

Forty-seven take away thirty-nine equals eight. _47 - 39 = 8_

Eighty-two decreased by five equals seventy-seven. _82 - 5 = 77_

Twenty-one subtracted from fifty-nine is thirty-eight. _59 - 21 = 38_

6. Multiply.

0	1	0	0	1	1	1	0	1
x 3	x 3	x 0	x 1	x 7	x 8	x 0	x 4	x 5
0	3	0	0	7	8	0	0	5

1	0	1	0	1	0	1	1	0
x 4	x 5	x 1	x 9	x 9	x 7	x 2	x 6	x 8
4	0	1	0	9	0	2	6	0

7. Add to find the sum.

672	291	354	647	504	593	163
+142	+652	+365	+315	+329	+ 90	+472
814	943	719	962	833	683	635

649	584	429	593	162	205	236
+243	+120	+247	+216	+567	+468	+549
892	704	676	809	729	673	785

136 (one hundred thirty-six)

① Match the number families.

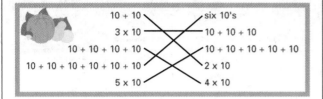

10 + 10	six 10's
3 x 10	10 + 10 + 10
10 + 10 + 10 + 10	10 + 10 + 10 + 10 + 10
10 + 10 + 10 + 10 + 10 + 10	2 x 10
5 x 10	4 x 10

② Draw both hands on the clocks.

3:35   11:25   6:50   10:20

③ Add to find the sum.

3,172	2,721	6,321	5,517	2,389	3,591
+5,490	+2,181	+3,439	+4,237	+4,140	+5,338
8,662	4,902	9,760	9,754	6,529	8,929

4,242	2,887	4,231	6,318	8,453	1,369
+2,176	+4,082	+1,597	+2,267	+1,417	+5,316
6,418	6,969	5,828	8,585	9,870	6,685

1,372	1,295	3,238	2,416	2,357	2,654
+6,453	+4,242	+6,435	+7,457	+5,421	+6,081
7,825	5,537	9,673	9,873	7,778	8,735

137 (one hundred thirty-seven)

---

④ Write the numbers.

<u>1</u> + 6 = 7	<u>6</u> + 3 = 9	<u>3</u> + 7 = 10
<u>4</u> + 2 = 6	<u>0</u> + 2 = 2	<u>6</u> + 9 = 15
<u>3</u> + 8 = 11	<u>7</u> + 7 = 14	<u>3</u> + 2 = 5
<u>6</u> + 2 = 8	<u>8</u> + 5 = 13	<u>5</u> + 7 = 12

⑤ Write as a number sentence.

The difference between forty-one and twenty-six is fifteen. <u>41 - 26 = 15</u>

Thirty-eight minus eighteen equals twenty. <u>38 - 18 = 20</u>

Sixty-three take away forty-nine equals fourteen. <u>63 - 49 = 14</u>

Eighty-nine take away fifty-two is thirty-seven. <u>89 - 52 = 37</u>

Seventy-six subtracted from seventy-eight is two. <u>78 - 76 = 2</u>

Fifty-four decreased by thirty-seven equals seventeen. <u>54 - 37 = 17</u>

⑥ Subtract to find the difference.

496	792	951	663	750	375	941
- 289	- 603	- 434	- 127	- 218	- 216	- 132
207	189	517	536	532	159	809

281	860	784	680	591	790	883
- 246	- 352	- 568	- 379	- 475	- 754	- 125
35	508	216	301	116	36	758

⑦ Chuck mowed the yard for 35 minutes. Bill finished the rest of the yard in 45 minutes. How long did it take both boys to mow the yard?

35
+ 45
80 minutes

138 (one hundred thirty-eight)

---

① Write = or ≠.

② Write the numbers.

<u>8</u> + 2 = 10	<u>7</u> + 1 = 8	<u>6</u> + 6 = 12
<u>5</u> + 6 = 11	<u>9</u> + 5 = 14	<u>5</u> + 4 = 9
<u>4</u> + 1 = 5	<u>2</u> + 7 = 9	<u>9</u> + 7 = 16

③ Subtract to find the difference.

975	762	456	932	623	867	854
- 826	- 509	- 147	- 715	- 217	- 549	- 106
149	253	309	217	406	318	748

139 (one hundred thirty-nine)

---

④ Multiply.

0	9	10	5	7	10	1	10	1
x 1	x 1	x 9	x 0	x 1	x 1	x 0	x 2	x 1
0	9	90	0	7	10	0	20	1

10	8	2	2	10	8	10	5	7
x 0	x 1	x 0	x 1	x 3	x 0	x 5	x 1	x 0
0	8	0	2	30	0	50	5	0

10	6	10	10	9	3	4	10	0
x 7	x 0	x 4	x 8	x 0	x 1	x 0	x 6	x 0
70	0	40	80	0	3	0	60	0

⑤ Write the next three numbers.

3	8	3	8	3	8	3	8	3
1	0	5	1	0	5	1	0	5
4	1	3	4	1	3	4	1	3
6	9	3	6	9	3	6	9	3
2	7	2	7	2	7	2	7	2

⑥ Add to find the sum.

4,173	6,529	7,514	2,093	2,328	5,665
+5,483	+2,046	+2,289	+2,625	+5,164	+3,152
9,656	8,575	9,803	4,718	7,492	8,817

3,162	4,327			3,343	7,556
+6,283	+2,156			+7,284	+2,253
9,445	6,483			10,627	9,809

140 (one hundred forty)

389

1 Write the number.

3,286 has a __8__ in the tens' place.

4,571 has a __4__ in the thousands' place.

8,942 has a __2__ in the ones' place.

1,765 has a __7__ in the hundreds' place.

6,423 has a __6__ in the thousands' place.

2,837 has a __7__ in the ones' place.

7,318 has a __3__ in the hundreds' place.

5,194 has a __9__ in the tens' place.

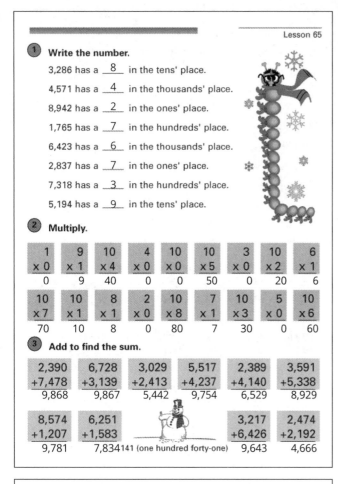

2 Multiply.

1	9	10	4	10	10	3	10	6
x 0	x 1	x 4	x 0	x 0	x 5	x 0	x 2	x 1
0	9	40	0	0	50	0	20	6

10	10	8	2	10	7	10	5	10
x 7	x 1	x 1	x 0	x 8	x 1	x 3	x 0	x 6
70	10	8	0	80	7	30	0	60

3 Add to find the sum.

2,390	6,728	3,029	5,517	2,389	3,591
+7,478	+3,139	+2,413	+4,237	+4,140	+5,338
9,868	9,867	5,442	9,754	6,529	8,929

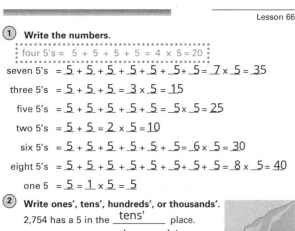

8,574	6,251			3,217	2,474
+1,207	+1,583			+6,426	+2,192
9,781	7,834			9,643	4,666

141 (one hundred forty-one)

---

4 Subtract to find the difference.

987	282	475	891	956	840	973
- 929	- 107	- 248	- 372	- 839	- 806	- 465
58	175	227	519	117	34	508

5 Match the word number to its number.

seven hundred three — 703

three hundred eighty-six — 386

four hundred twenty-eight — 428

five hundred seventy-four — 574

nine hundred fifty-seven — 957

two hundred ninety-one — 291

(matching lines: seven hundred three → 703, three hundred eighty-six → 386, four hundred twenty-eight → 428, five hundred seventy-four → 574, nine hundred fifty-seven → 957, two hundred ninety-one → 291)

Numbers listed on right: 386, 574, 291, 703, 428, 957

6 Write the next three numbers.

7	3	7	3	7	3	7	3	7
5	4	8	5	4	8	5	4	8
6	5	4	6	5	4	6	5	4
1	0	1	0	1	0	1	0	1
8	6	2	8	6	2	8	6	2

7 Write = or ≠.

16 - 7 _=_ 10 - 1	15 - 6 _≠_ 12 - 4	13 - 7 _=_ 11 - 5
12 - 5 _≠_ 15 - 7	10 - 8 _=_ 11 - 9	11 - 8 _≠_ 7 - 5
11 - 4 _≠_ 15 - 9	9 - 6 _=_ 8 - 5	10 - 4 _=_ 12 - 6

142 (one hundred forty-two)

---

1 Write the numbers.

four 5's = 5 + 5 + 5 + 5 = 4 x 5 = 20

seven 5's = _5_ + _5_ + _5_ + _5_ + _5_ + _5_ + _5_ = _7_ x _5_ = _35_

three 5's = _5_ + _5_ + _5_ = _3_ x _5_ = _15_

five 5's = _5_ + _5_ + _5_ + _5_ + _5_ = _5_ x _5_ = _25_

two 5's = _5_ + _5_ = _2_ x _5_ = _10_

six 5's = _5_ + _5_ + _5_ + _5_ + _5_ + _5_ = _6_ x _5_ = _30_

eight 5's = _5_ + _5_ + _5_ + _5_ + _5_ + _5_ + _5_ + _5_ = _8_ x _5_ = _40_

one 5 = _5_ = _1_ x _5_ = _5_

2 Write ones', tens', hundreds', or thousands'.

2,754 has a 5 in the __tens'__ place.

6,381 has a 6 in the __thousands'__ place.

5,902 has a 2 in the __ones'__ place.

8,467 has a 4 in the __hundreds'__ place.

4,839 has a 9 in the __ones'__ place.

9,015 has a 0 in the __hundreds'__ place.

3,278 has a 7 in the __tens'__ place.

1,523 has a 1 in the __thousands'__ place.

3 Add to find the sum.

4,307	3,251	3,192	4,271	5,205	3,418
+2,517	+1,691	+4,745	+1,356	+2,176	+2,221
6,824	4,942	7,937	5,627	7,381	5,639

143 (one hundred forty-three)

---

4 Write = or ≠.

three hundred seventy-six	_=_	376
two hundred fifty-four	_≠_	245
eight hundred eighteen	_≠_	819
six hundred four	_=_	604
five hundred three	_≠_	530
seven hundred fifty-eight	_=_	758

5 Write as a number sentence.

Thirty-five increased by ten equals forty-five. _35 + 10 = 45_

Twenty-three plus fifty-one equals seventy-four. _23 + 51 = 74_

Seventeen added to seven is twenty-four. _7 + 17 = 24_

The sum of forty and sixteen equals fifty-six. _40 + 16 = 56_

Eight and sixty-eight is seventy-six. _8 + 68 = 76_

6 Subtract to find the difference. Check your answers.

867	583	851	693	670	564	792
- 248	- 414	- 527	- 608	- 159	- 327	- 328
619	169	324	85	511	237	464

734	930	276	384	940	461	473
- 705	- 717	- 148	- 379	- 315	- 253	- 316
29	213	128	5	625	208	157

144 (one hundred forty-four)

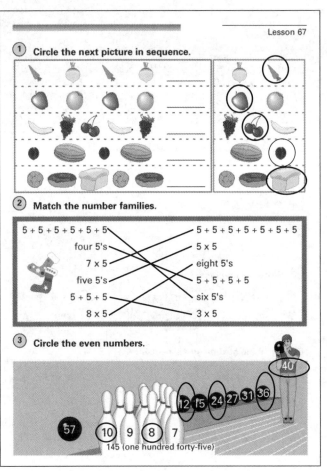

Lesson 67

① Circle the next picture in sequence.

② Match the number families.

5 + 5 + 5 + 5 + 5 + 5	5 + 5 + 5 + 5 + 5 + 5 + 5
four 5's	5 x 5
7 x 5	eight 5's
five 5's	5 + 5 + 5 + 5
5 + 5 + 5	six 5's
8 x 5	3 x 5

③ Circle the even numbers.

12 15 24 27 31 36
57 40
10 9 8 7

145 (one hundred forty-five)

---

④ Write as a number sentence.

The sum of thirty-six and forty-seven equals eighty-three. 36 + 47 = 83

Twenty-five and eighteen equals forty-three. 25 + 18 = 43

Thirty-two plus twenty-nine is sixty-one. 32 + 29 = 61

Forty-one increased by twelve equals fifty-three. 41 + 12 = 53

Fourteen added to fifty-three is sixty-seven. 53 + 14 = 67

⑤ Circle the number in the given place.

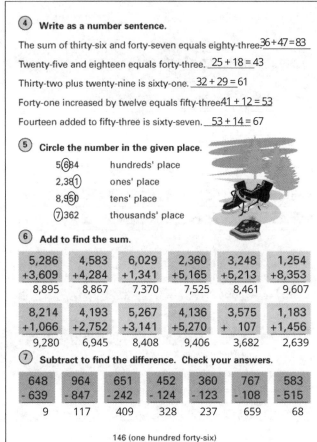

5,6̱8̱4̱	hundreds' place
2,38̱1̱	ones' place
8,95̱0̱	tens' place
7̱,362	thousands' place

⑥ Add to find the sum.

5,286	4,583	6,029	2,360	3,248	1,254
+3,609	+4,284	+1,341	+5,165	+5,213	+8,353
8,895	8,867	7,370	7,525	8,461	9,607

8,214	4,193	5,267	4,136	3,575	1,183
+1,066	+2,752	+3,141	+5,270	+ 107	+1,456
9,280	6,945	8,408	9,406	3,682	2,639

⑦ Subtract to find the difference. Check your answers.

648	964	651	452	360	767	583
- 639	- 847	- 242	- 124	- 123	- 108	- 515
9	117	409	328	237	659	68

146 (one hundred forty-six)

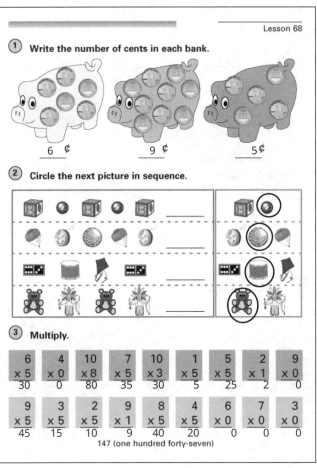

Lesson 68

① Write the number of cents in each bank.

6 ¢   9 ¢   5 ¢

② Circle the next picture in sequence.

③ Multiply.

6	4	10	7	10	1	5	2	9
x 5	x 0	x 8	x 5	x 3	x 5	x 5	x 1	x 0
30	0	80	35	30	5	25	2	0

9	3	2	9	8	4	6	7	3
x 5	x 5	x 5	x 1	x 5	x 5	x 0	x 0	x 0
45	15	10	9	40	20	0	0	0

147 (one hundred forty-seven)

---

④ Circle the odd numbers.

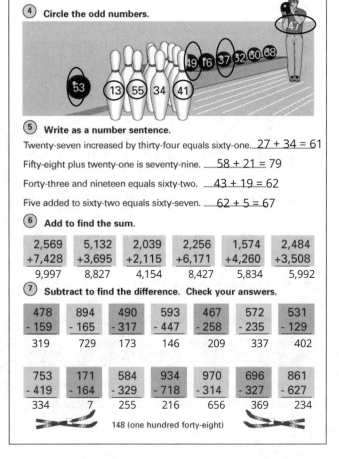

47
49 16 37 32 60 68
53
13 55 34 41

⑤ Write as a number sentence.

Twenty-seven increased by thirty-four equals sixty-one. 27 + 34 = 61

Fifty-eight plus twenty-one is seventy-nine. 58 + 21 = 79

Forty-three and nineteen equals sixty-two. 43 + 19 = 62

Five added to sixty-two equals sixty-seven. 62 + 5 = 67

⑥ Add to find the sum.

2,569	5,132	2,039	2,256	1,574	2,484
+7,428	+3,695	+2,115	+6,171	+4,260	+3,508
9,997	8,827	4,154	8,427	5,834	5,992

⑦ Subtract to find the difference. Check your answers.

478	894	490	593	467	572	531
- 159	- 165	- 317	- 447	- 258	- 235	- 129
319	729	173	146	209	337	402

753	171	584	934	970	696	861
- 419	- 164	- 329	- 718	- 314	- 327	- 627
334	7	255	216	656	369	234

148 (one hundred forty-eight)

December

Sunday	Monday	Tuesday	Wednesday	Thursday	Friday	Saturday
			1	**2**	**3**	**4**
5	**6**	**7**	**8**	**9**	**10**	**11**
12	**13**	**14**	**15**	**16**	**17**	**18**
19	**20**	**21**	**22**	**23**	**24**	**25**
26	**27**	**28**	**29**	**30**	**31**	

What is the first day of the week?	Sunday
What is the fourth day of the week?	Wednesday
What is the sixth day of the week?	Friday
How many Mondays in the month?	4
How many Saturdays in the month?	4
How many Thursdays in the month?	5
What date is the third Tuesday?	21
What date is the second Wednesday?	8
What date is the fifth Friday?	31

149 (one hundred forty-nine)

---

2. Multiply.

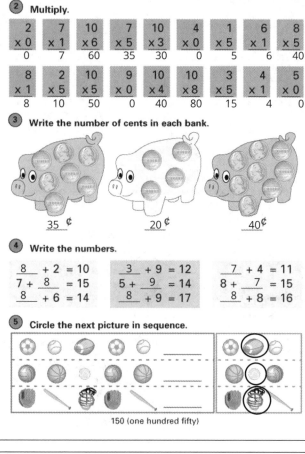

$\times$								
2 ×0 = 0	7 ×1 = 7	10 ×6 = 60	7 ×5 = 35	10 ×3 = 30	4 ×0 = 0	1 ×5 = 5	6 ×1 = 6	8 ×5 = 40
8 ×1 = 8	2 ×5 = 10	10 ×5 = 50	9 ×0 = 0	10 ×4 = 40	10 ×8 = 80	3 ×5 = 15	4 ×1 = 4	5 ×0 = 0

3. Write the number of cents in each bank.

35 ¢   20 ¢   40 ¢

4. Write the numbers.

8 + 2 = 10   3 + 9 = 12   7 + 4 = 11
7 + 8 = 15   5 + 9 = 14   8 + 7 = 15
8 + 6 = 14   8 + 9 = 17   8 + 8 = 16

5. Circle the next picture in sequence.

150 (one hundred fifty)

---

1. Write the next three numbers in the series. 18 pts.

4 5 4 5 4 __5__ __4__ __5__ | 1 0 0 1 0 __0__ __1__ __0__
1 2 3 1 2 __3__ __1__ __2__ | 9 4 6 9 4 __6__ __9__ __4__
6 8 7 6 8 __7__ __6__ __8__ | 7 3 7 3 7 __3__ __7__ __3__

2. Multiply. 27 pts.

9 ×1 = 9	4 ×0 = 0	4 ×1 = 4	8 ×1 = 8	10 ×5 = 50	1 ×0 = 0	10 ×6 = 60	5 ×1 = 5	10 ×1 = 10
7 ×1 = 7	2 ×0 = 0	3 ×1 = 3	10 ×7 = 70	8 ×0 = 0	10 ×2 = 20	10 ×4 = 40	5 ×0 = 0	6 ×1 = 6
3 ×0 = 0	10 ×9 = 90	9 ×0 = 0	10 ×3 = 30	7 ×0 = 0	1 ×1 = 1	10 ×8 = 80	2 ×1 = 2	6 ×0 = 0

3. Write 2 addition and 2 subtraction facts. 12 pts.

4 13 9	16 7 9	8 4 12
4 + 9 = 13	7 + 9 = 16	8 + 4 = 12
9 + 4 = 13	9 + 7 = 16	4 + 8 = 12
13 - 9 = 4	16 - 9 = 7	12 - 4 = 8
13 - 4 = 9	16 - 7 = 9	12 - 8 = 4

151 (one hundred fifty-one)

---

4. Add to find the sum. 12 pts.

2,392 +5,261	5,360 +2,141	1,581 +3,232	7,459 +2,139	5,042 +3,318	3,262 +6,580
7,653	7,501	4,813	9,598	8,360	9,842

1,250 +8,265	4,183 +5,793	4,624 +4,137	6,281 +1,345	3,776 +2,163	6,317 +2,549
9,515	9,976	8,761	7,626	5,939	8,866

5. Write = or ≠. 9 pts.

17 - 9 = 9 - 1   16 - 8 ≠ 11 - 2   13 - 6 ≠ 10 - 5
11 - 5 ≠ 6 - 1   12 - 6 = 9 - 3   15 - 7 = 14 - 6
13 - 9 ≠ 9 - 7   10 - 7 = 4 - 1   12 - 3 = 18 - 9

6. Andy weighs 64 pounds and Ed weighs 47 pounds. How many pounds do both boys weigh?

64
+ 47
111 pounds

If a balloon cost 28¢ and cotton candy cost 54¢, how much would both the balloon and cotton candy cost?

28¢
+ 54¢
82¢   2 pts.

7. Which animal would be about 10 inches tall: a camel, a ladybug, or a rabbit? __rabbit__   1 pt.

152 (one hundred fifty-two)

Lesson 70

1 Write the number of cents in each bank.

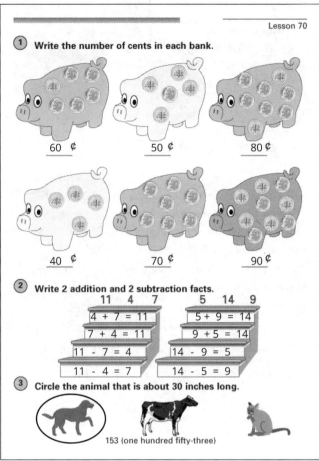

60 ¢   50 ¢   80 ¢

40 ¢   70 ¢   90 ¢

2 Write 2 addition and 2 subtraction facts.

11 4 7   5 14 9

4 + 7 = 11	5 + 9 = 14
7 + 4 = 11	9 + 5 = 14
11 - 7 = 4	14 - 9 = 5
11 - 4 = 7	14 - 5 = 9

3 Circle the animal that is about 30 inches long.

153 (one hundred fifty-three)

---

4 Subtract to find the difference. Check your answers.

692	360	785	883	570	992	476
- 686	- 259	- 179	- 239	- 266	- 963	- 339
6	101	606	644	304	29	137

868	581	593	460	734	981	893
- 639	- 347	- 146	- 213	- 417	- 504	- 724
229	234	447	247	317	477	169

5 Number the days of the week in the correct order.

3 Tuesday   6 Friday   5 Thursday
1 Sunday   4 Wednesday   2 Monday
7 Saturday

6 Write < or >.

4 x 5 > 15	8 x 5 > 30	10 x 5 < 60
1 x 5 > 0	0 x 5 < 5	3 x 0 < 1
10 x 7 < 80	5 x 5 > 20	6 x 5 > 20
9 x 5 < 55	7 x 1 > 6	2 x 5 < 15
7 x 5 > 25	6 x 0 < 1	3 x 5 < 25

7 Write the numbers.

3 + 5 = 8	1 + 5 = 6	9 + 5 = 14
3 + 3 = 6	8 + 6 = 14	2 + 4 = 6
0 + 4 = 4	4 + 8 = 12	7 + 6 = 13
6 + 5 = 11	7 + 8 = 15	4 + 5 = 9

154 (one hundred fifty-four)

Lesson 71

1 Write the number of cents in each bank.

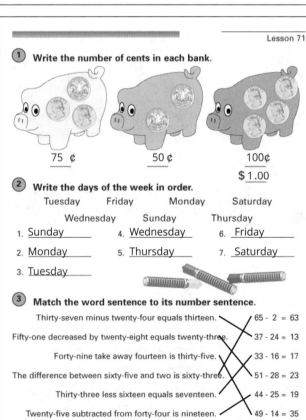

75 ¢   50 ¢   100¢
               $ 1.00

2 Write the days of the week in order.

Tuesday   Friday   Monday   Saturday
  Wednesday   Sunday   Thursday

1. Sunday   4. Wednesday   6. Friday
2. Monday   5. Thursday   7. Saturday
3. Tuesday

3 Match the word sentence to its number sentence.

Thirty-seven minus twenty-four equals thirteen. — 65 - 2 = 63
Fifty-one decreased by twenty-eight equals twenty-three. — 37 - 24 = 13
Forty-nine take away fourteen is thirty-five. — 33 - 16 = 17
The difference between sixty-five and two is sixty-three. — 51 - 28 = 23
Thirty-three less sixteen equals seventeen. — 44 - 25 = 19
Twenty-five subtracted from forty-four is nineteen. — 49 - 14 = 35

155 (one hundred fifty-five)

---

4 Write the numbers.

0 + 6 = 6	7 + 5 = 12	2 + 0 = 2
3 + 1 = 4	7 + 4 = 11	1 + 0 = 1
9 + 0 = 9	4 + 2 = 6	8 + 2 = 10
7 + 2 = 9	8 + 8 = 16	3 + 8 = 11

5 Draw three objects that are about 12 inches long.

answers will vary

6 Write < or >.

16 - 9 > 13 - 7	7 - 4 < 10 - 6	15 - 6 > 11 - 4
10 - 8 < 9 - 6	11 - 2 > 12 - 5	12 - 3 > 8 - 0
8 - 5 < 12 - 7	10 - 1 > 13 - 5	9 - 2 > 14 - 8
10 - 4 > 14 - 9	6 - 4 < 8 - 5	11 - 5 < 14 - 7

7 Michael had 376 pages in his book. He had read 158 pages. How many pages did he have left to read?

376
- 158
218 pages

Sally saved $3.48 in her bank. She earned $1.50 babysitting. How much does she have in all?

$3.48
+ 1.50
$4.98

156 (one hundred fifty-six)

393

① Write the answers.

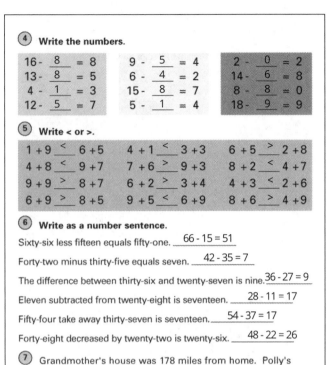

1 day	=	24	hours		1 minute	=	60	seconds
1 hour	=	60	minutes		1 week	=	7	days
1 year	=	12	months		1 year	=	52	weeks
1 year	=	365	days		½ hour	=	30	minutes

② Multiply.

10 ×2	1 ×0	6 ×5	1 ×1	3 ×0	1 ×5	10 ×6	1 ×2	10 ×9
20	0	30	1	0	5	60	2	90

4 ×0	2 ×5	1 ×4	10 ×8	1 ×3	9 ×5	1 ×7	5 ×0	10 ×3
0	10	4	80	3	45	7	0	30

8 ×5	10 ×5	8 ×0	1 ×9	4 ×5	7 ×0	10 ×4	1 ×8	3 ×5
40	50	0	9	20	0	40	8	15

③ Write 2 addition and 2 subtraction facts.

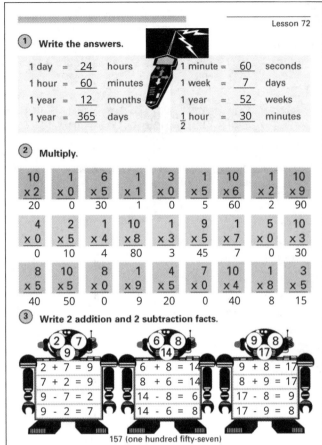

2 + 7 = 9
7 + 2 = 9
9 - 7 = 2
9 - 2 = 7

6 + 8 = 14
8 + 6 = 14
14 - 8 = 6
14 - 6 = 8

9 + 8 = 17
8 + 9 = 17
17 - 8 = 9
17 - 9 = 8

157 (one hundred fifty-seven)

---

④ Write the numbers.

16 - 8 = 8	9 - 5 = 4	2 - 0 = 2
13 - 8 = 5	6 - 4 = 2	14 - 6 = 8
4 - 1 = 3	15 - 8 = 7	8 - 8 = 0
12 - 5 = 7	5 - 1 = 4	18 - 9 = 9

⑤ Write < or >.

1 + 9 < 6 + 5	4 + 1 < 3 + 3	6 + 5 > 2 + 8
4 + 8 < 9 + 7	7 + 6 > 9 + 3	8 + 2 < 4 + 7
9 + 9 > 8 + 7	6 + 2 > 3 + 4	4 + 3 < 2 + 6
6 + 9 > 8 + 5	9 + 5 < 6 + 9	8 + 6 > 4 + 9

⑥ Write as a number sentence.

Sixty-six less fifteen equals fifty-one. 66 - 15 = 51

Forty-two minus thirty-five equals seven. 42 - 35 = 7

The difference between thirty-six and twenty-seven is nine. 36 - 27 = 9

Eleven subtracted from twenty-eight is seventeen. 28 - 11 = 17

Fifty-four take away thirty-seven is seventeen. 54 - 37 = 17

Forty-eight decreased by twenty-two is twenty-six. 48 - 22 = 26

⑦

Grandmother's house was 178 miles from home. Polly's family had already driven 105 miles to get there. How many miles do they have left to travel?

178
- 105
73 miles

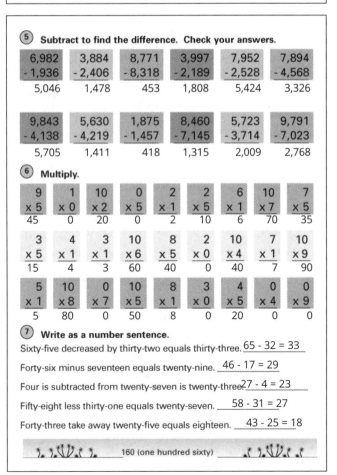

158 (one hundred fifty-eight)

---

① Write the numbers.

16 - 7 = 9	10 - 5 = 5	2 - 2 = 0
13 - 9 = 4	7 - 7 = 0	14 - 7 = 7
3 - 0 = 3	15 - 7 = 8	9 - 1 = 8
12 - 6 = 6	6 - 2 = 4	17 - 9 = 8
12 - 9 = 3	8 - 6 = 2	11 - 9 = 2

② Write the answers.

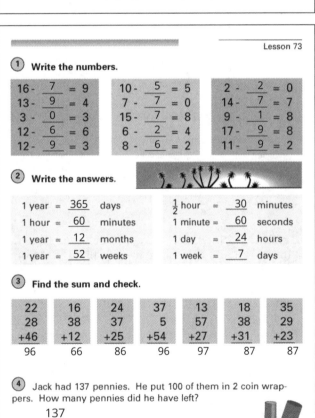

1 year	=	365	days		½ hour	=	30	minutes
1 hour	=	60	minutes		1 minute	=	60	seconds
1 year	=	12	months		1 day	=	24	hours
1 year	=	52	weeks		1 week	=	7	days

③ Find the sum and check.

22 28 +46	16 38 +12	24 37 +25	37 5 +54	13 57 +27	18 38 +31	35 29 +23
96	66	86	96	97	87	87

④

Jack had 137 pennies. He put 100 of them in 2 coin wrappers. How many pennies did he have left?

137
- 100
37 pennies

159 (one hundred fifty-nine)

---

⑤ Subtract to find the difference. Check your answers.

6,982 - 1,936	3,884 - 2,406	8,771 - 8,318	3,997 - 2,189	7,952 - 2,528	7,894 - 4,568
5,046	1,478	453	1,808	5,424	3,326

9,843 - 4,138	5,630 - 4,219	1,875 - 1,457	8,460 - 7,145	5,723 - 3,714	9,791 - 7,023
5,705	1,411	418	1,315	2,009	2,768

⑥ Multiply.

9 ×5	1 ×0	10 ×2	0 ×5	2 ×1	2 ×5	6 ×1	10 ×7	7 ×5
45	0	20	0	2	10	6	70	35

3 ×5	4 ×1	3 ×1	10 ×6	8 ×5	2 ×0	10 ×4	7 ×1	10 ×9
15	4	3	60	40	0	40	7	90

5 ×1	10 ×8	0 ×7	10 ×5	8 ×1	3 ×0	4 ×5	0 ×4	0 ×9
5	80	0	50	8	0	20	0	0

⑦ Write as a number sentence.

Sixty-five decreased by thirty-two equals thirty-three. 65 - 32 = 33

Forty-six minus seventeen equals twenty-nine. 46 - 17 = 29

Four is subtracted from twenty-seven is twenty-three. 27 - 4 = 23

Fifty-eight less thirty-one equals twenty-seven. 58 - 31 = 27

Forty-three take away twenty-five equals eighteen. 43 - 25 = 18

160 (one hundred sixty)

(1) Match the time equivalents.

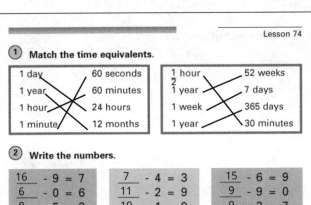

1 day	60 seconds
1 year	60 minutes
1 hour	24 hours
1 minute	12 months

1½ hour	52 weeks
1 year	7 days
1 week	365 days
1 year	30 minutes

(2) Write the numbers.

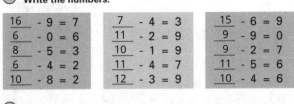

16 - 9 = 7	7 - 4 = 3	15 - 6 = 9
6 - 0 = 6	11 - 2 = 9	9 - 9 = 0
8 - 5 = 3	10 - 1 = 9	9 - 2 = 7
6 - 4 = 2	11 - 4 = 7	11 - 5 = 6
10 - 8 = 2	12 - 3 = 9	10 - 4 = 6

(3) Write the total value.

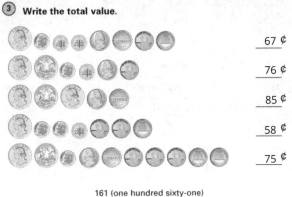

67 ¢
76 ¢
85 ¢
58 ¢
75 ¢

161 (one hundred sixty-one)

---

(4) Find the sum and check.

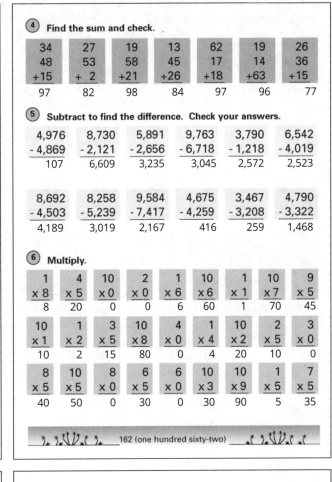

34	27	19	13	62	19	26
48	53	58	45	17	14	36
+15	+ 2	+21	+26	+18	+63	+15
97	82	98	84	97	96	77

(5) Subtract to find the difference. Check your answers.

4,976	8,730	5,891	9,763	3,790	6,542
- 4,869	- 2,121	- 2,656	- 6,718	- 1,218	- 4,019
107	6,609	3,235	3,045	2,572	2,523

8,692	8,258	9,584	4,675	3,467	4,790
- 4,503	- 5,239	- 7,417	- 4,259	- 3,208	- 3,322
4,189	3,019	2,167	416	259	1,468

(6) Multiply.

1	4	10	2	1	10	1	10	9
x 8	x 5	x 0	x 0	x 6	x 6	x 1	x 7	x 5
8	20	0	0	6	60	1	70	45

10	1	3	10	4	1	10	2	3
x 1	x 2	x 5	x 8	x 0	x 4	x 2	x 5	x 0
10	2	15	80	0	4	20	10	0

8	10	8	6	6	10	10	1	7
x 5	x 5	x 0	x 5	x 0	x 3	x 9	x 5	x 5
40	50	0	30	0	30	90	5	35

162 (one hundred sixty-two)

HALF DOLLAR

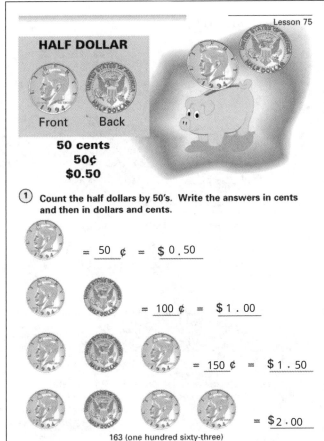

Front Back

50 cents
50¢
$0.50

(1) Count the half dollars by 50's. Write the answers in cents and then in dollars and cents.

= 50 ¢ = $ 0 . 50

= 100 ¢ = $ 1 . 00

= 150 ¢ = $ 1 . 50

= $ 2 . 00

163 (one hundred sixty-three)

---

(2) Write the correct time.

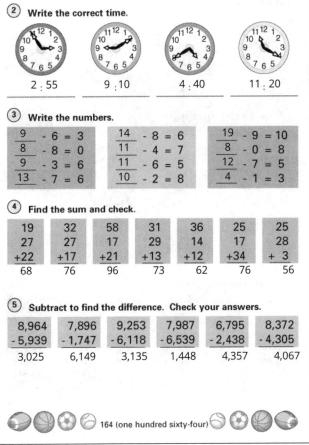

2 : 55   9 : 10   4 . 40   11 . 20

(3) Write the numbers.

9 - 6 = 3	14 - 8 = 6	19 - 9 = 10
8 - 8 = 0	11 - 4 = 7	8 - 0 = 8
9 - 3 = 6	11 - 6 = 5	12 - 7 = 5
13 - 7 = 6	10 - 2 = 8	4 - 1 = 3

(4) Find the sum and check.

19	32	58	31	36	25	25
27	27	17	29	14	17	28
+22	+17	+21	+13	+12	+34	+ 3
68	76	96	73	62	76	56

(5) Subtract to find the difference. Check your answers.

8,964	7,896	9,253	7,987	6,795	8,372
- 5,939	- 1,747	- 6,118	- 6,539	- 2,438	- 4,305
3,025	6,149	3,135	1,448	4,357	4,067

164 (one hundred sixty-four)

395

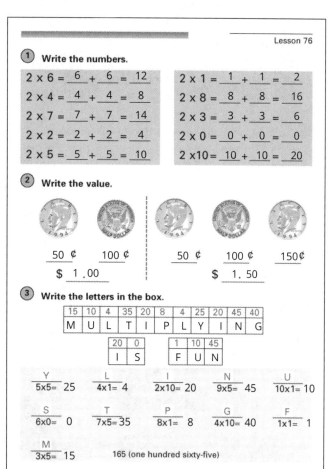

Lesson 76

① Write the numbers.

$2 \times 6 = \underline{6} + \underline{6} = \underline{12}$ $2 \times 1 = \underline{1} + \underline{1} = \underline{2}$

$2 \times 4 = \underline{4} + \underline{4} = \underline{8}$ $2 \times 8 = \underline{8} + \underline{8} = \underline{16}$

$2 \times 7 = \underline{7} + \underline{7} = \underline{14}$ $2 \times 3 = \underline{3} + \underline{3} = \underline{6}$

$2 \times 2 = \underline{2} + \underline{2} = \underline{4}$ $2 \times 0 = \underline{0} + \underline{0} = \underline{0}$

$2 \times 5 = \underline{5} + \underline{5} = \underline{10}$ $2 \times 10 = \underline{10} + \underline{10} = \underline{20}$

② Write the value.

50 ¢   100 ¢ | 50 ¢   100 ¢   150¢

$ 1 . 00 $ 1 . 50

③ Write the letters in the box.

15	10	4	35	20	8	4	25	20	45	40
M	U	L	T	I	P	L	Y	I	N	G

20	0		1	10	45
I	S		F	U	N

Y $5 \times 5 = 25$ L $4 \times 1 = 4$ I $2 \times 10 = 20$ N $9 \times 5 = 45$ U $10 \times 1 = 10$

S $6 \times 0 = 0$ T $7 \times 5 = 35$ P $8 \times 1 = 8$ G $4 \times 10 = 40$ F $1 \times 1 = 1$

M $3 \times 5 = 15$ 165 (one hundred sixty-five)

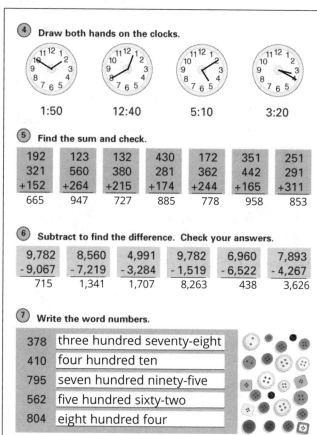

④ Draw both hands on the clocks.

1:50   12:40   5:10   3:20

⑤ Find the sum and check.

192	123	132	430	172	351	251
321	560	380	281	362	442	291
+152	+264	+215	+174	+244	+165	+311
665	947	727	885	778	958	853

⑥ Subtract to find the difference. Check your answers.

9,782	8,560	4,991	9,782	6,960	7,893
- 9,067	- 7,219	- 3,284	- 1,519	- 6,522	- 4,267
715	1,341	1,707	8,263	438	3,626

⑦ Write the word numbers.

378	three hundred seventy-eight
410	four hundred ten
795	seven hundred ninety-five
562	five hundred sixty-two
804	eight hundred four

166 (one hundred sixty-six)

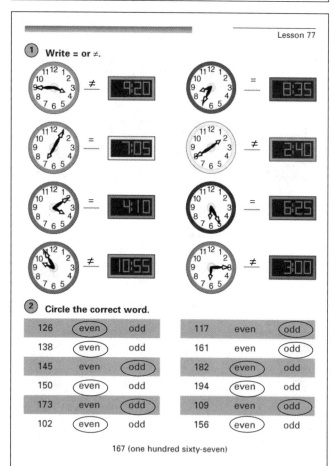

Lesson 77

① Write = or ≠.

≠   9:20
=   8:35
=   7:05
≠   2:40
=   4:10
=   6:25
≠   10:55
≠   3:00

② Circle the correct word.

126	(even)	odd		117	even	(odd)
138	(even)	odd		161	even	(odd)
145	even	(odd)		182	(even)	odd
150	(even)	odd		194	(even)	odd
173	even	(odd)		109	even	(odd)
102	(even)	odd		156	(even)	odd

167 (one hundred sixty-seven)

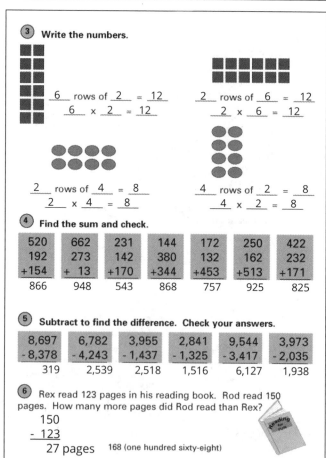

③ Write the numbers.

$\underline{6}$ rows of $\underline{2}$ = $\underline{12}$
$\underline{6}$ x $\underline{2}$ = $\underline{12}$

$\underline{2}$ rows of $\underline{6}$ = $\underline{12}$
$\underline{2}$ x $\underline{6}$ = $\underline{12}$

$\underline{2}$ rows of $\underline{4}$ = $\underline{8}$
$\underline{2}$ x $\underline{4}$ = $\underline{8}$

$\underline{4}$ rows of $\underline{2}$ = $\underline{8}$
$\underline{4}$ x $\underline{2}$ = $\underline{8}$

④ Find the sum and check.

520	662	231	144	172	250	422
192	273	142	380	132	162	232
+154	+ 13	+170	+344	+453	+513	+171
866	948	543	868	757	925	825

⑤ Subtract to find the difference. Check your answers.

8,697	6,782	3,955	2,841	9,544	3,973
- 8,378	- 4,243	- 1,437	- 1,325	- 3,417	- 2,035
319	2,539	2,518	1,516	6,127	1,938

⑥ Rex read 123 pages in his reading book. Rod read 150 pages. How many more pages did Rod read than Rex?

150
- 123
27 pages   168 (one hundred sixty-eight)

1 **Match pairs of multiplication facts.**

2 x 4 = 8 —— 4 x 2 = 8	3 x10= 30 7 x 1 = 7
3 x 2 = 6 2 x 6 = 12	2 x 5 = 10 0 x 6 = 0
5 x 1 = 5 2 x 3 = 6	6 x 0 = 0 2 x 7 = 14
6 x 2 = 12 8 x 2 = 16	1 x 7 = 7 10 x 3 = 30
8 x 1 = 8 1 x 5 = 5	7 x 2 = 14 5 x 2 = 10
2 x 8 = 16 1 x 8 = 8	10 x 5 = 50 —— 5 x10= 50

2 **Write the numbers.**

16 - 9 = 7	7 - 4 = 3	9 - 0 = 9
6 - 0 = 6	11 - 2 = 9	15 - 6 = 9
8 - 5 = 3	10 - 4 = 6	9 - 2 = 7
10 - 8 = 2	10 - 1 = 9	12 - 3 = 9

3 Lee picked 135 apples in his basket. Gene picked 118 apples in the same time. Lee picked how many more apples than Gene?

$$\begin{array}{r} 135 \\ -\ 118 \\ \hline 17 \text{ apples} \end{array}$$

There are 254 cabbage heads in the field. Allen picked 137 of them. How many more cabbage heads needed to be picked?

$$\begin{array}{r} 254 \\ -\ 137 \\ \hline 117 \text{ cabbage heads} \end{array}$$

169 (one hundred sixty-nine)

---

4 **Color the even numbers red and the odd numbers blue.**

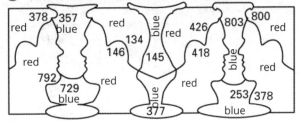

378 red   357 blue   red   134 blue   red   426   803 blue   800 red
146 red   145   418   red
792   729 blue   red   red   253 blue   378 red
377   blue

5 **Write = or ≠.**

3 x 5 ≠ 25	1 x 7 ≠ 1	10 x 6 ≠ 30
4 x 1 = 4	10 x 3 = 30	0 x 9 ≠ 9
6 x 5 = 30	5 x 4 ≠ 40	8 x 1 = 8
6 x 0 ≠ 6	1 x 6 ≠ 7	5 x 7 = 35

6 **Find the sum and check.**

193	421	52	20	572	113	124
241	183	674	397	140	640	62
+312	+152	+222	+341	+154	+185	+543
746	756	948	758	866	938	729

7 **Subtract to find the difference. Check your answers.**

5,274	6,872	5,986	2,873	7,735	6,981
- 1,265	- 3,418	- 2,259	- 1,736	- 1,406	- 5,709
4,009	3,454	3,727	1,137	6,329	1,272

170 (one hundred seventy)

---

1 **Multiply to find the product.**

5	2	6	9	10	2	10	1	10
x 5	x 5	x 0	x 1	x 2	x 1	x 8	x 5	x 3
25	10	0	9	20	2	80	5	30

1	2	3	10	8	0	5	1	5
x 3	x 3	x 5	x 4	x 0	x 4	x 9	x 1	x 6
3	6	15	40	0	0	45	1	30

5	0	7	5	10	7	10	2	4
x 8	x 7	x 2	x 7	x 5	x 1	x 6	x 4	x 5
40	0	14	35	50	7	60	8	20

2 **Write = or ≠.**

one hundred sixty-seven	=	167
five hundred forty-three	≠	5,403
eight hundred twenty-nine	=	829
three hundred fifty	≠	315
seven hundred four	≠	740

3 **Write the numbers.**

10 - 6 = 4	9 - 6 = 3	14 - 8 = 6
13 - 7 = 6	8 - 8 = 0	11 - 4 = 7
5 - 4 = 1	15 - 6 = 9	10 - 2 = 8
11 - 6 = 5	12 - 7 = 5	4 - 1 = 3
10 - 9 = 1	8 - 0 = 8	9 - 3 = 6

171 (one hundred seventy-one)

---

4 **Write as a number sentence.**

The sum of sixty-three and eighteen equals eighty-one. 63 + 18 = 81

Forty-five increased by twenty-seven is seventy-two. 45 + 27 = 72

Thirty-four plus fifty equals eighty-four. 34 + 50 = 84

Eight added to seventy-one equals seventy-nine. 71 + 8 = 79

Twenty-three and fifteen equals thirty-eight. 23 + 15 = 38

5 **Find the sum and check.**

241	274	210	212	318	314	341
219	351	239	150	218	356	398
+318	+152	+416	+386	+442	+125	+130
778	777	865	748	978	795	869

6 **Subtract to find the difference. Check your answers.**

9,546	8,351	8,568	5,621	9,745	6,982
- 1,418	- 6,302	- 5,529	- 3,517	- 6,539	- 1,526
8,128	2,049	3,039	2,104	3,206	5,456

4,273	7,962	5,874	2,675	7,621	9,952
- 1,145	- 2,416	- 3,459	- 1,126	- 4,306	- 3,708
3,128	5,546	2,415	1,549	3,315	6,244

7 Mr. High planted 153 strawberry plants and Mrs. High planted 128. Mr. High planted how many more strawberry plants than Mrs. High?

$$\begin{array}{r} 153 \\ -\ 128 \\ \hline 25 \text{ strawberry plants} \end{array}$$

172 (one hundred seventy-two)

397

① Circle the next animal in sequence.   4 pts.

② Write the number.   6 pts.

3,486 has a __6__ in the ones' place.

2,591 has a __5__ in the hundreds' place.

7,135 has a __3__ in the tens' place.

9,850 has a __9__ in the thousands' place.

5,324 has a __3__ in the hundreds' place.

8,762 has a __8__ in the thousands' place.

③ Write the value of each coin.   8 pts.

__10__ ¢   __25__ ¢   __25__ ¢

__5__ ¢   __1__ ¢   __10__ ¢

__1__ ¢   __5__ ¢

173 (one hundred seventy-three)

---

④ Write the numbers.   12 pts.

6 + __7__ = 13	1 + __1__ = 2	__0__ + 3 = 3
__3__ + 7 = 10	__1__ + 5 = 6	8 + __7__ = 15
6 + __9__ = 15	4 + __6__ = 10	__2__ + 8 = 10
8 + __8__ = 16	__3__ + 3 = 6	9 + __7__ = 16

⑤ Subtract to find the difference. Check your answers.   7 pts.

696	475	784	950	461	382	783
- 478	- 156	- 139	- 543	- 408	- 146	- 269
218	319	645	407	53	236	514

⑥ Circle the correct word.   8 pts.

38	(even) odd	280	(even) odd
96	(even) odd	477	even (odd)
153	even (odd)	651	even (odd)
381	even (odd)	892	(even) odd

⑦ Match the multiplication pairs.   10 pts.

2 x 5	10 x 8	4 x 1	8 x 5
3 x 1	0 x 6	0 x 9	1 x 4
8 x 10	5 x 2	10 x 7	2 x 6
6 x 0	2 x 9	6 x 2	9 x 0
9 x 2	1 x 3	5 x 8	7 x 10

174 (one hundred seventy-four)

---

① Circle the greatest number.

436   (581)   642   645   (726)

209   (603)   271   (648)   (792)

538   759

② Write the numbers.

1 - __0__ = 1	7 - __3__ = 4	__3__ - 1 = 2
12 - __6__ = 6	__5__ - 2 = 3	10 - __5__ = 5
__4__ - 3 = 1	15 - __7__ = 8	__9__ - 6 = 3
__13__ - 4 = 9	__18__ - 9 = 9	__10__ - 1 = 9
8 - __4__ = 4	__7__ - 0 = 7	__9__ - 3 = 6

③ Multiply to find the product.

2 x 1	10 x 1	10 x 2	3 x 1	2 x 4	10 x 8	5 x 5	0 x 6	10 x 5
2	10	20	3	8	80	25	0	50

7 x 5	6 x 2	8 x 0	6 x 5	8 x 2	10 x 3	8 x 5	2 x 2	7 x 1
35	12	0	30	16	30	40	4	7

5 x 4	1 x 9	2 x 3	5 x 3	10 x 6	0 x 3	9 x 5	9 x 2	1 x 8
20	9	6	15	60	0	45	18	8

175 (one hundred seventy-five)

---

④ Write as a number sentence.

The difference between forty-two and twelve is thirty. __42 - 12 = 30__

Fifty-four minus twenty-six equals twenty-eight. __54 - 26 = 28__

Seventy-five take away thirty-nine equals thirty-six. __75 - 39 = 36__

Eight subtracted from forty-seven equals thirty-nine. __47 - 8 = 39__

Eighty decreased by forty-six is thirty-four. __80 - 46 = 34__

⑤ Find the sum and check.

212	419	260	115	126	241	138
493	221	395	572	181	131	223
+171	+345	+121	+271	+460	+394	+121
876	985	776	958	767	766	482

⑥

8	5			1	4
2				0	
0		6	0		8
	5	3		1	8
		4			9
5	5		5	4	

Across

1. eighty-five
2. ___ - 8 = 6
3. 10 x 6
5. sixty take away seven
6. two 9's
7. next odd number after 53
8. next even number after 53

Down

1.
2.
3. 882
   -248
   634
4. 364
   182
   +343
   889

176 (one hundred seventy-six)

398

Lesson 81

1. Circle the least number.

(165) 289 401 · 751 (483) · (372) (351) 398 609

2. Write as a number sentence.

Sixty-five and twenty-eight equals ninety-three. 65 + 28 = 93

Ten added to seventy-four equals eighty-four. 74 + 10 = 84

Forty-three plus seventeen equals sixty. 43 + 17 = 60

The sum of thirty-one and fifty-eight is eighty-nine. 31 + 58 = 89

Twenty-five increased by thirteen is thirty-eight. 25 + 13 = 38

3. Find the sum and check.

374	102	360	326	139	342	111
182	584	286	471	329	282	539
+211	+192	+312	+192	+220	+121	+133
767	878	958	989	688	745	783

450	431	332	122	212	471	172
173	215	130	228	236	253	443
+122	+191	+291	+349	+438	+151	+150
745	837	753	699	886	875	765

1

4. Put an X on the numbers out of sequence.

236	238	240	✗	244	246	248
✗	252	✗	256	258	260	✗
264	266	268	✗	272	✗	276

5. Subtract to find the difference. Check your answers.

9,780	4,574	6,392	7,826	6,982	9,873
- 9,175	- 3,326	- 2,183	- 3,018	- 1,765	- 6,545
605	1,248	4,209	4,808	5,217	3,328

8,931	6,941	8,931	7,690	8,497	4,651
- 4,225	- 3,512	- 2,407	- 5,439	- 3,019	- 2,529
4,706	3,429	6,524	2,251	5,478	2,122

6. Write the numbers.

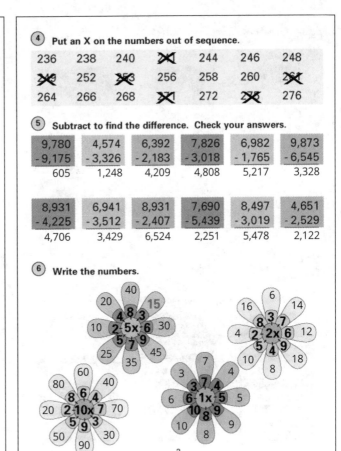

2

Lesson 82

1. Write the fraction that shows what part is shaded.

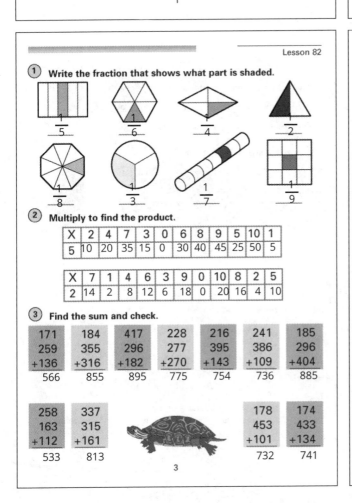

1/5   1/6   1/4   1/2

1/8   1/3   1/7   1/9

2. Multiply to find the product.

X	2	4	7	3	0	6	8	9	5	10	1
5	10	20	35	15	0	30	40	45	25	50	5

X	7	1	4	6	3	9	0	10	8	2	5
2	14	2	8	12	6	18	0	20	16	4	10

3. Find the sum and check.

171	184	417	228	216	241	185
259	355	296	277	395	386	296
+136	+316	+182	+270	+143	+109	+404
566	855	895	775	754	736	885

258	337			178	174
163	315			453	433
+112	+161			+101	+134
533	813			732	741

3

4. Write the value.

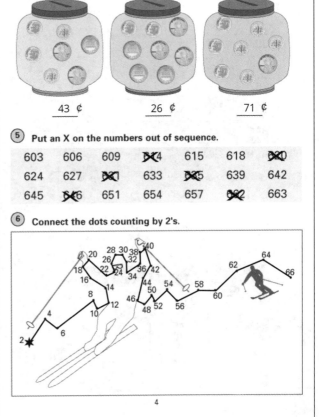

43 ¢   26 ¢   71 ¢

5. Put an X on the numbers out of sequence.

603	606	609	✗	615	618	✗
624	627	✗	633	✗	639	642
645	✗	651	654	657	✗	663

6. Connect the dots counting by 2's.

4

399

1 Write the value.

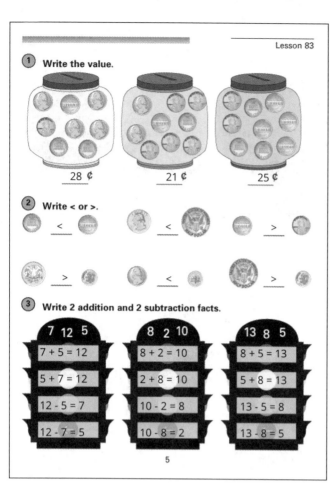

28 ¢   21 ¢   25 ¢

2 Write < or >.

<   <   >

>   <   >

3 Write 2 addition and 2 subtraction facts.

7 12 5	8 2 10	13 8 5
7 + 5 = 12	8 + 2 = 10	8 + 5 = 13
5 + 7 = 12	2 + 8 = 10	5 + 8 = 13
12 - 5 = 7	10 - 2 = 8	13 - 5 = 8
12 - 7 = 5	10 - 8 = 2	13 - 8 = 5

5

---

4 Write the fraction that shows what part is shaded.

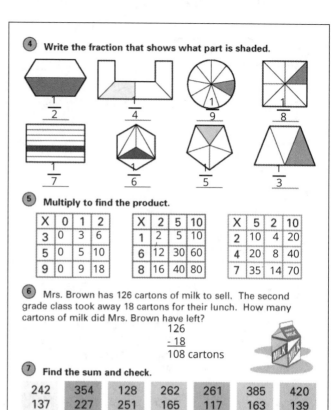

$\frac{1}{2}$ $\frac{1}{4}$ $\frac{1}{9}$ $\frac{1}{8}$

$\frac{1}{7}$ $\frac{1}{6}$ $\frac{1}{5}$ $\frac{1}{3}$

5 Multiply to find the product.

X	0	1	2
3	0	3	6
5	0	5	10
9	0	9	18

X	2	5	10
1	2	5	10
6	12	30	60
8	16	40	80

X	5	2	10
2	10	4	20
4	20	8	40
7	35	14	70

6 Mrs. Brown has 126 cartons of milk to sell. The second grade class took away 18 cartons for their lunch. How many cartons of milk did Mrs. Brown have left?

```
  126
 - 18
  108 cartons
```

7 Find the sum and check.

242	354	128	262	261	385	420
137	227	251	165	117	163	139
+194	+243	+383	+453	+359	+424	+179
573	824	762	880	737	972	738

6

Answers may vary.

1 Write the number of coins needed.

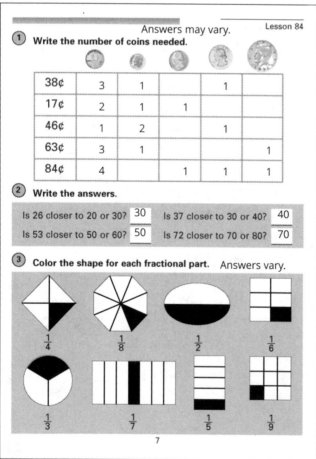

38¢	3	1		1	
17¢	2	1	1		
46¢	1	2		1	
63¢	3	1			1
84¢	4		1	1	1

2 Write the answers.

Is 26 closer to 20 or 30? 30   Is 37 closer to 30 or 40? 40

Is 53 closer to 50 or 60? 50   Is 72 closer to 70 or 80? 70

3 Color the shape for each fractional part. Answers vary.

$\frac{1}{4}$ $\frac{1}{8}$ $\frac{1}{2}$ $\frac{1}{6}$

$\frac{1}{3}$ $\frac{1}{7}$ $\frac{1}{5}$ $\frac{1}{9}$

7

---

4 Write as a number sentence.

Fifty-seven take away thirty-three equals twenty-four. 57 - 33 = 24

Forty-eight decreased by eleven is thirty-seven. 48 - 11 = 37

Sixty-four minus eighteen equals forty-six. 64 - 18 = 46

Seventy-five less twenty is fifty-five. 75 - 20 = 55

5 Write < or >.

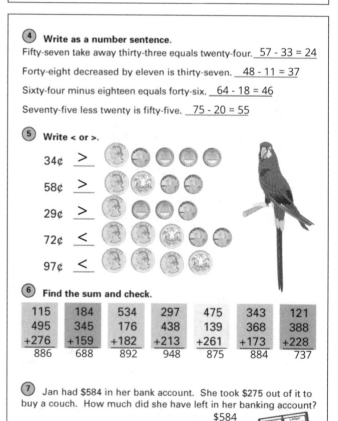

34¢ >

58¢ >

29¢ >

72¢ <

97¢ <

6 Find the sum and check.

115	184	534	297	475	343	121
495	345	176	438	139	368	388
+276	+159	+182	+213	+261	+173	+228
886	688	892	948	875	884	737

7 Jan had $584 in her bank account. She took $275 out of it to buy a couch. How much did she have left in her banking account?

```
 $584
 -275
 $309
```

8

400

① Match the time equivalents.

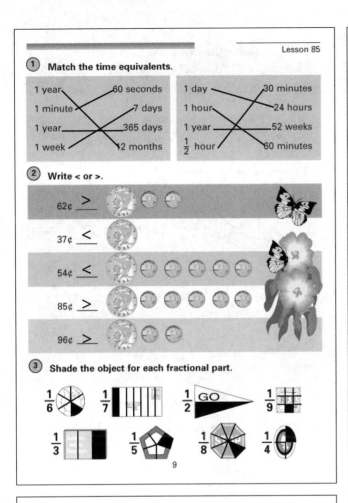

1 year — 60 seconds
1 minute — 7 days
1 year — 365 days
1 week — 12 months

1 day — 30 minutes
1 hour — 24 hours
1 year — 52 weeks
½ hour — 60 minutes

② Write < or >.

62¢ **>**

37¢ **<**

54¢ **<**

85¢ **>**

96¢ **>**

③ Shade the object for each fractional part.

$\frac{1}{6}$ $\frac{1}{7}$ $\frac{1}{2}$ $\frac{1}{9}$

$\frac{1}{3}$ $\frac{1}{5}$ $\frac{1}{8}$ $\frac{1}{4}$

9

---

④ Write the numbers.

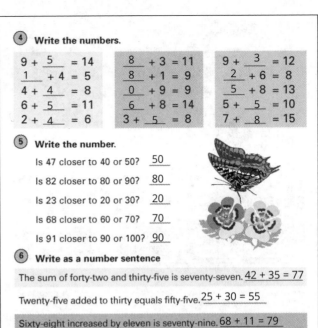

9 + **5** = 14	**8** + 3 = 11	9 + **3** = 12
1 + 4 = 5	**8** + 1 = 9	**2** + 6 = 8
4 + **4** = 8	**0** + 9 = 9	**5** + 8 = 13
6 + **5** = 11	**6** + 8 = 14	5 + **5** = 10
2 + **4** = 6	3 + **5** = 8	7 + **8** = 15

⑤ Write the number.

Is 47 closer to 40 or 50? **50**

Is 82 closer to 80 or 90? **80**

Is 23 closer to 20 or 30? **20**

Is 68 closer to 60 or 70? **70**

Is 91 closer to 90 or 100? **90**

⑥ Write as a number sentence

The sum of forty-two and thirty-five is seventy-seven. **42 + 35 = 77**

Twenty-five added to thirty equals fifty-five. **25 + 30 = 55**

Sixty-eight increased by eleven is seventy-nine. **68 + 11 = 79**

⑦ Write two addition and two subtraction facts.

Ⓐ 6, 10, 4   Ⓑ 4, 12, 8   Ⓒ 8, 9, 1

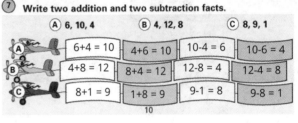

A	6+4 = 10	4+6 = 10	10-4 = 6	10-6 = 4
B	4+8 = 12	8+4 = 12	12-8 = 4	12-4 = 8
C	8+1 = 9	1+8 = 9	9-1 = 8	9-8 = 1

10

---

① Write the numbers.

four 3's = **3 + 3 + 3 + 3 = 4 x 3 = 12**

eight 3's = **3 + 3 + 3 + 3 + 3 + 3 + 3 + 3 = 8 x 3 = 24**

seven 3's = **3 + 3 + 3 + 3 + 3 + 3 + 3 = 7 x 3 = 21**

six 3's = **3 + 3 + 3 + 3 + 3 + 3 = 6 x 3 = 18**

three 3's = **3 + 3 + 3 = 3 x 3 = 9**

nine 3's = **3 + 3 + 3 + 3 + 3 + 3 + 3 + 3 + 3 = 9 x 3 = 27**

② Write the numbers.

1 day = **24** hours	1 minute = **60** seconds
1 year = **365** days	1 year = **52** weeks
1 week = **7** days	1 year = **12** months
1 hour = **60** minutes	½ hour = **30** minutes

③ Find the sum. Write even or odd.

4 **even**	6 **even**	8 **even**	2 **even**
+8 **even**	+2 **even**	+6 **even**	+8 **even**
12 **even**	8 **even**	14 **even**	10 **even**

3 **odd**	7 **odd**	5 **odd**	7 **odd**
+5 **odd**	+9 **odd**	+7 **odd**	+3 **odd**
8 **even**	16 **even**	12 **even**	10 **even**

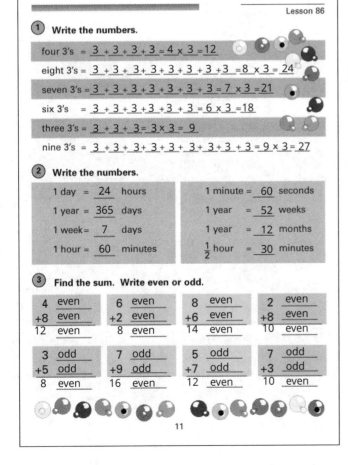

11

---

④ Write the numbers.

4 - **3** = 1	9 - **6** = 3	12 - **9** = 3
8 - 5 = 3	**13** - 8 = 5	**4** - 0 = 4
12 - **3** = 9	15 - **6** = 9	**11** - 6 = 5
11 - **2** = 9	10 - **4** = 6	**5** - 5 = 0
7 - **2** = 5	**10** - 2 = 8	**14** - 6 = 8

⑤ Find the sum and check.

3,242	2,449	2,320	1,017	2,438	1,130
1,581	2,165	3,295	3,296	1,042	2,589
+1,019	+2,243	+1,157	+3,522	+4,494	+4,055
5,842	6,857	6,772	7,835	7,974	7,774

⑥ Write as a number sentence.

Twenty-seven minus fifteen equals twelve. **27 - 15 = 12**
Forty-three decreased by twenty-eight is fifteen. **43 - 28 = 15**
Fifty-nine subtracted from sixty-six equals seven. **66 - 59 = 7**
Eighty-two take away thirty-four is forty-eight. **82 - 34 = 48**

⑦ Multiply to find the product.

X	5
3	15
8	40
5	25
7	35
9	45

X	10
3	30
8	80
5	50
7	70
9	90

X	2
3	6
8	16
5	10
7	14
9	18

X	0
3	0
8	0
5	0
7	0
9	0

12

$1.00 one dollar 100¢

$5.00 five dollars 500¢
$5.00 equals five one dollar bills

$10.00 ten dollars 1,000¢
$10.00 equals ten one dollar bills

$20.00 twenty dollars 2,000¢
$20.00 equals twenty one dollar bills

① **Write the value.**

$ __3.00__

$ __5.00__

13

---

② **Find the sum. Write even or odd.**

7 odd	5 odd	4 even	12 even
+6 even	+8 even	+9 odd	+15 odd
13 odd	13 odd	13 odd	27 odd

25 odd	17 odd	35 odd	26 even
+22 even	+11 odd	+32 even	+12 even
47 odd	28 even	67 odd	38 even

③ **Match the number families.**

3 + 3   5 x 3
eight 3's   nine 3's
3 + 3 + 3 + 3 + 3   30
9 x 3   8 x 3
10 x 3   two 3's

3 + 3 + 3 + 3   seven 3's
five threes   3 + 3 + 3
7 x 3   4 x 3
three 3's   6 x 3
3 + 3 + 3 + 3 + 3 + 3 5 x 3

④ **Write = or ≠.**

1 day	≠	12 hours		1 year	≠	356 days
1 year	=	52 weeks		1 hour	=	60 minutes
1 minute	≠	30 seconds		1 week	=	7 days
½ hour	≠	60 minutes		1 year	=	12 months

⑤ Ed and Barb invited 183 people to their wedding. There were 28 people that said they could not come. How many planned on attending the wedding?

```
 183
 -28
 155   people
```
14

---

① **Write the numbers.**

6 thousands + 5 hundreds + 4 tens + 3 ones = __6,000__ + __500__ + __40__ + __3__ = __6,543__

4 thousands + 7 hundreds + 2 tens + 8 ones = __4,000__ + __700__ + __20__ + __8__ = __4,728__

5 thousands + 9 hundreds + 3 tens + 1 one = __5,000__ + __900__ + __30__ + __1__ = __5,931__

8 thousands + 1 hundred + 5 tens + 6 ones = __8,000__ + __100__ + __50__ + __6__ = __8,156__

3 thousands + 0 hundreds + 7 tens + 4 ones = __3,000__ + __000__ + __70__ + __4__ = __3,074__

② **Write the numbers.**

__3__ rows of __4__
__3__ x __4__ = __12__

__3__ rows of __5__
__3__ x __5__ = __15__

__4__ rows of __3__
__4__ x __3__ = __12__

__5__ rows of __3__
__5__ x __3__ = __15__

③ **Draw the hands on the clocks.**

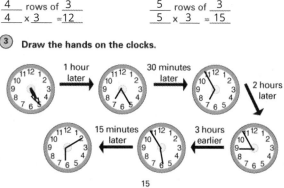

15

---

④ **Write the value.**

$ __20.00__

$ __40.00__

⑤ **Write the numbers.**

7 + __5__ = 12	2 + __2__ = 4	8 + __9__ = 17
__6__ + 1 = 7	__7__ + 3 = 10	__8__ + 4 = 12
4 + __4__ = 8	5 + __0__ = 5	6 + __9__ = 15
2 + __7__ = 9	__4__ + 3 = 7	__4__ + 1 = 5
7 + __7__ = 14	5 + __9__ = 14	__3__ + 7 = 10

⑥ **Find the sum and check.**

2,326	1,144	2,095	4,126	3,147	2,282
2,139	2,079	4,165	3,465	2,178	3,168
+2,191	+3,231	+1,316	+1,273	+3,551	+3,034
6,656	6,454	7,576	8,864	8,876	8,484

16

402

1 Match the fraction to its shaded part.

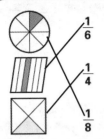

$\frac{1}{6}$

$\frac{1}{4}$

$\frac{1}{8}$

$\frac{1}{3}$

$\frac{1}{5}$

$\frac{1}{2}$

2 Match the multiplication pairs.

3 × 6 = 18	3 × 1 = 3	4 × 3 = 12	8 × 3 = 24
3 × 7 = 21	7 × 3 = 21	3 × 8 = 24	9 × 3 = 27
2 × 3 = 6	6 × 3 = 18	5 × 3 = 15	3 × 4 = 12
1 × 3 = 3	3 × 2 = 6	3 × 9 = 27	3 × 5 = 15

3 Write the numbers.

6 thousands + 2 hundreds + 0 tens + 7 ones = 6,000 + 200 + 00 + 7 = 6,207

5 thousands + 6 hundreds + 1 ten + 2 ones = 5,000 + 600 + 10 + 2 = 5,612

4 thousands + 9 hundreds + 8 tens + 7 ones = 4,000 + 900 + 80 + 7 = 4,987

8 thousands + 7 hundreds + 3 tens + 0 ones = 8,000 + 700 + 30 + 0 = 8,730

3 thousands + 5 hundreds + 6 tens + 7 ones = 3,000 + 500 + 60 + 7 = 3,567

1 thousand + 4 hundreds + 9 tens + 5 ones = 1,000 + 400 + 90 + 5 = 1,495

17

4 Draw both hands on the clocks.

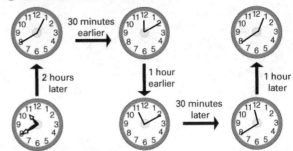

30 minutes earlier

2 hours later

1 hour earlier

1 hour later

30 minutes later

5 Write the numbers.

12 - 5 = 7	7 - 3 = 4	10 - 3 = 7
13 - 6 = 7	4 - 2 = 2	14 - 9 = 5
8 - 4 = 4	10 - 7 = 3	12 - 4 = 8
9 - 7 = 2	5 - 0 = 5	17 - 9 = 8
6 - 1 = 5	11 - 3 = 8	13 - 7 = 6

6 The basketball team scored 28 points in the first half and 34 points in the second half. They scored how many fewer points the first half than the second half?

```
 34
-28
  6 points
```

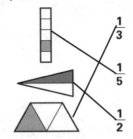

There were 72 plums in one basket and 26 grapefruit in another. There were how many fewer grapefruit than plums?

```
 72
-26
 46 grapefruit
```

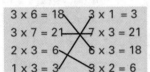

18

---

1 Write the value. 4 pts.

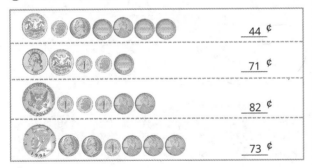

44 ¢

71 ¢

82 ¢

73 ¢

2 Multiply to find the product. 18 pts.

0 x 0	1 x 1	1 x 2	10 x 6	0 x 8	10 x 4	3 x 1	10 x 3	2 x 0
0	1	2	60	0	40	3	30	0

5 x 0	6 x 1	4 x 0	10 x 7	5 x 1	10 x 9	0 x 6	10 x 8	1 x 7
0	6	0	70	5	90	0	80	7

3 Write as a number sentence. 4 pts.

The sum of thirty-five and fifty-three is eighty-eight. 35 + 53 = 88

Twenty-seven increased by eleven equals thirty-eight. 27 + 11 = 38

Forty added to sixty equals one hundred. 40 + 60 = 100

Seventy-one plus fifteen equals eighty-six. 71 + 15 = 86

19

4 Write the numbers. 15 pts.

10 - 4 = 6	14 - 8 = 6	6 - 3 = 3
11 - 6 = 5	13 - 9 = 4	11 - 8 = 3
12 - 6 = 6	13 - 7 = 6	10 - 6 = 4
11 - 4 = 7	7 - 4 = 3	4 - 1 = 3
8 - 2 = 6	12 - 3 = 9	9 - 3 = 6

5 Find the sum and check. 7 pts.

191 172 +413	232 418 +126	161 394 +334	324 419 + 252	482 250 +213	354 293 +110	123 271 +275
776	776	889	995	945	757	669

6 Subtract to find the difference. Check your answers. 7 pts.

450 - 413	752 - 648	842 - 105	980 - 127	893 - 507	581 - 574	795 - 337
37	104	737	853	386	7	458

7 Karen sold 385 candy bars. Allen sold 257. Karen sold how many more candy bars than Allen?
How many candy bars did they sell in all?

```
 385
- 257
 128 candy bars
```

```
 385
+257
 642 candy bars
```

Stephanie and Paul walked their dog, Missy, for 20 minutes on Monday, 15 minutes on Tuesday, and 35 minutes on Wednesday.
How many total minutes did they walk on Monday and Wednesday?

```
 20
+35
 55  minutes
```

2 pts.

20

① Multiply to find the product.

2 ×6 **12**	3 ×7 **21**	8 ×0 **0**	1 ×9 **9**	0 ×2 **0**	6 ×1 **6**	0 ×3 **0**	10 ×2 **20**	2 ×5 **10**
5 ×5 **25**	1 ×2 **2**	4 ×3 **12**	5 ×9 **45**	2 ×8 **16**	3 ×9 **27**	4 ×5 **20**	4 ×2 **8**	7 ×5 **35**
3 ×8 **24**	2 ×7 **14**	1 ×3 **3**	2 ×9 **18**	3 ×2 **6**	5 ×8 **40**	5 ×3 **15**	6 ×5 **30**	2 ×2 **4**

② Draw both hands on the clocks for: Answers will vary.

 The time you get up in the morning

 The time you get home from school

 The time you eat lunch

 The time you play

③ Write the numbers.

1 + **4** = 5	9 + **8** = 17	**2** + 3 = 5
8 + 7 = 15	3 + **7** = 10	3 + **1** = 4
4 + **2** = 6	**7** + 5 = 12	1 + **0** = 1
7 + 0 = 7	**8** + 3 = 11	**5** + 4 = 9
9 + **4** = 13	**7** + 9 = 16	**6** + 6 = 12

21

---

④ Write = or ≠.

$\frac{1}{4}$ = $\frac{1}{3}$ ≠ $\frac{1}{5}$ =

$\frac{1}{6}$ = $\frac{1}{2}$ ≠ $\frac{1}{7}$ ≠

⑤ Write the value.

$ 20 00

$ 30 00

$ 60 00

$ 5 00

⑥ The auditorium at school will seat 380 people. The cafeteria will seat 175. How many fewer seats are there in the cafeteria than in the auditorium?

22

380
−175
205 seats

---

① Write the numbers.

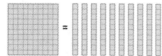 =

1 hundred = 10 tens	
3 hundreds = 2 hundreds + **10** tens	
6 hundreds = 5 hundreds + **10** tens	
8 hundreds = 7 hundreds + **10** tens	
4 hundreds = 3 hundreds + **10** tens	
7 hundreds = 6 hundreds + **10** tens	

② Write the numbers.

8 + **5** = 13	**6** + 6 = 12	7 − **3** = 4
3 − 1 = 2	1 + **2** = 3	**7** + 3 = 10
5 + 9 = 14	5 + **0** = 5	5 − **2** = 3
1 − 0 = 1	**5** − 0 = 5	**5** + 5 = 10
10 − **5** = 5	9 + **7** = 16	13 − **4** = 9

③ Multiply to find the product.

X	3	1	7	0	4	9	6	2	8	5	10
2	6	2	14	0	8	18	12	4	16	10	20

X	4	2	9	3	10	1	7	5	8	0	6
3	12	6	27	9	30	3	21	15	24	0	18

23

---

④ Write = or ≠.

$\frac{1}{3}$ ≠  $\frac{1}{4}$ = $\frac{1}{5}$ ≠

$\frac{1}{8}$ ≠  $\frac{1}{2}$ ≠ $\frac{1}{6}$ =

⑤ Find the sum and check.

197 183 +110 **490**	248 275 +243 **766**	202 388 +395 **985**	194 279 +423 **896**	132 145 +599 **876**	119 482 +283 **884**	336 180 +326 **842**

⑥ Subtract to find the difference.

973 − 869 **104**	894 − 346 **548**	762 − 248 **514**	893 − 504 **389**	341 − 128 **213**	954 − 318 **636**	382 − 215 **167**
694 − 585 **109**	240 − 119 **121**	785 − 479 **306**	963 − 239 **724**	470 − 246 **224**	882 − 863 **19**	576 − 437 **139**

⑦ Alice lives 283 miles from her grandmother. Anna lives 267 miles from her grandmother. Anna had how many fewer miles to travel to grandmother's than Alice?

283
−267
16 miles

24

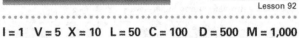

I = 1   V = 5   X = 10   L = 50   C = 100   D = 500   M = 1,000

Roman numerals	I	II	III	IV	V	VI	VII	VIII	IX	X
Arabic numbers	1	2	3	4	5	6	7	8	9	10

1 Write the Roman numerals.

11 = 10 + 1 = __XI__	16 = 10 + 6 = __XVI__
12 = 10 + 2 = __XII__	17 = 10 + 7 = __XVII__
13 = 10 + 3 = __XIII__	18 = 10 + 8 = __XVIII__
14 = 10 + 4 = __XIV__	19 = 10 + 9 = __XIX__
15 = 10 + 5 = __XV__	20 = 10 +10= __XX__

2 Write the value.

 $ __1.82__

 $ __5.46__

 $ __10.31__

25

---

3 Write the numbers.

4 hundreds + 3 tens = 3 hundreds + __13__ tens
7 hundreds + 5 tens = 6 hundreds + __15__ tens
2 hundreds + 7 tens = 1 hundred + __17__ tens
8 hundreds + 2 tens = 7 hundreds + __12__ tens
3 hundreds + 6 tens = 2 hundreds + __16__ tens

4 Multiply to find the product.

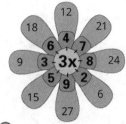   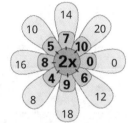

5 Circle the next shape in sequence.

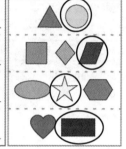

26

---

1 Match the shape to its name.

circle
triangle
octagon
square
oval
rectangle
diamond

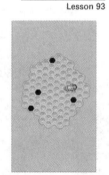

2 Write the Arabic numbers.

I	II	III	IV	V	VI	VII	VIII	IX	X	L	C	D	M
1	2	3	4	5	6	7	8	9	10	50	100	500	1,000

VII = __7__   IV = __4__   IX = __9__
XV = __15__   XVI = __16__   III = __3__
XIII = __13__   XX = __20__   XIX = __19__

3 Multiply to find the product.

X	2	3	5
6	12	18	30
4	8	12	20
8	16	24	40

X	1	3	10
5	5	15	50
2	2	6	20
7	7	21	70

X	0	2	5
3	0	6	15
9	0	18	45
0	0	0	0

27

---

4 Write the value.

 $ __3.36__

  $ __10.57__

  $ __40.45__

5 Write the numbers.

6 hundreds + 2 tens = __5__ hundreds + 12 tens
4 hundreds + 8 tens = __3__ hundreds + 18 tens
7 hundreds + 5 tens = __6__ hundreds + 15 tens
3 hundreds + 1 ten = __2__ hundreds + 11 tens
5 hundreds + 0 tens = __4__ hundreds + 10 tens

6 Circle the next shape in sequence.

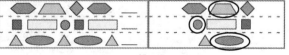

28

405

1 Put an X on the money needed. Answers may vary.

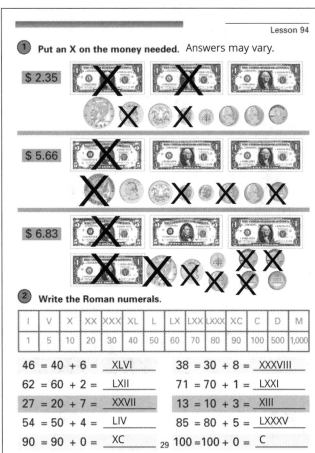

$ 2.35

$ 5.66

$ 6.83

2 Write the Roman numerals.

I	V	X	XX	XXX	XL	L	LX	LXX	LXXX	XC	C	D	M
1	5	10	20	30	40	50	60	70	80	90	100	500	1,000

46 = 40 + 6 = __XLVI__   38 = 30 + 8 = __XXXVIII__

62 = 60 + 2 = __LXII__   71 = 70 + 1 = __LXXI__

27 = 20 + 7 = __XXVII__   13 = 10 + 3 = __XIII__

54 = 50 + 4 = __LIV__   85 = 80 + 5 = __LXXXV__

90 = 90 + 0 = __XC__   29 100 = 100 + 0 = __C__

---

3 Circle the next shape in sequence.

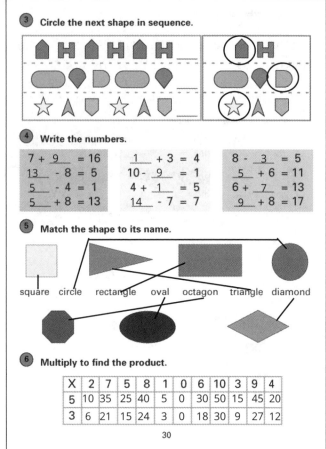

4 Write the numbers.

7 + __9__ = 16   __1__ + 3 = 4   8 - __3__ = 5

__13__ - 8 = 5   10 - __9__ = 1   __5__ + 6 = 11

__5__ - 4 = 1   4 + __1__ = 5   6 + __7__ = 13

__5__ + 8 = 13   __14__ - 7 = 7   __9__ + 8 = 17

5 Match the shape to its name.

square   circle   rectangle   oval   octagon   triangle   diamond

6 Multiply to find the product.

X	2	7	5	8	1	0	6	10	3	9	4
5	10	35	25	40	5	0	30	50	15	45	20
3	6	21	15	24	3	0	18	30	9	27	12

30

---

1 Write the name of each shape.

oval

square

circle

triangle

diamond

octagon

rectangle

2 Match the Roman numerals to the Arabic numbers.

II — 18
LXXV — 81
XVIII — 75
IX — 2
LXXXI — 9

XC — 14
XXXIII — 6
VI — 57
XIV — 90
LVII — 33

3 Write the numbers.

2 - __0__ = 2   7 - __7__ = 0   __6__ - 4 = 2

__8__ + 1 = 9   6 + __4__ = 10   16 - __8__ = 8

__11__ - 9 = 2   __5__ + 0 = 5   2 + __2__ = 4

5 + __2__ = 7   __11__ - 5 = 6   __7__ + 5 = 12

9 + __3__ = 12   9 - __2__ = 7   __8__ + 7 = 15

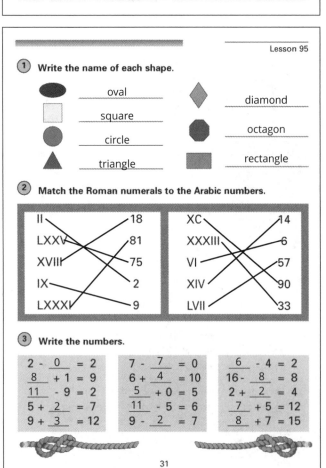

31

---

4 Write the value needed on the money.

$ 3.42

| 1 1 | 1 1 | 1 1 | | | |

25¢   10¢   5¢   1¢   1¢

$ 7.18

| 5 5 | 5 5 | 1 | 1 | 1 | |

10¢   5¢   1¢   1¢   1¢

$ 13.69

| 10 10 | 10 10 | 1 | 1 | 1 | 1 |

50¢   10¢   5¢   1¢   1¢   1¢   1¢

5 Burk Street has 43 houses on it. Gilbert Road has 61 houses on it. Burk Street has how many less houses than Gilbert?

```
  61
- 43
  18  houses
```

Anita made 68 snowballs behind her fort. Stan made 84 snowballs behind his fort. Anita made how many less snowballs than Stan?

```
  84
- 68
  16  snowballs
```

32

406

1 Subtract to find the difference.

504 - 211 293	705 - 461 244	305 - 245 60	705 - 673 32	604 - 323 281	802 - 441 361	607 - 451 156
604 - 192 412	704 - 524 180	807 - 133 674	608 - 252 356	307 - 177 130	508 - 463 45	607 - 512 95

2 Write the numbers.

three 6's = $\underline{6} + \underline{6} + \underline{6} = \underline{3} \times \underline{6} = \underline{18}$

four 6's = $\underline{6} + \underline{6} + \underline{6} + \underline{6} = \underline{4} \times \underline{6} = \underline{24}$

two 6's = $\underline{6} + \underline{6} = \underline{2} \times 6 = \underline{12}$

eight 6's = $\underline{6} + \underline{6} + \underline{6} + \underline{6} + \underline{6} + \underline{6} + \underline{6} + \underline{6} = \underline{8} \times \underline{6} = \underline{48}$

five 6's = $\underline{6} + \underline{6} + \underline{6} + \underline{6} + \underline{6} = \underline{5} \times \underline{6} = \underline{30}$

nine 6's = $\underline{6} + \underline{6} + \underline{6} + \underline{6} + \underline{6} + \underline{6} + \underline{6} + \underline{6} + \underline{6} = \underline{9} \times \underline{6} = \underline{54}$

six 6's = $\underline{6} + \underline{6} + \underline{6} + \underline{6} + \underline{6} + \underline{6} = \underline{6} \times \underline{6} = \underline{36}$

seven 6's = $\underline{6} + \underline{6} + \underline{6} + \underline{6} + \underline{6} + \underline{6} + \underline{6} = \underline{7} \times \underline{6} = \underline{42}$

3 Write the Roman numerals.

37	XXXVII		59	LIX
63	LXIII		78	LXXVIII
15	XV		42	XLII
24	XXIV		96	XCVI

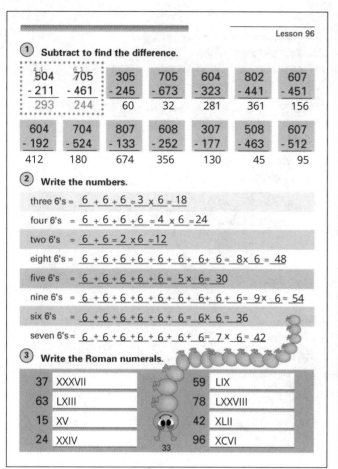

33

---

4 Write the letter on the shape.

square	-	S
rectangle	-	R
triangle	-	T
circle	-	C
oval	-	O
octagon	-	E
diamond	-	D

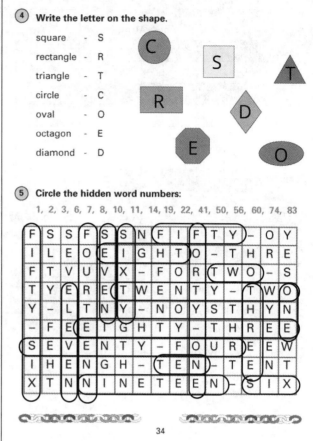

5 Circle the hidden word numbers:

1, 2, 3, 6, 7, 8, 10, 11, 14, 19, 22, 41, 50, 56, 60, 74, 83

F	S	S	F	S	S	N	F	I	F	T	Y	–	O	Y
I	L	E	O	E	I	G	H	T	O	–	T	H	R	E
F	T	V	U	V	X	–	F	O	R	T	W	O	–	S
T	Y	E	R	E	T	W	E	N	T	Y	–	T	W	O
Y	–	L	T	N	Y	–	N	O	Y	S	T	H	Y	N
–	F	E	E	I	G	H	T	Y	–	T	H	R	E	E
S	E	V	E	N	T	Y	–	F	O	U	R	E	E	W
I	H	E	N	G	H	–	T	E	N	–	T	E	N	T
X	T	N	N	I	N	E	T	E	E	N	–	S	I	X

34

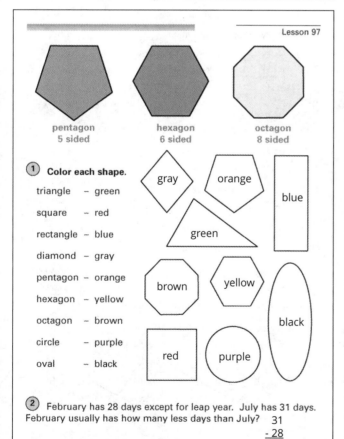

pentagon
5 sided

hexagon
6 sided

octagon
8 sided

1 Color each shape.

triangle	– green
square	– red
rectangle	– blue
diamond	– gray
pentagon	– orange
hexagon	– yellow
octagon	– brown
circle	– purple
oval	– black

Shapes labeled: gray, orange, blue, green, brown, yellow, black, red, purple

2 February has 28 days except for leap year. July has 31 days. February usually has how many less days than July?

31
- 28
3 days

35

---

3 Match the number families.

five 6's .... 7 x 6
8 x 6 .... 6 + 6 + 6 + 6
6 + 6 + 6 .... nine 6's
four 6's .... 3 x 6
6 + 6 + 6 + 6 + 6 + 6 + 6 .... 6 + 6 + 6 + 6 + 6
9 x 6 .... eight 6's

4 Write as a number sentence.

Eighty-five decreased by forty-one equals forty-four. $85 - 41 = 44$

Thirty-seven less sixteen equals twenty-one. $37 - 16 = 21$

The difference of fifty-three and twenty is thirty-three. $53 - 20 = 33$

Twenty-four minus seventeen equals seven. $24 - 17 = 7$

Thirty-two subtracted from forty-six is fourteen. $46 - 32 = 14$

5 Subtract to find the difference.

809 - 570 239	606 - 250 356	908 - 250 658	509 - 419 90	409 - 121 288	908 - 352 556	604 - 532 72
906 - 721 185	907 - 542 365	806 - 793 13	907 - 265 642	509 - 346 163	708 - 418 290	509 - 188 321

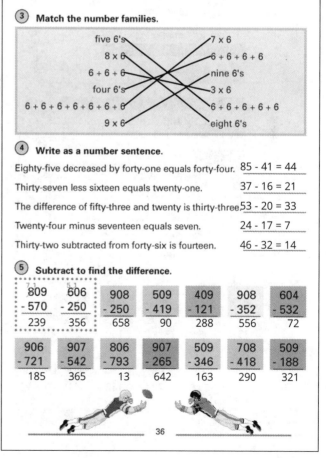

36

407

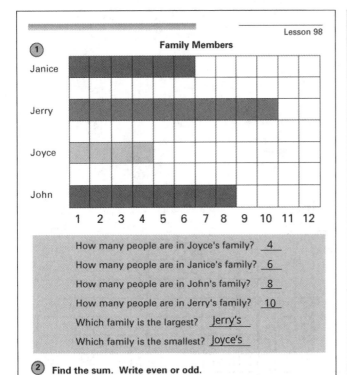

① Family Members

	1	2	3	4	5	6	7	8	9	10	11	12
Janice												
Jerry												
Joyce												
John												

How many people are in Joyce's family? 4

How many people are in Janice's family? 6

How many people are in John's family? 8

How many people are in Jerry's family? 10

Which family is the largest? Jerry's

Which family is the smallest? Joyce's

② Find the sum. Write even or odd.

243	odd	564	even	326	even
+685	odd	+172	even	+457	odd
928	even	736	even	783	odd

37

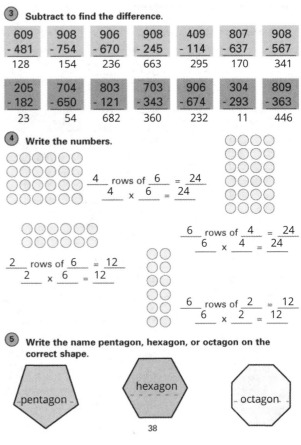

③ Subtract to find the difference.

609	908	906	908	409	807	908
- 481	- 754	- 670	- 245	- 114	- 637	- 567
128	154	236	663	295	170	341

205	704	803	703	906	304	809
- 182	- 650	- 121	- 343	- 674	- 293	- 363
23	54	682	360	232	11	446

④ Write the numbers.

 4 rows of 6 = 24
 4 x 6 = 24

 2 rows of 6 = 12
 2 x 6 = 12

 6 rows of 4 = 24
 6 x 4 = 24

 6 rows of 2 = 12
 6 x 2 = 12

⑤ Write the name pentagon, hexagon, or octagon on the correct shape.

pentagon   hexagon   octagon

38

---

① Money in the Bank

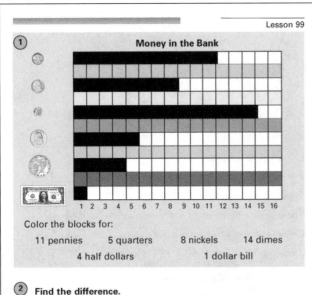

	1	2	3	4	5	6	7	8	9	10	11	12	13	14	15	16

Color the blocks for:

11 pennies   5 quarters   8 nickels   14 dimes

4 half dollars   1 dollar bill

② Find the difference.

304	206	504	601	603	507	406
- 242	- 171	- 413	- 280	- 453	- 234	- 195
62	35	91	321	150	273	211

807	702	508	702	307	705	608
- 321	- 350	- 371	- 632	- 145	- 261	- 382
486	352	137	70	162	444	226

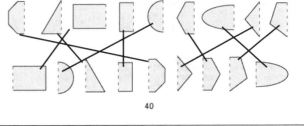

39

---

③ Multiply to find the product.

0	2	3	5	8	7	10	6	6
x 5	x 6	x 8	x 6	x 1	x 3	x 4	x 8	x 6
0	12	24	30	8	21	40	48	36

6	10	1	3	4	5	6	5	3
x 7	x 7	x 6	x 9	x 6	x 2	x 9	x 3	x 6
42	70	6	27	24	10	54	15	18

④ Write as a number sentence.

Twenty-five increased by seventeen equals forty-two. 25 + 17 = 42

Forty-eight plus thirteen equals sixty-one. 48 + 13 = 61

Thirty-six and fifty-one equals eighty-seven. 36 + 51 = 87

Eight added to thirty-four is forty-two. 34 + 8 = 42

⑤ Find the sum. Write even or odd.

58	even	47	odd	69	odd	42	even
+24	even	+36	even	+36	even	+15	odd
82	even	83	odd	105	odd	57	odd

⑥ Match one half to the other half.

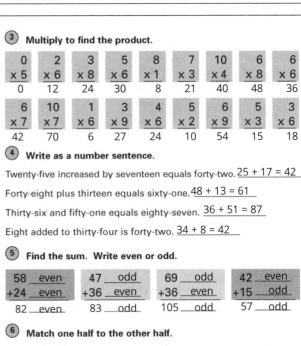

40

408

1 Circle the next shape in sequence. **3 pts.**

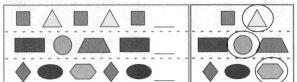

2 Write the fraction that shows what part is shaded. **4 pts.**

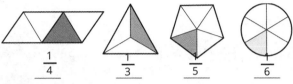

$\dfrac{1}{4}$ $\dfrac{1}{3}$ $\dfrac{1}{5}$ $\dfrac{1}{6}$

3 Write the numbers. **20 pts.**

6 thousands + 5 hundreds + 3 tens + 7 ones = 6,000 500 30 + 7 = 6,537

4 thousands + 7 hundreds + 1 ten + 6 ones = 4,000 700 10 + 6 = 4,716

8 thousands + 9 hundreds + 4 tens + 2 ones = 8,000 900 + 40 + 2 = 8942

2 thousands + 6 hundreds + 8 tens + 5 ones = 2,000 600 + 80 + 5 = 2,685

4 Find the sum. Write even or odd. **12 pts.**

75 odd	38 even	19 odd	22 even
+24 even	+46 even	+51 odd	+35 odd
99 odd	84 even	70 even	57 odd

41

---

5 Write the correct time. **4 pts.**

3:40   7:55   1:30   10:10

6 Write as a number sentence. **3 pts.**

Twenty-five minus twelve equals thirteen.   25 - 12 = 13

Fifty-one decreased by thirty-six is fifteen.   51 - 36 = 15

Nine subtracted from thirty equals twenty-one.   30 - 9 = 21

7 Write the numbers. **9 pts.**

16 - 9 = 7	15 - 8 = 7	7 + 4 = 11
8 + 6 = 14	8 + 5 = 13	0 + 3 = 3
13 - 9 = 4	11 - 9 = 2	6 + 9 = 15

8 Julia read a book with 264 pages. Joy's book had 238 pages. Joy's book had how many fewer pages than Julia's?

264
- 238
26 pages

There were 386 students in Kathy's high school. David's high school had 269 students. David's high school had how many fewer students than Kathy's?

2 pts.

386
- 269
117 students

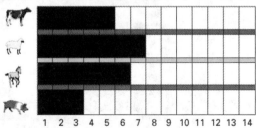

42

---

1 Find the sum.

3,902	7,531	2,824	4,210	5,617	3,851
+5,436	+1,546	+6,723	+3,870	+3,812	+2,348
9,338	9,077	9,547	8,080	9,429	6,199

4,741	5,467	2,906	6,728	1,530	4,136
+1,703	+1,630	+4,912	+1,931	+4,919	+2,930
6,444	7,097	7,818	8,659	6,449	7,066

2 Write = or ≠.

= pentagon   ≠ oval

= triangle   = hexagon

= oval   ≠ rectangle

≠ diamond

≠ rectangle   = octagon

3 Find the difference.

919	868	829	947	919	938	907
- 238	- 690	- 753	- 587	- 769	- 474	- 367
681	178	76	360	150	464	540

879	624	549		867	639	456
- 596	- 184	- 270		- 480	- 481	- 286
283	440	279		387	158	170

43

---

4 Make a bar graph from the picture below.

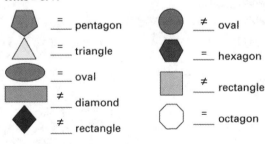

Animals in the Barnyard

1 2 3 4 5 6 7 8 9 10 11 12 13 14

5 Multiply to find the product.

4	3	9	1	7	3	6	7	3
x 6	x 3	x 3	x 6	x 6	x 5	x 6	x 2	x 6
24	9	27	6	42	15	36	14	18

3	2	1	8	8	6	8	9	0
x 2	x 6	x 4	x 6	x 3	x 5	x 2	x 6	x 6
6	12	4	48	24	30	16	54	0

44

409

1. Write the correct time.

2:50   11:40   4:05   8:25

2. Multiply to find the product.

0 ×7	6 ×3	9 ×2	3 ×7	6 ×5	2 ×3	9 ×6	2 ×4	6 ×0
0	18	18	21	30	6	54	8	0

10 ×9	3 ×8	6 ×1	4 ×3	8 ×6	0 ×8	10 ×3	6 ×4	8 ×1
90	24	6	12	48	0	30	24	8

2 ×7	6 ×6	5 ×3	10 ×7	4 ×5	6 ×2	3 ×9	4 ×1	7 ×6
14	36	15	70	20	12	27	4	42

3. Write the numbers.

1 + 4 = 5
2 - 0 = 2
8 + 7 = 15
5 - 1 = 4
2 + 3 = 5

16 - 8 = 8
13 - 4 = 9
13 - 8 = 5
14 - 6 = 8
6 + 6 = 12

9 - 5 = 4
9 + 8 = 17
6 - 4 = 2
7 + 9 = 16
8 - 3 = 5

45

---

4. Find the difference.

614 - 231	849 - 751	708 - 653	934 - 763	757 - 465	759 - 179	329 - 298
383	98	55	171	292	580	31

238 - 155	925 - 464	637 - 597	965 - 370	945 - 593	713 - 363	608 - 386
83	461	40	595	352	350	222

5. Find the sum.

4,736 +3,632	1,354 +7,824	3,652 +4,834	2,874 +6,315	2,463 +3,915	1,527 +5,750
8,368	9,178	8,486	9,189	6,378	7,277

4,273 +1,922	3,586 +1,913	1,925 +6,474	1,482 +2,702	4,819 +2,830	2,953 +1,916
6,195	5,499	8,399	4,184	7,649	4,869

6. Write = or ≠.

3 + 3 ≠ 15 - 8   5 + 1 = 14 - 8   1 + 0 ≠ 8 - 8
9 - 0 ≠ 9 + 4   11 - 8 ≠ 7 + 0   14 - 7 = 4 + 3
5 + 4 = 18 - 9   4 + 2 = 10 - 4   9 + 6 ≠ 4 - 1
9 - 6 ≠ 3 + 1   9 - 2 = 5 + 2   8 - 6 ≠ 9 - 4

46

---

1. Write the numbers.

4,861 = 4,000 + 800 + 60 + 1   6,153 = 6,000 + 100 + 50 + 3
2,573 = 2,000 + 500 + 70 + 3   2,709 = 2,000 + 700 + 00 + 9
9,804 = 9,000 + 800 + 00 + 4   1,645 = 1,000 + 600 + 40 + 5

2. Write = or ≠.

clock ≠ 2:05   clock ≠ 5:50
clock = 7:45   clock = 2:05
clock ≠ 7:30   clock ≠ 10:20

3. Write the numbers.

2 + 7 = 9
12 - 9 = 3
13 - 9 = 4
7 + 7 = 14
8 + 9 = 17

16 - 7 = 9
9 + 6 = 15
3 + 5 = 8
14 - 7 = 7
2 - 2 = 0

10 - 5 = 5
4 + 3 = 7
1 + 8 = 9
8 - 6 = 2
6 + 8 = 14

47

---

4. Multiply to find the product.

4 ×5	8 ×6	3 ×5	6 ×0	8 ×3	8 ×1	3 ×3	10 ×3	1 ×3
20	48	15	0	24	8	9	30	3

4 ×3	6 ×4	7 ×5	10 ×6	3 ×7	5 ×6	5 ×5	3 ×2	6 ×1
12	24	35	60	21	30	25	6	6

6 ×3	5 ×8	6 ×2	10 ×5	3 ×9	9 ×6	9 ×5	0 ×3	4 ×0
18	40	12	50	27	54	45	0	0

5. Find the sum.

5,212 +1,841	3,820 +5,421	1,614 +3,483	6,943 +2,826	2,764 +3,731	1,810 +1,946
7,053	9,241	5,097	9,769	6,495	3,756

3,534 +1,520	1,941 +7,542	1,358 +6,901	2,707 +6,431	2,653 +5,934	1,825 +5,742
5,054	9,483	8,259	9,138	8,587	7,567

6. Find the difference and check.

975 - 681	713 - 491	238 - 145	619 - 272	958 - 391	324 - 274	412 - 182
294	222	93	347	567	50	230

618 - 327	748 - 262	819 - 250	629 - 547	718 - 534	518 - 340	425 - 234
291	486	569	82	184	178	191

48

410

(1) Write the fraction that shows what part is shaded.

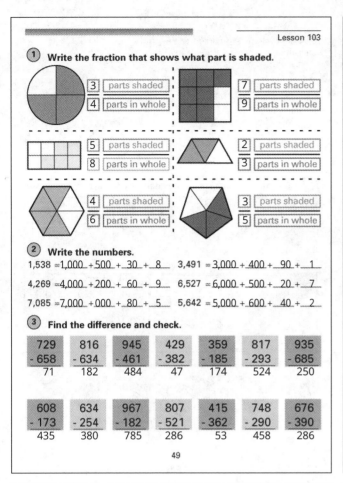

- [3] parts shaded / [4] parts in whole
- [7] parts shaded / [9] parts in whole
- [5] parts shaded / [8] parts in whole
- [2] parts shaded / [3] parts in whole
- [4] parts shaded / [6] parts in whole
- [3] parts shaded / [5] parts in whole

(2) Write the numbers.

1,538 = 1,000 + 500 + 30 + 8   3,491 = 3,000 + 400 + 90 + 1

4,269 = 4,000 + 200 + 60 + 9   6,527 = 6,000 + 500 + 20 + 7

7,085 = 7,000 + 000 + 80 + 5   5,642 = 5,000 + 600 + 40 + 2

(3) Find the difference and check.

729	816	945	429	359	817	935
- 658	- 634	- 461	- 382	- 185	- 293	- 685
71	182	484	47	174	524	250

608	634	967	807	415	748	676
- 173	- 254	- 182	- 521	- 362	- 290	- 390
435	380	785	286	53	458	286

49

(4) Draw both hands on the clocks.

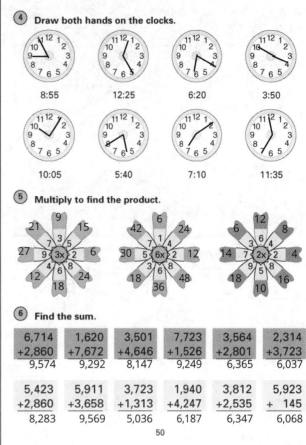

8:55   12:25   6:20   3:50

10:05   5:40   7:10   11:35

(5) Multiply to find the product.

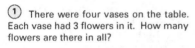
(3x, 6x, 2x multiplication flowers)

(6) Find the sum.

6,714	1,620	3,501	7,723	3,564	2,314
+2,860	+7,672	+4,646	+1,526	+2,801	+3,723
9,574	9,292	8,147	9,249	6,365	6,037

5,423	5,911	3,723	1,940	3,812	5,923
+2,860	+3,658	+1,313	+4,247	+2,535	+ 145
8,283	9,569	5,036	6,187	6,347	6,068

50

---

(1) There were four vases on the table. Each vase had 3 flowers in it. How many flowers are there in all?

4 x 3 = 12 flowers

Jason has five packs of pens with six pens in each pack. How many pens does Jason have?

5 x 6 = 30 pens

Mother bought 7 oranges at 10¢ an orange. What did the oranges cost Mother?

7 x 10 = 70 cents

(2) Find the difference and check.

978	457	739	658	847	528	836
- 281	- 291	- 649	- 361	- 354	- 237	- 274
697	166	90	297	493	291	562

719	649	704	519	863	626	509
- 383	- 278	- 591	- 346	- 592	- 576	- 134
336	371	113	173	271	50	375

51

(3) Write the fraction that shows what part is shaded.

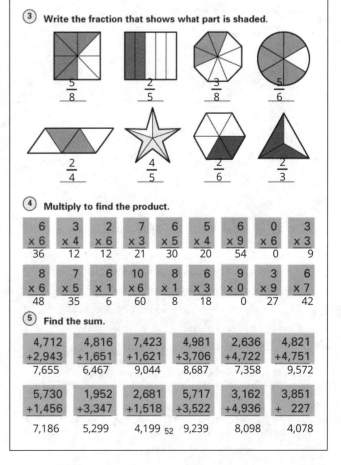

5/8   2/5   3/8   5/6

2/4   4/5   2/6   2/3

(4) Multiply to find the product.

6	3	2	7	6	5	6	0	3
x 6	x 4	x 6	x 3	x 5	x 4	x 9	x 6	x 3
36	12	12	21	30	20	54	0	9

8	7	6	10	8	6	9	3	6
x 6	x 5	x 1	x 6	x 1	x 3	x 0	x 9	x 7
48	35	6	60	8	18	0	27	42

(5) Find the sum.

4,712	4,816	7,423	4,981	2,636	4,821
+2,943	+1,651	+1,621	+3,706	+4,722	+4,751
7,655	6,467	9,044	8,687	7,358	9,572

5,730	1,952	2,681	5,717	3,162	3,851
+1,456	+3,347	+1,518	+3,522	+4,936	+ 227
7,186	5,299	4,199	9,239	8,098	4,078

52

411

① Write the ratio.

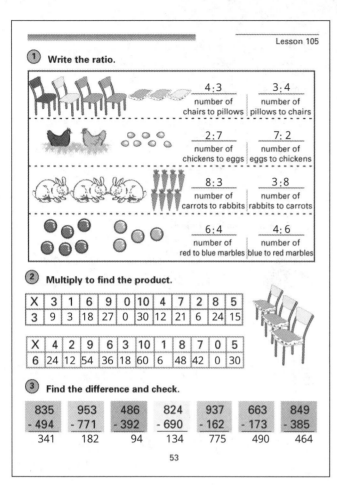

4:3 number of chairs to pillows	3:4 number of pillows to chairs
2:7 number of chickens to eggs	7:2 number of eggs to chickens
8:3 number of carrots to rabbits	3:8 number of rabbits to carrots
6:4 number of red to blue marbles	4:6 number of blue to red marbles

② Multiply to find the product.

X	3	1	6	9	0	10	4	7	2	8	5
3	9	3	18	27	0	30	12	21	6	24	15

X	4	2	9	63	3	10	1	8	7	0	5
6	24	12	54	36	18	60	6	48	42	0	30

③ Find the difference and check.

835	953	486	824	937	663	849
- 494	- 771	- 392	- 690	- 162	- 173	- 385
341	182	94	134	775	490	464

53

---

④ 6 bicycles were parked at the store. Each had 2 wheels. How many wheels were on the 6 bicycles?

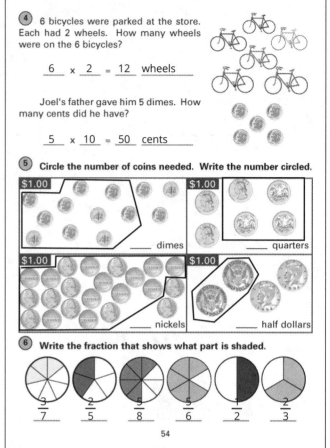

$\underline{\ 6\ } \times \underline{\ 2\ } = \underline{\ 12\ }$ wheels

Joel's father gave him 5 dimes. How many cents did he have?

$\underline{\ 5\ } \times \underline{\ 10\ } = \underline{\ 50\ }$ cents

⑤ Circle the number of coins needed. Write the number circled.

$1.00 ____ dimes $1.00 ____ quarters

$1.00 ____ nickels $1.00 ____ half dollars

⑥ Write the fraction that shows what part is shaded.

$\dfrac{3}{7}$ $\dfrac{2}{5}$ $\dfrac{5}{8}$ $\dfrac{5}{6}$ $\dfrac{1}{2}$ $\dfrac{2}{3}$

54

---

① Write the ratio.

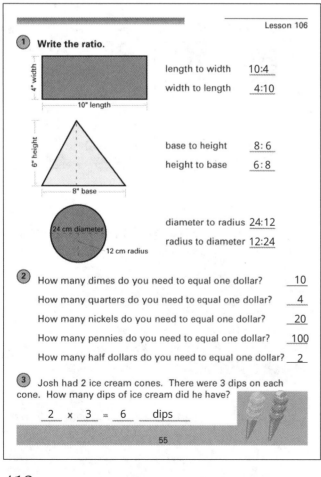

4" width, 10" length

length to width   10:4
width to length   4:10

6" height, 8" base

base to height   8:6
height to base   6:8

24 cm diameter, 12 cm radius

diameter to radius 24:12
radius to diameter 12:24

②

How many dimes do you need to equal one dollar?	10
How many quarters do you need to equal one dollar?	4
How many nickels do you need to equal one dollar?	20
How many pennies do you need to equal one dollar?	100
How many half dollars do you need to equal one dollar?	2

③ Josh had 2 ice cream cones. There were 3 dips on each cone. How many dips of ice cream did he have?

$\underline{\ 2\ } \times \underline{\ 3\ } = \underline{\ 6\ }$ dips

55

---

④ Write the numbers.

three 9's = $\underline{9} + \underline{9} + \underline{9} = 3 \times 9 = \underline{27}$

four 9's = $\underline{9} + \underline{9} + \underline{9} + \underline{9} = 4 \times 9 = \underline{36}$

two 9's = $\underline{9} + \underline{9} = 2 \times 9 = \underline{18}$

eight 9's = $\underline{9} + 9 + 9 + 9 + 9 + 9 + 9 + 9 = 8 \times 9 = \underline{72}$

five 9's = $\underline{9} + 9 + 9 + 9 + 9 = 5 \times 9 = \underline{45}$

nine 9's = $\underline{9} + 9 + 9 + 9 + 9 + 9 + 9 + 9 + 9 = 9 \times 9 = \underline{81}$

six 9's = $\underline{9} + 9 + 9 + 9 + 9 + 9 = 6 \times 9 = \underline{54}$

seven 9's = $\underline{9} + 9 + 9 + 9 + 9 + 9 + 9 = 7 \times 9 = \underline{63}$

⑤ Find the sum.

1,205	3,963	6,628	5,316	4,804	7,719
+1,846	+4,517	+2,426	+1,978	+1,277	+1,631
3,051	8,480	9,054	7,294	6,081	9,350

⑥ Write 2 addition and 2 subtraction facts.

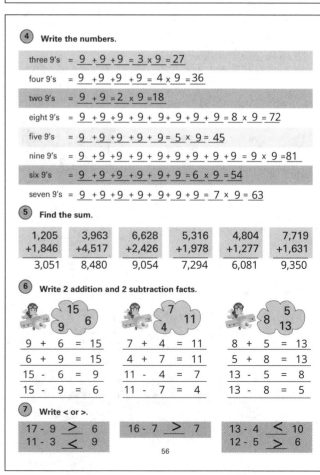

15, 6, 9

| 9 + 6 = 15 |
| 6 + 9 = 15 |
| 15 - 6 = 9 |
| 15 - 9 = 6 |

7, 11, 4

| 7 + 4 = 11 |
| 4 + 7 = 11 |
| 11 - 4 = 7 |
| 11 - 7 = 4 |

8, 5, 13

| 8 + 5 = 13 |
| 5 + 8 = 13 |
| 13 - 5 = 8 |
| 13 - 8 = 5 |

⑦ Write < or >.

17 - 9 $>$ 6   16 - 7 $>$ 7   13 - 4 $<$ 10

11 - 3 $<$ 9   12 - 5 $>$ 6

56

412

$$4 + n = 9 \qquad 6 + n = 13 \qquad 5 + n = 14$$
$$-4 \qquad\quad -4 \qquad\quad -6 \qquad\quad -6 \qquad\quad -5 \qquad\quad -5$$
$$n = 5 \qquad\qquad n = 7 \qquad\qquad n = 9$$

1 Solve the equations.

$2 + n = 11$	$7 + n = 15$	$3 + n = 6$	$4 + n = 13$
$-2 \quad -2$	$-7 \quad -7$	$-3 \quad -3$	$-4 \quad -4$
$n = 9$	$n = 8$	$n = 3$	$n = 9$
$1 + n = 8$	$5 + n = 10$	$5 + n = 7$	$9 + n = 12$
$-1 \quad -1$	$-5 \quad -5$	$-5 \quad -5$	$-9 \quad -9$
$n = 7$	$n = 5$	$n = 2$	$n = 3$

2 Find the sum.

1,509	2,821	3,923	1,506	4,426	5,738
+4,587	+5,849	+2,218	+6,759	+3,865	+3,713
6,096	8,670	6,141	8,265	8,291	9,451

3 Find the difference.

5,321	4,513	6,265	3,412	6,735	2,654
- 4,161	- 1,362	- 2,182	- 3,340	- 1,441	- 2,392
1,160	3,151	4,083	72	5,294	262

4 Write < or >.

$6 \times 9 \;\underline{<}\; 63 \qquad 9 \times 9 \;\underline{>}\; 72 \qquad 3 \times 9 \;\underline{>}\; 18$

$4 \times 9 \;\underline{<}\; 45 \qquad 8 \times 9 \;\underline{<}\; 81 \qquad 7 \times 9 \;\underline{>}\; 54$

57

---

5 Write the value.

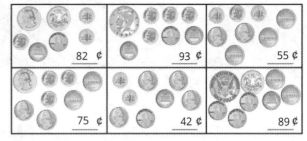

82 ¢ 　 93 ¢ 　 55 ¢

75 ¢ 　 42 ¢ 　 89 ¢

6 Write the ratio.

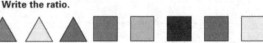

The number of triangles to the number of squares	3:5
The number of squares to the number of triangles	5:3
The number of triangles to the number of squares and triangles	3:8
The number of squares to the number of triangles and squares	5:8

7 Match the number families.

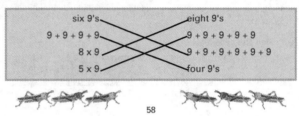

six 9's　　　　　　　　eight 9's

9 + 9 + 9 + 9　　　　9 + 9 + 9 + 9 + 9

8 x 9　　　　　　　　9 + 9 + 9 + 9 + 9 + 9

5 x 9　　　　　　　　four 9's

58

---

1 Write the Roman numerals.

I	IV	V	IX	X	XL	L	XC	C	CD	D	CM	M
1	4	5	9	10	40	50	90	100	400	500	900	1,000

7	VII
13	XIII
29	XXIX
48	XLVIII
52	LII

61	LXI
74	LXXIV
82	LXXXII
95	XCV
105	CV

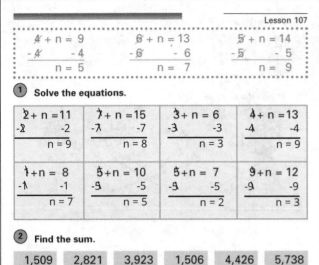

2 Find the difference.

9,877	7,948	7,809	8,936	8,926	9,718
- 9,382	- 5,882	- 6,157	- 4,696	- 6,445	- 5,085
495	2,066	1,652	4,240	2,481	4,633

3 Solve the equations.

$4 + n = 8$	$5 + n = 14$	$6 + n = 7$	$7 + n = 11$
$-4 \quad -4$	$-5 \quad -5$	$-6 \quad -6$	$-7 \quad -7$
$n = 4$	$n = 9$	$n = 1$	$n = 4$
$5 + n = 11$	$4 + n = 10$	$8 + n = 12$	$2 + n = 10$
$-5 \quad -5$	$-4 \quad -4$	$-8 \quad -8$	$-2 \quad -2$
$n = 6$	$n = 6$	$n = 4$	$n = 8$

59

---

4 Match the pairs of multiplication facts.

6 x 9	7 x 9	3 x 9	7 x 9
2 x 9	9 x 2	9 x 7	4 x 9
9 x 7	9 x 6	9 x 8	9 x 3
5 x 9	9 x 5	9 x 4	8 x 9

5 Find the sum.

6,784	4,857	3,542	1,826	1,937	1,809
+1,806	+4,923	+5,829	+2,536	+5,439	+1,428
8,590	9,780	9,371	4,362	7,376	3,237

6 Write the value.

$ 1.61 　 $ 10.72

$ 20.83 　 $ 5.49

7 Shade the shape for each fractional part.

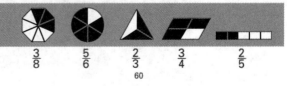

$\dfrac{3}{8} \qquad \dfrac{5}{6} \qquad \dfrac{2}{3} \qquad \dfrac{3}{4} \qquad \dfrac{2}{5}$

60

413

Number of Points Made by Ken in Basketball

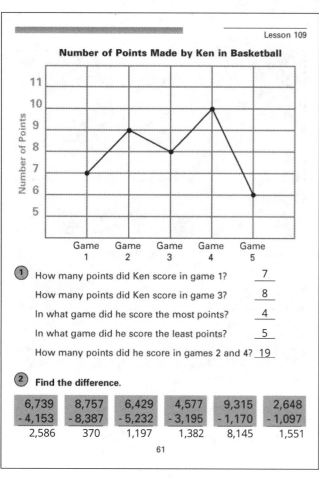

① How many points did Ken score in game 1? **7**

How many points did Ken score in game 3? **8**

In what game did he score the most points? **4**

In what game did he score the least points? **5**

How many points did he score in games 2 and 4? **19**

② **Find the difference.**

6,739	8,757	6,429	4,577	9,315	2,648
- 4,153	- 8,387	- 5,232	- 3,195	- 1,170	- 1,097
2,586	370	1,197	1,382	8,145	1,551

61

③ **Find the sum.**

2,319	3,824	4,636	1,707	5,945	6,908
+2,743	+1,858	+2,857	+5,845	+2,846	+1,153
5,062	5,682	7,493	7,552	8,791	8,061

④ **Match the solid to its name.**

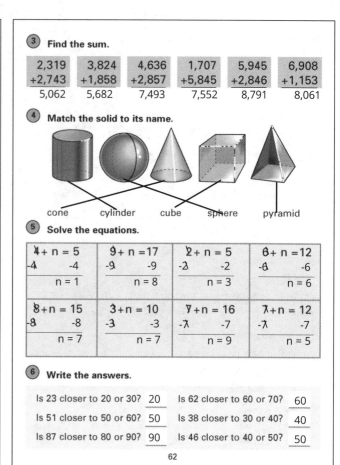

cone   cylinder   cube   sphere   pyramid

⑤ **Solve the equations.**

$4 + n = 5$	$9 + n = 17$	$2 + n = 5$	$6 + n = 12$
-4 -4	-9 -9	-2 -2	-6 -6
n = 1	n = 8	n = 3	n = 6
$8 + n = 15$	$3 + n = 10$	$7 + n = 16$	$7 + n = 12$
-8 -8	-3 -3	-7 -7	-7 -7
n = 7	n = 7	n = 9	n = 5

⑥ **Write the answers.**

Is 23 closer to 20 or 30? **20**   Is 62 closer to 60 or 70? **60**

Is 51 closer to 50 or 60? **50**   Is 38 closer to 30 or 40? **40**

Is 87 closer to 80 or 90? **90**   Is 46 closer to 40 or 50? **50**

62

⑦ **Shade the shape for each fractional part.**

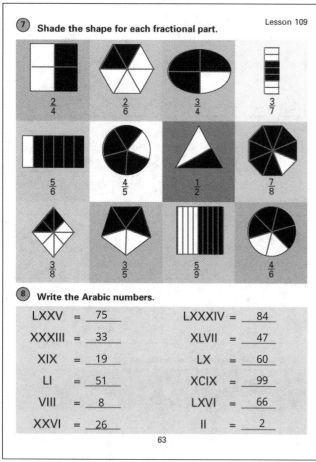

$\frac{2}{4}$ $\frac{2}{6}$ $\frac{3}{4}$ $\frac{3}{7}$

$\frac{5}{6}$ $\frac{4}{5}$ $\frac{1}{2}$ $\frac{7}{8}$

$\frac{3}{8}$ $\frac{3}{5}$ $\frac{5}{9}$ $\frac{4}{6}$

⑧ **Write the Arabic numbers.**

LXXV	=	75	LXXXIV	=	84
XXXIII	=	33	XLVII	=	47
XIX	=	19	LX	=	60
LI	=	51	XCIX	=	99
VIII	=	8	LXVI	=	66
XXVI	=	26	II	=	2

63

⑨ **Write the numbers.**

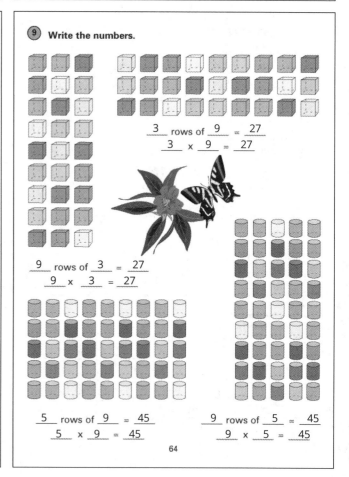

3 rows of **9** = **27**

3 x **9** = **27**

9 rows of **3** = **27**

9 x **3** = **27**

5 rows of **9** = **45**   **9** rows of **5** = **45**

5 x **9** = **45**   **9** x **5** = **45**

64

414

Panel 1 (top left)

1 Correct Spelling Words

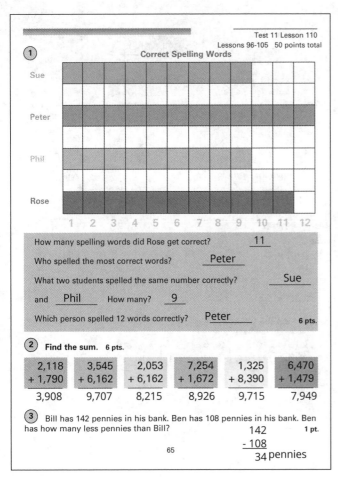

	1	2	3	4	5	6	7	8	9	10	11	12
Sue												
Peter												
Phil												
Rose												

How many spelling words did Rose get correct? __11__

Who spelled the most correct words? __Peter__

What two students spelled the same number correctly? __Sue__

and __Phil__   How many? __9__

Which person spelled 12 words correctly? __Peter__   **6 pts.**

2 Find the sum.   6 pts.

2,118 + 1,790	3,545 + 6,162	2,053 + 6,162	7,254 + 1,672	1,325 + 8,390	6,470 + 1,479
3,908	9,707	8,215	8,926	9,715	7,949

3 Bill has 142 pennies in his bank. Ben has 108 pennies in his bank. Ben has how many less pennies than Bill?   **1 pt.**

142
- 108
34 pennies

65

Panel 4 (top right)

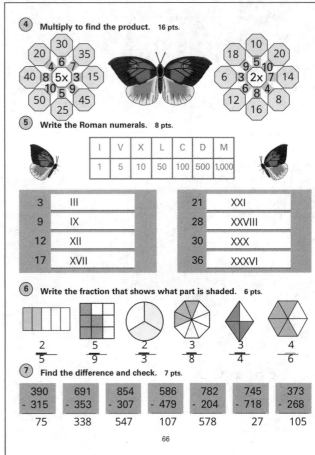

4 Multiply to find the product.   16 pts.

5 Write the Roman numerals.   8 pts.

I	V	X	L	C	D	M
1	5	10	50	100	500	1,000

3	III
9	IX
12	XII
17	XVII

21	XXI
28	XXVIII
30	XXX
36	XXXVI

6 Write the fraction that shows what part is shaded.   6 pts.

$\frac{2}{5}$ $\frac{5}{9}$ $\frac{2}{3}$ $\frac{3}{8}$ $\frac{3}{4}$ $\frac{4}{6}$

7 Find the difference and check.   7 pts.

390 - 315	691 - 353	854 - 307	586 - 479	782 - 204	745 - 718	373 - 268
75	338	547	107	578	27	105

66

Panel 2 (bottom left)

1 Kerry's Test Scores

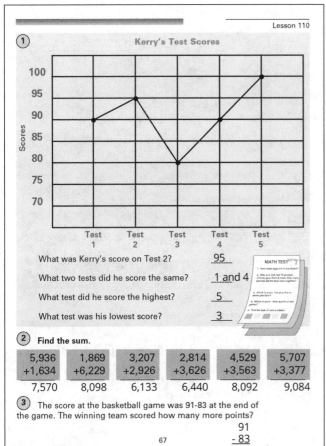

What was Kerry's score on Test 2? __95__

What two tests did he score the same? __1 and 4__

What test did he score the highest? __5__

What test was his lowest score? __3__

2 Find the sum.

5,936 +1,634	1,869 +6,229	3,207 +2,926	2,814 +3,626	4,529 +3,563	5,707 +3,377
7,570	8,098	6,133	6,440	8,092	9,084

3 The score at the basketball game was 91-83 at the end of the game. The winning team scored how many more points?

91
- 83
8 points

67

Panel 6 (bottom right)

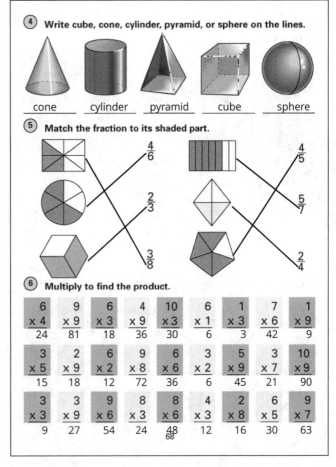

4 Write cube, cone, cylinder, pyramid, or sphere on the lines.

cone   cylinder   pyramid   cube   sphere

5 Match the fraction to its shaded part.

$\frac{4}{6}$ $\frac{4}{5}$

$\frac{2}{3}$ $\frac{5}{7}$

$\frac{3}{8}$ $\frac{2}{4}$

6 Multiply to find the product.

6 × 4	9 × 9	6 × 3	4 × 9	10 × 3	6 × 1	1 × 3	7 × 6	1 × 9
24	81	18	36	30	6	3	42	9

3 × 5	2 × 9	6 × 2	9 × 8	6 × 6	3 × 2	5 × 9	3 × 7	10 × 9
15	18	12	72	36	6	45	21	90

3 × 3	3 × 9	9 × 6	8 × 3	8 × 6	4 × 3	2 × 8	6 × 5	9 × 7
9	27	54	24	48	12	16	30	63

68

(1) Draw the line on the graph.

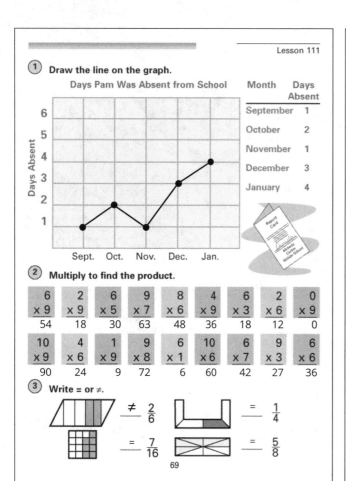

Days Pam Was Absent from School

Month	Days Absent
September	1
October	2
November	1
December	3
January	4

(2) Multiply to find the product.

6 × 9 54	2 × 9 18	6 × 5 30	9 × 7 63	8 × 6 48	4 × 9 36	6 × 3 18	2 × 6 12	0 × 9 0
10 × 9 90	4 × 6 24	1 × 9 9	9 × 8 72	6 × 1 6	10 × 6 60	6 × 7 42	9 × 3 27	6 × 6 36

(3) Write = or ≠.

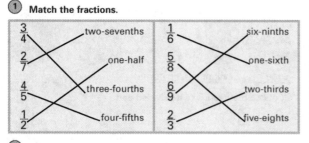

≠ $\frac{2}{6}$

= $\frac{1}{4}$

= $\frac{7}{16}$

= $\frac{5}{8}$

69

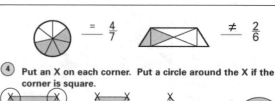

= $\frac{4}{7}$ ≠ $\frac{2}{6}$

(4) Put an X on each corner. Put a circle around the X if the corner is square.

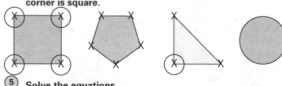

(5) Solve the equations.

6 + n = 11 -6 -6 n = 5	1 + n = 6 -1 -1 n = 5	4 + n = 10 -4 -4 n = 6	9 + n = 14 -9 -9 n = 5
3 + n = 8 -3 -3 n = 5	8 + n = 14 -8 -8 n = 6	0 + n = 8 -0 -0 n = 8	2 + n = 6 -2 -2 n = 4

(6) Find the difference and check.

213 - 193 20	309 - 172 137	429 - 251 178	547 - 363 184	664 - 390 274	438 - 172 266	889 - 493 396

(7) Pat had 142 sheets of notebook paper. She gave 8 sheets to Rick. How many sheets did Pat have left?

142
- 8
134 sheets

70

---

(1) Match the fractions.

$\frac{3}{4}$ — two-sevenths
$\frac{2}{7}$ — one-half
$\frac{4}{5}$ — three-fourths
$\frac{1}{2}$ — four-fifths

$\frac{1}{6}$ — six-ninths
$\frac{5}{8}$ — one-sixth
$\frac{6}{9}$ — two-thirds
$\frac{2}{3}$ — five-eights

(2) Find the sum.

1,640 +1,682 3,322	2,251 +1,964 4,215	3,574 +4,984 8,558	1,860 +7,398 9,258	3,784 +1,591 5,375	5,832 +2,694 8,526

(3) Match the shape to its name.

rectangle
diamond
oval

hexagon
square
circle

pentagon
octagon
triangle

(4) Find the difference and check.

9,765 - 7,575 2,190	8,853 - 762 8,091	9,648 - 2,084 7,564	6,419 - 4,352 2,067	4,925 - 4,584 341	5,337 - 2,084 3,253

71

---

(5) Draw the line graph.

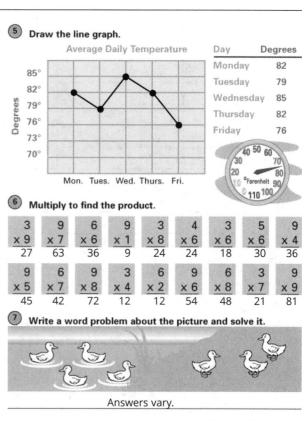

Average Daily Temperature

Day	Degrees
Monday	82
Tuesday	79
Wednesday	85
Thursday	82
Friday	76

(6) Multiply to find the product.

3 × 9 27	9 × 7 63	6 × 6 36	9 × 1 9	3 × 8 24	4 × 6 24	3 × 6 18	5 × 6 30	9 × 4 36
9 × 5 45	6 × 7 42	9 × 8 72	3 × 4 12	6 × 2 12	9 × 6 54	6 × 8 48	3 × 7 21	9 × 9 81

(7) Write a word problem about the picture and solve it.

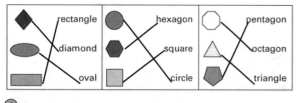

Answers vary.

72

416

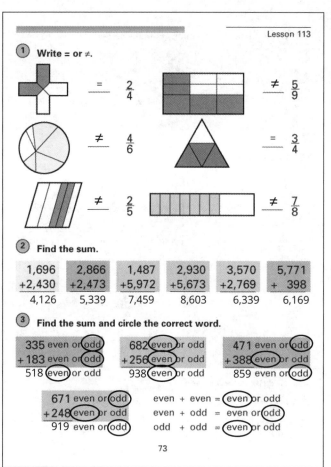

1 Write = or ≠.

= $\frac{2}{4}$ ≠ $\frac{5}{9}$

≠ $\frac{4}{6}$ = $\frac{3}{4}$

≠ $\frac{2}{5}$ ≠ $\frac{7}{8}$

2 Find the sum.

1,696	2,866	1,487	2,930	3,570	5,771
+2,430	+2,473	+5,972	+5,673	+2,769	+ 398
4,126	5,339	7,459	8,603	6,339	6,169

3 Find the sum and circle the correct word.

335 even or (odd)
+ 183 even or (odd)
518 (even) or odd

682 (even) or odd
+256 (even) or odd
938 (even) or odd

471 even or (odd)
+388 (even) or odd
859 even or (odd)

671 even or (odd)
+248 (even) or odd
919 even or (odd)

even + even = (even) or odd
even + odd = even or (odd)
odd + odd = (even) or odd

73

---

4 Find the difference and check.

7,859	7,824	9,738	6,905	3,846	7,819
- 6,679	- 2,590	- 4,168	- 1,831	- 3,195	- 1,320
1,180	5,234	5,570	5,074	651	6,499

5 Write the name of each shape.

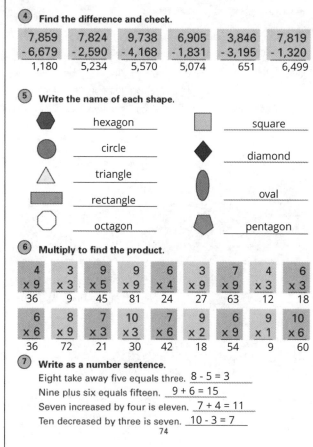

hexagon   square

circle   diamond

triangle

rectangle   oval

octagon   pentagon

6 Multiply to find the product.

4	3	9	9	6	3	7	4	6
x 9	x 3	x 5	x 9	x 4	x 9	x 9	x 3	x 3
36	9	45	81	24	27	63	12	18

6	8	7	10	7	9	6	9	10
x 6	x 9	x 3	x 3	x 6	x 2	x 9	x 1	x 6
36	72	21	30	42	18	54	9	60

7 Write as a number sentence.

Eight take away five equals three. 8 - 5 = 3

Nine plus six equals fifteen. 9 + 6 = 15

Seven increased by four is eleven. 7 + 4 = 11

Ten decreased by three is seven. 10 - 3 = 7

74

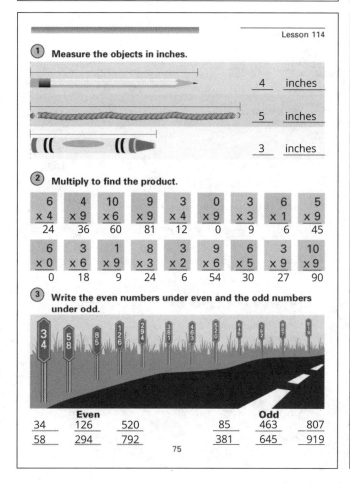

1 Measure the objects in inches.

4 inches

5 inches

3 inches

2 Multiply to find the product.

6	4	10	9	3	0	3	6	5
x 4	x 9	x 6	x 9	x 4	x 9	x 3	x 1	x 9
24	36	60	81	12	0	9	6	45

6	3	1	8	3	9	6	3	10
x 0	x 6	x 9	x 3	x 2	x 6	x 5	x 9	x 9
0	18	9	24	6	54	30	27	90

3 Write the even numbers under even and the odd numbers under odd.

	Even				Odd	
34	126	520		85	463	807
58	294	792		381	645	919

75

---

4 Match the solid to its name.

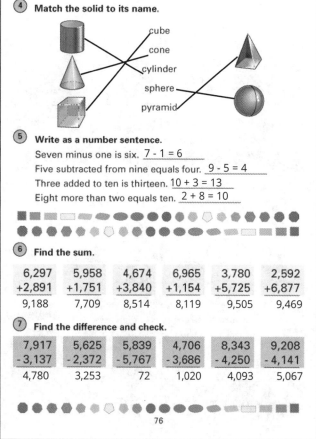

cube
cone
cylinder
sphere
pyramid

5 Write as a number sentence.

Seven minus one is six. 7 - 1 = 6

Five subtracted from nine equals four. 9 - 5 = 4

Three added to ten is thirteen. 10 + 3 = 13

Eight more than two equals ten. 2 + 8 = 10

6 Find the sum.

6,297	5,958	4,674	6,965	3,780	2,592
+2,891	+1,751	+3,840	+1,154	+5,725	+6,877
9,188	7,709	8,514	8,119	9,505	9,469

7 Find the difference and check.

7,917	5,625	5,839	4,706	8,343	9,208
- 3,137	- 2,372	- 5,767	- 3,686	- 4,250	- 4,141
4,780	3,253	72	1,020	4,093	5,067

76

417

1 Write the numbers.

5,000 + 600 + 70 + 4 = 5,674   4,000 + 200 + 10 + 3 = 4,213

2,000 + 400 + 30 + 9 = 2,439   9,000 + 700 + 80 + 1 = 9,781

7,000 + 800 + 00 + 6 = 7,806   3,000 + 100 + 50 + 2 = 3,152

8,000 + 500 + 60 + 5 = 8,565   6,000 + 300 + 20 + 7 = 6,327

2 Write the number of inches for each object. Label the answer.

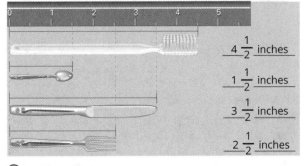

$4\frac{1}{2}$ inches

$1\frac{1}{2}$ inches

$3\frac{1}{2}$ inches

$2\frac{1}{2}$ inches

3 Find the sum.

1,492	4,792	1,490	3,765	4,871	5,630
+3,783	+2,496	+2,654	+3,841	+3,865	+ 2,587
5,275	7,288	4,144	7,606	8,736	8,217

2,953	3,853	3,967	4,894	3,581	5,184
+3,670	+1,796	+5,280	+4,915	+2,656	+ 3,942
6,623	5,649	9,247	9,809	6,237	9,126

77

---

4 Write the next three numbers in the series.

1	6	9	1	6	9	1	6
4	8	7	4	8	7	4	8
3	5	3	5	3	5	3	5
7	2	0	7	2	0	7	2

5 Write the name of the solid.

cone   cube   cylinder   pyramid   sphere

6 Multiply to find the product.

8	3	9	4	9	7	9	3	9
x 9	x 7	x 2	x 3	x 9	x 6	x 4	x 3	x 0
72	21	18	12	81	42	36	9	0

5	10	9	6	3	9	9	6	4
x 9	x 3	x 1	x 8	x 8	x 3	x 9	x 6	x 6
45	30	9	48	24	27	81	36	24

7 Find the difference and check.

6,802	4,956	7,714	5,703	9,848	9,573
- 1,562	- 1,282	- 1,562	- 3,421	- 6,283	- 8,190
5,240	3,674	6,152	2,282	3,565	1,383

78

---

1 Write the numbers.

three 4's = 4 + 4 + 4 = 3 x 4 = 12

seven 4's = 4 + 4 + 4 + 4 + 4 + 4 + 4 = 7 x 4 = 28

five 4's = 4 + 4 + 4 + 4 + 4 = 5 x 4 = 20

eight 4's = 4 + 4 + 4 + 4 + 4 + 4 + 4 + 4 = 8 x 4 = 32

two 4's = 4 + 4 = 2 x 4 = 8

six 4's = 4 + 4 + 4 + 4 + 4 + 4 = 6 x 4 = 24

four 4's = 4 + 4 + 4 + 4 = 4 x 4 = 16

2 Circle the solid that is different.

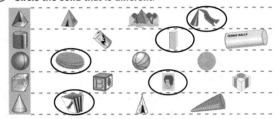

3 Write the next three numbers in the series.

3	5	6	1	3	5	6	1	3
2	7	8	2	7	8	2	7	8
4	0	4	0	4	0	4	0	4
1	9	3	4	1	9	3	4	1

79

---

4 Find the sum.

7,986	3,765	2,898	4,565	1,894	6,572
+1,232	+4,960	+5,671	+1,573	+7,535	+1,852
9,218	8,725	8,569	6,138	9,429	8,424

5 Write the numbers.

7,000 + 100 + 30 + 5 = 7,135   2,000 + 500 + 60 + 4 = 2,564

3,000 + 600 + 00 + 1 = 3,601   9,000 + 300 + 10 + 2 = 9,312

6,000 + 400 + 70 + 3 = 6,473   1,000 + 900 + 50 + 9 = 1,959

8,000 + 200 + 40 + 7 = 8,247   5,000 + 700 + 20 + 6 = 5,726

6 Measure the objects in inches.

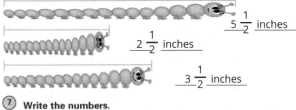

$5\frac{1}{2}$ inches

$2\frac{1}{2}$ inches

$3\frac{1}{2}$ inches

7 Write the numbers.

12 inches = 1 foot   3 feet = 1 yard   36 inches = 1 yard

8

John wanted to buy 7 apples at 9¢ each. How much would the apples cost John?   7 x 9 = 63¢

80

418

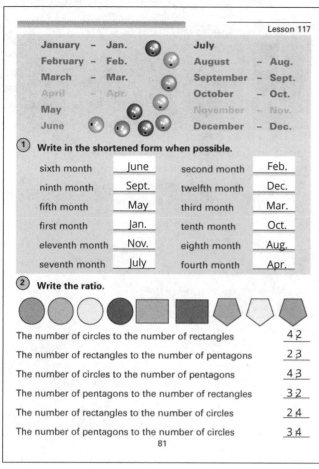

January – Jan.	July
February – Feb.	August – Aug.
March – Mar.	September – Sept.
April – Apr.	October – Oct.
May	November – Nov.
June	December – Dec.

① Write in the shortened form when possible.

sixth month	June	second month	Feb.
ninth month	Sept.	twelfth month	Dec.
fifth month	May	third month	Mar.
first month	Jan.	tenth month	Oct.
eleventh month	Nov.	eighth month	Aug.
seventh month	July	fourth month	Apr.

② Write the ratio.

The number of circles to the number of rectangles — 4 2

The number of rectangles to the number of pentagons — 2 3

The number of circles to the number of pentagons — 4 3

The number of pentagons to the number of rectangles — 3 2

The number of rectangles to the number of circles — 2 4

The number of pentagons to the number of circles — 3 4

81

---

③ Write the numbers.

3,000 + 100 + 00 + 5 = 3,105   4,000 + 600 + 10 + 3 = 4,613

8,000 + 700 + 60 + 2 = 8,762   5,000 + 800 + 30 + 7 = 5,837

④ There were 6 chairs at the table. Each chair had 4 legs. How many chair legs were there altogether?

6 x 4 = 24 legs

⑤ Measure the objects in inches.

3 ½ inches

5 ½ inches

2 ½ inches

36 inches = 1 yard   12 inches = 1 foot   3 feet = 1 yard

⑥ Match the number families.

3 x 4 — nine 4's
four 4's — 2 x 4
4 + 4 + 4 + 4 + 4 — 4 + 4 + 4 + 4
six 4's — five 4's
9 x 4 — 6 x 4
4 + 4 — 4 + 4 + 4

⑦ Kay had $36. She wanted to buy a coat for $50. How much more money did she need?

$50
82   - 36
$14

---

① Number of Mini Cars Owned

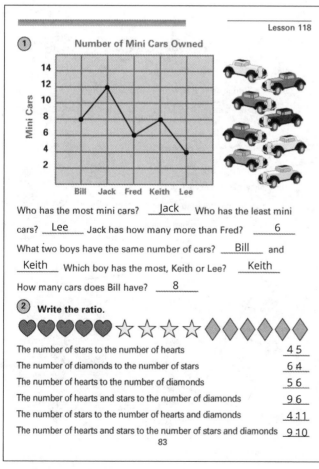

Who has the most mini cars? __Jack__ Who has the least mini cars? __Lee__ Jack has how many more than Fred? __6__

What two boys have the same number of cars? __Bill__ and __Keith__ Which boy has the most, Keith or Lee? __Keith__

How many cars does Bill have? __8__

② Write the ratio.

The number of stars to the number of hearts — 4 5

The number of diamonds to the number of stars — 6 4

The number of hearts to the number of diamonds — 5 6

The number of hearts and stars to the number of diamonds — 9 6

The number of stars to the number of hearts and diamonds — 4 11

The number of hearts and stars to the number of stars and diamonds — 9 10

83

---

③ Write the value. Find the sum.

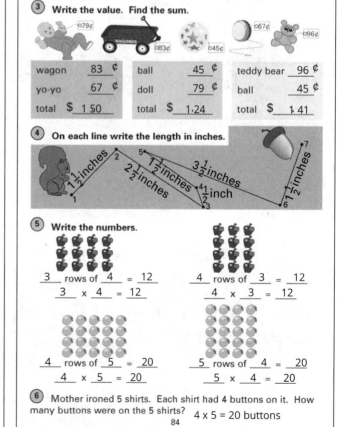

wagon	83 ¢	ball	45 ¢	teddy bear	96 ¢
yo-yo	67 ¢	doll	79 ¢	ball	45 ¢
total	$ 1 50	total	$ 1.24	total	$ 1.41

④ On each line write the length in inches.

1 ½ inches   2 ½ inches   1 ½ inches   3 ½ inches   ½ inch   1 ½ inches

⑤ Write the numbers.

3 rows of 4 = 12   4 rows of 3 = 12
3 x 4 = 12   4 x 3 = 12

4 rows of 5 = 20   5 rows of 4 = 20
4 x 5 = 20   5 x 4 = 20

⑥ Mother ironed 5 shirts. Each shirt had 4 buttons on it. How many buttons were on the 5 shirts? 4 x 5 = 20 buttons

84

419

① Solve the equations.

n+3 = 6 -3 -3 n = 3	n+8 = 12 -8 -8 n = 4	n+2 = 8 -2 -2 n = 6	n+6 = 13 -6 -6 n = 7
n+4 = 4 -4 -4 n = 0	n+5 = 9 -5 -5 n = 4	n+8 = 15 -8 -8 n = 7	n+9 = 10 -9 -9 n = 1

②

Girls' Ages

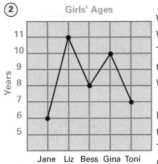

Who is the oldest? __Liz__

Who is the youngest? __Jane__

Toni is how much younger than Gina? __3 years__

Who is oldest, Bess or Jane? __Bess__

Bess is how much older than Jane? __2 years__

There are how many years between Liz and Gina? __1 year__

③ Match the multiplication pairs.

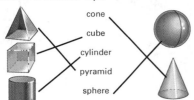

3 x 4 = 12 7 x 4 = 28	2 x 4 = 8 4 x 1 = 4
4 x 7 = 28 4 x 8 = 32	4 x 9 = 36 4 x 6 = 24
8 x 4 = 32 5 x 4 = 20	1 x 4 = 4 4 x 2 = 8
4 x 5 = 20 4 x 3 = 12	6 x 4 = 24 9 x 4 = 36

85

---

④ Write the ratio using the picture below.

The number of cats to the number of pigs	2:3
The number of goats and cows to the number of horses	7:6
The number of pigs and cats to the number of horses	5:6
The number of goats to the number of cows and cats	3:6
The number of cows and horses to the number of pigs and goats	10:6

⑤ Write the cost.

Cherries 3¢ each   Bananas 8¢ each   Oranges 5¢ each   Apples 7¢ each

4 apples	= __28__ ¢
5 bananas	= __40__ ¢
9 cherries	= __27__ ¢
6 oranges	= __30__ ¢

⑥ Write < or >.

   <

  >

  >

86

---

① Match the solid to its name. 5 pts.

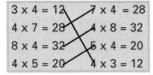

cone
cube
cylinder
pyramid
sphere

② Write the answers. 6 pts.

Is 16 closer to 10 or 20?	20	Is 49 closer to 40 or 50?	50
Is 38 closer to 30 or 40?	40	Is 66 closer to 60 or 70?	70
Is 52 closer to 50 or 60?	50	Is 72 closer to 70 or 80?	70

③ Solve the equations. 8 pts.

5+n = 11 -5 -5 n = 6	3+n = 12 -3 -3 n = 9	7+n = 16 -7 -7 n = 9	8+n = 14 -8 -8 n = 6
3+n = 8 -3 -3 n = 5	6+n = 15 -6 -6 n = 9	4+n = 7 -4 -4 n = 3	8+n = 17 -8 -8 n = 9

④ Write = or ≠. 6 pts.

5 x 9 = 45	2 x 4 = 8	7 x 5 ≠ 70
3 x 6 ≠ 24	8 x 3 ≠ 32	6 x 9 ≠ 36

87

---

⑤

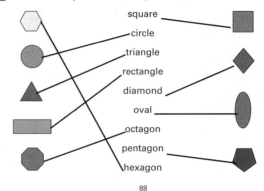

How many tricycles are in the picture? __6__

If each has three wheels, how many wheels are there altogether? __6 x 3 = 18 wheels__   2 pts.

(Write the fact, answer, and label.)

⑥

How many dimes equal a dollar?	10
How many nickels equal a dollar?	20
How many quarters equal a dollar?	4
How many pennies equal a dollar?	100
How many half dollars equal a dollar?	2

5 pts.

⑦ Match the shape to its name. 9 pts.

square
circle
triangle
rectangle
diamond
oval
octagon
pentagon
hexagon

88

420

Lesson 120

1 Measure the objects in centimeters. Label the answers.

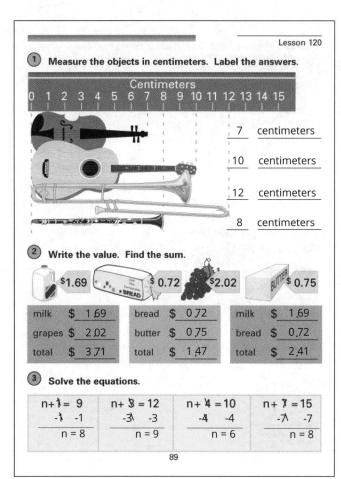

Centimeters
0 1 2 3 4 5 6 7 8 9 10 11 12 13 14 15

7 centimeters

10 centimeters

12 centimeters

8 centimeters

2 Write the value. Find the sum.

$1.69 $0.72 $2.02 $0.75 BUTTER

milk	$ 1.69	bread	$ 0.72	milk	$ 1.69
grapes	$ 2.02	butter	$ 0.75	bread	$ 0.72
total	$ 3.71	total	$ 1.47	total	$ 2.41

3 Solve the equations.

n + 1 = 9	n + 3 = 12	n + 4 = 10	n + 7 = 15
-1 -1	-3 -3	-4 -4	-7 -7
n = 8	n = 9	n = 6	n = 8

89

---

4 Write the multiplication fact to make a pair.

5 x 6 = 30 $\underline{6 \times 5 = 30}$ 3 x 9 = 27 $\underline{9 \times 3 = 27}$

7 x 4 = 28 $\underline{4 \times 7 = 28}$ 10 x 6 = 60 $\underline{6 \times 10 = 60}$

2 x 8 = 16 $\underline{8 \times 2 = 16}$ 1 x 8 = 8 $\underline{8 \times 1 = 8}$

5 Multiply to find the product.

9 x 2	3 x 4	3 x 6	9 x 3	3 x 2	0 x 4	10 x 9	10 x 4	9 x 5
18	12	18	27	6	0	90	40	45

5 x 6	6 x 9	1 x 4	3 x 5	4 x 7	9 x 9	3 x 3	2 x 4	6 x 7
30	54	4	15	28	81	9	8	42

4 x 4	9 x 4	7 x 3	4 x 8	3 x 8	4 x 5	7 x 9	6 x 8	4 x 9
16	36	21	32	24	20	63	48	36

6 Write < or >.

8 + 5 $\underline{>}$ 13 - 4   6 + 6 $\underline{>}$ 7 - 3   10 - 5 $\underline{<}$ 9 + 7

12 - 6 $\underline{<}$ 5 + 9   5 - 3 $\underline{<}$ 1 + 2   5 + 5 $\underline{>}$ 9 - 6

7 Write an addition or subtraction fact. Answers may vary.

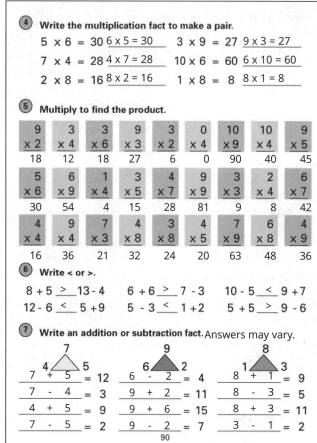

7   9   8
4 ◁ 5   6 ◁ 2   1 ◁ 3

7 + 5 = 12   6 - 2 = 4   8 + 1 = 9

7 - 4 = 3   9 + 2 = 11   8 - 3 = 5

4 + 5 = 9   9 + 6 = 15   8 + 3 = 11

7 - 5 = 2   9 - 2 = 7   3 - 1 = 2

90

Lesson 121

1 Write the fractional part that is colored.

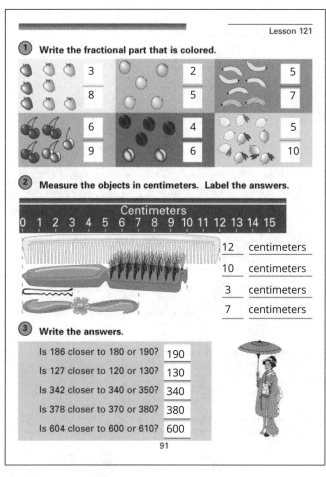

$\dfrac{3}{8}$ $\dfrac{2}{5}$ $\dfrac{5}{7}$

$\dfrac{6}{9}$ $\dfrac{4}{6}$ $\dfrac{5}{10}$

2 Measure the objects in centimeters. Label the answers.

Centimeters
0 1 2 3 4 5 6 7 8 9 10 11 12 13 14 15

12 centimeters

10 centimeters

3 centimeters

7 centimeters

3 Write the answers.

Is 186 closer to 180 or 190?	190
Is 127 closer to 120 or 130?	130
Is 342 closer to 340 or 350?	340
Is 378 closer to 370 or 380?	380
Is 604 closer to 600 or 610?	600

91

4

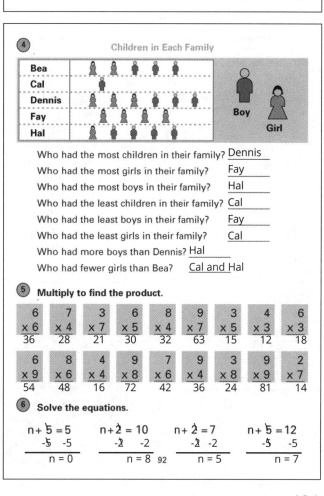

Children in Each Family

Bea	
Cal	
Dennis	
Fay	
Hal	

Boy   Girl

Who had the most children in their family? Dennis

Who had the most girls in their family? Fay

Who had the most boys in their family? Hal

Who had the least children in their family? Cal

Who had the least boys in their family? Fay

Who had the least girls in their family? Cal

Who had more boys than Dennis? Hal

Who had fewer girls than Bea? Cal and Hal

5 Multiply to find the product.

6 x 6	7 x 4	3 x 7	6 x 5	8 x 4	9 x 7	3 x 5	4 x 3	6 x 3
36	28	21	30	32	63	15	12	18

6 x 9	8 x 6	4 x 4	9 x 8	7 x 6	9 x 4	3 x 8	9 x 9	2 x 7
54	48	16	72	42	36	24	81	14

6 Solve the equations.

n + 5 = 5	n + 2 = 10	n + 2 = 7	n + 5 = 12
-5 -5	-2 -2	-2 -2	-5 -5
n = 0	n = 8	n = 5	n = 7

92

421

① Write the Roman numerals.

I	IV	V	IX	X	XL	L	XC	C	CD	D	CM	M
1	4	5	9	10	40	50	90	100	400	500	900	1,000

138	CXXXVIII		550	DL
162	CLXII		673	DCLXXIII
214	CCXIV		746	DCCXLVI
397	CCCXCVII		881	DCCCLXXXI

② Write the fractional part that is colored.

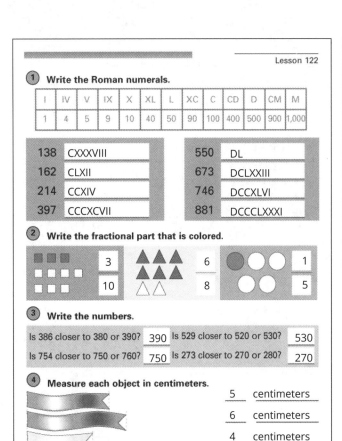

$\dfrac{3}{10}$ $\dfrac{6}{8}$ $\dfrac{1}{5}$

③ Write the numbers.

Is 386 closer to 380 or 390? 390   Is 529 closer to 520 or 530? 530

Is 754 closer to 750 or 760? 750   Is 273 closer to 270 or 280? 270

④ Measure each object in centimeters.

5 centimeters
6 centimeters
4 centimeters
10 centimeters

93

---

⑤ Write the multiplication fact to represent how many cans each person collected.

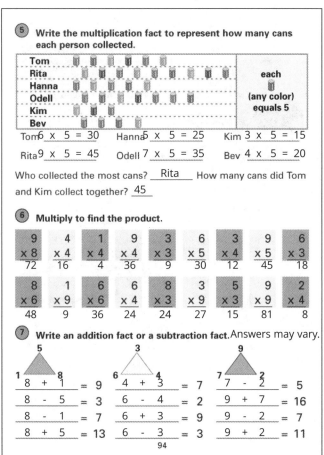

| Tom | Rita | Hanna | Odell | Kim | Bev | each (any color) equals 5 |

Tom 6 x 5 = 30   Hanna 5 x 5 = 25   Kim 3 x 5 = 15
Rita 9 x 5 = 45   Odell 7 x 5 = 35   Bev 4 x 5 = 20

Who collected the most cans? Rita   How many cans did Tom and Kim collect together? 45

⑥ Multiply to find the product.

9	4	1	9	3	6	3	9	6
x8	x4	x4	x4	x3	x5	x4	x5	x3
72	16	4	36	9	30	12	45	18

8	1	6	6	8	3	5	9	2
x6	x9	x6	x4	x3	x9	x3	x9	x4
48	9	36	24	24	27	15	81	8

⑦ Write an addition fact or a subtraction fact. Answers may vary.

8 + 1 = 9   4 + 3 = 7   7 - 2 = 5
8 - 5 = 3   6 - 4 = 2   9 + 7 = 16
8 - 1 = 7   6 + 3 = 9   9 - 2 = 7
8 + 5 = 13   6 - 3 = 3   9 + 2 = 11

94

---

① Find the sum.

3,621	3,971	1,958	2,437	8,239	2,661
+3,119	+1,505	+4,022	+5,661	+1,458	+3,292
6,740	5,476	5,980	8,098	9,697	5,953

5,473	1,754	1,243	2,198	7,314	5,416
+1,332	+3,741	+1,629	+7,640	+2,439	+3,873
6,805	5,495	2,872	9,838	9,753	9,289

n - 5 = 7   n - 8 = 3   n - 7 = 6
+ 5 + 5   + 8 + 8   + 7 + 7
n   = 12   n   = 11   n   = 13

② Solve the equations.

n - 8 = 8	n - 5 = 9	n - 0 = 2	n - 4 = 9
+8 +8	+5 +5	+0 +0	+4 +4
n = 16	n = 14	n = 2	n = 13

n - 8 = 5	n - 4 = 2	n - 6 = 8	n - 3 = 5
+8 +8	+4 +4	+6 +6	+3 +3
n = 13	n = 6	n = 14	n = 8

③ Measure the lines in centimeters.

10 centimeters
7 centimeters
3 centimeters
15 centimeters

95

---

④ Write the Arabic numbers.

I	IV	V	IX	X	XL	L	XC	C	CD	D	CM	M
1	4	5	9	10	40	50	90	100	400	500	900	1,000

CLVI	=	156		DCCXCII	=	792
DCXLIII	=	643		CCCXVIII	=	318
DCCCXXV	=	825		DIX	=	509
CDXXXVII	=	437		CMLXI	=	961
CCLXXX	=	280		CCLXXIV	=	274

⑤ Shade the objects for each fractional part. Answers vary.

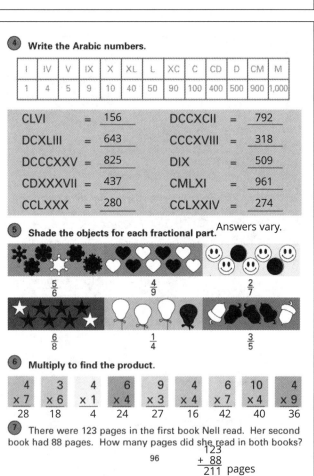

$\dfrac{5}{6}$ $\dfrac{4}{9}$ $\dfrac{2}{7}$

$\dfrac{6}{8}$ $\dfrac{1}{4}$ $\dfrac{3}{5}$

⑥ Multiply to find the product.

4	3	4	6	9	4	6	10	4
x7	x6	x1	x4	x3	x4	x7	x4	x9
28	18	4	24	27	16	42	40	36

⑦ There were 123 pages in the first book Nell read. Her second book had 88 pages. How many pages did she read in both books?

123
+ 88
211 pages

96

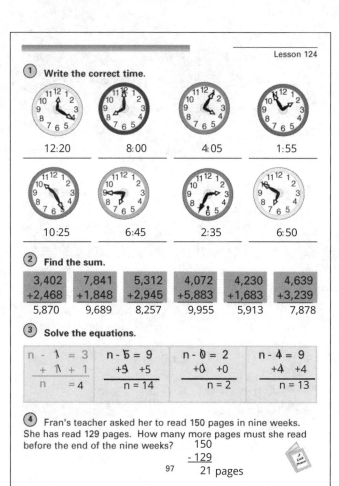

1 Write the correct time.

12:20   8:00   4:05   1:55

10:25   6:45   2:35   6:50

2 Find the sum.

3,402	7,841	5,312	4,072	4,230	4,639
+2,468	+1,848	+2,945	+5,883	+1,683	+3,239
5,870	9,689	8,257	9,955	5,913	7,878

3 Solve the equations.

n - 1 = 3	n - 5 = 9	n - 0 = 2	n - 4 = 9
+ 1 + 1	+5 +5	+0 +0	+4 +4
n = 4	n = 14	n = 2	n = 13

4 Fran's teacher asked her to read 150 pages in nine weeks. She has read 129 pages. How many more pages must she read before the end of the nine weeks?

150
- 129
21 pages

97

---

5 Shade the objects for each fractional part.

Answers may vary.

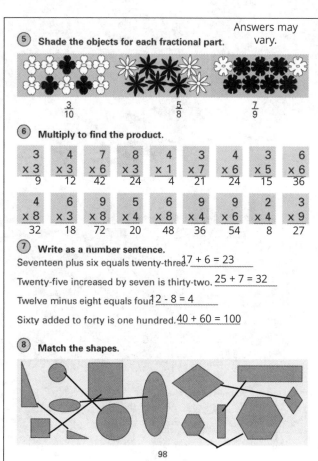

$\frac{3}{10}$ $\frac{5}{8}$ $\frac{7}{9}$

6 Multiply to find the product.

3	4	7	8	4	3	4	3	6
x 3	x 3	x 6	x 3	x 1	x 7	x 6	x 5	x 6
9	12	42	24	4	21	24	15	36

4	6	9	5	9	9	9	2	3
x 8	x 3	x 8	x 4	x 8	x 4	x 6	x 4	x 9
32	18	72	20	48	36	54	8	27

7 Write as a number sentence.

Seventeen plus six equals twenty-three. 17 + 6 = 23

Twenty-five increased by seven is thirty-two. 25 + 7 = 32

Twelve minus eight equals four. 12 - 8 = 4

Sixty added to forty is one hundred. 40 + 60 = 100

8 Match the shapes.

98

---

1 Write the numbers.

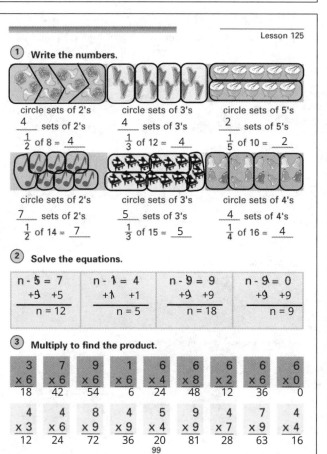

circle sets of 2's   circle sets of 3's   circle sets of 5's

4 sets of 2's   4 sets of 3's   2 sets of 5's

$\frac{1}{2}$ of 8 = 4 $\frac{1}{3}$ of 12 = 4 $\frac{1}{5}$ of 10 = 2

circle sets of 2's   circle sets of 3's   circle sets of 4's

7 sets of 2's   5 sets of 3's   4 sets of 4's

$\frac{1}{2}$ of 14 = 7 $\frac{1}{3}$ of 15 = 5 $\frac{1}{4}$ of 16 = 4

2 Solve the equations.

n - 5 = 7	n - 1 = 4	n - 9 = 9	n - 9 = 0
+5 +5	+1 +1	+9 +9	+9 +9
n = 12	n = 5	n = 18	n = 9

3 Multiply to find the product.

3	7	9	1	6	6	6	6	6
x 6	x 6	x 6	x 6	x 4	x 8	x 2	x 6	x 0
18	42	54	6	24	48	12	36	0

4	4	8	4	5	9	4	7	4
x 3	x 6	x 9	x 9	x 4	x 9	x 7	x 9	x 4
12	24	72	36	20	81	28	63	16

99

---

4 Draw both hands on the clocks.

5:20   8:50   3:05   11:30

5 Find the sum.

5,089	1,363	2,590	6,822	4,257	5,514
+4,312	+6,576	+4,167	+1,402	+2,705	+3,925
9,401	7,939	6,757	8,224	6,962	9,439

6 Match the shape to its name.

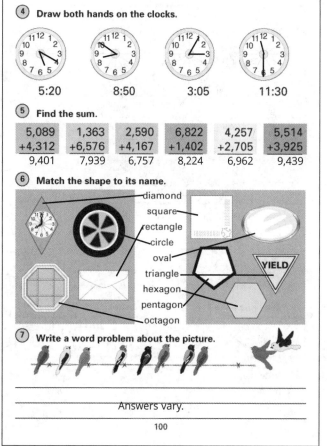

diamond
square
rectangle
circle
oval
triangle
hexagon
pentagon
octagon

YIELD

7 Write a word problem about the picture.

Answers vary.

100

423

16 ounces (oz.) = 1 pound (lb.)

2,000 pounds (lbs.) = 1 Ton (T.)

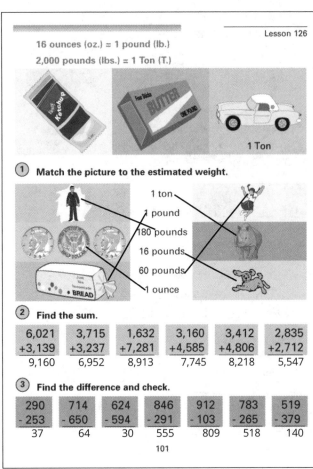

1 Ton

① **Match the picture to the estimated weight.**

1 ton
1 pound
180 pounds
16 pounds
60 pounds
1 ounce

② **Find the sum.**

6,021	3,715	1,632	3,160	3,412	2,835
+3,139	+3,237	+7,281	+4,585	+4,806	+2,712
9,160	6,952	8,913	7,745	8,218	5,547

③ **Find the difference and check.**

290	714	624	846	912	783	519
- 253	- 650	- 594	- 291	- 103	- 265	- 379
37	64	30	555	809	518	140

101

---

④ **Write = or ≠.**

△ _=_ triangle	⬠ _=_ pentagon	⬭ _≠_ circle
▮ _=_ rectangle	● _≠_ oval	⬡ _≠_ octagon
⯃ _≠_ hexagon	◻ _=_ square	◆ _=_ diamond

⑤ **Write the numbers.**

1 year = __12__ months	1 week = __7__ days
1 hour = __60__ minutes	1 minute= __60__ seconds
1 day = __24__ hours	$\frac{1}{2}$ hour = __30__ minutes
1 year = __52__ weeks	1 year = __365__ days

⑥ **Write the numbers.**

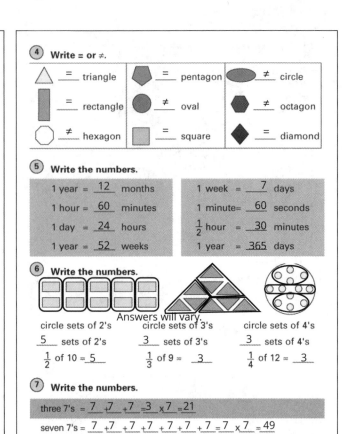

Answers will vary.

circle sets of 2's	circle sets of 3's	circle sets of 4's
__5__ sets of 2's	__3__ sets of 3's	__3__ sets of 4's
$\frac{1}{2}$ of 10 = __5__	$\frac{1}{3}$ of 9 = __3__	$\frac{1}{4}$ of 12 = __3__

⑦ **Write the numbers.**

three 7's = __7__ __7__ +__7__ =3 x 7 =21

seven 7's = __7__ +__7__ +7 +7 + 7 + 7 + 7 = 7 x 7 = 49

four 7's = __7__ +7 + 7 + 7 = 4 x 7 = 28

102

---

① **Draw the nickels needed on the pictograph.**

Nickels Spent at Lunch

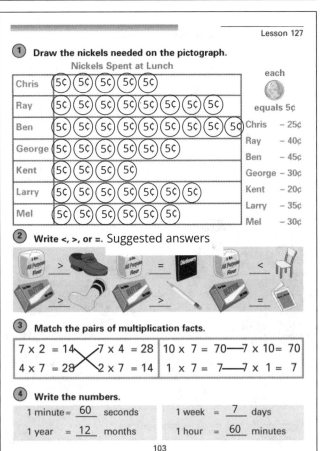

each ⬤ equals 5¢

Chris – 25¢
Ray – 40¢
Ben – 45¢
George – 30¢
Kent – 20¢
Larry – 35¢
Mel – 30¢

② **Write <, >, or =.** Suggested answers

③ **Match the pairs of multiplication facts.**

7 x 2 = 14	7 x 4 = 28	10 x 7 = 70 — 7 x 10= 70
4 x 7 = 28	2 x 7 = 14	1 x 7 = 7 — 7 x 1 = 7

④ **Write the numbers.**

1 minute= __60__ seconds	1 week = __7__ days
1 year = __12__ months	1 hour = __60__ minutes

103

---

⑤ **Match the solid to its picture.**

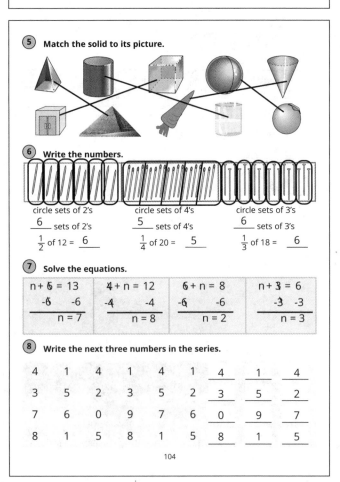

⑥ **Write the numbers.**

circle sets of 2's	circle sets of 4's	circle sets of 3's
__6__ sets of 2's	__5__ sets of 4's	__6__ sets of 3's
$\frac{1}{2}$ of 12 = __6__	$\frac{1}{4}$ of 20 = __5__	$\frac{1}{3}$ of 18 = __6__

⑦ **Solve the equations.**

n + 6 = 13	4 + n = 12	6 + n = 8	n + 3 = 6
-6 -6	-4 -4	-6 -6	-3 -3
n = 7	n = 8	n = 2	n = 3

⑧ **Write the next three numbers in the series.**

4	1	4	1	4	1	4	1	4
3	5	2	3	5	2	3	5	2
7	6	0	9	7	6	0	9	7
8	1	5	8	1	5	8	1	5

104

424

1) Write ones', tens', hundreds', or thousands'.

2,483 has an 8 in the <u>tens'</u> place.

2,483 has a 2 in the <u>thousands'</u> place.

9,048 has an 8 in the <u>ones'</u> place.

9,048 has a 0 in the <u>hundreds'</u> place.

5,617 has a 5 in the <u>thousands'</u> place.

5,617 has a 7 in the <u>ones'</u> place.

3,564 has a 6 in the <u>tens'</u> place.

3,564 has a 5 in the <u>hundreds'</u> place.

2) Write the next three numbers in the series.

1	2	5	3	1	2	5	3	1
4	7	6	8	4	7	6	8	4
9	3	0	2	9	3	0	2	9
5	4	1	7	5	4	1	7	5

3) Write the name of the solid.

cube   sphere   pyramid   cone   cylinder

4) Josh's mother bought 4 bags of apples. There were 9 apples in each bag. How many apples did Josh's mother buy?

4 x 9 = 36 apples

105

5) Solve the equations.

0 + n = 4	4 + n = 9	n + 8 = 15	n + 9 = 10
-0 -0	-4 -4	-8 -8	-9 -9
n = 4	n = 5	n = 7	n = 1

6) Write the number of points each boy scored.

Touchdowns in a Year

each
equals 6
points

Leroy <u>30</u>   John <u>24</u>   Porter <u>42</u>   Matt <u>48</u>   Craig <u>18</u>

7) Find the product.

4	7	9	4	10	7	4	3	9
x 0	x 8	x 5	x 1	x 4	x 5	x 2	x 7	x 3
0	56	45	4	40	35	8	21	27

9	4	4	6	10	7	9	7	6
x 9	x 5	x 7	x 3	x 9	x 7	x 8	x 4	x 4
81	20	28	18	90	49	72	28	24

8) Find the difference.

877	582	639	405	367	291	685
- 808	- 147	- 377	- 265	- 284	- 38	- 208
69	435	262	140	83	253	477

106

---

1) Measure the lines in inches.

$4 \frac{1}{4}$ inches

$2 \frac{3}{4}$ inches

$4 \frac{3}{4}$ inches

$3 \frac{3}{4}$ inches

2) Find the sum.

2,902	7,579	1,068	4,744	1,569	1,839
+1,829	+2,333	+5,859	+1,663	+2,507	+ 6,224
4,731	9,912	6,927	6,407	4,076	8,063

3) Write ones', tens', hundreds', or thousands'.

3,956 has a 5 in the <u>tens'</u> place.

3,956 has a 3 in the <u>thousands'</u> place.

3,956 has a 6 in the <u>ones'</u> place.

3,956 has a 9 in the <u>hundreds'</u> place.

4) Find the difference.

590	737	472	653	181	942	845
- 468	- 387	- 313	- 471	- 154	- 217	- 392
122	350	159	182	27	725	453

107

5) Write the ratio using the picture below.

The number of dogs to hamsters.   <u>3 :5</u>

The number of cats to dogs.   <u>4 :3</u>

The number of dogs and cats to hamsters.   <u>7 :5</u>

The number of hamsters and dogs to cats.   <u>8 :4</u>

6) Multiply to find the product.

7	4	9	3	7	4	8	3	10
x 2	x 3	x 9	x 9	x 5	x 8	x 7	x 7	x 5
14	12	81	27	35	32	56	21	50

9	4	8	7	4	9	6	4	7
x 4	x 7	x 9	x 7	x 5	x 6	x 7	x 4	x 4
36	28	72	49	20	54	42	16	28

7) Solve the equations.

n + 5 = 13	6 + n = 12	9 + n = 16	n + 3 = 10
-5 -5	-6 -6	-9 -9	-3 -3
n = 8	n = 6	n = 7	n = 7

8) Jacob found 5 bird nests. Each nest had 3 eggs. How many eggs did Jacob find in all?

5 x 3 = 15 eggs

Mother bought 8 yards of cloth for $4.00 a yard. How much did she spend? 8 x $4.00 = $32.00

108

425

(1)

Temperature Highs

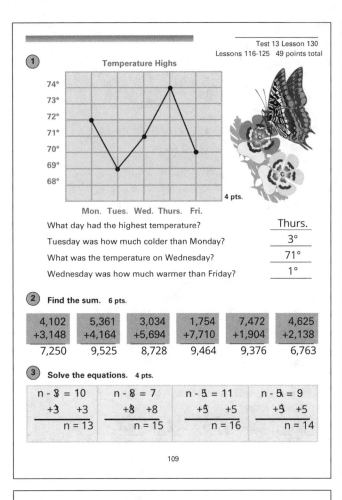

| | Mon. | Tues. | Wed. | Thurs. | Fri. |

4 pts.

What day had the highest temperature? Thurs.

Tuesday was how much colder than Monday? 3°

What was the temperature on Wednesday? 71°

Wednesday was how much warmer than Friday? 1°

(2) Find the sum. 6 pts.

4,102	5,361	3,034	1,754	7,472	4,625
+3,148	+4,164	+5,694	+7,710	+1,904	+2,138
7,250	9,525	8,728	9,464	9,376	6,763

(3) Solve the equations. 4 pts.

n - 3 = 10	n - 8 = 7	n - 5 = 11	n - 5 = 9
+3 +3	+8 +8	+5 +5	+5 +5
n = 13	n = 15	n = 16	n = 14

109

---

(4) Write the numbers. 6 pts.

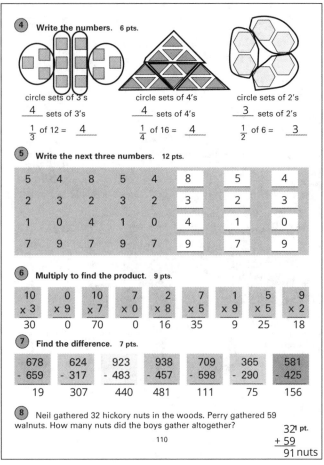

circle sets of 3's	circle sets of 4's	circle sets of 2's
__4__ sets of 3's	__4__ sets of 4's	__3__ sets of 2's
$\frac{1}{3}$ of 12 = __4__	$\frac{1}{4}$ of 16 = __4__	$\frac{1}{2}$ of 6 = __3__

(5) Write the next three numbers. 12 pts.

5	4	8	5	4	8	5	4
2	3	2	3	2	3	2	3
1	0	4	1	0	4	1	0
7	9	7	9	7	9	7	9

(6) Multiply to find the product. 9 pts.

10	0	10	7	2	7	1	5	9
x 3	x 9	x 7	x 0	x 8	x 5	x 9	x 5	x 2
30	0	70	0	16	35	9	25	18

(7) Find the difference. 7 pts.

678	624	923	938	709	365	581
- 659	- 317	- 483	- 457	- 598	- 290	- 425
19	307	440	481	111	75	156

(8) Neil gathered 32 hickory nuts in the woods. Perry gathered 59 walnuts. How many nuts did the boys gather altogether?

110

1 pt.

32
+ 59
91 nuts

Sunday	–	Sun.		
Monday	–	Mon.	Thursday	– Thurs.
Tuesday	–	Tues.	Friday	– Fri.
Wednesday	–	Wed.	Saturday	– Sat.

(1) Write the shortened form for the days of the week.

third day	Tues.	second day	Mon.	first day	Sun.
fifth day	Thurs.	sixth day	Fri.	fourth day	Wed.
seventh day	Sat.				

(2) Find the difference.

215	894	927	840	853	758	696
- 185	- 76	- 560	- 321	- 419	- 498	- 437
30	818	367	519	434	260	259

(3) Write the correct letter in the blank.

G	P	I	N
543	362	604	710

R	S	T
827	469	975

276	583	307	180
+328	+392	+297	+289
604	975	604	469
I	T	I	S

235	149	352	521	526	276
+234	+213	+475	+ 83	+184	+267
469	362	827	604	710	543
S	P	R	I	N	G

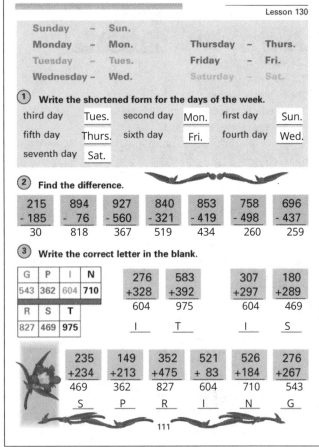

111

---

(4) Measure the lines in inches.

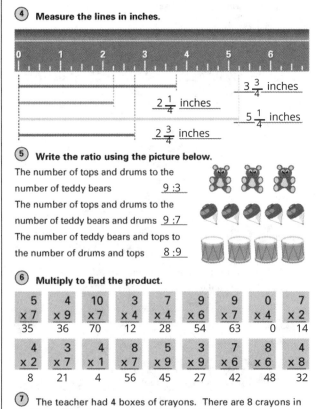

$3\frac{3}{4}$ inches

$2\frac{1}{4}$ inches

$5\frac{1}{4}$ inches

$2\frac{3}{4}$ inches

(5) Write the ratio using the picture below.

The number of tops and drums to the number of teddy bears __9 :3__

The number of tops and drums to the number of teddy bears and drums __9 :7__

The number of teddy bears and tops to the number of drums and tops __8 :9__

(6) Multiply to find the product.

5	4	10	3	7	9	9	0	7
x 7	x 9	x 7	x 4	x 4	x 6	x 7	x 4	x 2
35	36	70	12	28	54	63	0	14

4	3	4	8	5	3	7	8	4
x 2	x 7	x 1	x 7	x 9	x 9	x 6	x 6	x 8
8	21	4	56	45	27	42	48	32

(7) The teacher had **4** boxes of crayons. There are 8 crayons in each box. How many crayons does the teacher have?

112   4 x 8 = 32 crayons

1 **Find the sum.**

$ 4.83 + $ 2.75 =	$4.83 +2.75 $7.58
$32.15 + $21.85 =	$32.15 + 21.85 $54.00
$12.97 + $ 5.60 =	$12.97 + 5.60 $18.57

$ 6.28 + $ 0.64 =	$6.28 +0.64 $6.92
$68.94 + $ 0.76 =	$68.94 + 0.76 $69.70
$84.80 + $12.31 =	$84.80 + 12.31 $97.11

2 **Measure the lines in inches.**

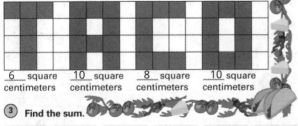

$3\frac{3}{4}$ inches

$2\frac{3}{4}$ inches

$1\frac{1}{4}$ inches

$5\frac{1}{4}$ inches

3 At the basketball game there were 5 rows of bleachers. If 9 students could sit in each row, how many students could sit on the bleachers?

5 x 9 = 45 students

113

---

4 **Solve the equations.**

n - 7 = 9 +7 +7 n = 16	n - 5 = 5 +5 +5 n = 10	n - 2 = 0 +2 +2 n = 2	n - 9 = 3 +9 +9 n = 12

5 **Count the squares to find the area. We measure area in square units.**

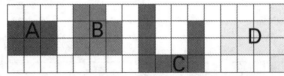

The area of A is __6__ square centimeters.

The area of B is __8__ square centimeters.

The area of C is __9__ square centimeters.

The area of D is __10__ square centimeters.

6 **Find the difference.**

682 - 569 113	507 - 343 164	977 - 887 90	914 - 631 283	693 - 124 569	671 - 262 409	929 - 140 789

7 **Multiply to find the product.**

3 x 4 12	6 x 4 24	9 x 8 72	4 x 7 28	1 x 4 4	4 x 9 36	5 x 6 30	4 x 2 8	0 x 3 0

114

---

1 **Find the difference.**

$33.28 - $31.31 =	$33.28 - 31.31 $ 1.97
$27.80 - $ 1.51 =	$27.80 - 1.51 $26.29
$45.18 - $ 0.97 =	$45.18 - 0.97 $44.21

$65.04 - $32.74 =	$65.04 - 32.74 $32.30
$74.73 - $ 3.28 =	$74.73 - 3.28 $71.45
$51.56 - $ 0.76 =	$51.56 - 0.76 $50.80

2 **Count the squares to find the area.**

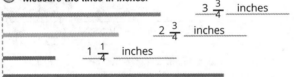

__6__ square centimeters   __10__ square centimeters   __8__ square centimeters   __10__ square centimeters

3 **Find the sum.**

1,579 +1,645 3,224	5,787 +3,749 9,536	3,863 +2,297 6,160	4,856 +1,684 6,540	2,948 +4,173 7,121	3,978 + 1,465 5,443

115

---

4 **Write the length in inches on each line.**

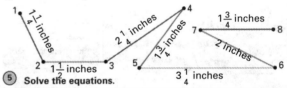

$1\frac{1}{4}$ inches

$1\frac{1}{2}$ inches

$2\frac{1}{4}$ inches

$1\frac{3}{4}$ inches

$3\frac{1}{4}$ inches

$1\frac{3}{4}$ inches

2 inches

5 **Solve the equations.**

n - 9 = 4 +9 +9 n = 13	n - 7 = 0 +7 +7 n = 7	n - 7 = 7 +7 +7 n = 14	n - 6 = 2 +6 +6 n = 8

6 **Multiply to find the product.**

9 x 9 81	4 x 4 16	8 x 7 56	7 x 1 7	8 x 9 72	4 x 7 28	10 x 7 70	7 x 2 14	2 x 4 8
4 x 6 24	7 x 3 21	5 x 6 30	3 x 4 12	6 x 7 42	6 x 3 18	7 x 5 35	9 x 5 45	10 x 4 40

7 **Circle the lines that are the same length as line AB.**

A_____B

Measure with an inch ruler to see if you are correct.

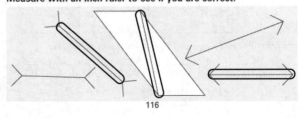

116

427

① **Measure the line to the nearest inch.**

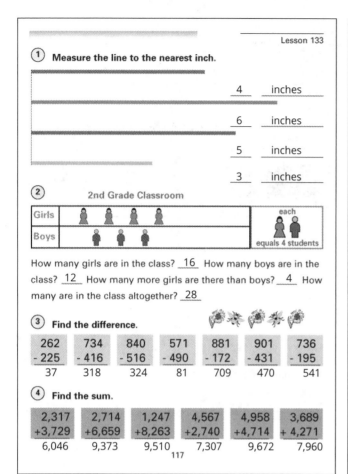

4 inches

6 inches

5 inches

3 inches

② 2nd Grade Classroom

| Girls | 👩 👩 👩 👩 | each |
| Boys | 🧒 🧒 🧒 | 👩🧒 equals 4 students |

How many girls are in the class? __16__ How many boys are in the class? __12__ How many more girls are there than boys? __4__ How many are in the class altogether? __28__

③ **Find the difference.**

262	734	840	571	881	901	736
- 225	- 416	- 516	- 490	- 172	- 431	- 195
37	318	324	81	709	470	541

④ **Find the sum.**

2,317	2,714	1,247	4,567	4,958	3,689
+3,729	+6,659	+8,263	+2,740	+4,714	+ 4,271
6,046	9,373	9,510	7,307	9,672	7,960

117

---

⑤ **Shade the number of squares needed to equal the following areas:** Answers vary.

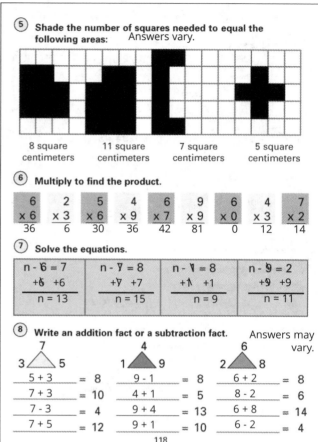

8 square centimeters   11 square centimeters   7 square centimeters   5 square centimeters

⑥ **Multiply to find the product.**

6	2	5	4	6	9	6	4	7
x 6	x 3	x 6	x 9	x 7	x 9	x 0	x 3	x 2
36	6	30	36	42	81	0	12	14

⑦ **Solve the equations.**

n - 6 = 7	n - 7 = 8	n - 1 = 8	n - 9 = 2
+6 +6	+7 +7	+1 +1	+9 +9
n = 13	n = 15	n = 9	n = 11

⑧ **Write an addition fact or a subtraction fact.** Answers may vary.

7: 3△5
5 + 3 = 8
7 + 3 = 10
7 - 3 = 4
7 + 5 = 12

4: 1△9
9 - 1 = 8
4 + 1 = 5
9 + 4 = 13
9 + 1 = 10

6: 2△8
6 + 2 = 8
8 - 2 = 6
6 + 8 = 14
6 - 2 = 4

118

Lesson 134
Suggested answers.

① **Write the numbers.**

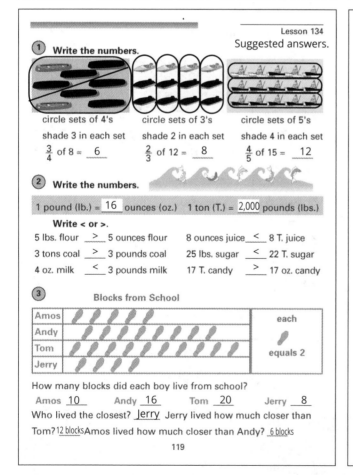

circle sets of 4's   circle sets of 3's   circle sets of 5's
shade 3 in each set   shade 2 in each set   shade 4 in each set

$\frac{3}{4}$ of 8 = __6__ $\frac{2}{3}$ of 12 = __8__ $\frac{4}{5}$ of 15 = __12__

② **Write the numbers.**

1 pound (lb.) = __16__ ounces (oz.)   1 ton (T.) = __2,000__ pounds (lbs.)

Write < or >.

5 lbs. flour __>__ 5 ounces flour   8 ounces juice __<__ 8 T. juice
3 tons coal __>__ 3 pounds coal   25 lbs. sugar __<__ 22 T. sugar
4 oz. milk __<__ 3 pounds milk   17 T. candy __>__ 17 oz. candy

③ Blocks from School

Amos	///// /////	each
Andy	///// ///// ///// /	
Tom	///// ///// ///// /////	👣
Jerry	///// /	equals 2

How many blocks did each boy live from school?
Amos __10__   Andy __16__   Tom __20__   Jerry __8__
Who lived the closest? __Jerry__ Jerry lived how much closer than Tom? __12 blocks__ Amos lived how much closer than Andy? __6 blocks__

119

---

④ **Measure the lines to the nearest inch.**

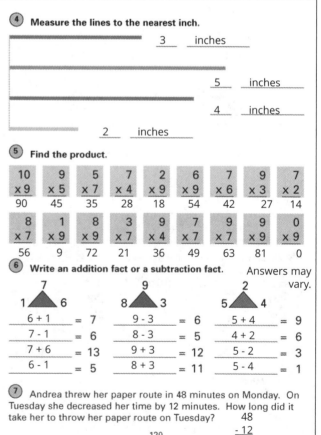

3 inches

5 inches

4 inches

2 inches

⑤ **Find the product.**

10	9	5	7	2	6	7	9	7
x 9	x 5	x 7	x 4	x 9	x 9	x 6	x 3	x 2
90	45	35	28	18	54	42	27	14

8	1	8	3	9	7	9	9	0
x 7	x 9	x 9	x 7	x 4	x 7	x 7	x 9	x 9
56	9	72	21	36	49	63	81	0

⑥ **Write an addition fact or a subtraction fact.** Answers may vary.

7: 1△6
6 + 1 = 7
7 - 1 = 6
7 + 6 = 13
6 - 1 = 5

9: 8△3
9 - 3 = 6
8 - 3 = 5
9 + 3 = 12
8 + 3 = 11

2: 5△4
5 + 4 = 9
4 + 2 = 6
5 - 2 = 3
5 - 4 = 1

⑦ Andrea threw her paper route in 48 minutes on Monday. On Tuesday she decreased her time by 12 minutes. How long did it take her to throw her paper route on Tuesday?

48
- 12
36 minutes

120

428

① **Write the numbers.**

1 hour = __60__ minutes	1 year = __52__ weeks
1 day = __24__ hours	1 minute = __60__ seconds
1 year = __365__ days	1 week = __7__ days
½ hour = __30__ minutes	1 year = __12__ months

② **Write the numbers.**

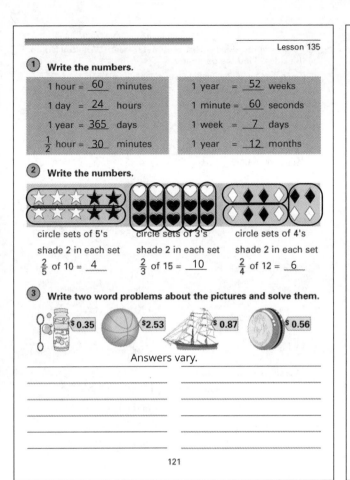

circle sets of 5's
shade 2 in each set
$\frac{2}{5}$ of 10 = __4__

circle sets of 3's
shade 2 in each set
$\frac{2}{3}$ of 15 = __10__

circle sets of 4's
shade 2 in each set
$\frac{2}{4}$ of 12 = __6__

③ **Write two word problems about the pictures and solve them.**

$ 0.35 $2.53 $ 0.87 $ 0.56

Answers vary.

121

---

④ **Find the perimeter.**

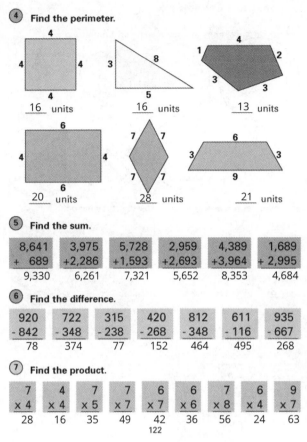

__16__ units   __16__ units   __13__ units

__20__ units   __28__ units   __21__ units

⑤ **Find the sum.**

8,641	3,975	5,728	2,959	4,389	1,689
+ 689	+2,286	+1,593	+2,693	+3,964	+ 2,995
9,330	6,261	7,321	5,652	8,353	4,684

⑥ **Find the difference.**

920	722	315	420	812	611	935
- 842	- 348	- 238	- 268	- 348	- 116	- 667
78	374	77	152	464	495	268

⑦ **Find the product.**

7	4	7	7	6	6	7	6	9
x 4	x 4	x 5	x 7	x 7	x 6	x 8	x 4	x 7
28	16	35	49	42	36	56	24	63

122

---

① **Write the numbers.**

three 8's = __8__ +__8__ +__8__ = 3 × 8 = __24__
four 8's = __8__ +__8__ +__8__ +__8__ = 4 × 8 = __32__
two 8's = __8__ +__8__ = 2 × 8 = __16__
eight 8's = __8__ +__8__ +__8__ +__8__ +__8__ + __8__ + __8__ + __8__ = 8× 8 = __64__
five 8's = __8__ +__8__ +__8__ +__8__ + __8__ = 5 × 8 = __40__
nine 8's = __8__ +__8__ +__8__ +__8__ +__8__ + __8__ + __8__ + __8__ + __8__= 9× 8= __72__
six 8's = __8__ +__8__ +__8__ +__8__ +__8__ + __8__ = 6 × 8 = __48__
seven 8's = __8__ +__8__ +__8__ +__8__ +__8__ + __8__ + __8__ = 7 × 8= __56__

② **Write the numbers.**

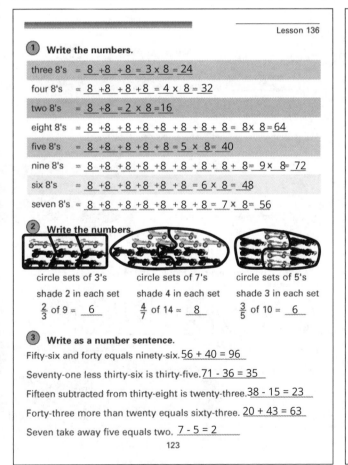

circle sets of 3's
shade 2 in each set
$\frac{2}{3}$ of 9 = __6__

circle sets of 7's
shade 4 in each set
$\frac{4}{7}$ of 14 = __8__

circle sets of 5's
shade 3 in each set
$\frac{3}{5}$ of 10 = __6__

③ **Write as a number sentence.**

Fifty-six and forty equals ninety-six. __56 + 40 = 96__

Seventy-one less thirty-six is thirty-five. __71 - 36 = 35__

Fifteen subtracted from thirty-eight is twenty-three. __38 - 15 = 23__

Forty-three more than twenty equals sixty-three. __20 + 43 = 63__

Seven take away five equals two. __7 - 5 = 2__

123

---

④ **Find the difference.**

512	713	840	734	646	450	965
- 346	- 594	- 475	- 285	- 387	- 379	- 396
166	119	365	449	259	71	569

⑤ **Find the perimeter.**

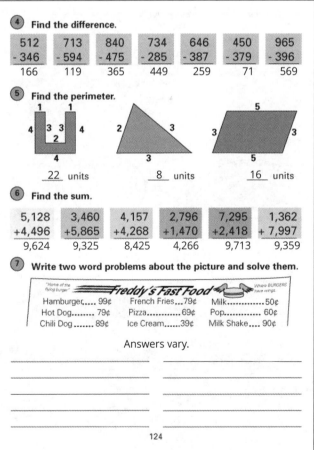

__22__ units   __8__ units   __16__ units

⑥ **Find the sum.**

5,128	3,460	4,157	2,796	7,295	1,362
+4,496	+5,865	+4,268	+1,470	+2,418	+ 7,997
9,624	9,325	8,425	4,266	9,713	9,359

⑦ **Write two word problems about the picture and solve them.**

"Home of the flying burger" **Freddy's Fast Food** Where BURGERS have wings

Hamburger..... 99¢   French Fries...79¢   Milk..............50¢
Hot Dog......... 79¢   Pizza..............69¢   Pop..............60¢
Chili Dog .... 89¢   Ice Cream......39¢   Milk Shake.... 90¢

Answers vary.

124

429

1 Circle the shapes that have a line of symmetry drawn.

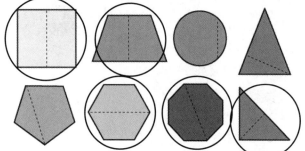

2 Number the events in the order that they happen.

_2_ I chose a book at the library.
_1_ I went to the library.
_3_ I read my library book.

_3_ I wore my new shoes to school.
_2_ I bought a new pair of shoes.
_1_ I went shopping.

3 Write <, >, or =.

7 x 5 _<_ 42	8 x 7 _>_ 49	7 x 7 _<_ 56
7 x 3 _>_ 14	9 x 7 _>_ 56	7 x 6 _<_ 49
4 x 7 _=_ 28	2 x 7 _=_ 14	7 x 1 _=_ 7

125

---

4 Measure the sides with a centimeter ruler. Write the length by the sides. Find the perimeter.

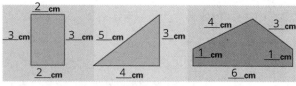

_2_ cm   _3_ cm   _3_ cm   _2_ cm

_5_ cm   _3_ cm   _4_ cm

_4_ cm   _3_ cm   _1_ cm   _1_ cm   _6_ cm

_10_ centimeters   _12_ centimeters   _15_ centimeters

5 Find the difference and check.

918	350	931	820	834	542	750
- 539	- 191	- 248	- 654	- 276	- 179	- 487
379	159	683	166	558	363	263

6 Write the numbers.

1 week = _7_ days
1 year = _365_ days
1 hour = _60_ minutes
1 minute = _60_ seconds

1 year = _52_ weeks
1 day = _24_ hours
1 year = _12_ months
½ hour = _30_ minutes

7 Write as a number sentence.

Forty-two plus sixteen equals fifty-eight. _42 + 16 = 58_

Fifty-six decreased by twenty-three is thirty-three. _56 - 23 = 33_

Eighty-four minus seventy-two is twelve. _84 - 72 = 12_

Thirty-five plus twenty-one is fifty-six. _35 + 21 = 56_

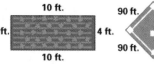

126

---

1 Write the ratio.

3 cars to 8 trucks	_3 :8_
3 cats and 2 dogs to 7 hamsters	_5 :7_
5 fingers to 5 toes	_5 :5_
2 legs to 10 toes and 10 fingers	_2 :20_
2 apples and 3 oranges to 4 pears and 5 peaches	_5 :9_

2 Circle the shapes that have a line of symmetry drawn.

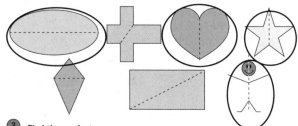

3 Find the product.

9	3	7	3	6	5	6	4	10
x 7	x 8	x 3	x 9	x 8	x 7	x 4	x 2	x 7
63	24	21	27	48	35	24	8	70

5	4	5	4	3	0	6	3	8
x 9	x 4	x 8	x 7	x 4	x 8	x 9	x 6	x 8
45	16	40	28	12	0	54	18	64

2	6	6	7	9	5	7	10	9
x 7	x 6	x 5	x 8	x 9	x 4	x 7	x 8	x 4
14	36	30	56	81	20	49	80	36

127

---

4 Find the perimeter.

10 ft.   90 ft.   90 ft.   10 in.
4 ft.   4 ft.   10 in.   10 in.
90 ft.   90 ft.
10 ft.   10 in.

_28_ feet   _360_ feet   _40_ inches

5 Number the events in the order that they happen.

_1_ Gerald went to Grandma's house in the afternoon.
_3_ Gerald slept all night at Grandma's house.
_2_ Gerald ate supper with Grandpa.

_2_ We ate on the ground.
_3_ We left some crumbs for the squirrels.
_1_ We went on a picnic.

6 Write the fractional part that is shaded. Write <, >, or = between each set of fractions.

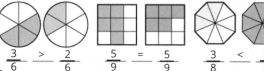

$\frac{3}{6}$ > $\frac{2}{6}$ $\frac{5}{9}$ = $\frac{5}{9}$ $\frac{3}{8}$ < $\frac{6}{8}$

7 Find the difference and check.

731	820	843	725	916	664	975
- 252	- 748	- 359	- 586	- 159	- 378	- 897
479	72	484	139	757	286	78

128

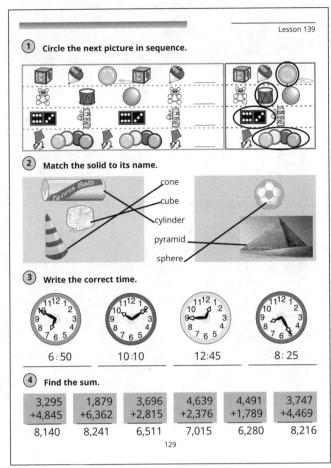

1 Circle the next picture in sequence.

2 Match the solid to its name.

cone
cube
cylinder
pyramid
sphere

3 Write the correct time.

6:50   10:10   12:45   8:25

4 Find the sum.

3,295	1,879	3,696	4,639	4,491	3,747
+4,845	+6,362	+2,815	+2,376	+1,789	+4,469
8,140	8,241	6,511	7,015	6,280	8,216

129

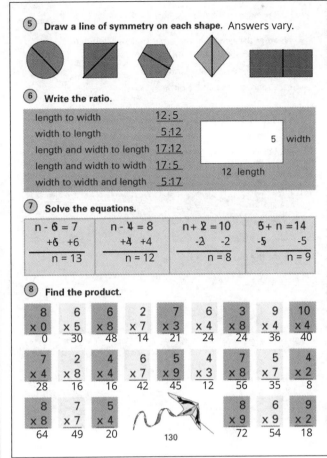

5 Draw a line of symmetry on each shape. Answers vary.

6 Write the ratio.

length to width	12:5
width to length	5:12
length and width to length	17:12
length and width to width	17:5
width to width and length	5:17

5 width
12 length

7 Solve the equations.

n - 6 = 7	n - 4 = 8	n + 2 = 10	5 + n = 14
+6 +6	+4 +4	-2 -2	-5 -5
n = 13	n = 12	n = 8	n = 9

8 Find the product.

8	6	6	2	7	6	3	9	10
×0	×5	×8	×7	×3	×4	×8	×4	×4
0	30	48	14	21	24	24	36	40

7	2	4	6	5	4	7	5	4
×4	×8	×4	×7	×9	×3	×8	×7	×2
28	16	16	42	45	12	56	35	8

8	7	5		8	6	9
×8	×7	×4		×9	×9	×2
64	49	20		72	54	18

130

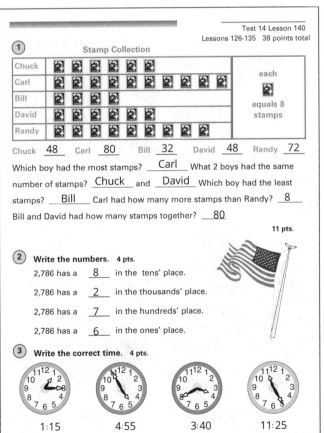

1 Stamp Collection

Chuck	
Carl	
Bill	
David	
Randy	

each ▣ equals 8 stamps

Chuck __48__ Carl __80__ Bill __32__ David __48__ Randy __72__

Which boy had the most stamps? ___Carl___ What 2 boys had the same number of stamps? __Chuck__ and __David__ Which boy had the least stamps? __Bill__ Carl had how many more stamps than Randy? __8__

Bill and David had how many stamps together? __80__

11 pts.

2 Write the numbers. 4 pts.

2,786 has a __8__ in the tens' place.

2,786 has a __2__ in the thousands' place.

2,786 has a __7__ in the hundreds' place.

2,786 has a __6__ in the ones' place.

3 Write the correct time. 4 pts.

1:15   4:55   3:40   11:25

131

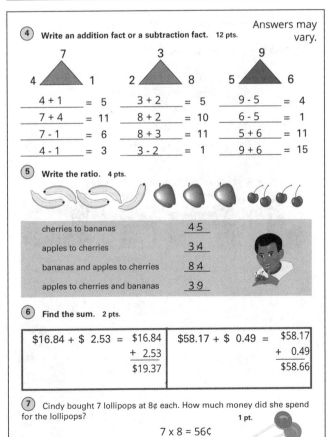

Answers may vary.

4 Write an addition fact or a subtraction fact. 12 pts.

7
4 1

4 + 1	= 5
7 + 4	= 11
7 - 1	= 6
4 - 1	= 3

3
2 8

3 + 2	= 5
8 + 2	= 10
8 + 3	= 11
3 - 2	= 1

9
5 6

9 - 5	= 4
6 - 5	= 1
5 + 6	= 11
9 + 6	= 15

5 Write the ratio. 4 pts.

cherries to bananas	4 5
apples to cherries	3 4
bananas and apples to cherries	8 4
apples to cherries and bananas	3 9

6 Find the sum. 2 pts.

| $16.84 + $ 2.53 = | $16.84 + 2.53 = $19.37 | $58.17 + $ 0.49 = | $58.17 + 0.49 = $58.66 |

7 Cindy bought 7 lollipops at 8¢ each. How much money did she spend for the lollipops? 1 pt.

7 × 8 = 56¢

132

431

1 **Number the events in the order that they happen.**

_1_ John bought Jack a birthday gift.

_3_ John gave Jack his birthday gift.

_2_ John went to Jack's birthday party.

_2_ Susie pulled weeds from around the young tomato plants.

_1_ Susie helped Mother plant tomatoes.

_3_ Susie picked tomatoes from the plants.

2 **Solve the equations.**

$n + 3 = 10$	$n - 8 = 7$	$5 + n = 14$	$n - 1 = 5$
$-3 \quad -3$	$+8 \quad +8$	$-5 \quad \quad -5$	$+1 \quad +1$
$n = 7$	$n = 15$	$n = 9$	$n = 6$

3 **Circle the next picture in sequence.**

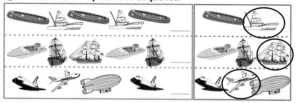

4 **Find the sum.**

7,495	1,966	3,479	4,287	6,846	2,577
+1,557	+5,358	+3,632	+3,893	+2,294	+6,954
9,052	7,324	7,111	8,180	9,140	9,531

133

---

5 **Find the difference and check.**

624	930	815	562	713	480	371
- 479	- 566	- 449	- 286	- 468	- 195	- 289
145	364	366	276	245	285	82

6 **Draw a line of symmetry on each object.**

7 **Write the name of each solid.**

cone   cube   cylinder   pyramid   sphere

8 **Find the product.**

7	3	2	3	8	4	3	3	10
x 8	x 1	x 8	x 3	x 5	x 3	x 2	x 8	x 3
56	3	16	9	40	12	6	24	30

5	8	8	3	8	10	6	8	3
x 3	x 4	x 8	x 7	x 0	x 8	x 3	x 1	x 9
15	32	64	21	0	80	18	8	27

134

---

1 **Find the difference and check.**

600	100	900	400	600	500	300
- 169	- 46	- 518	- 236	- 425	- 317	- 136
431	54	382	164	175	183	164

800	700	500	400	800	200	700
- 642	- 351	- 453	- 277	- 234	- 182	- 196
158	349	47	123	566	18	504

2 **Draw a shape equal to the area.**   Answers vary.

4 square centimeters	7 square centimeters	5 square centimeters	10 square centimeters

3 **Write <, >, or =.**

1 cup = 8 ounces   1 quart = 2 pints   1 gallon = 4 quarts

1 pint = 2 cups   1 quart = 4 cups

1 cup _<_ 1 pint	1 quart _>_ 1 pint	1 gallon _>_ 1 pint
1 ounce _<_ 1 cup	1 quart _<_ 1 gallon	1 pint _=_ 2 cups

135

---

4 **Animal Heights**

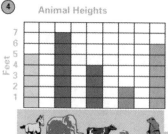

Which animal is about 4 feet tall? __cow__ Which animal is the shortest? ___dog___

How tall is the bear? __6 feet__

Which animal is the tallest? __elephant__

How tall is the horse? __5 feet__

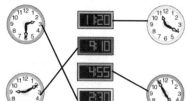

5 **Match the clock.**

1 year = __12__ months

1 hour = __60__ minutes

1 week = __7__ days

1 day = __24__ hours

1 year = __365__ days

6 **Solve the equations.**

$n + 7 = 15$	$4 + n = 12$	$n - 6 = 6$	$n - 3 = 6$
$-7 \quad -7$	$-4 \quad \quad -4$	$+6 \quad +6$	$+3 \quad +3$
$n = 8$	$n = 8$	$n = 12$	$n = 9$

7 Ann had 4 boxes of pencils with 8 pencils in each box. How many pencils did Ann have altogether?

$4 \times 8 = 32$ pencils   136

432

① Write the temperature.

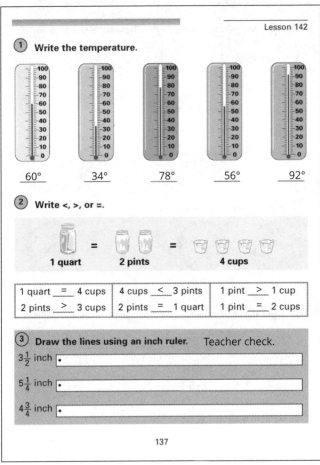

60° 34° 78° 56° 92°

② Write <, >, or =.

1 quart = 2 pints = 4 cups

1 quart $=$ 4 cups	4 cups $<$ 3 pints	1 pint $>$ 1 cup
2 pints $>$ 3 cups	2 pints $=$ 1 quart	1 pint $=$ 2 cups

③ Draw the lines using an inch ruler.   Teacher check.

$3\frac{1}{2}$ inch •

$5\frac{1}{4}$ inch •

$4\frac{3}{4}$ inch •

137

---

④

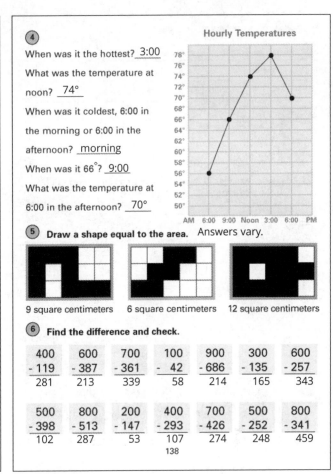

Hourly Temperatures

When was it the hottest? 3:00

What was the temperature at noon? 74°

When was it coldest, 6:00 in the morning or 6:00 in the afternoon? morning

When was it 66°? 9:00

What was the temperature at 6:00 in the afternoon? 70°

⑤ Draw a shape equal to the area.   Answers vary.

9 square centimeters   6 square centimeters   12 square centimeters

⑥ Find the difference and check.

400	600	700	100	900	300	600
- 119	- 387	- 361	- 42	- 686	- 135	- 257
281	213	339	58	214	165	343

500	800	200	400	700	500	800
- 398	- 513	- 147	- 293	- 426	- 252	- 341
102	287	53	107	274	248	459

138

---

① Fill in the blanks.

Number Correct on Speed Drill

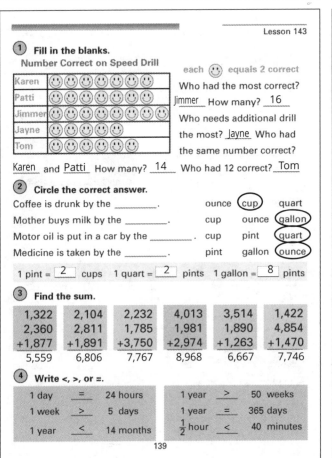

each ☺ equals 2 correct

Who had the most correct? Jimmer How many? 16

Who needs additional drill the most? Jayne Who had the same number correct?

Karen and Patti How many? 14 Who had 12 correct? Tom

② Circle the correct answer.

Coffee is drunk by the _____.   ounce (cup) quart

Mother buys milk by the _____.   cup   ounce (gallon)

Motor oil is put in a car by the _____.   cup   pint   (quart)

Medicine is taken by the _____.   pint   gallon   (ounce)

1 pint = 2 cups   1 quart = 2 pints   1 gallon = 8 pints

③ Find the sum.

1,322	2,104	2,232	4,013	3,514	1,422
2,360	2,811	1,785	1,981	1,890	4,854
+1,877	+1,891	+3,750	+2,974	+1,263	+1,470
5,559	6,806	7,767	8,968	6,667	7,746

④ Write <, >, or =.

1 day	$=$	24 hours	1 year	$>$	50 weeks
1 week	$>$	5 days	1 year	$=$	365 days
1 year	$<$	14 months	$\frac{1}{2}$ hour	$<$	40 minutes

139

---

⑤ Draw the lines using an inch ruler.   Teacher check.

$4\frac{1}{2}$ inch •

$2\frac{1}{4}$ inch •

$3\frac{3}{4}$ inch •

⑥ Find the product.

8	4	8	6	4	8	10	5	4
× 8	× 2	× 4	× 9	× 7	× 2	× 8	× 8	× 4
64	8	32	54	28	16	80	40	16

4	1	6	6	5	9	9	8	4
× 3	× 8	× 4	× 8	× 4	× 8	× 7	× 3	× 9
12	8	24	48	20	72	63	24	36

⑦ Write the correct temperature.

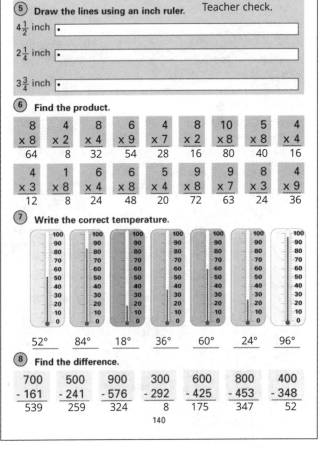

52° 84° 18° 36° 60° 24° 96°

⑧ Find the difference.

700	500	900	300	600	800	400
- 161	- 241	- 576	- 292	- 425	- 453	- 348
539	259	324	8	175	347	52

140

433

1 Write the Roman numerals.

I	IV	V	IX	X	XL	L	XC	C	CD	D	CM	M
1	4	5	9	10	40	50	90	100	400	500	900	1,000

183	CLXXXIII		392	CCCXCII
457	CDLVII		946	CMXLVI
824	DCCCXXIV		709	DCCIX

2 Measure the sides of each shape with a centimeter ruler. Find the perimeter.

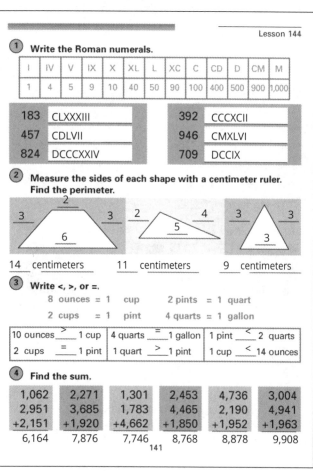

14 centimeters   11 centimeters   9 centimeters

3 Write <, >, or =.

8 ounces = 1 cup   2 pints = 1 quart
2 cups = 1 pint   4 quarts = 1 gallon

10 ounces > 1 cup	4 quarts = 1 gallon	1 pint < 2 quarts
2 cups = 1 pint	1 quart > 1 pint	1 cup < 14 ounces

4 Find the sum.

1,062	2,271	1,301	2,453	4,736	3,004
2,951	3,685	1,783	4,465	2,190	4,941
+2,151	+1,920	+4,662	+1,850	+1,952	+1,963
6,164	7,876	7,746	8,768	8,878	9,908

141

5 Put a dot (●) at the intersection. Connect the dots in order.

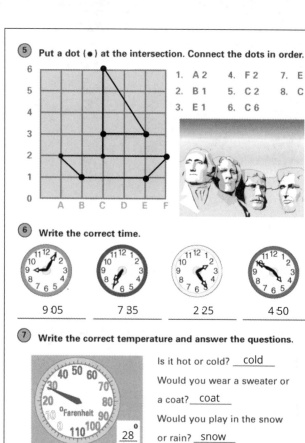

1. A 2	4. F 2	7. E 3
2. B 1	5. C 2	8. C 3
3. E 1	6. C 6	

6 Write the correct time.

9 05   7 35   2 25   4 50

7 Write the correct temperature and answer the questions.

Is it hot or cold? __cold__

Would you wear a sweater or a coat? __coat__

Would you play in the snow or rain? __snow__

28

142

---

1 Write the numbers.

Is 185 closer to 100 or 200?	200	Is 138 closer to 100 or 200?	100
Is 160 closer to 100 or 200?	200	Is 114 closer to 100 or 200?	100
Is 176 closer to 100 or 200?	200	Is 127 closer to 100 or 200?	100

2 Find the difference.

$6.00	$4.00	$8.00	$7.00	$3.00	$9.00	$5.00
- 4.18	- 2.45	- 4.24	- 2.37	- 1.26	- 5.19	- 4.03
$1.82	$1.55	$3.76	$4.63	$1.74	$3.81	$0.97

3 Write the Arabic numbers.

CLVI	=	156		DCCXCII	=	792
DCXLIII	=	643		CCCXVIII	=	318
DCCCXXV	=	825		DIX	=	509
CDXXXVII	=	437		CMLXI	=	961

4 Mark the thermometer at the correct temperature. Color the liquid red.

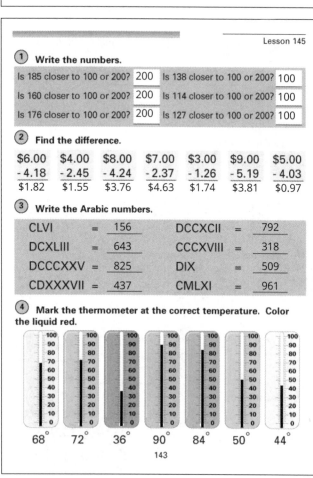

68°   72°   36°   90°   84°   50°   44°

143

5 Put a dot (●) at the intersection. Connect the dots in order.

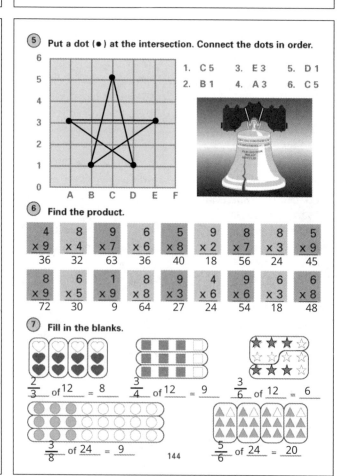

| 1. C 5 | 3. E 3 | 5. D 1 |
| 2. B 1 | 4. A 3 | 6. C 5 |

6 Find the product.

4	8	9	6	5	9	8	8	5
x 9	x 4	x 7	x 6	x 8	x 2	x 7	x 3	x 9
36	32	63	36	40	18	56	24	45

8	6	1	8	9	4	9	6	6
x 9	x 5	x 9	x 8	x 3	x 6	x 6	x 3	x 8
72	30	9	64	27	24	54	18	48

7 Fill in the blanks.

$\frac{2}{3}$ of 12 = 8 $\frac{3}{4}$ of 12 = 9 $\frac{3}{6}$ of 12 = 6

$\frac{3}{8}$ of 24 = 9 $\frac{5}{6}$ of 24 = 20

144

434

1 Find the volume for each set by counting the cubes.

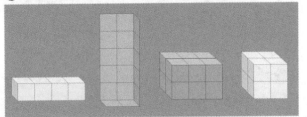

__4__ cubic units __10__ cubic units __12__ cubic units __8__ cubic units

2 Find the difference and check.

$4.02	$6.07	$3.01	$8.03	$2.06	$5.05	$7.04
- 2.65	- 3.78	- 1.34	- 4.26	- 1.58	- 2.49	- 3.17
$1.37	$2.29	$1.67	$3.77	$0.48	$2.56	$3.87

3 Write the numbers.

Is 242 closer to 200 or 300?	200	Is 375 closer to 300 or 400?	400
Is 569 closer to 500 or 600?	600	Is 628 closer to 600 or 700?	600
Is 803 closer to 800 or 900?	800	Is 454 closer to 400 or 500?	500
Is 758 closer to 700 or 800?	800	Is 160 closer to 100 or 200?	200

4 Maria's father drove 27 miles to work. Sam's father drove 36 miles to work. Sam's father drove how many miles more than Maria's father?

36
- 27
9 miles 145

5 Fill in the blanks.

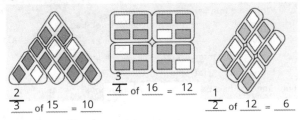

$\frac{2}{3}$ of __15__ = __10__ $\frac{3}{4}$ of __16__ = __12__ $\frac{1}{2}$ of __12__ = __6__

6 Find the sum.

2,161	2,673	1,851	1,451	4,982	3,044
1,781	1,452	4,963	2,784	3,434	1,993
+4,921	+2,341	+2,073	+4,653	+1,173	+2,822
8,863	6,466	8,887	8,888	9,589	7,859

7 Find the product.

0	6	4	9	3	7	1	0	6
x 7	x 8	x 2	x 7	x 8	x 7	x 4	x 8	x 7
0	48	8	63	24	49	4	0	42

2	4	2	8	8	5	4	4	10
x 8	x 4	x 7	x 9	x 8	x 7	x 8	x 3	x 7
16	16	14	72	64	35	32	12	70

5	5	4	1	4	10	0	9	7
x 4	x 8	x 7	x 8	x 6	x 8	x 4	x 4	x 8
20	40	28	8	24	80	0	36	56

146

1 Number the events in the order that they appear.

__3__ The teacher graded the students' math sheets.

__1__ The teacher handed out the math sheets.

__2__ The students completed their math sheets.

2 Write <, >, or =.

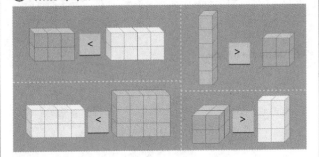

3 Solve the equations.

n - 8 = 5	n - 4 = 9	n + 6 = 13	n + 3 = 11
+8 +8	+4 +4	-6 -6	-3 -3
n = 13	n = 13	n = 7	n = 8

4 Find the difference and check.

$6.03	$2.01	$9.04	$3.06	$5.02	$7.07	$4.05
- 4.88	- 1.19	- 5.27	- 1.68	- 2.35	- 3.59	- 3.46
$1.15	$0.82	$3.77	$1.38	$2.67	$3.48	$0.59

147

5 Fill in the blanks.

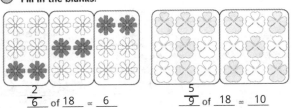

$\frac{2}{6}$ of __18__ = __6__ $\frac{5}{9}$ of __18__ = __10__

6 Find the sum.

1,493	1,181	2,174	3,571	2,404	2,901
3,872	3,782	1,831	1,971	1,863	2,272
+4,304	+1,403	+3,731	+4,322	+4,472	+1,181
9,669	6,366	7,736	9,864	8,739	6,354

7 Find the product.

9	9	4	6	4	4	5	6	6
x 3	x 6	x 3	x 7	x 2	x 9	x 3	x 5	x 4
27	54	12	42	8	36	15	30	24

4	3	6	8	4	3	8	5	3
x 4	x 0	x 6	x 3	x 8	x 3	x 6	x 4	x 2
16	0	36	24	32	9	48	20	6

8 There were 86 birds on the pond. At dusk 95 more birds landed on the pond. How many birds were now on the pond?

86
+ 95
181 birds

148

435

Lesson 148

① Write as a number sentence.

Three hundred eighty plus fifty-one is four hundred

thirty-one.   380 + 51 = 431

Two hundred fifty-three decreased by one hundred thirty-nine

is one hundred fourteen.   253 - 139 = 114

Four hundred nine minus one hundred ten equals two hundred

ninety-nine.   409 - 110 = 299

Five hundred twenty-seven and two hundred forty-two equals

seven hundred sixty-nine.   527 + 242 = 769

② Number the events in the order that they appear.

  2   We played baseball at recess.

  3   The teacher read us a story after recess.

  1   The bell rang for recess.

③ Write two word problems about the pictures and solve them.

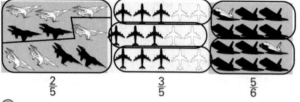

Answers vary.

149

---

④ Write <, >, or =.

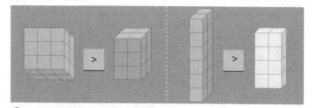

⑤ Solve the equations.

n - 5 = 6	n - 7 = 11	n + 8 = 17	n + 4 = 12
+5 +5	+7 +7	-8 -8	-4 -4
n = 11	n = 18	n = 9	n = 8

⑥ Find the sum.

1,332	4,023	3,311	4,242	2,553	2,541
1,293	2,594	1,794	3,873	4,691	1,694
+2,811	+1,871	+1,671	+1,844	+1,632	+1,532
5,436	8,488	6,776	9,959	8,876	5,767

⑦ Find the product.

7	4	6	7	4	7	2	4	6
x 9	x 7	x 5	x 8	x 1	x 1	x 7	x 4	x 3
63	28	30	56	4	7	14	16	18

7	4	6	7	7	4	4	9	5
x 6	x 3	x 6	x 3	x 7	x 6	x 2	x 6	x 7
42	12	36	21	49	24	8	54	35

150

Lesson 149

① Shade the fractional part of each set.

$\dfrac{2}{5}$ $\dfrac{3}{5}$ $\dfrac{5}{6}$

② Number the events in the order that they happen.

  1   Mother fixes dinner.

  3   I wash the dinner dishes.

  2   The family eats dinner.

③ Write the Roman numerals.

458	CDLVIII	543	DXLIII
627	DCXXVII	789	DCCLXXXIX
962	CMLXII	231	CCXXXI
314	CCCXIV	796	DCCXCVI

④ Write as a number sentence.

Six hundred twenty-two increased by fifty-three is six hundred

seventy-five.   622 + 53 = 675

Eight hundred seventy-one take away one hundred thirty-five is

seven hundred thirty-six.   871 - 135 = 736

Five hundred eighty-four less ninety equals four hundred

ninety-four.   584 - 90 = 494

151

---

⑤ Draw a line of symmetry on each shape.

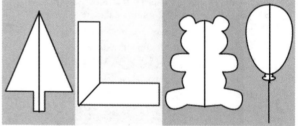

⑥ Write the numbers.

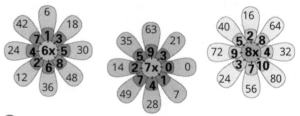

⑦ Find the difference.

901	503	206	704	402	307	605
- 515	- 468	- 139	- 676	- 223	- 159	- 347
386	35	67	28	179	148	258

808	501	606	403	902	305	704
- 349	- 162	- 449	- 217	- 333	- 159	- 428
459	339	157	186	569	146	276

152

436

1 Circle the next picture in sequence.   4 pts.

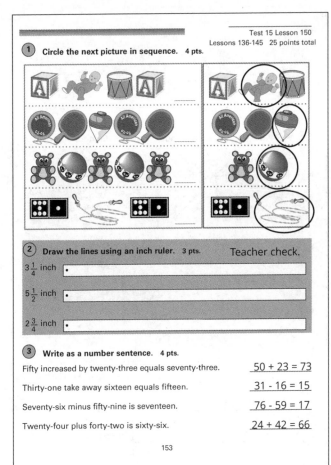

2 Draw the lines using an inch ruler.   3 pts.   Teacher check.

$3\frac{1}{4}$ inch

$5\frac{1}{2}$ inch

$2\frac{3}{4}$ inch

3 Write as a number sentence.   4 pts.

Fifty increased by twenty-three equals seventy-three. $50 + 23 = 73$

Thirty-one take away sixteen equals fifteen. $31 - 16 = 15$

Seventy-six minus fifty-nine is seventeen. $76 - 59 = 17$

Twenty-four plus forty-two is sixty-six. $24 + 42 = 66$

153

---

4 Solve the equations.   4 pts.

$n + 3 = 9$	$n - 8 = 5$	$5 + n = 11$	$n - 4 = 9$
-3 -3	$+8$ $+8$	-5 -5	$+4$ $+4$
$n = 6$	$n = 13$	$n = 6$	$n = 13$

5 Find the perimeter.   6 pts.

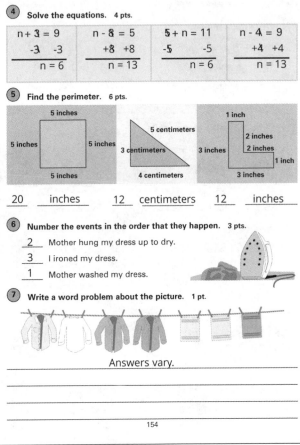

__20__ inches   __12__ centimeters   __12__ inches

6 Number the events in the order that they happen.   3 pts.

_2_ Mother hung my dress up to dry.

_3_ I ironed my dress.

_1_ Mother washed my dress.

7 Write a word problem about the picture.   1 pt.

Answers vary.

154

---

1 Write the point of intersection.   Connect the dots in order.

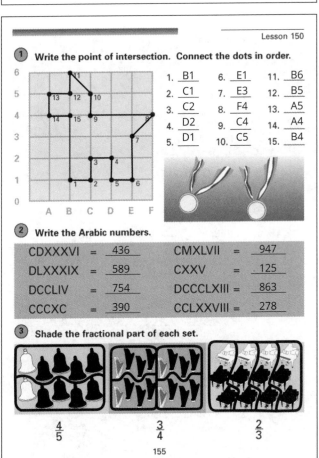

1. __B1__   6. __E1__   11. __B6__
2. __C1__   7. __E3__   12. __B5__
3. __C2__   8. __F4__   13. __A5__
4. __D2__   9. __C4__   14. __A4__
5. __D1__   10. __C5__   15. __B4__

2 Write the Arabic numbers.

CDXXXVI	=	436	CMXLVII	=	947
DLXXXIX	=	589	CXXV	=	125
DCCLIV	=	754	DCCCLXIII	=	863
CCCXC	=	390	CCLXXVIII	=	278

3 Shade the fractional part of each set.

$\frac{4}{5}$ $\frac{3}{4}$ $\frac{2}{3}$

155

---

4 Find the difference.

506	803	301	902	403	704	601
- 158	- 275	- 145	- 367	- 126	- 438	- 518
348	528	156	535	277	266	83

5 Draw a line of symmetry on each object.

6 Write the ratio.

apples to bananas   __3__ : __6__   oranges to apples   __4__ : __3__

oranges to cherries   __4__ : __5__   cherries to apples   __5__ : __3__

bananas to oranges   __6__ : __4__   bananas to cherries   __6__ : __5__

7 Find the sum.

1,191	2,081	1,924	1,740	1,953	4,334
2,791	1,733	2,261	4,781	1,561	1,670
+4,501	+2,962	+2,382	+3,158	+4,242	+3,645
8,483	6,776	6,567	9,679	7,756	9,649

8 Find the product.

4	9	5	4	3	6	9	7	3
x 3	x 7	x 3	x 8	x 3	x 7	x 3	x 0	x 2
12	63	15	32	9	42	27	0	6

8	8	7	5	3	8	7	8	8
x 7	x 8	x 1	x 8	x 6	x 3	x 3	x 6	x 2
56	64	7	40	18	24	21	48	16

156

1 Write the numbers.

1 day	= 24 hours	1 hour	= 60 minutes
1 week	= 7 days	1 minute	= 60 seconds
1 year	= 52 weeks	1 year	= 12 months
1 pound	= 16 ounces	1 ton	= 2,000 pounds

2 Write the name of each solid.

cube   pyramid   sphere   cone   cylinder

3 Find the sum.

1,143	1,613	6,546	1,133	3,437	1,355
2,286	3,748	1,829	1,795	2,656	3,751
+3,925	+4,092	+1,380	+3,429	+1,274	+1,849
7,354	9,453	9,755	6,357	7,367	6,955

4 Find the difference and check.

421	642	727	952	816	525	843
- 247	- 159	- 339	- 485	- 128	- 376	- 597
174	483	388	467	688	149	246

914	721	673		538	331	916
- 266	- 684	- 289		- 169	- 158	- 657
648	37	384	157	369	173	259

5 Write the correct time.

12 35   6 05   5 00   7 20

6 Write the point of intersection. Connect the dots in order.

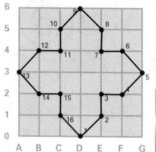

1. D0	6. F4	11. C4
2. E1	7. E4	12. B4
3. E2	8. E5	13. A3
4. F2	9. D6	14. B2
5. G3	10. C5	15. C2
		16. C1

7 Write the ratio.

soccer balls to baseballs 4:5   baseballs to footballs 5:2

basketballs to footballs 4:2   basketballs to soccer balls 4:4

8 Find the product.

X	5	3	6	9	2	8	4	7
9	45	27	54	81	18	72	36	63

X	7	4	8	0	6	3	5	1
4	28	16	32	0	24	12	20	4

---

1 Circle the next shape in sequence.

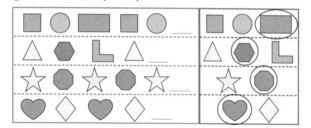

2 Draw both hands on the clock.

6:40   1:25   8:05   2:40

3 Find the product.

7	8	9	1	9	4	9	7	4
x 7	x 4	x 2	x 7	x 8	x 2	x 3	x 3	x 6
49	32	18	7	72	8	27	21	24

9	6	5	3	8	7	4	8	10
x 4	x 7	x 9	x 4	x 3	x 5	x 7	x 8	x 4
36	42	45	12	24	35	28	64	40

5	4	10	2	7	5	6	4	9
x 8	x 4	x 7	x 7	x 8	x 4	x 8	x 0	x 9
40	16	70	14	56	20	48	0	81

4 Write the numbers.

1 pound = 16 ounces	1 ton = 2,000 pounds
1 year = 12 months	½ hour = 30 minutes
1 week = 7 days	1 year = 365 days
1 minute = 60 seconds	1 day = 24 hours
1 cup = 8 ounces	1 pint = 2 cups
1 quart = 2 pints	1 gallon = 4 quarts
1 yard = 36 inches	1 foot = 12 inches

5 Find the sum.

1,803	1,162	2,834	1,184	3,220	2,456
2,487	4,948	1,797	5,669	1,387	1,967
+5,195	+3,832	+4,241	+1,806	+2,939	+2,155
9,485	9,942	8,872	8,659	7,546	6,578

6 Find the difference and check.

410	914	432	925	803	726	531
- 395	- 738	- 86	- 377	- 274	- 149	- 37
15	176	346	548	529	577	494

7 Mother planted 5 rows of tomato plants. There were 8 plants in each row. How many tomato plants did she plant?

5 x 8 = 40 tomato plants

1 Write the correct temperature.

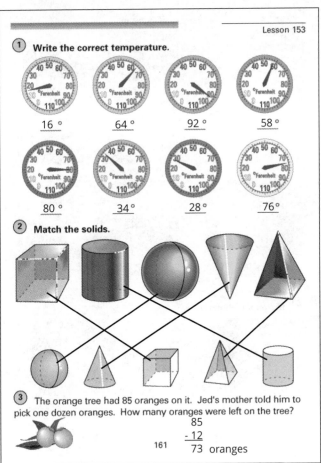

16 °   64 °   92 °   58 °

80 °   34 °   28 °   76°

2 Match the solids.

3 The orange tree had 85 oranges on it. Jed's mother told him to pick one dozen oranges. How many oranges were left on the tree?

85
- 12
73 oranges

161

---

4 Draw both hands on the clocks.   Answers vary.

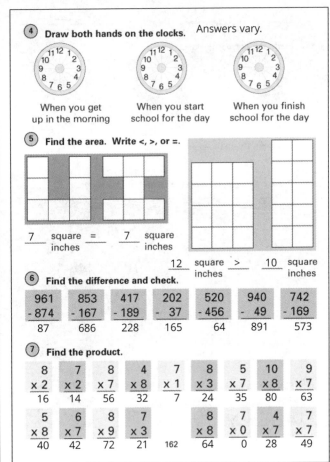

When you get up in the morning

When you start school for the day

When you finish school for the day

5 Find the area. Write <, >, or =.

7 square inches = 7 square inches

12 square inches > 10 square inches

6 Find the difference and check.

961	853	417	202	520	940	742
- 874	- 167	- 189	- 37	- 456	- 49	- 169
87	686	228	165	64	891	573

7 Find the product.

8	7	8	4	7	8	5	10	9
x 2	x 2	x 7	x 8	x 1	x 3	x 7	x 8	x 7
16	14	56	32	7	24	35	80	63

5	6	8	7		8	7	4	7
x 8	x 7	x 9	x 3		x 8	x 0	x 7	x 7
40	42	72	21	162	64	0	28	49

1

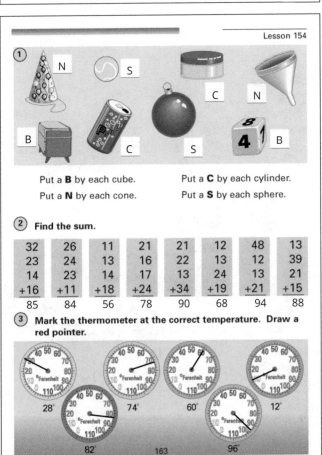

N   S   C   N

B   C   S   B

Put a **B** by each cube.   Put a **C** by each cylinder.
Put a **N** by each cone.   Put a **S** by each sphere.

2 Find the sum.

32	26	11	21	21	12	48	13
23	24	13	16	22	13	12	39
14	23	14	17	13	24	13	21
+16	+11	+18	+24	+34	+19	+21	+15
85	84	56	78	90	68	94	88

3 Mark the thermometer at the correct temperature. Draw a red pointer.

28°   74°   60°   12°

82°   96°

163

---

4 Find the perimeter.

3 cm.   4 cm.   2 cm.

12 cm.   12 cm.

20 cm.

5 Find the difference.

926	751	514	603	830	327	705
- 469	- 486	- 128	- 358	- 542	- 138	- 577
457	265	386	245	288	189	128

6 Find the product.

6	8	9	1	5	10	0	8	9
x 9	x 0	x 5	x 9	x 8	x 9	x 9	x 1	x 3
54	0	45	9	40	90	0	8	27

8	2	8	7	4	8	9	3	9
x 7	x 9	x 2	x 9	x 8	x 9	x 4	x 8	x 9
56	18	16	63	32	72	36	24	81

7 Brenda had 21 red balloons, 14 blue balloons, 33 green balloons, and 27 orange balloons. How many balloons did she have altogether?

21
14
33
+ 27
95 balloons

164

439

1 Write the correct temperature.

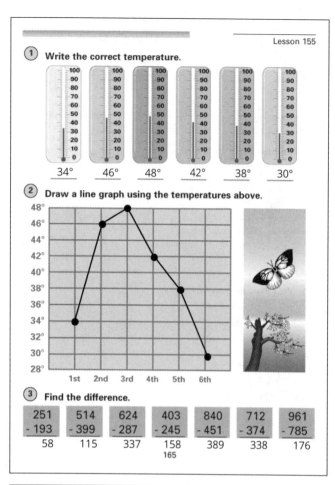

34°   46°   48°   42°   38°   30°

2 Draw a line graph using the temperatures above.

48°
46°
44°
42°
40°
38°
36°
34°
32°
30°
28°
    1st   2nd   3rd   4th   5th   6th

3 Find the difference.

251	514	624	403	840	712	961
- 193	- 399	- 287	- 245	- 451	- 374	- 785
58	115	337	158	389	338	176

165

---

4 Find the volume.

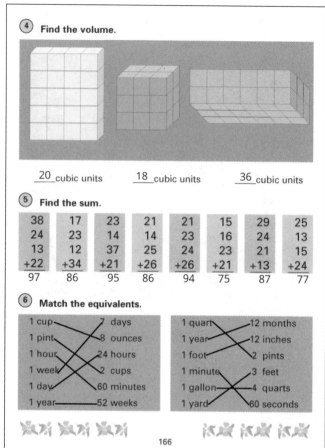

20 cubic units   18 cubic units   36 cubic units

5 Find the sum.

38	17	23	21	21	15	29	25
24	23	14	14	23	16	24	13
13	12	37	25	24	23	21	15
+22	+34	+21	+26	+26	+21	+13	+24
97	86	95	86	94	75	87	77

6 Match the equivalents.

1 cup ———— 7 days
1 pint ———— 8 ounces
1 hour ———— 24 hours
1 week ———— 2 cups
1 day ———— 60 minutes
1 year ———— 52 weeks

1 quart ———— 12 months
1 year ———— 12 inches
1 foot ———— 2 pints
1 minute ———— 3 feet
1 gallon ———— 4 quarts
1 yard ———— 60 seconds

166

---

1 Write the letter on the blank.

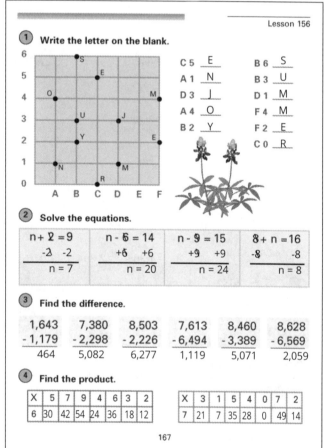

6 | S
5 | E
4 | O   M
3 | U   J
2 | Y   E
1 | N   M
0 | R
   A B C D E F

C 5 E   B 6 S
A 1 N   B 3 U
D 3 J   D 1 M
A 4 O   F 4 M
B 2 Y   F 2 E
             C 0 R

2 Solve the equations.

n + 2 = 9	n - 6 = 14	n - 9 = 15	8 + n = 16
-2 -2	+6 +6	+9 +9	-8 -8
n = 7	n = 20	n = 24	n = 8

3 Find the difference.

1,643	7,380	8,503	7,613	8,460	8,628
- 1,179	- 2,298	- 2,226	- 6,494	- 3,389	- 6,569
464	5,082	6,277	1,119	5,071	2,059

4 Find the product.

X	5	7	9	4	6	3	2
6	30	42	54	24	36	18	12

X	3	1	5	4	0	7	2
7	21	7	35	28	0	49	14

167

X	3	7	5	8	4	6
8	24	56	40	64	32	48

X	4	3	9	5	8	7
9	36	27	81	45	72	63

5 Find the sum.

33	28	23	11	13	24	16	17
16	33	29	14	24	23	21	32
24	24	24	23	12	31	25	15
+22	+12	+22	+27	+17	+19	+21	+23
95	97	98	75	66	97	83	87

6 Draw a bar graph.

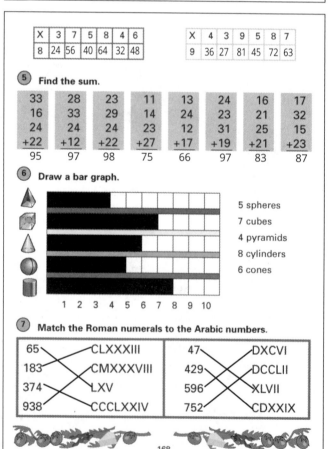

5 spheres
7 cubes
4 pyramids
8 cylinders
6 cones

1 2 3 4 5 6 7 8 9 10

7 Match the Roman numerals to the Arabic numbers.

65 ———— CLXXXIII
183 ———— CMXXXVIII
374 ———— LXV
938 ———— CCCLXXIV

47 ———— DXCVI
429 ———— DCCLII
596 ———— XLVII
752 ———— CDXXIX

168

440

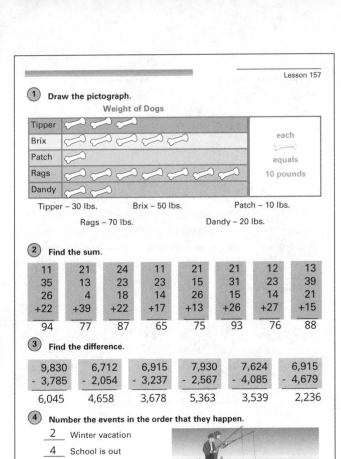

Lesson 157

1 Draw the pictograph.

Weight of Dogs

Tipper	🦴 🦴 🦴	
Brix	🦴 🦴 🦴 🦴 🦴	each
Patch	🦴	🦴
Rags	🦴 🦴 🦴 🦴 🦴 🦴 🦴	equals
Dandy	🦴 🦴	10 pounds

Tipper – 30 lbs.   Brix – 50 lbs.   Patch – 10 lbs.

Rags – 70 lbs.   Dandy – 20 lbs.

2 Find the sum.

11	21	24	11	21	21	12	13
35	13	23	23	15	31	23	39
26	4	18	14	26	15	14	21
+22	+39	+22	+17	+13	+26	+27	+15
94	77	87	65	75	93	76	88

3 Find the difference.

9,830	6,712	6,915	7,930	7,624	6,915
- 3,785	- 2,054	- 3,237	- 2,567	- 4,085	- 4,679
6,045	4,658	3,678	5,363	3,539	2,236

4 Number the events in the order that they happen.

2   Winter vacation

4   School is out

3   Spring break

1   Thanksgiving

169

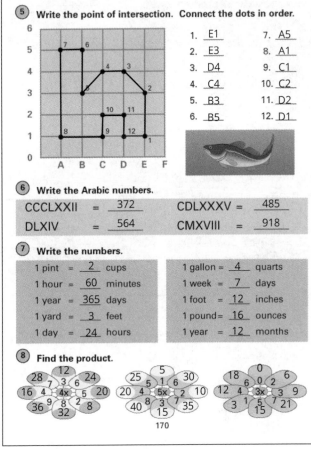

5 Write the point of intersection. Connect the dots in order.

1. E1   7. A5
2. E3   8. A1
3. D4   9. C1
4. C4   10. C2
5. B3   11. D2
6. B5   12. D1

6 Write the Arabic numbers.

CCCLXXII = 372   CDLXXXV = 485

DLXIV = 564   CMXVIII = 918

7 Write the numbers.

1 pint	=	2	cups		1 gallon	=	4	quarts
1 hour	=	60	minutes		1 week	=	7	days
1 year	=	365	days		1 foot	=	12	inches
1 yard	=	3	feet		1 pound	=	16	ounces
1 day	=	24	hours		1 year	=	12	months

8 Find the product.

[4x wheel: 28, 12, 3, 7, 6, 24, 16, 4, 5, 20, 36, 9, 8, 8, 32]

[5x wheel: 25, 5, 1, 6, 30, 20, 4, 2, 10, 40, 8, 3, 7, 35, 15]

[3x wheel: 18, 0, 0, 6, 2, 6, 12, 4, 3, 9, 3, 1, 7, 21, 15]

170

Lesson 158

1 Write the numbers.

$4 + 4 = 8$	$6 + 6 = 12$	$2 + 2 = 4$
$\frac{1}{2}$ of 8 = 4	$\frac{1}{2}$ of 12 = 6	$\frac{1}{2}$ of 4 = 2

$5 + 5 = 10$	$7 + 7 = 14$	$8 + 8 = 16$
$\frac{1}{2}$ of 10 = 5	$\frac{1}{2}$ of 14 = 7	$\frac{1}{2}$ of 16 = 8

$3 + 3 = 6$	$1 + 1 = 2$	$9 + 9 = 18$
$\frac{1}{2}$ of 6 = 3	$\frac{1}{2}$ of 2 = 1	$\frac{1}{2}$ of 18 = 9

2 Write the numbers.

$4 \times 6 = 24$ $9 \times 6 = 54$ $7 \times 9 = 63$ $9 \times 4 = 36$

$8 \times 9 = 72$ $4 \times 7 = 28$ $6 \times 4 = 24$ $3 \times 6 = 18$

$2 \times 7 = 14$ $5 \times 9 = 45$ $3 \times 2 = 6$ $5 \times 4 = 20$

$6 \times 3 = 18$ $8 \times 2 = 16$ $7 \times 5 = 35$ $2 \times 5 = 10$

$4 \times 9 = 36$ $6 \times 8 = 48$ $3 \times 8 = 24$ $2 \times 9 = 18$

$2 \times 4 = 8$ $5 \times 7 = 35$ $7 \times 4 = 28$ $8 \times 3 = 24$

$3 \times 3 = 9$ $7 \times 6 = 42$ $6 \times 2 = 12$ $9 \times 5 = 45$

3 Find the sum.

41	12	63	51	42	11	42	42
32	41	53	14	81	73	32	62
23	51	11	11	13	42	21	13
+72	+61	+31	+62	+31	+32	+92	+72
168	165	158	138	167	158	187	189

171

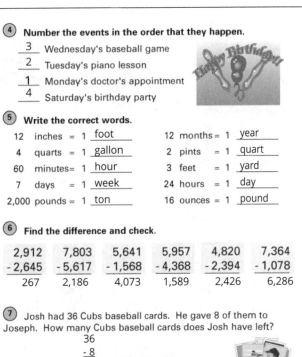

4 Number the events in the order that they happen.

3   Wednesday's baseball game

2   Tuesday's piano lesson

1   Monday's doctor's appointment

4   Saturday's birthday party

5 Write the correct words.

12 inches = 1 foot   12 months = 1 year

4 quarts = 1 gallon   2 pints = 1 quart

60 minutes = 1 hour   3 feet = 1 yard

7 days = 1 week   24 hours = 1 day

2,000 pounds = 1 ton   16 ounces = 1 pound

6 Find the difference and check.

2,912	7,803	5,641	5,957	4,820	7,364
- 2,645	- 5,617	- 1,568	- 4,368	- 2,394	- 1,078
267	2,186	4,073	1,589	2,426	6,286

7 Josh had 36 Cubs baseball cards. He gave 8 of them to Joseph. How many Cubs baseball cards does Josh have left?

36
- 8
28 Cubs baseball cards

Cindy had 7 girls at her birthday party. She gave each of them 3 suckers. How many suckers did Cindy give to the girls?

$7 \times 3 = 21$ suckers

172

441

1

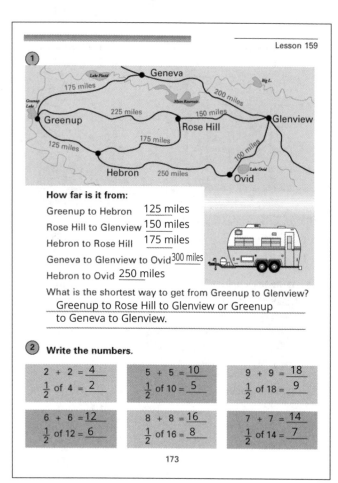

How far is it from:

Greenup to Hebron ___125 miles___

Rose Hill to Glenview ___150 miles___

Hebron to Rose Hill ___175 miles___

Geneva to Glenview to Ovid ___300 miles___

Hebron to Ovid ___250 miles___

What is the shortest way to get from Greenup to Glenview?
___Greenup to Rose Hill to Glenview or Greenup___
___to Geneva to Glenview.___

2 Write the numbers.

2 + 2 = **4**	5 + 5 = **10**	9 + 9 = **18**
$\frac{1}{2}$ of 4 = **2**	$\frac{1}{2}$ of 10 = **5**	$\frac{1}{2}$ of 18 = **9**
6 + 6 = **12**	8 + 8 = **16**	7 + 7 = **14**
$\frac{1}{2}$ of 12 = **6**	$\frac{1}{2}$ of 16 = **8**	$\frac{1}{2}$ of 14 = **7**

173

---

3 Write the numbers.

4 x __5__ = 20   8 x __5__ = 40   4 x __2__ = 8   9 x __2__ = 18

7 x __3__ = 21   6 x __6__ = 36   5 x __8__ = 40   4 x __4__ = 16

2 x __6__ = 12   3 x __4__ = 12   6 x __9__ = 54   3 x __9__ = 27

8 x __7__ = 56   6 x __5__ = 30   9 x __3__ = 27   3 x __7__ = 21

4

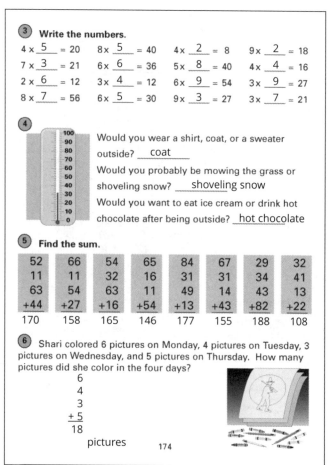

Would you wear a shirt, coat, or a sweater outside? ___coat___

Would you probably be mowing the grass or shoveling snow? ___shoveling snow___

Would you want to eat ice cream or drink hot chocolate after being outside? ___hot chocolate___

5 Find the sum.

52	66	54	65	84	67	29	32
11	11	32	16	31	31	34	41
63	54	63	11	49	14	43	13
+44	+27	+16	+54	+13	+43	+82	+22
170	158	165	146	177	155	188	108

6 Shari colored 6 pictures on Monday, 4 pictures on Tuesday, 3 pictures on Wednesday, and 5 pictures on Thursday. How many pictures did she color in the four days?

```
  6
  4
  3
+ 5
 18
```
pictures

174

---

1 Write the numbers.

$\frac{1}{2}$ of 10 = **5**	$\frac{1}{2}$ of 16 = **8**	$\frac{1}{2}$ of 8 = **4**
$\frac{1}{2}$ of 18 = **9**	$\frac{1}{2}$ of 6 = **3**	$\frac{1}{2}$ of 12 = **6**
$\frac{1}{2}$ of 2 = **1**	$\frac{1}{2}$ of 14 = **7**	$\frac{1}{2}$ of 4 = **2**

2 Write the correct words.

16 ounces = 1 ___pound___   52 weeks = 1 ___year___

365 days = 1 ___year___   2 cups = 1 ___pint___

60 seconds = 1 ___minute___   30 minutes = $\frac{1}{2}$ ___hour___

36 inches = 1 ___yard___   12 inches = 1 ___foot___

3 Mark the thermometer at the correct temperature. Color the liquid red.

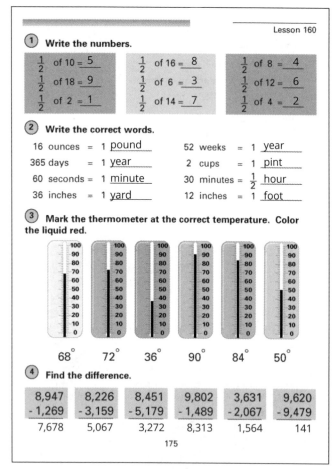

68°   72°   36°   90°   84°   50°

4 Find the difference.

8,947	8,226	8,451	9,802	3,631	9,620
- 1,269	- 3,159	- 5,179	- 1,489	- 2,067	- 9,479
7,678	5,067	3,272	8,313	1,564	141

175

5

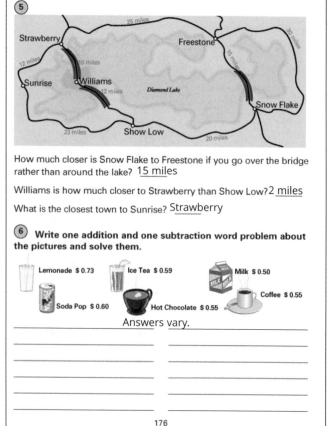

How much closer is Snow Flake to Freestone if you go over the bridge rather than around the lake? ___15 miles___

Williams is how much closer to Strawberry than Show Low? ___2 miles___

What is the closest town to Sunrise? ___Strawberry___

6 Write one addition and one subtraction word problem about the pictures and solve them.

Lemonade $0.73   Ice Tea $0.59   Milk $0.50

Soda Pop $0.60   Hot Chocolate $0.55   Coffee $0.55

___Answers vary.___

176

442

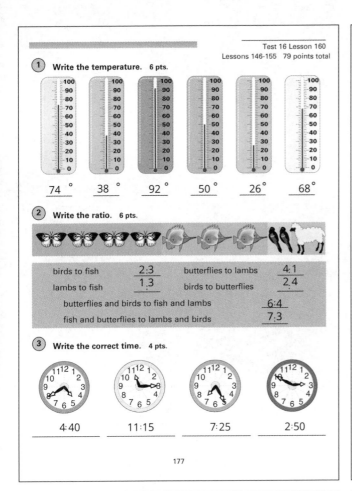

1 Write the temperature. 6 pts.

74 °   38 °   92 °   50 °   26°   68°

2 Write the ratio. 6 pts.

birds to fish	2:3	butterflies to lambs	4:1
lambs to fish	1:3	birds to butterflies	2:4
butterflies and birds to fish and lambs			6:4
fish and butterflies to lambs and birds			7:3

3 Write the correct time. 4 pts.

4:40   11:15   7:25   2:50

177

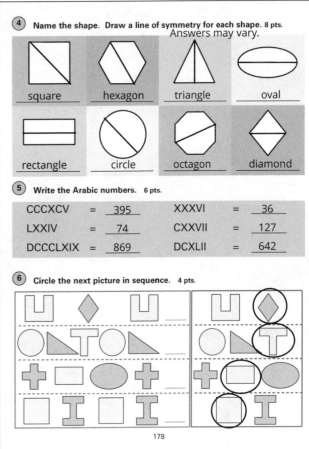

4 Name the shape. Draw a line of symmetry for each shape. 8 pts.
Answers may vary.

square   hexagon   triangle   oval

rectangle   circle   octagon   diamond

5 Write the Arabic numbers. 6 pts.

CCCXCV	=	395	XXXVI	=	36
LXXIV	=	74	CXXVII	=	127
DCCCLXIX	=	869	DCXLII	=	642

6 Circle the next picture in sequence. 4 pts.

178

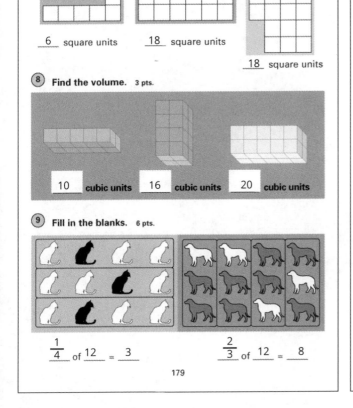

7 Find the area. 3 pts.

6 square units   18 square units   18 square units

8 Find the volume. 3 pts.

10 cubic units   16 cubic units   20 cubic units

9 Fill in the blanks. 6 pts.

$\frac{1}{4}$ of 12 = 3 $\frac{2}{3}$ of 12 = 8

179

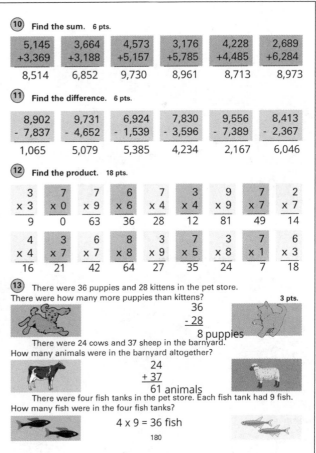

10 Find the sum. 6 pts.

5,145	3,664	4,573	3,176	4,228	2,689
+3,369	+3,188	+5,157	+5,785	+4,485	+6,284
8,514	6,852	9,730	8,961	8,713	8,973

11 Find the difference. 6 pts.

8,902	9,731	6,924	7,830	9,556	8,413
- 7,837	- 4,652	- 1,539	- 3,596	- 7,389	- 2,367
1,065	5,079	5,385	4,234	2,167	6,046

12 Find the product. 18 pts.

3	7	7	6	7	3	9	7	2
× 3	× 0	× 9	× 6	× 4	× 4	× 9	× 7	× 7
9	0	63	36	28	12	81	49	14

4	3	6	8	3	7	3	7	6
× 4	× 7	× 7	× 8	× 9	× 5	× 8	× 1	× 3
16	21	42	64	27	35	24	7	18

13 There were 36 puppies and 28 kittens in the pet store.
There were how many more puppies than kittens?   3 pts.

36
- 28
8 puppies

There were 24 cows and 37 sheep in the barnyard.
How many animals were in the barnyard altogether?

24
+ 37
61 animals

There were four fish tanks in the pet store. Each fish tank had 9 fish.
How many fish were in the four fish tanks?

4 x 9 = 36 fish

180

443

Worksheets

Reproducible Worksheets
for use with Horizons
Mathematics 2

0	1	2	3	4	5	6	7	8	9
10	11	12	13	14	15	16	17	18	19
20	21	22	23	24	25	26	27	28	29
30	31	32	33	34	35	36	37	38	39
40	41	42	43	44	45	46	47	48	49
50	51	52	53	54	55	56	57	58	59
60	61	62	63	64	65	66	67	68	69
70	71	72	73	74	75	76	77	78	79
80	81	82	83	84	85	86	87	88	89
90	91	92	93	94	95	96	97	98	99

1. **Color the first square red.**
2. **Draw a tree on the fourth square.**
3. **Write "STOP" on the ninth square.**
4. **Put a circle in the thirteenth square.**
5. **Color the fifteenth square blue.**
6. **Write "GO" on the eighteenth square.**
7. **Draw a house on the twentieth square.**

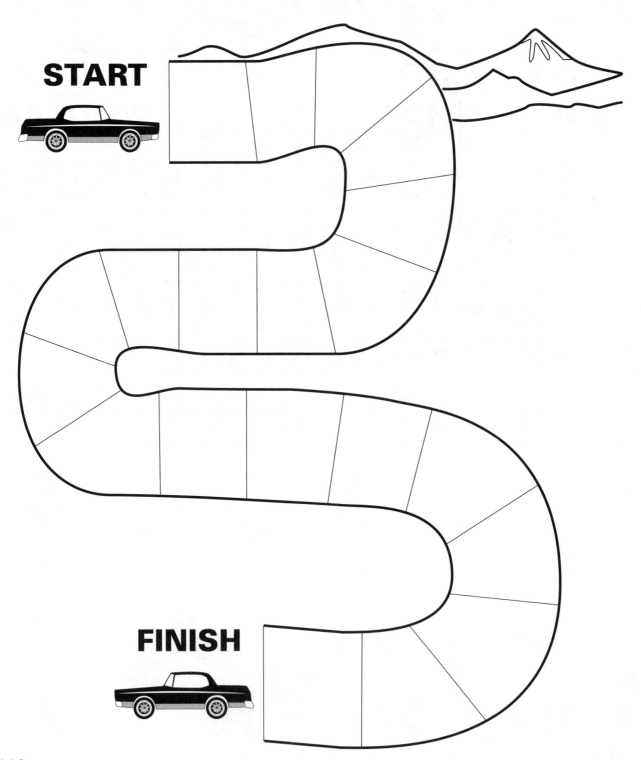

START

FINISH

Write the numbers.

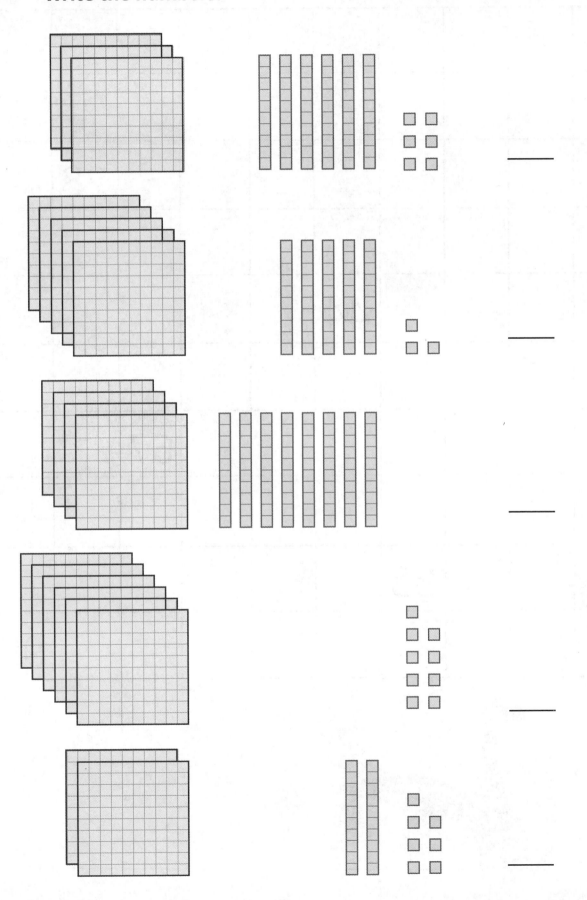

Write the missing numbers on the number chart.

0									
								28	
				44					
							67		
			83						
									99

**Add each number to the given number
at the bottom of the ladder.**

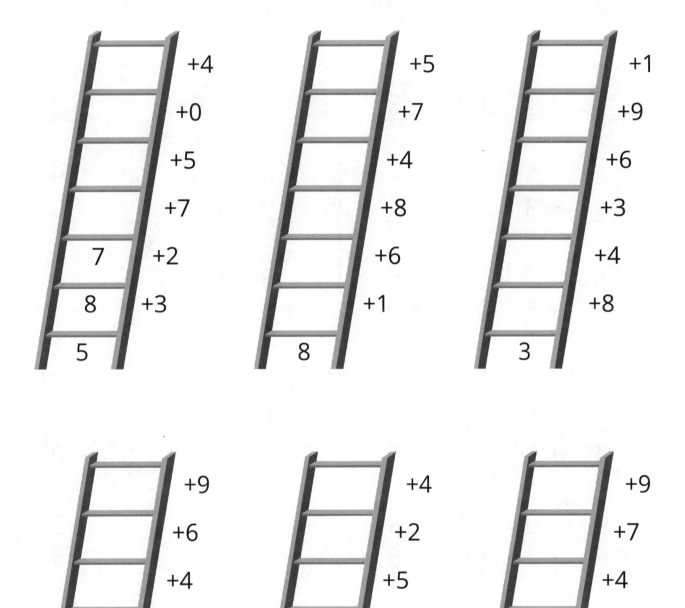

+4
+0
+5
+7
7 +2
8 +3
5

+5
+7
+4
+8
+6
+1
8

+1
+9
+6
+3
+4
+8
3

+9
+6
+4
+5
+3
+8
2

+4
+2
+5
+9
+8
+7
6

+9
+7
+4
+3
+6
+5
9

Drill #1

6	2	9	0
+ 8	+ 1	+ 4	+ 5

9	4	7	8
+ 1	+ 4	+ 4	+ 3

2	1	5	7
+ 4	+ 3	+ 6	+ 2

3	9	4	5
+ 0	+ 5	+ 7	+ 9

Drill #2

7	1	7	2
+ 5	+ 4	+ 3	+ 6

4	4	5	3
+ 1	+ 8	+ 5	+ 2

4	8	0	9
+ 9	+ 4	+ 9	+ 3

9	2	1	8
+ 7	+ 3	+ 2	+ 1

Drill #3

5	2	8	5
+ 4	+ 9	+ 2	+ 0

9	0	5	3
+ 6	+ 2	+ 8	+ 6

1	7	5	8
+ 9	+ 6	+ 3	+ 6

2	5	1	6
+ 5	+ 1	+ 7	+ 5

Drill #4

6	3	1	7
+ 6	+ 9	+ 8	+ 0

5	6	8	3
+ 7	+ 1	+ 5	+ 5

7	6	3	4
+ 9	+ 4	+ 8	+ 2

9	0	8	6
+ 8	+ 6	+ 8	+ 3

Write the numbers.

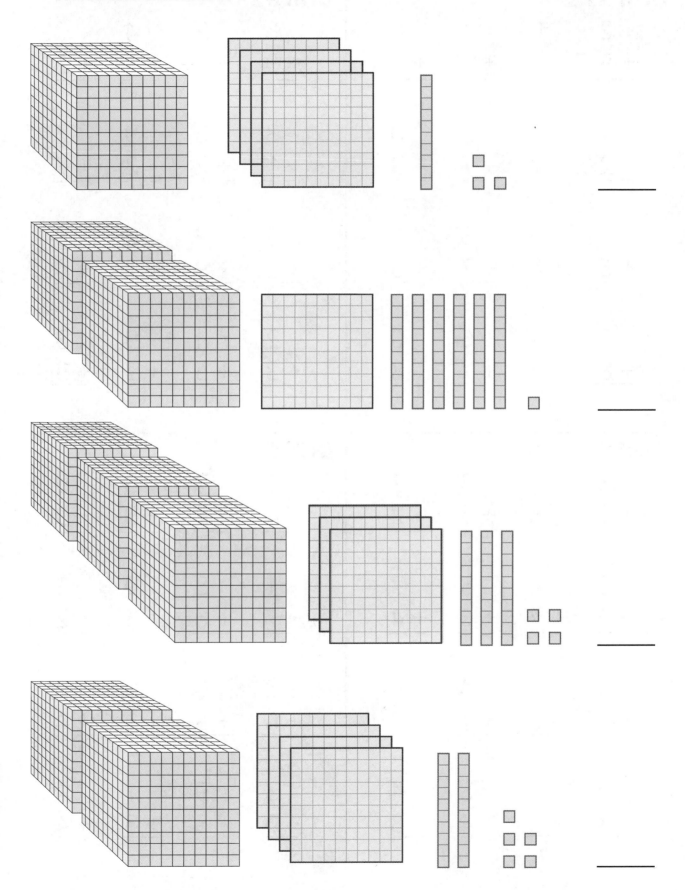

Drill #1

2	0	1	6
+ 8	+ 1	+ 1	+ 9

1	7	3	0
+ 2	+ 7	+ 7	+ 3

4	0	8	1
+ 6	+ 4	+ 7	+ 5

7	1	6	0
+ 8	+ 6	+ 7	+ 8

Drill #2

8	2	4	7
+ 9	+ 0	+ 3	+ 1

3	6	9	2
+ 1	+ 2	+ 2	+ 7

5	9	2	3
+ 2	+ 9	+ 2	+ 4

2	4	9	3
+ 3	+ 5	+ 7	+ 3

Drill #3

8	0	8	7
+ 1	+ 5	+ 3	+ 2

5	4	5	7
+ 9	+ 7	+ 6	+ 4

9	7	4	4
+ 4	+ 5	+ 1	+ 9

9	2	8	4
+ 8	+ 5	+ 4	+ 8

Drill #4

1	7	5	0
+ 4	+ 3	+ 5	+ 9

1	8	9	3
+ 7	+ 6	+ 3	+ 2

2	6	9	2
+ 6	+ 8	+ 1	+ 4

3	9	1	4
+ 0	+ 5	+ 3	+ 4

Write the missing numbers.

346 347 ____ ____ ____ ____ 352 ____ ____ ____

420 ____ ____ ____ ____ 425 ____ ____ ____ ____

489 ____ ____ ____ ____ ____ 496 ____ ____

513 ____ ____ ____ ____ 518 ____ ____ ____ ____

672 ____ ____ ____ ____ ____ 678 ____ ____ ____

705 706 ____ ____ ____ ____ ____ ____ ____ ____

794 795 ____ ____ ____ ____ ____ ____ 802 ____

847 ____ ____ ____ ____ 852 ____ ____ ____ ____

991 ____ ____ ____ ____ ____ ____ ____ ____ 1,000

Draw both hands on the clocks.

6:00

8:00

2:00

11:00

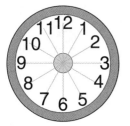

7:00

1:00

10:00

5:00

3:00

12:00

9:00

4:00

Drill #1

2	5	9	1
+ 1	+ 4	+ 6	+ 9

2	2	0	7
+ 5	+ 9	+ 2	+ 6

5	6	3	5
+ 1	+ 6	+ 9	+ 7

6	7	6	9
+ 1	+ 9	+ 4	+ 8

Drill #2

0	8	5	3
+ 6	+ 2	+ 8	+ 6

5	5	8	1
+ 3	+ 0	+ 6	+ 7

6	1	8	3
+ 5	+ 8	+ 5	+ 8

8	7	3	4
+ 8	+ 0	+ 5	+ 2

Drill #3

6	6	0	1
+ 3	+ 9	+ 3	+ 5

0	1	3	8
+ 8	+ 1	+ 7	+ 7

6	3	7	0
+ 7	+ 4	+ 7	+ 4

1	2	1	4
+ 6	+ 8	+ 2	+ 6

Drill #4

7	7	2	0
+ 8	+ 1	+ 7	+ 1

3	4	9	2
+ 3	+ 3	+ 2	+ 2

9	2	6	9
+ 7	+ 0	+ 2	+ 9

4	8	3	5
+ 5	+ 9	+ 1	+ 2

Write the correct time.

    :

    :

    :

    :

    :

    :

    :

    :

    :

    :

    :

    :

    :

    :

    :

    :

Drill #1

2	7	7	4
+3	+2	+4	+9

4	8	5	4
+ 8	+ 3	+ 6	+ 1

8	0	4	7
+ 4	+ 5	+ 7	+ 5

6	8	5	9
+ 3	+ 8	+ 9	+ 4

Drill #2

9	0	3	2
+ 7	+ 9	+ 2	+ 4

4	5	9	9
+ 4	+ 5	+ 3	+ 1

1	7	8	6
+ 3	+ 3	+ 1	+ 8

9	1	1	2
+ 5	+ 4	+ 2	+ 6

Drill #3

3	1	7	5
+ 0	+ 9	+ 6	+ 7

9	9	0	3
+ 8	+ 6	+ 2	+ 9

6	5	2	6
+ 4	+ 4	+ 9	+ 6

7	2	2	5
+ 9	+ 1	+ 5	+ 1

Drill #4

6	3	1	3
+ 1	+ 6	+ 7	+ 8

3	4	9	2
+ 2	+ 8	+ 6	+ 5

3	8	5	1
+ 5	+ 2	+ 0	+ 8

7	0	5	6
+ 0	+ 6	+ 3	+ 5

Follow the pattern of the arrows to complete the ladders.

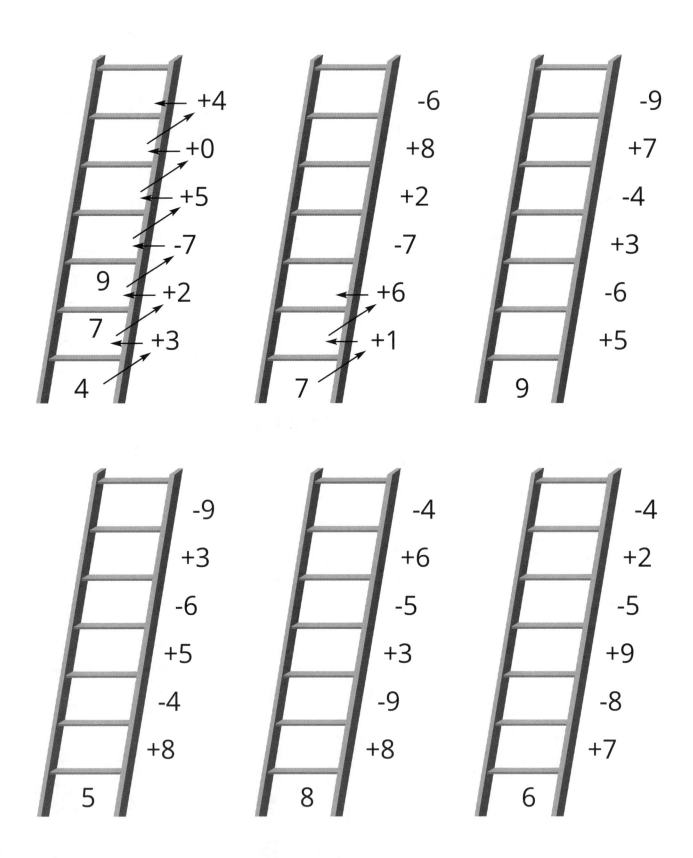

16	10	3	12	10	10	7	13	9	6
-7	-1	-3	-9	-8	-6	-3	-9	-9	-5

4	11	7	15	6	9	11	8	17	13
-4	-9	-4	-8	-3	-4	-8	-5	-9	-7

6	11	9	15	13	4	12	8	7	11
-4	-4	-6	-9	-5	-3	-7	-2	-6	-2

12	6	17	4	9	8	16	14	10	13
-3	-6	-8	-2	-3	-7	-9	-5	-4	-8

13	8	11	7	15	5	9	12	10	10
-6	-6	-5	-5	-7	-4	-8	-8	-7	-9

5	14	8	16	10	7	14	6	9	12
-2	-6	-3	-8	-3	-7	-7	-2	-5	-4

10	12	5	9	15	11	8	10	13	14
-2	-6	-5	-7	-6	-7	-4	-5	-4	-8

12	18	9	14	3	7	11	5	8	11
-5	-9	-2	-9	-2	-2	-6	-3	-8	-3

Drill #1

8	1	8	0
+ 8	+ 5	+ 7	+ 4

4	0	3	7
+ 6	+ 3	+ 7	+ 7

1	6	1	0
+ 2	+ 9	+ 1	+ 1

2	6	0	6
+ 8	+ 3	+ 8	+ 7

Drill #2

15	9	5	13
- 7	- 6	- 0	- 4

8	2	10	3
- 7	- 2	- 5	- 1

6	18	5	7
- 6	- 9	- 2	- 3

10	4	12	1
- 1	- 3	- 6	- 0

Drill #3

1	3	2	9
+ 6	+ 4	+ 2	+ 9

5	2	9	6
+ 2	+ 7	+ 2	+ 2

3	7	4	2
+ 1	+ 1	+ 3	+ 0

8	7	3	9
+ 9	+ 8	+ 3	+ 7

Drill #4

6	16	4	8
- 0	- 8	- 1	- 3

11	2	6	13
- 5	- 0	- 2	- 8

9	6	14	3
- 2	- 4	- 7	- 3

11	7	5	10
- 9	- 7	- 4	- 9

210	174	371	393	281	642	481
+ 590	+ 292	+ 136	+ 256	+ 490	+ 184	+ 275

137	152	581	320	497	374	592
+ 191	+ 453	+ 283	+ 381	+ 432	+ 250	+ 391

270	231	593	371	742	154	485
+ 534	+ 692	+ 145	+ 578	+ 180	+ 693	+ 174

271	487	460	152	261	123	396
+ 697	+ 160	+ 293	+ 382	+ 371	+ 594	+ 423

175	664	281	683	248	390	572
+ 463	+ 145	+ 354	+ 241	+ 170	+ 312	+ 183

362	190	631	162	586	253	374
+ 467	+ 365	+ 276	+ 145	+ 240	+ 163	+ 164

458	185	463	576	790	631	362
+ 361	+ 730	+ 352	+ 241	+ 186	+ 285	+ 482

426	340	255	581	143	492	362
+ 492	+ 267	+ 271	+ 327	+ 290	+ 176	+ 574

Drill #1

6	0	5	4
+ 3	+ 5	+ 6	+ 9

8	8	7	9
+ 4	+ 3	+ 4	+ 4

7	4	5	7
+ 2	+ 8	+ 9	+ 5

2	8	4	4
+ 3	+ 1	+ 7	+ 1

Drill #2

8	17	9	15
- 1	- 8	- 3	- 6

9	16	14	8
- 4	- 7	- 5	- 5

9	12	12	11
- 7	- 8	- 9	- 4

7	10	8	11
- 1	- 3	- 8	- 7

Drill #3

7	5	0	5
+ 9	+ 4	+ 2	+ 7

2	2	3	3
+ 1	+ 9	+ 9	+ 0

2	6	9	1
+ 5	+ 6	+ 8	+ 9

5	6	9	7
+ 1	+ 4	+ 6	+ 6

Drill #4

12	15	14	11
- 5	- 9	- 6	- 8

11	7	13	9
- 3	- 5	- 6	- 0

12	17	10	13
- 4	- 9	- 7	- 7

9	10	14	10
- 8	- 8	- 9	- 4

_____ thousands + _____ hundreds + _____ tens + _____ ones

_____ = _____ + _____ + _____ + _____ = _____

_____ thousands + _____ hundreds + _____ tens + _____ ones

_____ = _____ + _____ + _____ + _____ = _____

_____ thousands + _____ hundreds + _____ tens + _____ ones

_____ = _____ + _____ + _____ + _____ = _____

_____ thousands + _____ hundreds + _____ tens + _____ ones

_____ = _____ + _____ + _____ + _____ = _____

Drill #1

9 + 5	7 + 3	9 + 3	2 + 4
1 + 4	8 + 1	9 + 1	9 + 7
1 + 2	6 + 8	4 + 4	0 + 9
2 + 6	1 + 3	5 + 5	3 + 2

Drill #2

7 - 2	4 - 4	10 - 2	6 - 5
13 - 5	1 - 1	12 - 7	16 - 9
5 - 3	15 - 8	8 - 6	14 - 9
11 - 2	9 - 1	16 - 7	3 - 2

Drill #3

7 + 0	8 + 2	8 + 6	3 + 8
0 + 6	5 + 0	8 + 5	6 + 1
5 + 3	1 + 8	4 + 2	3 + 6
6 + 5	3 + 5	5 + 8	1 + 7

Drill #4

7 - 4	11 - 8	8 - 0	9 - 5
14 - 8	2 - 1	10 - 6	12 - 3
11 - 6	12 - 6	13 - 9	5 - 5
4 - 2	6 - 3	13 - 7	8 - 2

Write the correct time.

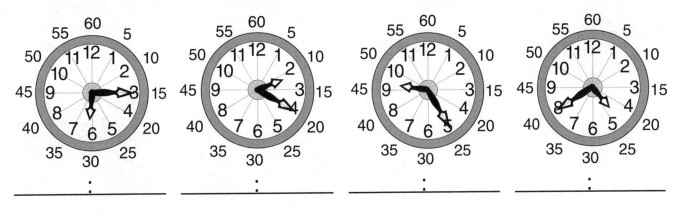

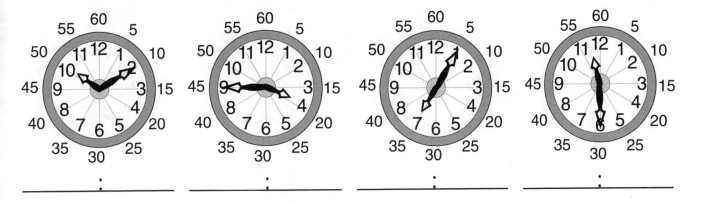

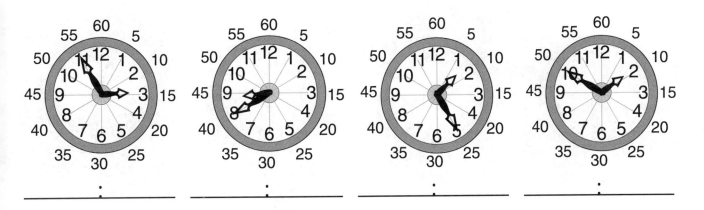

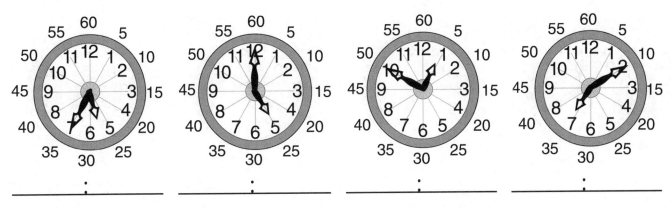

Write the correct time.

:   :   :   :

:   :   :   :

:   :   :   :

:   :   :   :

Drill #1

6	1	0	8
+ 7	+ 1	+ 3	+ 8

0	3	1	0
+ 1	+ 7	+ 5	+ 4

7	8	1	6
+ 7	+ 7	+ 2	+ 3

0	6	4	2
+ 8	+ 9	+ 6	+ 8

Drill #2

8	13	3	9
- 4	- 5	- 0	- 8

14	5	10	7
- 7	- 1	- 3	- 1

11	8	12	15
- 3	- 7	- 4	- 7

6	10	7	5
- 3	- 8	- 6	- 3

Drill #3

9	4	2	1
+ 7	+ 3	+ 7	+ 6

2	9	3	9
+ 0	+ 2	+ 4	+ 9

6	2	7	3
+ 2	+ 2	+ 8	+ 1

8	3	7	5
+ 9	+ 3	+ 1	+ 2

Drill #4

9	12	10	13
- 9	- 7	- 6	- 9

8	14	6	16
- 2	- 5	- 1	- 8

5	7	11	9
- 2	- 0	- 5	- 4

7	17	6	11
- 4	- 8	- 6	- 7

Add to find the sum.

$$
\begin{array}{r} 365 \\ + 549 \end{array} \qquad \begin{array}{r} 481 \\ + 439 \end{array} \qquad \begin{array}{r} 565 \\ + 295 \end{array} \qquad \begin{array}{r} 243 \\ + 198 \end{array} \qquad \begin{array}{r} 789 \\ + 127 \end{array} \qquad \begin{array}{r} 374 \\ + 576 \end{array} \qquad \begin{array}{r} 198 \\ + 642 \end{array}
$$

$$
\begin{array}{r} 627 \\ + 186 \end{array} \qquad \begin{array}{r} 169 \\ + 143 \end{array} \qquad \begin{array}{r} 698 \\ + 196 \end{array} \qquad \begin{array}{r} 237 \\ + 396 \end{array} \qquad \begin{array}{r} 598 \\ + 354 \end{array} \qquad \begin{array}{r} 245 \\ + 679 \end{array} \qquad \begin{array}{r} 364 \\ + 398 \end{array}
$$

$$
\begin{array}{r} 396 \\ + 127 \end{array} \qquad \begin{array}{r} 194 \\ + 526 \end{array} \qquad \begin{array}{r} 548 \\ + 175 \end{array} \qquad \begin{array}{r} 457 \\ + 169 \end{array} \qquad \begin{array}{r} 396 \\ + 485 \end{array} \qquad \begin{array}{r} 286 \\ + 475 \end{array} \qquad \begin{array}{r} 565 \\ + 287 \end{array}
$$

$$
\begin{array}{r} 276 \\ + 486 \end{array} \qquad \begin{array}{r} 798 \\ + 168 \end{array} \qquad \begin{array}{r} 261 \\ + 259 \end{array} \qquad \begin{array}{r} 459 \\ + 286 \end{array} \qquad \begin{array}{r} 187 \\ + 264 \end{array} \qquad \begin{array}{r} 672 \\ + 289 \end{array} \qquad \begin{array}{r} 154 \\ + 478 \end{array}
$$

$$
\begin{array}{r} 383 \\ + 469 \end{array} \qquad \begin{array}{r} 548 \\ + 387 \end{array} \qquad \begin{array}{r} 238 \\ + 575 \end{array} \qquad \begin{array}{r} 477 \\ + 235 \end{array} \qquad \begin{array}{r} 369 \\ + 275 \end{array} \qquad \begin{array}{r} 367 \\ + 289 \end{array} \qquad \begin{array}{r} 429 \\ + 381 \end{array}
$$

$$
\begin{array}{r} 393 \\ + 378 \end{array} \qquad \begin{array}{r} 179 \\ + 349 \end{array} \qquad \begin{array}{r} 686 \\ + 247 \end{array} \qquad \begin{array}{r} 196 \\ + 746 \end{array} \qquad \begin{array}{r} 458 \\ + 169 \end{array} \qquad \begin{array}{r} 435 \\ + 487 \end{array} \qquad \begin{array}{r} 287 \\ + 394 \end{array}
$$

$$
\begin{array}{r} 254 \\ + 187 \end{array} \qquad \begin{array}{r} 489 \\ + 381 \end{array} \qquad \begin{array}{r} 547 \\ + 193 \end{array} \qquad \begin{array}{r} 285 \\ + 635 \end{array} \qquad \begin{array}{r} 393 \\ + 187 \end{array} \qquad \begin{array}{r} 279 \\ + 253 \end{array} \qquad \begin{array}{r} 252 \\ + 589 \end{array}
$$

Draw both hands on the clocks and write the time the teacher indicates.

:   :   :   :

:   :   :   :

:   :   :   :

  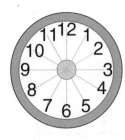 

:   :   :   :

Drill #1

0	1	4	6
+ 3	+ 9	+ 1	+ 5

4	9	1	7
+ 8	+ 1	+ 1	+ 6

8	2	9	6
+ 2	+ 0	+ 9	+ 2

4	5	7	3
+ 3	+ 1	+ 2	+ 0

Drill #2

4	9	10	5
- 3	- 6	- 2	- 5

8	13	12	12
- 5	- 8	- 9	- 3

11	15	4	14
- 2	- 6	- 0	- 6

7	10	11	18
- 2	- 4	- 6	- 9

Drill #3

2	4	3	0
+ 6	+ 5	+ 6	+ 7

1	2	3	6
+ 5	+ 2	+ 8	+ 9

9	8	2	5
+ 5	+ 6	+ 4	+ 3

3	7	3	5
+ 4	+ 5	+ 2	+ 7

Drill #4

9	11	10	3
- 2	- 3	- 5	- 3

11	14	2	13
- 9	- 8	- 1	- 6

15	6	16	9
- 8	- 5	- 9	- 0

7	12	15	10
- 6	- 8	- 9	- 1

Subtract to find the difference.

90 − 81	23 − 4	92 − 13	42 − 34	74 − 69	64 − 15	91 − 62
53 − 19	96 − 58	91 − 79	27 − 18	80 − 12	62 − 35	86 − 47
83 − 15	30 − 26	85 − 66	91 − 86	54 − 26	74 − 58	65 − 56
82 − 26	90 − 25	67 − 29	73 − 46	93 − 26	32 − 7	96 − 58
81 − 77	73 − 28	64 − 47	75 − 27	81 − 55	40 − 13	51 − 47
95 − 39	31 − 18	50 − 37	71 − 54	42 − 28	86 − 39	72 − 36
78 − 19	60 − 54	51 − 43	82 − 49	64 − 18	93 − 47	85 − 78

Drill #1

0	2	6	7
+ 5	+ 9	+ 7	+ 8

3	4	1	5
+ 3	+ 9	+ 7	+ 5

5	1	4	9
+ 2	+ 2	+ 0	+ 3

9	6	3	2
+ 0	+ 4	+ 9	+ 5

Drill #2

1	12	7	10
- 0	- 5	- 3	- 3

6	13	4	14
- 1	- 6	- 2	- 9

11	8	10	3
- 3	- 4	- 7	- 1

12	15	9	5
- 4	- 9	- 7	- 0

Drill #3

4	5	6	0
+ 4	+ 9	+ 1	+ 9

1	7	4	1
+ 6	+ 4	+ 6	+ 3

5	6	8	7
+ 6	+ 0	+ 4	+ 1

2	8	9	2
+ 1	+ 8	+ 7	+ 8

Drill #4

17	1	10	6
- 9	- 1	- 5	- 0

14	3	12	13
- 5	- 2	- 8	- 4

4	10	7	11
- 4	- 9	- 5	- 7

5	17	8	9
- 4	- 8	- 1	- 3

Write any three-digit number.

START HERE

___ ___ ___

Write the number
that is 100 more.

___ ___ ___

Write the number
that is 10 less.

___ ___ ___

Write the number
that is 100 less.

___ ___ ___

Write the number
that is 10 more.

___ ___ ___

Write the number
that is 100 less.

___ ___ ___

Write the number
that is 10 more

___ ___ ___

Write the number
that is 100 more.

___ ___ ___

Write the number
that is 10 less.

___ ___ ___

Compare your last number
with your first number.

475

Drill #1

1	9	2	6
+ 4	+ 8	+ 3	+ 6

8	3	3	7
+ 7	+ 7	+ 1	+ 9

4	7	1	9
+ 2	+ 5	+ 0	+ 4

7	8	5	4
+ 0	+ 3	+ 4	+ 7

Drill #2

16	9	2	13
- 8	- 5	- 0	- 4

13	6	14	8
- 8	- 4	- 6	- 3

4	15	8	11
- 1	- 8	- 8	- 8

12	5	18	9
- 5	- 1	- 9	- 9

Drill #3

2	9	1	6
+ 7	+ 6	+ 8	+ 8

8	4	3	7
+ 9	+ 3	+ 5	+ 7

6	7	5	9
+ 3	+ 3	+ 0	+ 2

0	8	9	5
+ 1	+ 5	+ 7	+ 8

Drill #4

16	10	2	12
- 7	- 5	- 2	- 9

13	7	14	8
- 9	- 7	- 7	- 6

3	15	9	11
- 0	- 7	- 1	- 9

12	6	17	5
- 6	- 2	- 9	- 2

X	0	1	2	3	4	5	6	7	8	9	10
0	0	0	0	0	0	0	0	0	0	0	0
1	0	1	2	3	4	5	6	7	8	9	10
2	0	2	4	6	8	10	12	14	16	18	20
3	0	3	6	9	12	15	18	21	24	27	30
4	0	4	8	12	16	20	24	28	32	36	40
5	0	5	10	15	20	25	30	35	40	45	50
6	0	6	12	18	24	30	36	42	48	54	60
7	0	7	14	21	28	35	42	49	56	63	70
8	0	8	16	24	32	40	48	56	64	72	80
9	0	9	18	27	36	45	54	63	72	81	90
10	0	10	20	30	40	50	60	70	80	90	100

Write the missing numbers in the blanks.

0 + __ = 0	2 + __ = 5	7 + __ = 16	__ + 9 = 10
__ + 3 = 11	__ + 1 = 3	9 + __ = 12	__ + 9 = 15
3 + __ = 10	5 + __ = 13	__ + 2 = 8	__ + 6 = 8
7 + __ = 14	1 + __ = 7	8 + __ = 9	0 + __ = 6
2 + __ = 4	__ + 3 = 10	9 + __ = 18	__ + 4 = 7
__ + 9 = 14	__ + 8 = 9	__ + 8 = 11	__ + 2 = 5
__ + 7 = 11	1 + __ = 2	4 + __ = 4	5 + __ = 12
6 + __ = 9	4 + __ = 6	2 + __ = 11	1 + __ = 5
9 + __ = 14	__ + 5 = 11	8 + __ = 16	__ + 8 = 12
__ + 5 = 9	__ + 6 = 10	3 + __ = 6	3 + __ = 12

Drill #1

0	5	2	9
+ 6	+ 7	+ 0	+ 9

3	7	8	1
+ 1	+ 4	+ 0	+ 1

5	9	4	8
+ 3	+ 1	+ 2	+ 2

6	7	8	3
+ 9	+ 2	+ 8	+ 8

Drill #2

16	7	15	10
- 9	- 4	- 6	- 8

6	11	9	5
- 0	- 2	- 9	- 5

12	8	10	9
- 3	- 5	- 1	- 2

10	6	7	11
- 4	- 4	- 0	- 5

Drill #3

6	1	4	9
+ 5	+ 5	+ 6	+ 5

3	8	0	2
+ 5	+ 6	+ 8	+ 4

3	4	6	7
+ 3	+ 8	+ 2	+ 6

0	4	7	1
+ 4	+ 5	+ 8	+ 9

Drill #4

10	9	14	10
- 6	- 6	- 8	- 9

13	8	11	8
- 7	- 8	- 4	- 0

5	6	10	9
- 0	- 6	- 2	- 3

11	12	4	3
- 6	- 7	- 1	- 1

Circle the picture that comes next in each sequence.

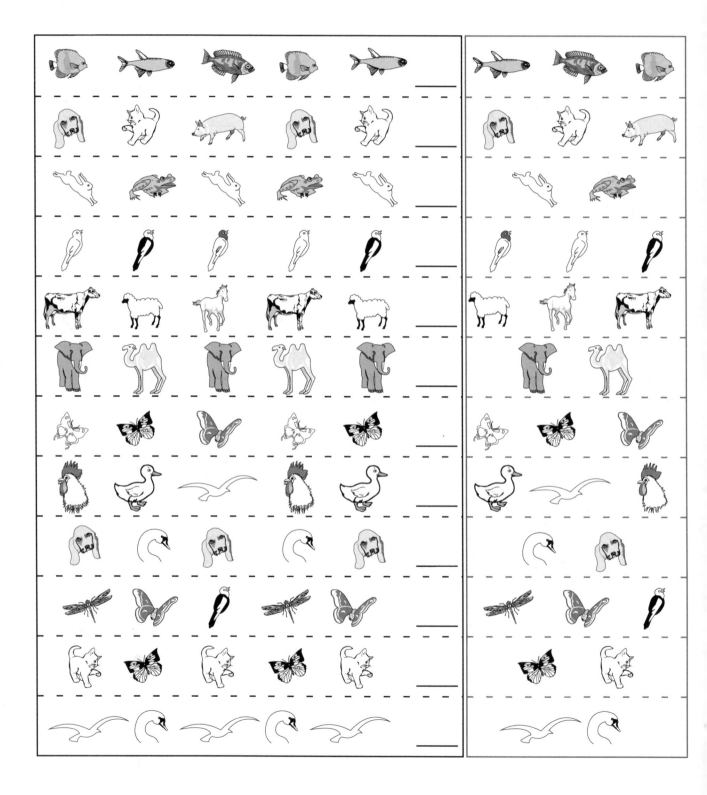

Drill #1

8	6	9	7
+ 5	+ 6	+ 7	+ 3

5	1	0	5
+ 9	+ 2	+ 0	+ 5

3	9	2	8
+ 4	+ 2	+ 1	+ 9

2	7	6	7
+ 6	+ 0	+ 3	+ 7

Drill #2

1	7	3	13
- 0	- 3	- 1	- 4

12	5	10	5
- 6	- 2	- 5	- 0

4	18	2	9
- 3	- 9	- 2	- 6

10	6	8	15
- 1	- 6	- 7	- 7

Drill #3

7	1	6	9
+ 9	+ 3	+ 7	+ 8

5	4	0	5
+ 8	+ 1	+ 2	+ 6

8	9	6	8
+ 1	+ 3	+ 4	+ 7

5	2	5	7
+ 0	+ 2	+ 2	+ 5

Drill #4

10	3	13	8
- 9	- 3	- 8	- 3

5	14	6	4
- 4	- 7	- 2	- 1

7	6	2	16
- 7	- 4	- 0	- 8

11	9	11	6
- 9	- 2	- 5	- 0

Write the total value of each line.

¢ _____

¢ _____

¢ _____

¢ _____

¢ _____

¢ _____

¢ _____

¢ _____

Drill #1

6 + 7	0 + 1	7 + 7	0 + 4
0 + 8	1 + 1	3 + 7	8 + 7
6 + 3	6 + 9	0 + 3	1 + 5
2 + 8	1 + 2	4 + 6	8 + 8

Drill #2

11 - 7	11 - 4	8 - 5	15 - 6
8 - 8	12 - 9	14 - 5	9 - 3
10 - 3	12 - 8	16 - 7	17 - 8
7 - 1	9 - 7	9 - 4	8 - 1

Drill #3

9 + 7	2 + 0	6 + 2	9 + 9
3 + 3	4 + 3	9 + 2	2 + 2
7 + 8	7 + 1	2 + 7	3 + 4
8 + 9	3 + 1	5 + 2	1 + 6

Drill #4

10 - 4	13 - 7	9 - 0	11 - 8
14 - 9	10 - 6	13 - 6	14 - 6
10 - 8	17 - 9	7 - 5	15 - 9
9 - 8	12 - 4	11 - 3	12 - 5

Write the numbers.

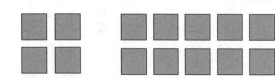

___ rows of ___

___ x ___ = ___

___ rows of ___

___ x ___ = ___

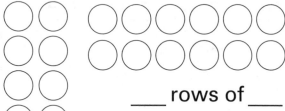

___ rows of ___

___ x ___ = ___

___ rows of ___

___ x ___ = ___

___ rows of ___

___ x ___ = ___

___ rows of ___

___ x ___ = ___

___ rows of ___

___ x ___ = ___

___ rows of ___

___ x ___ = ___

___ rows of ___

___ x ___ = ___

___ rows of ___

___ x ___ = ___

Write the numbers.

1. two hundred seventy-six _____

2. three hundred ten _____

3. five hundred eighty-four _____

4. nine hundred three _____

5. seven hundred forty-eight _____

6. four hundred thirty _____

7. one hundred sixty-two _____

8. eight hundred nine _____

9. six hundred one _____

10. five hundred twenty-five _____

11. eight hundred ninety-seven _____

12. three hundred fifty-nine _____

13. seven hundred thirteen _____

14. one hundred sixty-two _____

15. two hundred seventy-one _____

16. five hundred sixty-nine _____

17. three hundred four _____

18. nine hundred thirty-six _____

19. four hundred eighty _____

20. six hundred forty-eight _____

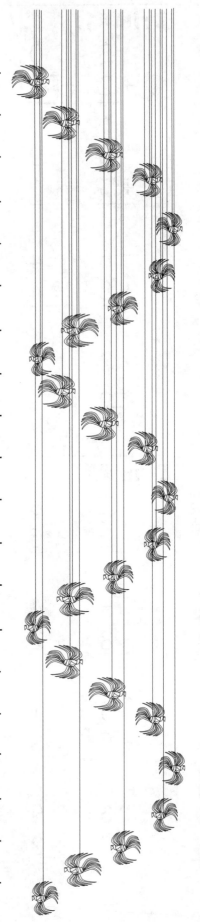

Drill #1

3	0	9	2
+ 2	+ 9	+ 7	+ 4

5	9	9	1
+ 5	+ 1	+ 3	+ 3

6	4	8	7
+ 8	+ 4	+ 1	+ 3

2	1	9	1
+ 6	+ 2	+ 5	+ 4

Drill #2

3	14	16	6
- 2	- 9	- 9	- 5

16	8	12	10
- 7	- 6	- 7	- 2

9	15	1	11
- 1	- 8	- 1	- 2

5	4	13	7
- 3	- 4	- 5	- 2

Drill #3

7	3	6	3
+ 0	+ 6	+ 1	+ 8

5	4	8	8
+ 8	+ 2	+ 5	+ 6

3	1	5	8
+ 5	+ 8	+ 0	+ 2

6	5	0	1
+ 5	+ 3	+ 6	+ 7

Drill #4

8	5	12	9
- 2	- 5	- 3	- 5

13	13	10	8
- 7	- 9	- 6	- 0

6	12	2	11
- 3	- 6	- 1	- 8

4	11	14	7
- 2	- 6	- 8	- 4

Multiply to find the products.

X	0	1	2	3	4	5	6	7	8	9	10
0											
1											
2											
3											
4											
5											
6											
7											
8											
9											
10											

Multiply to find the products.

X	5	2	7	0	1	6	10	4	9	3	8
0											

X	0	4	7	1	6	10	8	2	5	9	3
1											

X	1	5	0	10	8	4	2	7	9	3	6
2											

X	4	7	1	9	5	0	3	10	6	8	2
5											

X	4	8	6	3	0	9	7	2	10	5	1
10											

Drill #1

2	6	0	8
+ 8	+ 3	+ 4	+ 8

4	1	1	0
+ 6	+ 2	+ 5	+ 3

6	8	3	1
+ 9	+ 7	+ 7	+ 1

0	7	0	6
+ 8	+ 7	+ 1	+ 7

Drill #2

5	15	7	9
- 3	- 7	- 1	- 8

7	12	10	3
- 6	- 4	- 3	- 0

10	8	5	13
- 8	- 7	- 1	- 5

6	11	14	8
- 3	- 3	- 7	- 4

Drill #3

5	3	9	1
+ 2	+ 1	+ 9	+ 6

7	7	3	2
+ 1	+ 8	+ 4	+ 7

3	2	9	4
+ 3	+ 2	+ 2	+ 3

8	6	2	9
+ 9	+ 2	+ 0	+ 7

Drill #4

11	9	16	13
- 7	- 4	- 8	- 9

6	11	6	10
- 6	- 5	- 1	- 6

17	7	14	12
- 8	- 0	- 5	- 7

7	5	8	9
- 4	- 2	- 2	- 9

Write the value.

$ _____ . _____

$ _____ . _____

$ _____ . _____

$ _____ . _____

Drill #1

3	6	7	6
+ 0	+ 2	+ 6	+ 5

7	9	1	4
+ 2	+ 9	+ 1	+ 1

5	2	9	1
+ 1	+ 0	+ 1	+ 9

4	8	4	0
+ 3	+ 2	+ 8	+ 3

Drill #2

18	14	12	5
- 9	- 6	- 3	- 5

11	4	12	10
- 6	- 0	- 9	- 2

10	15	13	9
- 4	- 6	- 8	- 6

7	11	8	4
- 2	- 2	- 5	- 3

Drill #3

5	5	6	0
+ 7	+ 3	+ 9	+ 7

3	2	3	3
+ 2	+ 4	+ 8	+ 6

7	8	2	4
+ 7	+ 6	+ 2	+ 5

3	9	1	2
+ 4	+ 5	+ 5	+ 6

Drill #4

10	9	13	3
- 1	- 0	- 6	- 3

15	16	2	10
- 9	- 9	- 1	- 5

12	6	14	11
- 8	- 5	- 8	- 4

7	15	11	9
- 6	- 8	- 9	- 2

Circle the next shape in sequence.

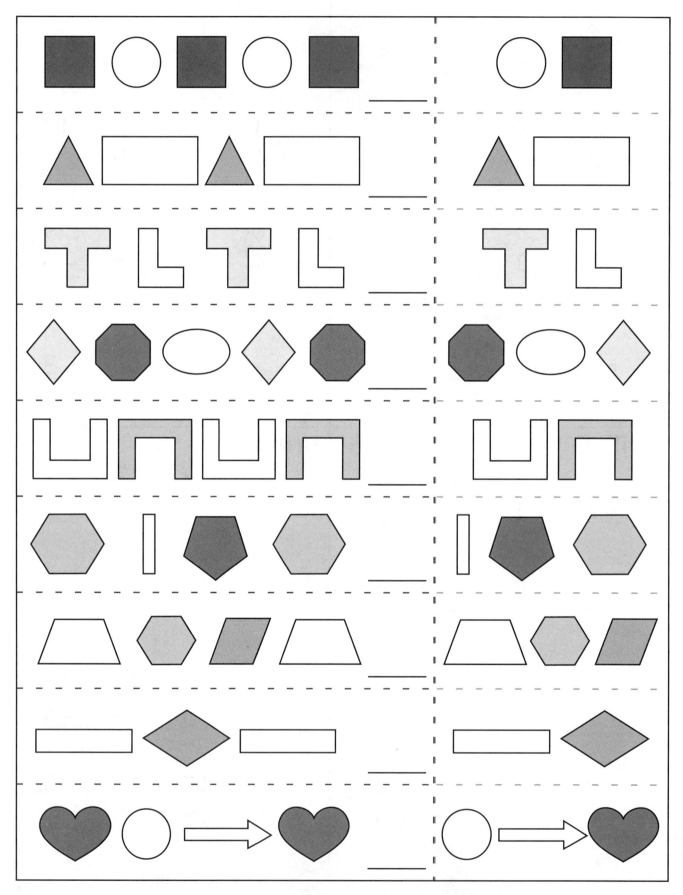

Put an "X" on the money needed.

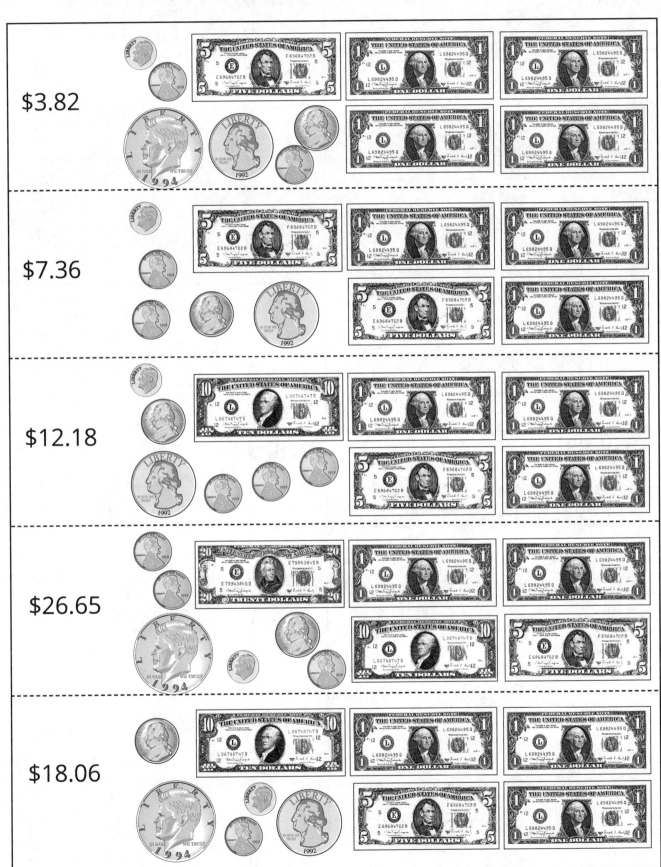

$3.82

$7.36

$12.18

$26.65

$18.06

Drill #1

2	9	5	7
+ 5	+ 3	+ 5	+ 8

3	4	1	6
+ 9	+ 0	+ 7	+ 7

6	1	4	2
+ 4	+ 2	+ 9	+ 9

9	5	3	0
+ 0	+ 2	+ 3	+ 5

Drill #2

5	3	14	10
- 0	- 1	- 9	- 3

9	10	4	7
- 7	- 7	- 2	- 3

15	8	13	12
- 9	- 4	- 6	- 5

12	11	6	1
- 4	- 3	- 1	- 0

Drill #3

2	7	1	0
+ 8	+ 1	+ 3	+ 9

9	8	4	6
+ 7	+ 4	+ 6	+ 1

8	6	7	5
+ 8	+ 0	+ 4	+ 9

2	5	1	4
+ 1	+ 6	+ 6	+ 4

Drill #4

9	11	13	6
- 3	- 7	- 4	- 0

8	7	12	10
- 1	- 5	- 8	- 4

1	3	10	17
- 1	- 2	- 9	- 8

5	4	14	17
- 4	- 4	- 5	- 9

Write the numbers.

____ rows of ____
____ x ____ = ____

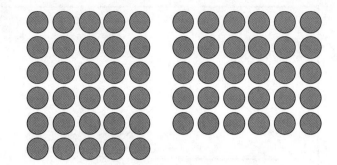

____ rows of ____
____ x ____ = ____

____ rows of ____
____ x ____ = ____

____ rows of ____
____ x ____ = ____

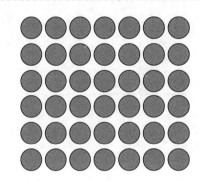

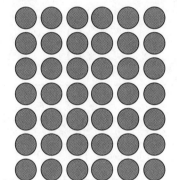

____ rows of ____
____ x ____ = ____

____ rows of ____
____ x ____ = ____

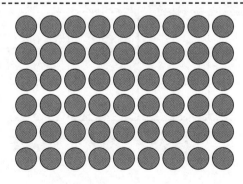

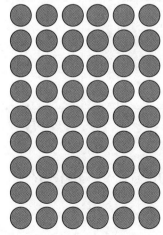

____ rows of ____
____ x ____ = ____

____ rows of ____
____ x ____ = ____

Make a bar graph from the picture.

Shapes in the picture

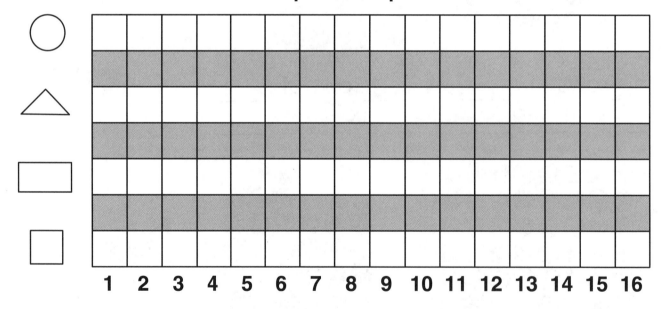

Which shape appears the most times? _____

Which shape appears the least times? _____

Does the circle or the triangle appear more times? _____

Does the square or the triangle appear more times? _____

Drill #1

4	9	7	6
+ 7	+ 4	+ 9	+ 6

5	1	3	2
+ 4	+ 0	+ 1	+ 3

8	7	3	9
+ 3	+ 5	+ 7	+ 8

7	4	8	1
+ 0	+ 2	+ 7	+ 4

Drill #2

9	11	8	13
- 9	- 8	- 3	- 4

18	8	14	2
- 9	- 8	- 6	- 0

5	15	6	9
- 1	- 8	- 4	- 5

12	4	13	16
- 5	- 1	- 8	- 8

Drill #3

5	9	7	6
+ 8	+ 2	+ 7	+ 8

9	5	3	1
+ 3	+ 0	+ 5	+ 8

8	7	4	9
+ 5	+ 3	+ 3	+ 6

0	6	8	2
+ 1	+ 3	+ 9	+ 7

Drill #4

5	11	8	12
- 2	- 9	- 6	- 9

17	9	14	2
- 9	- 1	- 7	- 2

6	15	7	10
- 2	- 7	- 7	- 5

12	3	13	16
- 6	- 0	- 9	- 7

Write the fraction that shows what part is shaded.

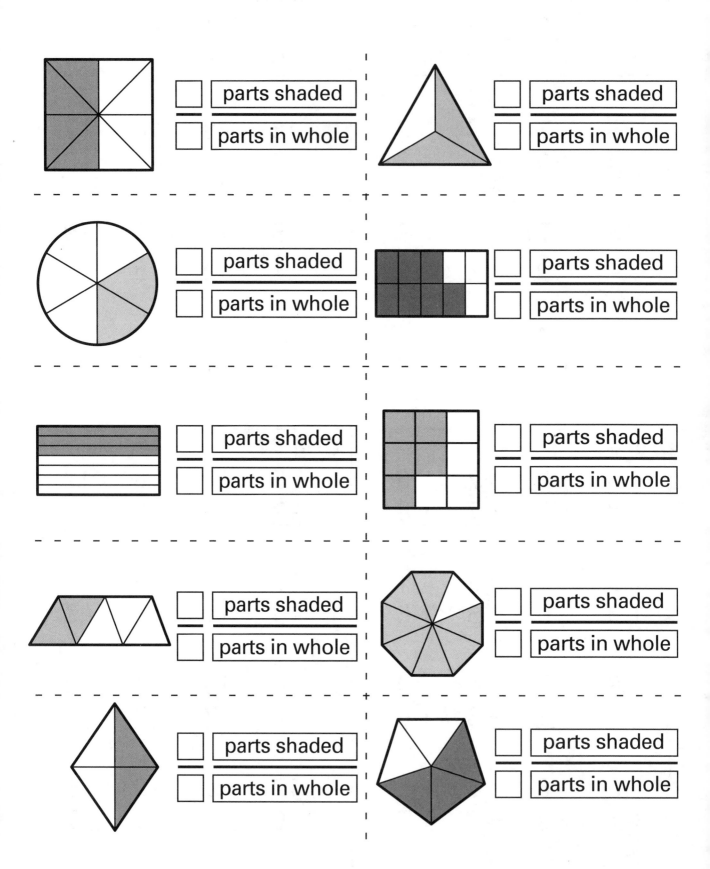

Drill #1

3	8	1	9
+ 8	+ 2	+ 1	+ 9

8	4	8	7
+ 8	+ 2	+ 0	+ 2

9	7	2	5
+ 1	+ 4	+ 0	+ 7

6	5	3	0
+ 9	+ 3	+ 1	+ 6

Drill #2

11	9	5	10
- 5	- 2	- 5	- 8

7	10	9	15
- 0	- 1	- 9	- 6

6	8	11	7
- 4	- 5	- 2	- 4

10	12	6	16
- 4	- 3	- 0	- 9

Drill #3

1	7	2	9
+ 9	+ 6	+ 4	+ 5

7	6	0	4
+ 8	+ 2	+ 8	+ 6

4	4	8	1
+ 5	+ 8	+ 6	+ 5

0	3	3	6
+ 4	+ 3	+ 5	+ 5

Drill #4

3	9	8	10
- 1	- 3	- 0	- 9

4	10	11	14
- 1	- 2	- 4	- 8

12	6	9	11
- 7	- 6	- 6	- 6

5	13	10	8
- 0	- 7	- 6	- 8

Solve the equations.

$2 + n = 9$	$9 + n = 15$	$1 + n = 9$	$6 + n = 14$
$8 + n = 17$	$4 + n = 7$	$3 + n = 8$	$7 + n = 14$
$6 + n = 9$	$7 + n = 10$	$5 + n = 5$	$9 + n = 11$
$0 + n = 1$	$8 + n = 13$	$9 + n = 13$	$5 + n = 13$
$7 + n = 13$	$8 + n = 11$	$5 + n = 9$	$4 + n = 11$
$0 + n = 6$	$5 + n = 12$	$2 + n = 2$	$9 + n = 18$

I	II	III	IV	V	VI	VII	VIII	IX	X	XX	XXX
1	2	3	4	5	6	7	8	9	10	20	30

XL	L	LX	LXX	LXXX	XC	C	CD	D	CM	M
40	50	60	70	80	90	100	400	500	900	1,000

Write the Roman numerals.

36 _____   5 _____

24 _____   61 _____

12 _____   80 _____

48 _____   77 _____

59 _____   96 _____

3 _____   17 _____

Write the Arabic numbers.

LV _____   IV _____

XXVII _____   LXXXIII _____

VII _____   XXXIII _____

XLIII _____   XIX _____

LXVI _____   XIV _____

C _____   LXXI _____

Drill #1

2	9	0	7
+ 6	+ 2	+ 0	+ 3

3	1	9	7
+ 4	+ 2	+ 7	+ 7

5	6	6	8
+ 9	+ 6	+ 3	+ 9

8	7	2	5
+ 5	+ 0	+ 1	+ 5

Drill #2

1	0	8	10
x 5	x 2	x 0	x 9

10	10	4	10
x 0	x 7	x 1	x 1

1	1	0	3
x 2	x 9	x 6	x 1

0	10	1	10
x 4	x 5	x 6	x 2

Drill #3

1	0	1	7
x 8	x 1	x 1	x 0

0	1	10	2
x 5	x 7	x 3	x 1

5	10	0	10
x 1	x 8	x 3	x 6

9	10	0	9
x 1	x 4	x 0	x 0

Drill #4

10	18	10	13
- 1	- 9	- 5	- 4

4	5	3	15
- 3	- 2	- 1	- 7

12	7	8	9
- 6	- 3	- 7	- 6

1	6	2	5
- 0	- 6	- 2	- 0

Measure the objects in inches. Label each answer.

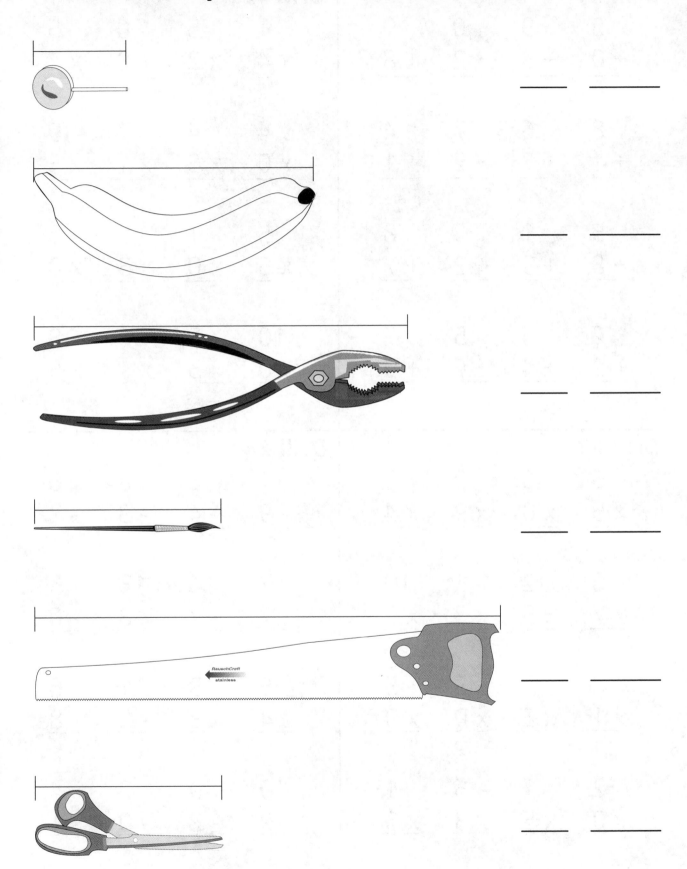

_____ _____

_____ _____

_____ _____

_____ _____

_____ _____

_____ _____

Drill #1

5	9	0	9
+ 0	+ 3	+ 2	+ 8

8	6	7	4
+ 1	+ 7	+ 5	+ 1

5	1	5	8
+ 8	+ 3	+ 2	+ 7

2	6	5	7
+ 2	+ 4	+ 6	+ 9

Drill #2

1	5	0	5
x 4	x 2	x 8	x 7

4	4	7	9
x 0	x 5	x 1	x 5

5	1	5	3
x 6	x 0	x 3	x 0

10	5	6	8
x 10	x 5	x 1	x 5

Drill #3

6	6	0	5
x 5	x 0	x 9	x 4

0	2	1	10
x 7	x 5	x 3	x 5

8	3	5	5
x 1	x 5	x 0	x 9

2	7	5	1
x 0	x 5	x 8	x 5

Drill #4

11	6	8	6
- 9	- 4	- 3	- 2

7	14	13	6
- 7	- 7	- 8	- 0

5	3	11	16
- 4	- 3	- 5	- 8

10	9	2	4
- 9	- 2	- 0	- 1

Solve the equations.

$n + 5 = 13$	$n + 6 = 12$	$n + 7 = 16$	$n + 3 = 10$
$n + 9 = 14$	$n + 2 = 3$	$n + 0 = 0$	$n + 5 = 10$
$n + 4 = 7$	$n + 2 = 11$	$n + 1 = 3$	$n + 9 = 17$
$n + 6 = 8$	$n + 0 = 7$	$n + 3 = 9$	$n + 7 = 14$
$n + 9 = 16$	$n + 3 = 4$	$n + 7 = 13$	$n + 8 = 17$
$n + 8 = 13$	$n + 1 = 5$	$n + 2 = 2$	$n + 6 = 11$

Drill #1

2	6	3	0
+ 8	+ 9	+ 7	+ 4

6	1	7	8
+ 3	+ 1	+ 7	+ 8

0	4	1	0
+ 8	+ 6	+ 5	+ 1

1	0	8	6
+ 2	+ 3	+ 7	+ 7

Drill #2

7	1	10	6
x 5	x 2	x 10	x 0

10	5	2	8
x 5	x 8	x 1	x 5

0	0	1	5
x 8	x 0	x 8	x 9

5	10	8	1
x 5	x 0	x 1	x 0

Drill #3

5	3	4	10
x 1	x 0	x 5	x 8

5	1	0	3
x 7	x 5	x 5	x 1

9	10	9	0
x 1	x 2	x 0	x 2

10	4	5	10
x 3	x 0	x 3	x 6

Drill #4

7	12	14	15
- 1	- 8	- 5	- 6

10	12	8	8
- 3	- 9	- 5	- 1

8	11	9	17
- 8	- 4	- 4	- 8

11	9	16	9
- 7	- 7	- 7	- 3

Books Read by Students

Gale									Each
Lois									
Penny									
Roberto									equals 6
Stan									
Bruce									

Write the multiplication fact to represent how many books each student read.

Gale_____ **Penny**_____ **Stan** _____

Lois _____ **Roberto** _____ **Bruce** _____

Who read the most books?_____

How many students read more books than Stan? _____

How many books did Penny and Lois read together? _____

Points Scored in Basketball

Adam									Each
Guy									
Dale									equals 2
Cliff									
Kevin									Each
Jamal									equals 1

Write the number of points each boy scored.

Adam _____ **Dale**_____ **Kevin** _____

Guy _____ **Cliff** _____ **Jamal** _____

Who scored the most points? _____

How many boys scored over fifteen points? _____

How many boys scored an odd number of points?_____

**Draw a line across each ribbon at the given length.
Then color the ribbons.**

3 centimeters

11 centimeters

6 centimeters

2 centimeters

4 centimeters

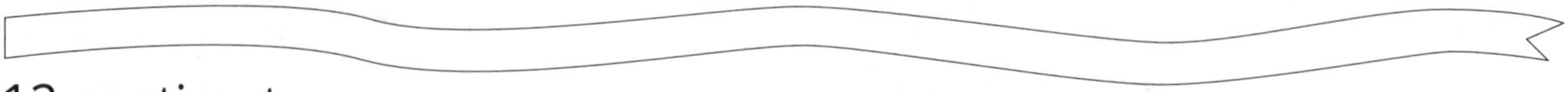

12 centimeters

9 centimeters

15 centimeters

5 centimeters

8 centimeters

1 centimeter

10 centimeters

7 centimeters

14 centimeters

Drill #1

8	7	9	9
+ 9	+ 1	+ 2	+ 9

7	4	6	1
+ 8	+ 3	+ 2	+ 6

3	2	5	3
+ 3	+ 0	+ 2	+ 4

9	3	2	2
+ 7	+ 1	+ 7	+ 2

Drill #2

6	2	2	10
x 2	x 0	x 2	x 7

4	1	9	8
x 2	x 4	x 5	x 2

7	10	2	2
x 5	x 1	x 3	x 9

2	3	5	0
x 7	x 5	x 6	x 4

Drill #3

2	0	5	7
x 8	x 5	x 8	x 2

2	7	3	9
x 6	x 1	x 2	x 0

5	10	9	4
x 4	x 4	x 2	x 1

6	1	10	2
x 5	x 9	x 3	x 4

Drill #4

9	17	13	11
- 8	- 9	- 6	- 8

10	10	9	12
- 8	- 7	- 0	- 5

14	13	11	15
- 9	- 7	- 3	- 9

10	12	7	14
- 4	- 4	- 5	- 6

circle sets of 2's
$\frac{1}{2}$ of 10 =____

circle sets of 5's
$\frac{1}{5}$ of 10 =____

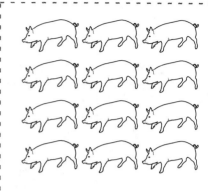

circle sets of 3's
$\frac{1}{3}$ of 12 =____

circle sets of 4's
$\frac{1}{4}$ of 12 =____

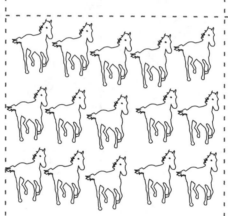

circle sets of 5's
$\frac{1}{5}$ of 15 =____

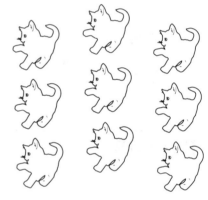

circle sets of 3's
$\frac{1}{3}$ of 9 = ____

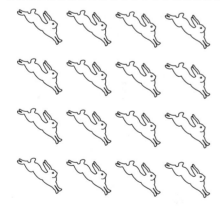

circle sets of 4's
$\frac{1}{4}$ of 16 =____

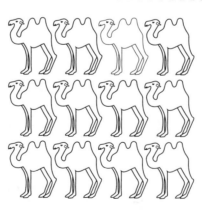

circle sets of 6's
$\frac{1}{6}$ of 12 =____

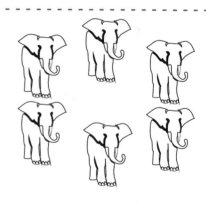

circle sets of 2's
$\frac{1}{2}$ of 6 = ____

Drill #1

2	8	9	2
+ 6	+ 1	+ 3	+ 4

6	9	9	1
+ 8	+ 1	+ 7	+ 4

5	0	9	7
+ 5	+ 9	+ 5	+ 3

3	1	4	1
+ 2	+ 2	+ 4	+ 3

Drill #2

9	7	7	2
x 2	x 0	x 5	x 7

6	1	3	6
x 3	x 6	x 2	x 1

5	3	10	6
x 2	x 7	x 10	x 2

1	2	0	3
x 7	x 2	x 3	x 5

Drill #3

8	8	5	3
x 2	x 3	x 8	x 4

6	1	4	10
x 5	x 3	x 2	x 0

8	2	5	7
x 0	x 3	x 9	x 2

10	1	2	0
x 9	x 1	x 5	x 7

Drill #4

5	15	12	6
- 3	- 8	- 7	- 5

9	8	1	7
- 1	- 6	- 1	- 2

16	14	13	11
- 7	- 9	- 5	- 2

3	4	16	10
- 2	- 4	- 9	- 2

Find the sum.

$56.20 + $0.86 =

\+ _____

$10.41 + $14.73 =

\+ _____

$15.73 + $2.18 =

\+ _____

$35.65 + $50.15 =

\+ _____

$92.45 + $1.38 =

\+ _____

$71.63 + $0.53 =

\+ _____

$81.36 + $4.58 =

\+ _____

$42.73 + $3.41 =

\+ _____

$48.72 + $20.77 =

\+ _____

$71.18 + $7.62 =

\+ _____

circle sets of 4's

shade 2 in each set

$\dfrac{2}{4}$ of   8 = _____

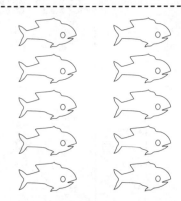

circle sets of 5's

shade 2 in each set

$\dfrac{2}{5}$ of 10 = _____

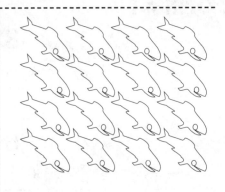

circle sets of 8's

shade 3 in each set

$\dfrac{3}{8}$ of 16 = _____

circle sets of 5's

shade 3 in each set

$\dfrac{3}{5}$ of 15 = _____

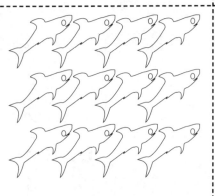

circle sets of 3's

shade 2 in each set

$\dfrac{2}{3}$ of 12 = _____

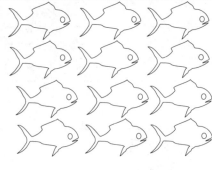

circle sets of 4's

shade 3 in each set

$\dfrac{3}{4}$ of 12 = _____

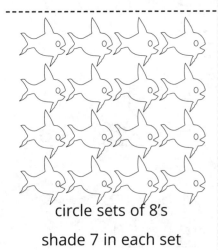

circle sets of 8's

shade 7 in each set

$\dfrac{7}{8}$ of 16 = _____

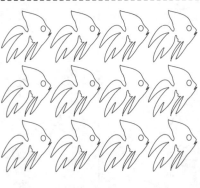

circle sets of 6's

shade 5 in each set

$\dfrac{5}{6}$ of 12 = _____

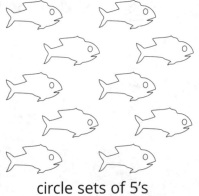

circle sets of 5's

shade 4 in each set

$\dfrac{4}{5}$ of 10 = _____

Drill #1

6	1	8	3
+ 5	+ 8	+ 5	+ 8

3	4	6	1
+ 5	+ 2	+ 1	+ 7

5	3	0	8
+ 8	+ 6	+ 6	+ 2

7	5	5	8
+ 0	+ 3	+ 0	+ 6

Drill #2

9	4	9	3
x 3	x 5	x 5	x 3

5	3	6	7
x 7	x 0	x 1	x 1

0	7	5	1
x 8	x 3	x 5	x 0

4	5	5	5
x 5	x 2	x 3	x 6

Drill #3

8	1	1	5
x 3	x 5	x 3	x 9

10	5	8	3
x 5	x 4	x 5	x 4

2	0	7	3
x 3	x 9	x 5	x 5

2	3	8	6
x 5	x 6	x 1	x 5

Drill #4

4	12	10	9
- 2	- 6	- 6	- 5

6	13	12	7
- 3	- 9	- 3	- 4

13	5	14	11
- 7	- 5	- 8	- 8

8	11	2	8
- 2	- 6	- 1	- 0

Draw a line of symmetry on each shape.

Write two word problems for each set of pictures.
Solve the word problems.

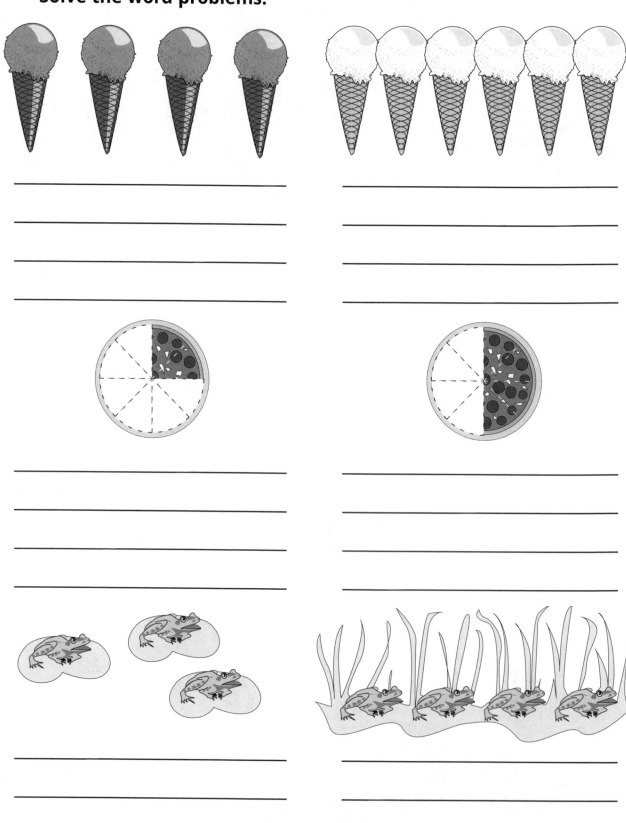

Drill #1

0 + 8	8 + 7	1 + 5	8 + 8
6 + 9	1 + 2	0 + 4	6 + 7
4 + 6	6 + 3	0 + 1	1 + 1
2 + 8	7 + 7	3 + 7	0 + 3

Drill #2

7 x 5	3 x 8	1 x 2	10 x 7
6 x 0	5 x 8	3 x 6	8 x 5
8 x 3	0 x 8	5 x 9	1 x 8
5 x 5	8 x 1	4 x 3	10 x 0

Drill #3

2 x 3	10 x 3	7 x 3	4 x 0
5 x 3	9 x 1	10 x 2	3 x 5
9 x 0	5 x 7	3 x 0	4 x 5
3 x 1	3 x 9	5 x 1	10 x 8

Drill #4

6 - 3	8 - 7	10 - 3	9 - 8
10 - 8	12 - 4	7 - 1	8 - 4
7 - 6	15 - 7	14 - 7	13 - 5
5 - 3	11 - 3	5 - 1	3 - 0

Draw each shape. Write the name of the shape on it.

Draw the shapes.

Drill #1

8 + 9	2 + 2	3 + 4	1 + 6
3 + 3	7 + 8	9 + 9	9 + 7
7 + 1	3 + 1	2 + 0	4 + 6
5 + 2	6 + 2	9 + 2	2 + 7

Drill #2

1 x 3	9 x 3	9 x 2	2 x 6
5 x 6	7 x 0	3 x 3	6 x 6
6 x 3	9 x 6	7 x 5	4 x 3
2 x 7	0 x 6	5 x 2	8 x 6

Drill #3

3 x 6	5 x 3	2 x 3	3 x 7
2 x 2	7 x 6	1 x 7	4 x 6
8 x 2	1 x 6	7 x 3	10 x 10
0 x 3	8 x 3	5 x 8	10 x 6

Drill #4

7 - 4	7 - 0	6 - 1	13 - 9
17 - 8	11 - 5	16 - 8	9 - 9
6 - 6	9 - 4	8 - 2	12 - 7
11 - 7	5 - 2	14 - 5	10 - 0

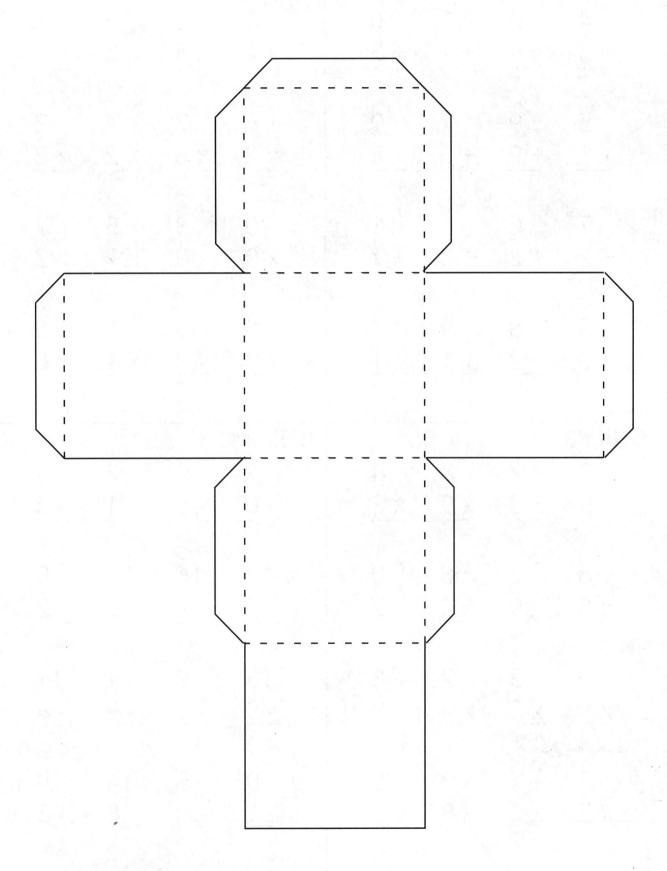

Drill #1

4	2	1	6
+ 3	+ 0	+ 1	+ 5

5	9	7	0
+ 1	+ 9	+ 6	+ 8

7	6	4	1
+ 2	+ 2	+ 8	+ 7

3	8	9	4
+ 0	+ 2	+ 1	+ 1

Drill #2

8	6	5	1
x 2	x 3	x 8	x 3

6	7	4	3
x 2	x 6	x 2	x 2

10	3	5	7
x 0	x 9	x 7	x 2

10	5	1	6
x 9	x 3	x 1	x 6

Drill #3

2	7	8	4
x 5	x 3	x 0	x 3

8	2	6	0
x 6	x 9	x 4	x 7

5	3	2	6
x 9	x 3	x 4	x 9

2	4	3	5
x 2	x 5	x 8	x 6

Drill #4

7	6	2	3
- 6	- 5	- 1	- 3

12	16	13	9
- 8	- 9	- 6	- 2

15	9	11	11
- 9	- 0	- 9	- 4

10	15	14	10
- 1	- 8	- 8	- 5

Find the area by adding.

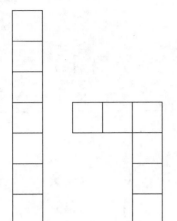 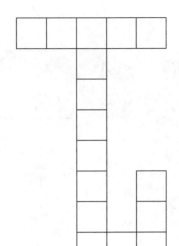 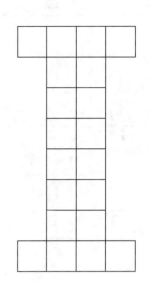

_____ square units   _____ square units   _____ square units

Find the area by multiplying.

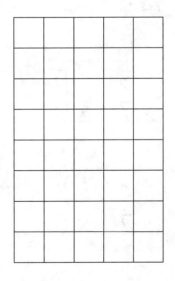 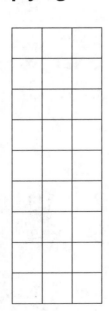 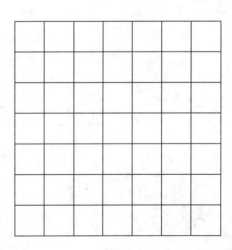

_____ square units   _____ square units   _____ square units

7	8	10	2	4	5	0	6	3	1
x 8	x 3	x 5	x 2	x 6	x 8	x 7	x 8	x 5	x 1

10	9	1	0	4	9	2	7	10	1
x 10	x 3	x 5	x 2	x 9	x 8	x 9	x 3	x 1	x 9

10	0	9	2	5	1	4	0	3	6
x 2	x 8	x 7	x 3	x 7	x 6	x 5	x 1	x 4	x 7

5	6	3	9	0	10	2	7	1	10
x 4	x 4	x 9	x 4	x 6	x 8	x 8	x 4	x 4	x 9

6	9	0	10	3	4	8	1	8	2
x 6	x 5	x 3	x 3	x 3	x 8	x 8	x 8	x 4	x 4

8	2	9	4	1	0	10	3	0	5
x 5	x 7	x 9	x 4	x 2	x 0	x 6	x 7	x 9	x 6

5	0	7	8	2	10	1	4	3	6
x 9	x 4	x 5	x 9	x 5	x 4	x 7	x 7	x 8	x 9

2	10	1	8	3	7	9	0	5	7
x 6	x 7	x 3	x 6	x 6	x 7	x 6	x 5	x 5	x 6

Drill #1

3	8	3	0
+ 4	+ 6	+ 8	+ 7

7	2	6	2
+ 2	+ 4	+ 9	+ 6

3	5	1	4
+ 2	+ 3	+ 5	+ 5

5	9	2	3
+ 7	+ 5	+ 2	+ 6

Drill #2

5	10	9	5
x 3	x 7	x 2	x 8

1	7	5	9
x 4	x 0	x 6	x 6

6	5	7	5
x 6	x 9	x 7	x 5

8	8	3	9
x 2	x 6	x 7	x 9

Drill #3

9	7	7	3
x 7	x 5	x 8	x 8

8	6	9	2
x 4	x 3	x 3	x 7

1	7	4	8
x 9	x 1	x 6	x 9

6	4	8	4
x 7	x 5	x 8	x 9

Drill #4

7	6	8	11
- 3	- 1	- 1	- 3

17	13	13	6
- 8	- 9	- 7	- 2

18	5	11	9
- 9	- 0	- 6	- 4

10	11	14	13
- 8	- 8	- 7	- 5

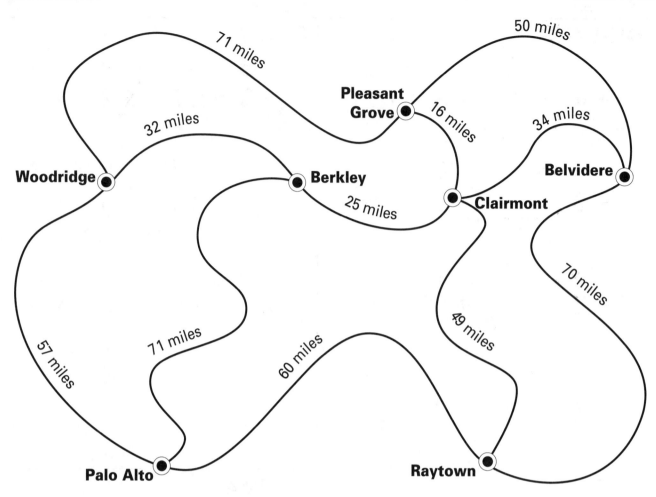

Is Raytown closer to Clairmont or Palo Alto? _____

Name two ways to go from Woodridge to Raytown.

_____

_____

What town is closest to Clairmont? _____

Name two ways to go from Palo Alto to Pleasant Grove.

_____

_____

What is the shortest way to go from Berkley to Raytown?

_____

Is Belvidere closer to Berkley or to Woodridge? _____

Worksheet

Answer
Key

Worksheet 1 — Lesson 1

0	1	2	3	4	5	6	7	8	9
10	11	12	13	14	15	16	17	18	19
20	21	22	23	24	25	26	27	28	29
30	31	32	33	34	35	36	37	38	39
40	41	42	43	44	45	46	47	48	49
50	51	52	53	54	55	56	57	58	59
60	61	62	63	64	65	66	67	68	69
70	71	72	73	74	75	76	77	78	79
80	81	82	83	84	85	86	87	88	89
90	91	92	93	94	95	96	97	98	99

Worksheet 2 — Lesson 3

1. Color the first square red.
2. Draw a tree on the fourth square.
3. Write "STOP" on the ninth square.
4. Put a circle in the thirteenth square.
5. Color the fifteenth square blue.
6. Write "GO" on the eighteenth square.
7. Draw a house on the twentieth square.

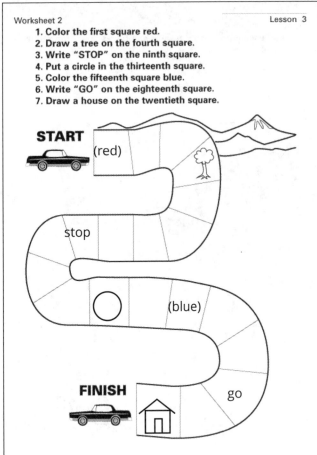

Worksheet 3 — Lesson 5

Write the numbers.

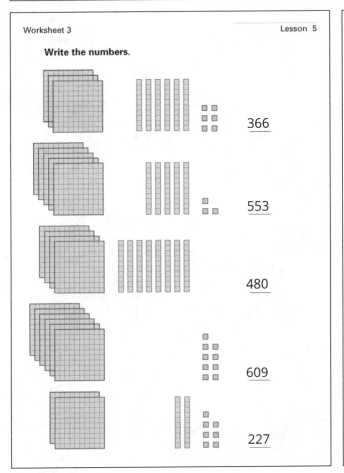

366

553

480

609

227

Worksheet 4 — Lesson 6

Write the missing numbers on the number chart.

0	1	2	3	4	5	6	7	8	9
10	11	12	13	14	15	16	17	18	19
20	21	22	23	24	25	26	27	28	29
30	31	32	33	34	35	36	37	38	39
40	41	42	43	44	45	46	47	48	49
50	51	52	53	54	55	56	57	58	59
60	61	62	63	64	65	66	67	68	69
70	71	72	73	74	75	76	77	78	79
80	81	82	83	84	85	86	87	88	89
90	91	92	93	94	95	96	97	98	99

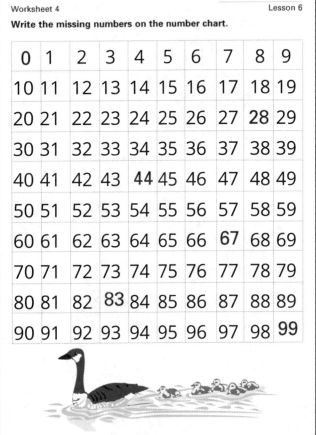

Worksheet 5 — Lesson 9

Add each number to the given number at the bottom of the ladder.

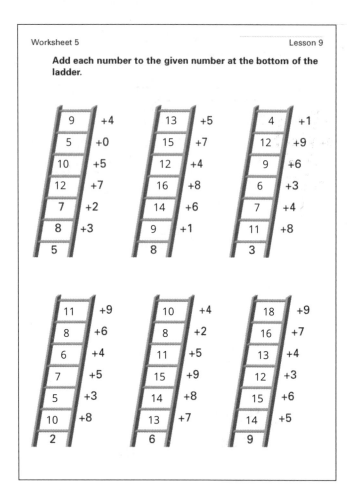

Ladder		Ladder		Ladder	
9	+4	13	+5	4	+1
5	+0	15	+7	12	+9
10	+5	12	+4	9	+6
12	+7	16	+8	6	+3
7	+2	14	+6	7	+4
8	+3	9	+1	11	+8
5		8		3	

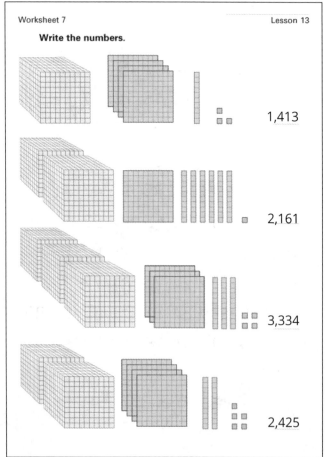

Ladder		Ladder		Ladder	
11	+9	10	+4	18	+9
8	+6	8	+2	16	+7
6	+4	11	+5	13	+4
7	+5	15	+9	12	+3
5	+3	14	+8	15	+6
10	+8	13	+7	14	+5
2		6		9	

Worksheet 6 — Lesson 11

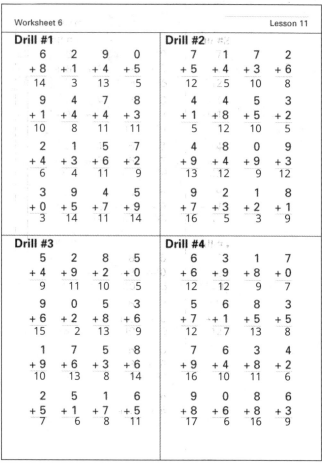

Drill #1

6 +8 = 14	2 +1 = 3	9 +4 = 13	0 +5 = 5
9 +1 = 10	4 +4 = 8	7 +4 = 11	8 +3 = 11
2 +4 = 6	1 +3 = 4	5 +6 = 11	7 +2 = 9
3 +0 = 3	9 +5 = 14	4 +7 = 11	5 +9 = 14

Drill #2

7 +5 = 12	1 +4 = 5	7 +3 = 10	2 +6 = 8
4 +1 = 5	4 +8 = 12	5 +5 = 10	3 +2 = 5
4 +9 = 13	8 +4 = 12	0 +9 = 9	9 +3 = 12
9 +7 = 16	2 +3 = 5	1 +2 = 3	8 +1 = 9

Drill #3

5 +4 = 9	2 +9 = 11	8 +2 = 10	5 +0 = 5
9 +6 = 15	0 +2 = 2	5 +8 = 13	3 +6 = 9
1 +9 = 10	7 +6 = 13	5 +3 = 8	8 +6 = 14
2 +5 = 7	5 +1 = 6	1 +7 = 8	6 +5 = 11

Drill #4

6 +6 = 12	3 +9 = 12	1 +8 = 9	7 +0 = 7
5 +7 = 12	6 +1 = 7	8 +5 = 13	3 +5 = 8
7 +9 = 16	6 +4 = 10	3 +8 = 11	4 +2 = 6
9 +8 = 17	0 +6 = 6	8 +8 = 16	6 +3 = 9

Worksheet 7 — Lesson 13

Write the numbers.

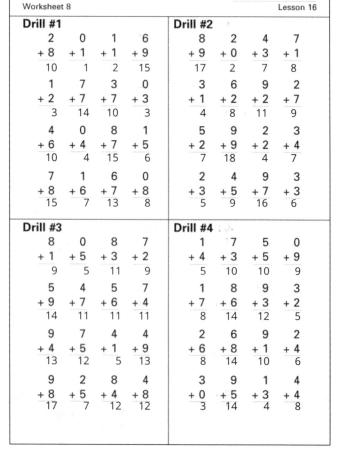

1,413

2,161

3,334

2,425

Worksheet 8 — Lesson 16

Drill #1

2 +8 = 10	0 +1 = 1	1 +1 = 2	6 +9 = 15
1 +2 = 3	7 +7 = 14	3 +7 = 10	0 +3 = 3
4 +6 = 10	0 +4 = 4	8 +7 = 15	1 +5 = 6
7 +8 = 15	1 +6 = 7	6 +7 = 13	0 +8 = 8

Drill #2

8 +9 = 17	2 +0 = 2	4 +3 = 7	7 +1 = 8
3 +1 = 4	6 +2 = 8	9 +2 = 11	2 +7 = 9
5 +2 = 7	9 +9 = 18	2 +2 = 4	3 +4 = 7
2 +3 = 5	4 +5 = 9	9 +7 = 16	3 +3 = 6

Drill #3

8 +1 = 9	0 +5 = 5	8 +3 = 11	7 +2 = 9
5 +9 = 14	4 +7 = 11	5 +6 = 11	7 +4 = 11
9 +4 = 13	7 +5 = 12	4 +1 = 5	4 +9 = 13
9 +8 = 17	2 +5 = 7	8 +4 = 12	4 +8 = 12

Drill #4

1 +4 = 5	7 +3 = 10	5 +5 = 10	0 +9 = 9
1 +7 = 8	8 +6 = 14	9 +3 = 12	3 +2 = 5
2 +6 = 8	6 +8 = 14	9 +1 = 10	2 +4 = 6
3 +0 = 3	9 +5 = 14	1 +3 = 4	4 +4 = 8

Write the missing numbers.

346   347   348   349   350   351   352   353   354   355

420   421   422   423   424   425   426   427   428   429

489   490   491   492   493   494   495   496   497   498

513   514   515   516   517   518   519   520   521   522

672   673   674   675   676   677   678   679   680   681

705   706   707   708   709   710   711   712   713   714

794   795   796   797   798   799   800   801   802   803

847   848   849   850   851   852   853   854   855   856

991   992   993   994   995   996   997   998   999   1,000

Draw both hands on the clocks.

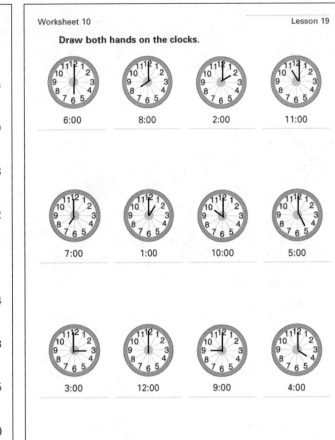

6:00   8:00   2:00   11:00

7:00   1:00   10:00   5:00

3:00   12:00   9:00   4:00

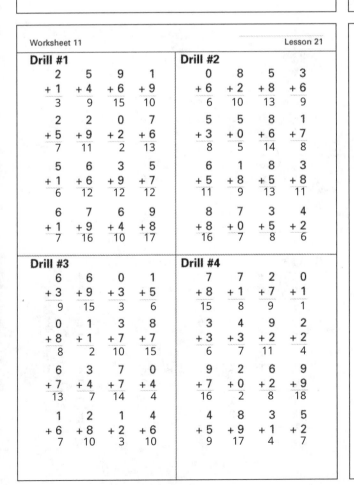

Drill #1

2	5	9	1
+1	+4	+6	+9
3	9	15	10

2	2	0	7
+5	+9	+2	+6
7	11	2	13

5	6	3	5
+1	+6	+9	+7
6	12	12	12

6	7	6	9
+1	+9	+4	+8
7	16	10	17

Drill #2

0	8	5	3
+6	+2	+8	+6
6	10	13	9

5	5	8	1
+3	+0	+6	+7
8	5	14	8

6	1	8	3
+5	+8	+5	+8
11	9	13	11

8	7	3	4
+8	+0	+5	+2
16	7	8	6

Drill #3

6	6	0	1
+3	+9	+3	+5
9	15	3	6

0	1	3	8
+8	+1	+7	+7
8	2	10	15

6	3	7	0
+7	+4	+7	+4
13	7	14	4

1	2	1	4
+6	+8	+2	+6
7	10	3	10

Drill #4

7	7	2	0
+8	+1	+7	+1
15	8	9	1

3	4	9	2
+3	+3	+2	+2
6	7	11	4

9	2	6	9
+7	+0	+2	+9
16	2	8	18

4	8	3	5
+5	+9	+1	+2
9	17	4	7

Write the correct time.

3:00   8:00   12:00   5:00

2:30   4:30   7:30   11:30

1:45   10:45   6:15   9:15

9:30   6:00   11:45   4:15

Drill #1

2	7	7	4
+3	+2	+4	+9
5	9	11	13
4	8	5	4
+ 8	+ 3	+ 6	+ 1
12	11	11	5
8	0	4	7
+ 4	+ 5	+ 7	+ 5
12	5	11	12
6	8	5	9
+ 3	+ 8	+ 9	+ 4
9	16	14	13

Drill #2

9	0	3	2
+ 7	+ 9	+ 2	+ 4
16	9	5	6
4	5	9	9
+ 4	+ 5	+ 3	+ 1
8	10	12	10
1	7	8	6
+ 3	+ 3	+ 1	+ 8
4	10	9	14
9	1	1	2
+ 5	+ 4	+ 2	+ 6
14	5	3	8

Drill #3

3	1	7	5
+ 0	+ 9	+ 6	+ 7
3	10	13	12
9	9	0	3
+ 8	+ 6	+ 2	+ 9
17	15	2	12
6	5	2	6
+ 4	+ 4	+ 9	+ 6
10	9	11	12
7	2	2	5
+ 9	+ 1	+ 5	+ 1
16	3	7	6

Drill #4

6	3	1	3
+ 1	+ 6	+ 7	+ 8
7	9	8	11
3	4	9	2
+ 2	+ 8	+ 6	+ 5
5	12	15	7
3	8	5	1
+ 5	+ 2	+ 0	+ 8
8	10	5	9
7	0	5	6
+ 0	+ 6	+ 3	+ 5
7	6	8	11

Follow the pattern of the arrows to complete the ladders.

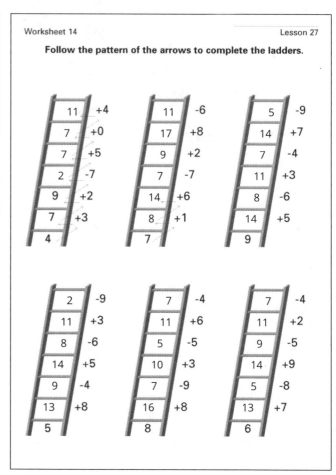

16	10	3	12	10	10	7	13	9	6
-7	-1	-3	-9	-8	-6	-3	-9	-9	-5
9	9	0	3	2	4	4	4	0	1
4	11	7	15	6	9	11	8	17	13
-4	-9	-4	-8	-3	-4	-8	-5	-9	-7
0	2	3	7	3	5	3	3	8	6
6	11	9	15	13	4	12	8	7	11
-4	-4	-6	-9	-5	-3	-7	-2	-6	-2
2	7	3	6	8	1	5	6	1	9
12	6	17	4	9	8	16	14	10	13
-3	-6	-8	-2	-3	-7	-9	-5	-4	-8
9	0	9	2	6	1	7	9	6	5
13	8	11	7	15	5	9	12	10	10
-6	-6	-5	-5	-7	-4	-8	-8	-7	-9
7	2	6	2	8	1	1	4	3	1
5	14	8	16	10	7	14	6	9	12
-2	-6	-3	-8	-3	-7	-7	-2	-5	-4
3	8	5	8	7	0	7	4	4	8
10	12	5	9	15	11	8	10	13	14
-2	-6	-5	-7	-6	-7	-4	-5	-4	-8
8	6	0	2	9	4	4	5	9	6
12	18	9	14	3	7	11	5	8	11
-5	-9	-2	-9	-2	-2	-6	-3	-8	-3
7	9	7	5	1	5	5	2	0	8

Drill #1

8	1	8	0
+ 8	+ 5	+ 7	+ 4
16	6	15	4
4	0	3	7
+ 6	+ 3	+ 7	+ 7
10	3	10	14
1	6	1	0
+ 2	+ 9	+ 1	+ 1
3	15	2	1
2	6	0	6
+ 8	+ 3	+ 8	+ 7
10	9	8	13

Drill #2

15	9	5	13
- 7	- 6	- 0	- 4
8	3	5	9
8	2	10	3
- 7	- 2	- 5	- 1
1	0	5	2
6	18	5	7
- 6	- 9	- 2	- 3
0	9	3	4
10	4	12	1
- 1	- 3	- 6	- 0
9	1	6	1

Drill #3

1	3	2	9
+ 6	+ 4	+ 2	+ 9
7	7	4	18
5	2	9	6
+ 2	+ 7	+ 2	+ 2
7	9	11	8
3	7	4	2
+ 1	+ 1	+ 3	+ 0
4	8	7	2
8	7	3	9
+ 9	+ 8	+ 3	+ 7
17	15	6	16

Drill #4

6	16	4	8
- 0	- 8	- 1	- 3
6	8	3	5
11	2	6	13
- 5	- 0	- 2	- 8
6	2	4	5
9	6	14	3
- 2	- 4	- 7	- 3
7	2	7	0
11	7	5	10
- 9	- 7	- 4	- 9
2	0	1	1

210	174	371	393	281	642	481
+ 590	+ 292	+ 136	+ 256	+ 490	+ 184	+ 275
800	466	507	649	771	826	756

137	152	581	320	497	374	592
+ 191	+ 453	+ 283	+ 381	+ 432	+ 250	+ 391
328	605	864	701	929	624	983

270	231	593	371	742	154	485
+ 534	+ 692	+ 145	+ 578	+ 180	+ 693	+ 174
804	923	738	949	922	847	659

271	487	460	152	261	123	396
+ 697	+ 160	+ 293	+ 382	+ 371	+ 594	+ 423
968	647	753	534	632	717	819

175	664	281	683	248	390	572
+ 463	+ 145	+ 354	+ 241	+ 170	+ 312	+ 183
638	809	635	924	418	702	755

362	190	631	162	586	253	374
+ 467	+ 365	+ 276	+ 145	+ 240	+ 163	+ 164
829	555	907	307	826	416	538

458	185	463	576	790	631	362
+ 361	+ 730	+ 352	+ 241	+ 186	+ 285	+ 482
819	915	815	817	976	916	844

426	340	255	581	143	492	362
+ 492	+ 267	+ 271	+ 327	+ 290	+ 176	+ 574
918	607	526	908	433	668	936

Drill #1

6	0	5	4
+ 3	+ 5	+ 6	+ 9
9	5	11	13

8	8	7	9
+ 4	+ 3	+ 4	+ 4
12	11	11	13

7	4	5	7
+ 2	+ 8	+ 9	+ 5
9	12	14	12

2	8	4	4
+ 3	+ 1	+ 7	+ 1
5	9	11	5

Drill #2

8	17	9	15
- 1	- 8	- 3	- 6
7	9	6	9

9	16	14	8
- 4	- 7	- 5	- 5
5	9	9	3

9	12	12	11
- 7	- 8	- 9	- 4
2	4	3	7

7	10	8	11
- 1	- 3	- 8	- 7
6	7	0	4

Drill #3

7	5	0	5
+ 9	+ 4	+ 2	+ 7
16	9	2	12

2	2	3	3
+ 1	+ 9	+ 9	+ 0
3	11	12	3

2	6	9	1
+ 5	+ 6	+ 8	+ 9
7	12	17	10

5	6	9	7
+ 1	+ 4	+ 6	+ 6
6	10	15	13

Drill #4

12	15	14	11
- 5	- 9	- 6	- 8
7	6	8	3

11	7	13	9
- 3	- 5	- 6	- 0
8	2	7	9

12	17	10	13
- 4	- 9	- 7	- 7
8	8	3	6

9	10	14	10
- 8	- 8	- 9	- 4
1	2	5	6

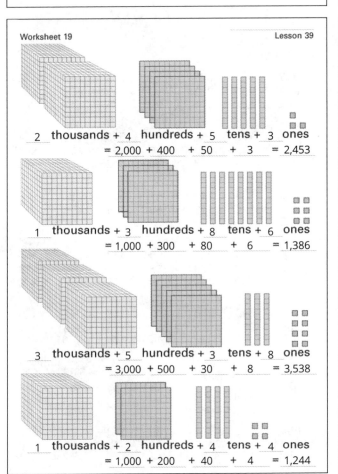

2 thousands + 4 hundreds + 5 tens + 3 ones
= 2,000 + 400 + 50 + 3 = 2,453

1 thousands + 3 hundreds + 8 tens + 6 ones
= 1,000 + 300 + 80 + 6 = 1,386

3 thousands + 5 hundreds + 3 tens + 8 ones
= 3,000 + 500 + 30 + 8 = 3,538

1 thousands + 2 hundreds + 4 tens + 4 ones
= 1,000 + 200 + 40 + 4 = 1,244

Drill #1

9	7	9	2
+ 5	+ 3	+ 3	+ 4
14	10	12	6

1	8	9	9
+ 4	+ 1	+ 1	+ 7
5	9	10	16

1	6	4	0
+ 2	+ 8	+ 4	+ 9
3	14	8	9

2	1	5	3
+ 6	+ 3	+ 5	+ 2
8	4	10	5

Drill #2

7	4	10	6
- 2	- 4	- 2	- 5
5	0	8	1

13	1	12	16
- 5	- 1	- 7	- 9
8	0	5	7

5	15	8	14
- 3	- 8	- 6	- 9
2	7	2	5

11	9	16	3
- 2	- 1	- 7	- 2
9	8	9	1

Drill #3

7	8	8	3
+ 0	+ 2	+ 6	+ 8
7	10	14	11

0	5	8	6
+ 6	+ 0	+ 5	+ 1
6	5	13	7

5	1	4	3
+ 3	+ 8	+ 2	+ 6
8	9	6	9

6	3	5	1
+ 5	+ 5	+ 8	+ 7
11	8	13	8

Drill #4

7	11	8	9
- 4	- 8	- 0	- 5
3	3	8	4

14	2	10	12
- 8	- 1	- 6	- 3
6	1	4	9

11	12	13	5
- 6	- 6	- 9	- 5
5	6	4	0

4	6	13	8
- 2	- 3	- 7	- 2
2	3	6	6

Worksheet 21 — Lesson 42

Write the correct time.

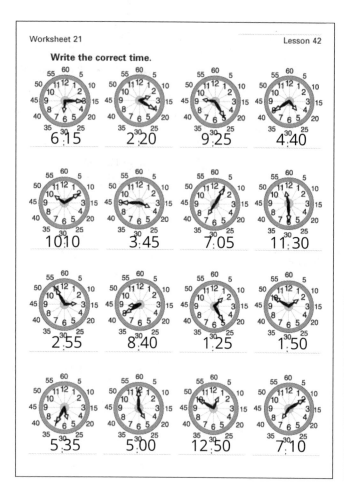

6:15	2:20	9:25	4:40
10:10	3:45	7:05	11:30
2:55	8:40	1:25	1:50
5:35	5:00	12:50	7:10

Worksheet 22 — Lesson 45

Write the correct time.

10:50	1:15	6:45	5:40
7:00	2:05	4:05	11:35
3:30	9:20	2:35	8:55
12:20	5:10	11:40	8:25

Worksheet 23 — Lesson 46

Drill #1

```
  6    1    0    8
+ 7  + 1  + 3  + 8
 13    2    3   16

  0    3    1    0
+ 1  + 7  + 5  + 4
  1   10    6    4

  7    8    1    6
+ 7  + 7  + 2  + 3
 14   15    3    9

  0    6    4    2
+ 8  + 9  + 6  + 8
  8   15   10   10
```

Drill #2

```
  8   13    3    9
- 4  - 5  - 0  - 8
  4    8    3    1

 14    5   10    7
- 7  - 1  - 3  - 1
  7    4    7    6

 11    8   12   15
- 3  - 7  - 4  - 7
  8    1    8    8

  6   10    7    5
- 3  - 8  - 6  - 3
  3    2    1    2
```

Drill #3

```
  9    4    2    1
+ 7  + 3  + 7  + 6
 16    7    9    7

  2    9    3    9
+ 0  + 2  + 4  + 9
  2   11    7   18

  6    2    7    3
+ 2  + 2  + 8  + 1
  8    4   15    4

  8    3    7    5
+ 9  + 3  + 1  + 2
 17    6    8    7
```

Drill #4

```
  9   12   10   13
- 9  - 7  - 6  - 9
  0    5    4    4

  8   14    6   16
- 2  - 5  - 1  - 8
  6    9    5    8

  5    7   11    9
- 2  - 0  - 5  - 4
  3    7    6    5

  7   17    6   11
- 4  - 8  - 6  - 7
  3    9    0    4
```

Worksheet 24 — Lesson 48

Add to find the sum.

```
  365     481     565     243     789     374     198
+ 549   + 439   + 295   + 198   + 127   + 576   + 642
  914     920     860     441     916     950     840

  627     169     698     237     598     245     364
+ 186   + 143   + 196   + 396   + 354   + 679   + 398
  813     312     894     633     952     924     762

  396     194     548     457     396     286     565
+ 127   + 526   + 175   + 169   + 485   + 475   + 287
  523     720     723     626     881     761     852

  276     798     261     459     187     672     154
+ 486   + 168   + 259   + 286   + 264   + 289   + 478
  762     966     520     745     451     961     632

  383     548     238     477     369     367     429
+ 469   + 387   + 575   + 235   + 275   + 289   + 381
  852     935     813     712     644     656     810

  393     179     686     196     458     435     287
+ 378   + 349   + 247   + 746   + 169   + 487   + 394
  771     528     933     942     627     922     681

  254     489     547     285     393     279     252
+ 187   + 381   + 193   + 635   + 187   + 253   + 589
  441     870     740     920     580     532     841
```

Worksheet 25 — Teacher check — Lesson 49

Draw both hands on the clocks and write the time the teacher indicates.

Worksheet 26 — Lesson 51

Drill #1

0	1	4	6
+ 3	+ 9	+ 1	+ 5
3	10	5	11
4	9	1	7
+ 8	+ 1	+ 1	+ 6
12	10	2	13
8	2	9	6
+ 2	+ 0	+ 9	+ 2
10	2	18	8
4	5	7	3
+ 3	+ 1	+ 2	+ 0
7	6	9	3

Drill #2

4	9	10	5
- 3	- 6	- 2	- 5
1	3	8	0
8	13	12	12
- 5	- 8	- 9	- 3
3	5	3	9
11	15	4	14
- 2	- 6	- 0	- 6
9	9	4	8
7	10	11	18
- 2	- 4	- 6	- 9
5	6	5	9

Drill #3

2	4	3	0
+ 6	+ 5	+ 6	+ 7
8	9	9	7
1	2	3	6
+ 5	+ 2	+ 8	+ 9
6	4	11	15
9	8	2	5
+ 5	+ 6	+ 4	+ 3
14	14	6	8
3	7	3	5
+ 4	+ 5	+ 2	+ 7
7	12	5	12

Drill #4

9	11	10	3
- 2	- 3	- 5	- 3
7	8	5	0
11	14	2	13
- 9	- 8	- 1	- 6
2	6	1	7
15	6	16	9
- 8	- 5	- 9	- 0
7	1	7	9
7	12	15	10
- 6	- 8	- 9	- 1
1	4	6	9

Worksheet 27 — Lesson 54

Subtract to find the difference.

90	23	92	42	74	64	91
- 81	- 4	- 13	- 34	- 69	- 15	- 62
9	19	79	8	5	49	29
53	96	91	27	80	62	86
- 19	- 58	- 79	- 18	- 12	- 35	- 47
34	38	12	9	68	27	39
83	30	85	91	54	74	65
- 15	- 26	- 66	- 86	- 26	- 58	- 56
68	4	19	5	28	16	9
82	90	67	73	93	32	96
- 26	- 25	- 29	- 46	- 26	- 7	- 58
56	65	38	27	67	25	38
81	73	64	75	81	40	51
- 77	- 28	- 47	- 27	- 55	- 13	- 47
4	45	17	48	26	27	4
95	31	50	71	42	86	72
- 39	- 18	- 37	- 54	- 28	- 39	- 36
56	13	13	17	14	47	36
78	60	51	82	64	93	85
- 19	- 54	- 43	- 49	- 18	- 47	- 78
59	6	8	33	46	46	7

Worksheet 28 — Lesson 56

Drill #1

0	2	6	7
+ 5	+ 9	+ 7	+ 8
5	11	13	15
3	4	1	5
+ 3	+ 9	+ 7	+ 5
6	13	8	10
5	1	4	9
+ 2	+ 2	+ 0	+ 3
7	3	4	12
9	6	3	2
+ 0	+ 4	+ 9	+ 5
9	10	12	7

Drill #2

1	12	7	10
- 0	- 5	- 3	- 3
1	7	4	7
6	13	4	14
- 1	- 6	- 2	- 9
5	7	2	5
11	8	10	3
- 3	- 4	- 7	- 1
8	4	3	2
12	15	9	5
- 4	- 9	- 7	- 0
8	6	2	5

Drill #3

4	5	6	0
+ 4	+ 9	+ 1	+ 9
8	14	7	9
1	7	4	1
+ 6	+ 4	+ 6	+ 3
7	11	10	4
5	6	8	7
+ 6	+ 0	+ 4	+ 1
11	6	12	8
2	8	9	2
+ 1	+ 8	+ 7	+ 8
3	16	16	10

Drill #4

17	1	10	6
- 9	- 1	- 5	- 0
8	0	5	6
14	3	12	13
- 5	- 2	- 8	- 4
9	1	4	9
4	10	7	11
- 4	- 9	- 5	- 7
0	1	2	4
5	17	8	9
- 4	- 8	- 1	- 3
1	9	7	6

Write any three-digit number. Answers vary

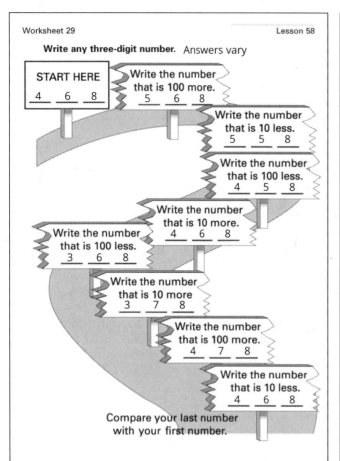

START HERE
4   6   8

Write the number that is 100 more.
5   6   8

Write the number that is 10 less.
5   5   8

Write the number that is 100 less.
4   5   8

Write the number that is 10 more.
4   6   8

Write the number that is 100 less.
3   6   8

Write the number that is 10 more.
3   7   8

Write the number that is 100 more.
4   7   8

Write the number that is 10 less.
4   6   8

Compare your last number with your first number.

Drill #1

1	9	2	6
+ 4	+ 8	+ 3	+ 6
5	17	5	12
8	3	3	7
+ 7	+ 7	+ 1	+ 9
15	10	4	16
4	7	1	9
+ 2	+ 5	+ 0	+ 4
6	12	1	13
7	8	5	4
+ 0	+ 3	+ 4	+ 7
7	11	9	11

Drill #2

16	9	2	13
- 8	- 5	- 0	- 4
8	4	2	9
13	6	14	8
- 8	- 4	- 6	- 3
5	2	8	5
4	15	8	11
- 1	- 8	- 8	- 8
3	7	0	3
12	5	18	9
- 5	- 1	- 9	- 9
7	4	9	0

Drill #3

2	9	1	6
+ 7	+ 6	+ 8	+ 8
9	15	9	14
8	4	3	7
+ 9	+ 3	+ 5	+ 7
17	7	8	14
6	7	5	9
+ 3	+ 3	+ 0	+ 2
9	10	5	11
0	8	9	5
+ 1	+ 5	+ 7	+ 8
1	13	16	13

Drill #4

16	10	2	12
- 7	- 5	- 2	- 9
9	5	0	3
13	7	14	8
- 9	- 7	- 7	- 6
4	0	7	2
3	15	9	11
- 0	- 7	- 1	- 9
3	8	8	2
12	6	17	5
- 6	- 2	- 9	- 2
6	4	8	3

X	0	1	2	3	4	5	6	7	8	9	10
0	0	0	0	0	0	0	0	0	0	0	0
1	0	1	2	3	4	5	6	7	8	9	10
2	0	2	4	6	8	10	12	14	16	18	20
3	0	3	6	9	12	15	18	21	24	27	30
4	0	4	8	12	16	20	24	28	32	36	40
5	0	5	10	15	20	25	30	35	40	45	50
6	0	6	12	18	24	30	36	42	48	54	60
7	0	7	14	21	28	35	42	49	56	63	70
8	0	8	16	24	32	40	48	56	64	72	80
9	0	9	18	27	36	45	54	63	72	81	90
10	0	10	20	30	40	50	60	70	80	90	100

Write the missing numbers in the blanks.

0 + 0 = 0	2 + 3 = 5	7 + 9 = 16	1 + 9 = 10
8 + 3 = 11	2 + 1 = 3	9 + 3 = 12	6 + 9 = 15
3 + 7 = 10	5 + 8 = 13	6 + 2 = 8	2 + 6 = 8
7 + 7 = 14	1 + 6 = 7	8 + 1 = 9	0 + 6 = 6
2 + 2 = 4	7 + 3 = 10	9 + 9 = 18	3 + 4 = 7
5 + 9 = 14	1 + 8 = 9	3 + 8 = 11	3 + 2 = 5
4 + 7 = 11	1 + 1 = 2	4 + 0 = 4	5 + 7 = 12
6 + 3 = 9	4 + 2 = 6	2 + 9 = 11	1 + 4 = 5
9 + 5 = 14	6 + 5 = 11	8 + 8 = 16	4 + 8 = 12
4 + 5 = 9	4 + 6 = 10	3 + 3 = 6	3 + 9 = 12

Drill #1

0	5	2	9
+ 6	+ 7	+ 0	+ 9
6	12	2	18
3	7	8	1
+ 1	+ 4	+ 0	+ 1
4	11	8	2
5	9	4	8
+ 3	+ 1	+ 2	+ 2
8	10	6	10
6	7	8	3
+ 9	+ 2	+ 8	+ 8
15	9	16	11

Drill #2

16	7	15	10
- 9	- 4	- 6	- 8
7	3	9	2
6	11	9	5
- 0	- 2	- 9	- 5
6	9	0	0
12	8	10	9
- 3	- 5	- 1	- 2
9	3	9	7
10	6	7	11
- 4	- 4	- 0	- 5
6	2	7	6

Drill #3

6	1	4	9
+ 5	+ 5	+ 6	+ 5
11	6	10	14
3	8	0	2
+ 5	+ 6	+ 8	+ 4
8	14	8	6
3	4	6	7
+ 3	+ 8	+ 2	+ 6
6	12	8	13
0	4	7	1
+ 4	+ 5	+ 8	+ 9
4	9	15	10

Drill #4

10	9	14	10
- 6	- 6	- 8	- 9
4	3	6	1
13	8	11	8
- 7	- 8	- 4	- 0
6	0	7	8
5	6	10	9
- 0	- 6	- 2	- 3
5	0	8	6
11	12	4	3
- 6	- 7	- 1	- 1
5	5	3	2

Circle the picture that comes next in each sequence.

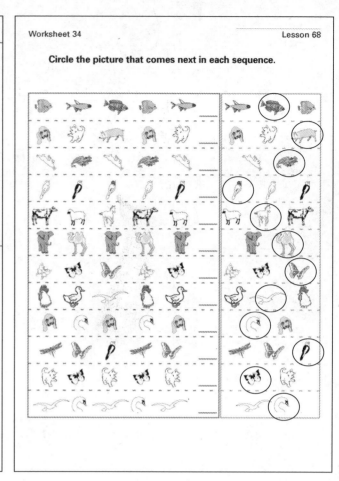

Drill #1

8	6	9	7
+ 5	+ 6	+ 7	+ 3
13	12	16	10
5	1	0	5
+ 9	+ 2	+ 0	+ 5
14	3	0	10
3	9	2	8
+ 4	+ 2	+ 1	+ 9
7	11	3	17
2	7	6	7
+ 6	+ 0	+ 3	+ 7
8	7	9	14

Drill #2

1	7	3	13
- 0	- 3	- 1	- 4
1	4	2	9
12	5	10	5
- 6	- 2	- 5	- 0
6	3	5	5
4	18	2	9
- 3	- 9	- 2	- 6
1	9	0	3
10	6	8	15
- 1	- 6	- 7	- 7
9	0	1	8

Drill #3

7	1	6	9
+ 9	+ 3	+ 7	+ 8
16	4	13	17
5	4	0	5
+ 8	+ 1	+ 2	+ 6
13	5	2	11
8	9	6	8
+ 1	+ 3	+ 4	+ 7
9	12	10	15
5	2	5	7
+ 0	+ 2	+ 2	+ 5
5	4	7	12

Drill #4

10	3	13	8
- 9	- 3	- 8	- 3
1	0	5	5
5	14	6	4
- 4	- 7	- 2	- 1
1	7	4	3
7	6	2	16
- 7	- 4	- 0	- 8
0	2	2	8
11	9	11	6
- 9	- 2	- 5	- 0
2	7	6	6

Write the total value of each line.

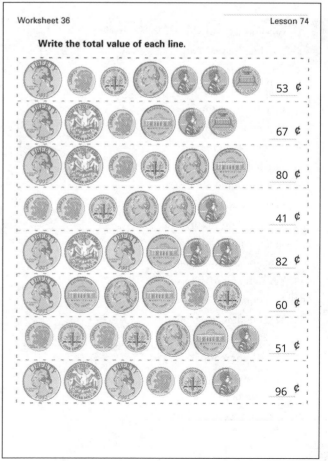

53 ¢

67 ¢

80 ¢

41 ¢

82 ¢

60 ¢

51 ¢

96 ¢

Drill #1

6	0	7	0
+7	+1	+7	+4
13	1	14	4
0	1	3	8
+8	+1	+7	+7
8	2	10	15
6	6	0	1
+3	+9	+3	+5
9	15	3	6
2	1	4	8
+8	+2	+6	+8
10	3	10	16

Drill #2

11	11	8	15
-7	-4	-5	-6
4	7	3	9
8	12	14	9
-8	-9	-5	-3
0	3	9	6
10	12	16	17
-3	-8	-7	-8
7	4	9	9
7	9	9	8
-1	-7	-4	-1
6	2	5	7

Drill #3

9	2	6	9
+7	+0	+2	+9
16	2	8	18
3	4	9	2
+3	+3	+2	+2
6	7	11	4
7	7	2	3
+8	+1	+7	+4
15	8	9	7
8	3	5	1
+9	+1	+2	+6
17	4	7	7

Drill #4

10	13	9	11
-4	-7	-0	-8
6	6	9	3
14	10	13	14
-9	-6	-6	-6
5	4	7	8
10	17	7	15
-8	-9	-5	-9
2	8	2	6
9	12	11	12
-8	-4	-3	-5
1	8	8	7

Write the numbers.

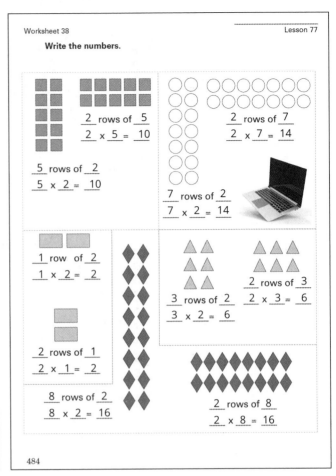

2 rows of 5
2 x 5 = 10

5 rows of 2
5 x 2 = 10

2 rows of 7
2 x 7 = 14

7 rows of 2
7 x 2 = 14

1 row of 2
1 x 2 = 2

2 rows of 1
2 x 1 = 2

8 rows of 2
8 x 2 = 16

3 rows of 2
3 x 2 = 6

2 rows of 3
2 x 3 = 6

2 rows of 8
2 x 8 = 16

484

Write the numbers.

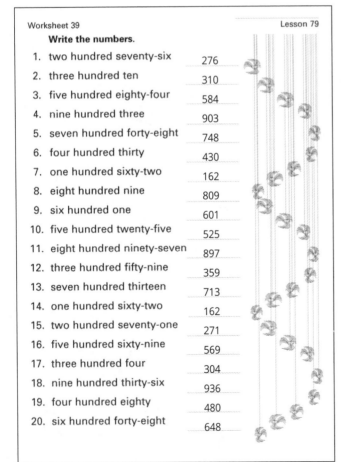

1. two hundred seventy-six — 276
2. three hundred ten — 310
3. five hundred eighty-four — 584
4. nine hundred three — 903
5. seven hundred forty-eight — 748
6. four hundred thirty — 430
7. one hundred sixty-two — 162
8. eight hundred nine — 809
9. six hundred one — 601
10. five hundred twenty-five — 525
11. eight hundred ninety-seven — 897
12. three hundred fifty-nine — 359
13. seven hundred thirteen — 713
14. one hundred sixty-two — 162
15. two hundred seventy-one — 271
16. five hundred sixty-nine — 569
17. three hundred four — 304
18. nine hundred thirty-six — 936
19. four hundred eighty — 480
20. six hundred forty-eight — 648

Drill #1

3	0	9	2
+2	+9	+7	+4
5	9	16	6
5	9	9	1
+5	+1	+3	+3
10	10	12	4
6	4	8	7
+8	+4	+1	+3
14	8	9	10
2	1	9	1
+6	+2	+5	+4
8	3	14	5

Drill #2

3	14	16	6
-2	-9	-9	-5
1	5	7	1
16	8	12	10
-7	-6	-7	-2
9	2	5	8
9	15	1	11
-1	-8	-1	-2
8	7	0	9
5	4	13	7
-3	-4	-5	-2
2	0	8	5

Drill #3

7	3	6	3
+0	+6	+1	+8
7	9	7	11
5	4	8	8
+8	+2	+5	+6
13	6	13	14
3	1	5	8
+5	+8	+0	+2
8	9	5	10
6	5	0	1
+5	+3	+6	+7
11	8	6	8

Drill #4

8	5	12	9
-2	-5	-3	-5
6	0	9	4
13	13	10	8
-7	-9	-6	-0
6	4	4	8
6	12	2	11
-3	-6	-1	-8
3	6	1	3
4	11	14	7
-2	-6	-8	-4
2	5	6	3

Multiply to find the products.

X	0	1	2	3	4	5	6	7	8	9	10
0	0	0	0	0	0	0	0	0	0	0	0
1	0	1	2	3	4	5	6	7	8	9	10
2	0	2	4	6	8	10	12	14	16	18	20
3	0	3	6	9	12	15	18	21	24	27	30
4	0	4	8	12	16	20	24	28	32	36	40
5	0	5	10	15	20	25	30	35	40	45	50
6	0	6	12	18	24	30	36	42	48	54	60
7	0	7	14	21	28	35	42	49	56	63	70
8	0	8	16	24	32	40	48	56	64	72	80
9	0	9	18	27	36	45	54	63	72	81	90
10	0	10	20	30	40	50	60	70	80	90	100

Multiply to find the products.

X	5	2	7	0	1	6	10	4	9	3	8
0	0	0	0	0	0	0	0	0	0	0	0

X	0	4	7	1	6	10	8	2	5	9	3
1	0	4	7	1	6	10	8	2	5	9	3

X	1	5	0	10	8	4	2	7	9	3	6
2	2	10	0	20	16	8	4	14	18	6	12

X	4	7	1	9	5	0	3	10	6	8	2
5	20	35	5	45	25	0	15	50	30	40	10

X	4	8	6	3	0	9	7	2	10	5	1
10	40	80	60	30	0	90	70	20	100	50	10

Drill #1

2	6	0	8
+8	+3	+4	+8
10	9	4	16

4	1	1	0
+6	+2	+5	+3
10	3	6	3

6	8	3	1
+9	+7	+7	+1
15	15	10	2

0	7	0	6
+8	+7	+1	+7
8	14	1	13

Drill #2

5	15	7	9
-3	-7	-1	-8
2	8	6	1

7	12	10	3
-6	-4	-3	-0
1	8	7	3

10	8	5	13
-8	-7	-1	-5
2	1	4	8

6	11	14	8
-3	-3	-7	-4
3	8	7	4

Drill #3

5	3	9	1
+2	+1	+9	+6
7	4	18	7

7	7	3	2
+1	+8	+4	+7
8	15	7	9

3	2	9	4
+3	+2	+2	+3
6	4	11	7

8	6	2	9
+9	+2	+0	+7
17	8	2	16

Drill #4

11	9	16	13
-7	-4	-8	-9
4	5	8	4

6	11	6	10
-6	-5	-1	-6
0	6	5	4

17	7	14	12
-8	-0	-5	-7
9	7	9	5

7	5	8	9
-4	-2	-2	-9
3	3	6	0

Write the value.

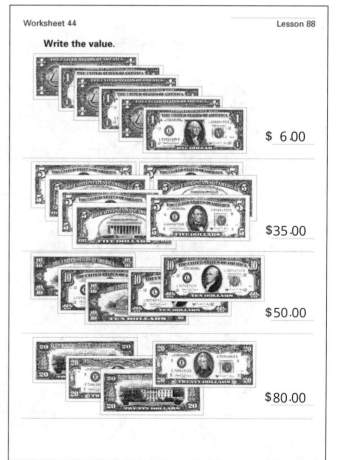

$ 6.00

$35.00

$50.00

$80.00

Drill #1

3	6	7	6
+ 0	+ 2	+ 6	+ 5
3	8	13	11
7	9	1	4
+ 2	+ 9	+ 1	+ 1
9	18	2	5
5	2	9	1
+ 1	+ 0	+ 1	+ 9
6	2	10	10
4	8	4	0
+ 3	+ 2	+ 8	+ 3
7	10	12	3

Drill #2

18	14	12	5
- 9	- 6	- 3	- 5
9	8	9	0
11	4	12	10
- 6	- 0	- 9	- 2
5	4	3	8
10	15	13	9
- 4	- 6	- 8	- 6
6	9	5	3
7	11	8	4
- 2	- 2	- 5	- 3
5	9	3	1

Drill #3

5	5	6	0
+ 7	+ 3	+ 9	+ 7
12	8	15	7
3	2	3	3
+ 2	+ 4	+ 8	+ 6
5	6	11	9
7	8	2	4
+ 7	+ 6	+ 2	+ 5
14	14	4	9
3	9	1	2
+ 4	+ 5	+ 5	+ 6
7	14	6	8

Drill #4

10	9	13	3
- 1	- 0	- 6	- 3
9	9	7	0
15	16	2	10
- 9	- 9	- 1	- 5
6	7	1	5
12	6	14	11
- 8	- 5	- 8	- 4
4	1	6	7
7	15	11	9
- 6	- 8	- 9	- 2
1	7	2	7

Circle the next shape in sequence.

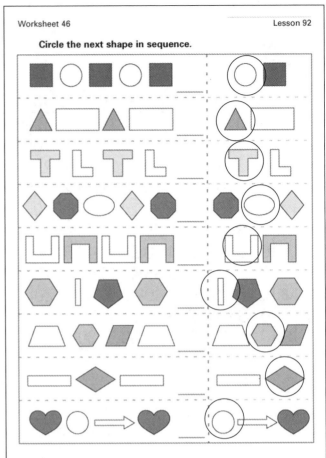

Put an "X" on the money needed.

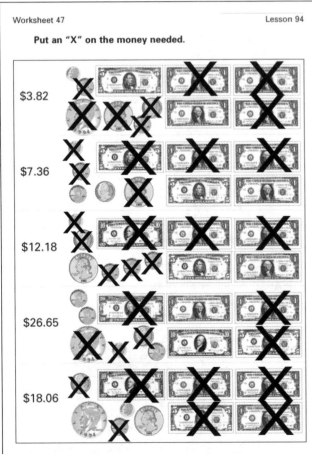

$3.82

$7.36

$12.18

$26.65

$18.06

Drill #1

2	9	5	7
+ 5	+ 3	+ 5	+ 8
7	12	10	15
3	4	1	6
+ 9	+ 0	+ 7	+ 7
12	4	8	13
6	1	4	2
+ 4	+ 2	+ 9	+ 9
10	3	13	11
9	5	3	0
+ 0	+ 2	+ 3	+ 5
9	7	6	5

Drill #2

5	3	14	10
- 0	- 1	- 9	- 3
5	2	5	7
9	10	4	7
- 7	- 7	- 2	- 3
2	3	2	4
15	8	13	12
- 9	- 4	- 6	- 5
6	4	7	7
12	11	6	1
- 4	- 3	- 1	- 0
8	8	5	1

Drill #3

2	7	1	0
+ 8	+ 1	+ 3	+ 9
10	8	4	9
9	8	4	6
+ 7	+ 4	+ 6	+ 1
16	12	10	7
8	6	7	5
+ 8	+ 0	+ 4	+ 9
16	6	11	14
2	5	1	4
+ 1	+ 6	+ 6	+ 4
3	11	7	8

Drill #4

9	11	13	6
- 3	- 7	- 4	- 0
6	4	9	6
8	7	12	10
- 1	- 5	- 8	- 4
7	2	4	6
1	3	10	17
- 1	- 2	- 9	- 8
0	1	1	9
5	4	14	17
- 4	- 4	- 5	- 9
1	0	9	8

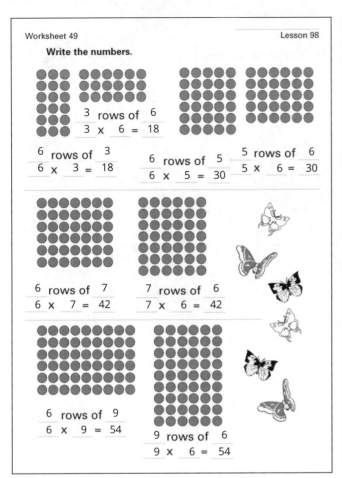

Worksheet 49 — Lesson 98

Write the numbers.

3 rows of 6
3 x 6 = 18

6 rows of 3
6 x 3 = 18

6 rows of 5
6 x 5 = 30

5 rows of 6
5 x 6 = 30

6 rows of 7
6 x 7 = 42

7 rows of 6
7 x 6 = 42

6 rows of 9
6 x 9 = 54

9 rows of 6
9 x 6 = 54

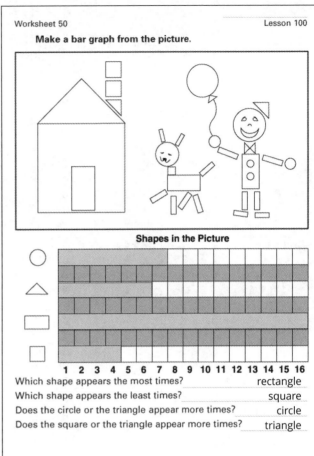

Worksheet 50 — Lesson 100

Make a bar graph from the picture.

Shapes in the Picture

	1 2 3 4 5 6 7 8 9 10 11 12 13 14 15 16

Which shape appears the most times? — rectangle
Which shape appears the least times? — square
Does the circle or the triangle appear more times? — circle
Does the square or the triangle appear more times? — triangle

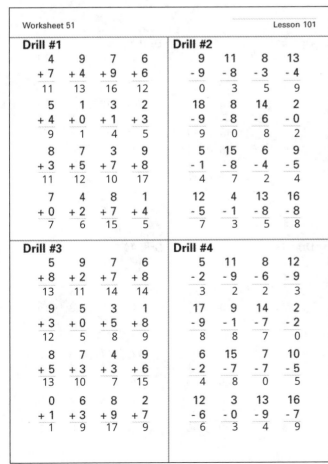

Worksheet 51 — Lesson 101

Drill #1

4	9	7	6
+ 7	+ 4	+ 9	+ 6
11	13	16	12
5	1	3	2
+ 4	+ 0	+ 1	+ 3
9	1	4	5
8	7	3	9
+ 3	+ 5	+ 7	+ 8
11	12	10	17
7	4	8	1
+ 0	+ 2	+ 7	+ 4
7	6	15	5

Drill #2

9	11	8	13
- 9	- 8	- 3	- 4
0	3	5	9
18	8	14	2
- 9	- 8	- 6	- 0
9	0	8	2
5	15	6	9
- 1	- 8	- 4	- 5
4	7	2	4
12	4	13	16
- 5	- 1	- 8	- 8
7	3	5	8

Drill #3

5	9	7	6
+ 8	+ 2	+ 7	+ 8
13	11	14	14
9	5	3	1
+ 3	+ 0	+ 5	+ 8
12	5	8	9
8	7	4	9
+ 5	+ 3	+ 3	+ 6
13	10	7	15
0	6	8	2
+ 1	+ 3	+ 9	+ 7
1	9	17	9

Drill #4

5	11	8	12
- 2	- 9	- 6	- 9
3	2	2	3
17	9	14	2
- 9	- 1	- 7	- 2
8	8	7	0
6	15	7	10
- 2	- 7	- 7	- 5
4	8	0	5
12	3	13	16
- 6	- 0	- 9	- 7
6	3	4	9

Worksheet 52 — Lesson 103

Write the fraction that shows what part is shaded.

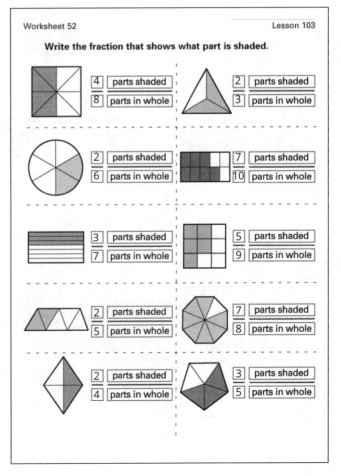

4 parts shaded / 8 parts in whole

2 parts shaded / 3 parts in whole

2 parts shaded / 6 parts in whole

7 parts shaded / 10 parts in whole

3 parts shaded / 7 parts in whole

5 parts shaded / 9 parts in whole

2 parts shaded / 5 parts in whole

7 parts shaded / 8 parts in whole

2 parts shaded / 4 parts in whole

3 parts shaded / 5 parts in whole

Drill #1

3	8	1	9
+8	+2	+1	+9
11	10	2	18

8	4	8	7
+8	+2	+0	+2
16	6	8	9

9	7	2	5
+1	+4	+0	+7
10	11	2	12

6	5	3	0
+9	+3	+1	+6
15	8	4	6

Drill #2

11	9	5	10
-5	-2	-5	-8
6	7	0	2

7	10	9	15
-0	-1	-9	-6
7	9	0	9

6	8	11	7
-4	-5	-2	-4
2	3	9	3

10	12	6	16
-4	-3	-0	-9
6	9	6	7

Drill #3

1	7	2	9
+9	+6	+4	+5
10	13	6	14

7	6	0	4
+8	+2	+8	+6
15	8	8	10

4	4	8	1
+5	+8	+6	+5
9	12	14	6

0	3	3	6
+4	+3	+5	+5
4	6	8	11

Drill #4

3	9	8	10
-1	-3	-0	-9
2	6	8	1

4	10	11	14
-1	-2	-4	-8
3	8	7	6

12	6	9	11
-7	-6	-6	-6
5	0	3	5

5	13	10	8
-0	-7	-6	-8
5	6	4	0

Solve the equations.

$7 + n = 9$ → $-7 \quad -7$ → $n = 7$

$9 + n = 15$ → $-9 \quad -9$ → $n = 6$

$1 + n = 9$ → $-1 \quad -1$ → $n = 8$

$6 + n = 14$ → $-6 \quad -6$ → $n = 8$

$8 + n = 17$ → $-8 \quad -8$ → $n = 9$

$4 + n = 7$ → $-4 \quad -4$ → $n = 3$

$3 + n = 8$ → $-3 \quad -3$ → $n = 5$

$7 + n = 14$ → $-7 \quad -7$ → $n = 7$

$6 + n = 9$ → $-6 \quad -6$ → $n = 3$

$7 + n = 10$ → $-7 \quad -7$ → $n = 3$

$5 + n = 5$ → $-5 \quad -5$ → $n = 0$

$9 + n = 11$ → $-9 \quad -9$ → $n = 2$

$0 + n = 1$ → $-0 \quad -0$ → $n = 1$

$8 + n = 13$ → $-8 \quad -8$ → $n = 5$

$9 + n = 13$ → $-9 \quad -9$ → $n = 4$

$5 + n = 13$ → $-5 \quad -5$ → $n = 8$

$7 + n = 13$ → $-7 \quad -7$ → $n = 6$

$8 + n = 11$ → $-8 \quad -8$ → $n = 3$

$5 + n = 9$ → $-5 \quad -5$ → $n = 4$

$4 + n = 11$ → $-4 \quad -4$ → $n = 7$

$0 + n = 6$ → $-0 \quad -0$ → $n = 6$

$5 + n = 12$ → $-5 \quad -5$ → $n = 7$

$2 + n = 2$ → $-2 \quad -2$ → $n = 0$

$9 + n = 18$ → $-9 \quad -9$ → $n = 9$

I	II	III	IV	V	VI	VII	VIII	IX	X	XX	XXX
1	2	3	4	5	6	7	8	9	10	20	30

XL	L	LX	LXX	LXXX	XC	C	CD	D	CM	M
40	50	60	70	80	90	100	400	500	900	1,000

Write the Roman numerals.

36	XXXVI	5	V
24	XXIV	61	LXI
12	XII	80	LXXX
48	XLVIII	77	LXXVII
59	LIX	96	XCVI
3	III	17	XVII

Write the Arabic numbers.

LV	55	IV	4
XXVII	27	LXXXIII	83
VII	7	XXXIII	33
XLIII	43	XIX	19
LXVI	66	XIV	14
C	100	LXXI	71

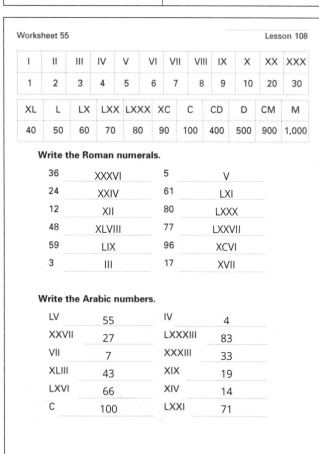

Drill #1

2	9	0	7
+6	+2	+0	+3
8	11	0	10

3	1	9	7
+4	+2	+7	+7
7	3	16	14

5	6	6	8
+9	+6	+3	+9
14	12	9	17

8	7	2	5
+5	+0	+1	+5
13	7	3	10

Drill #2

1	0	8	10
x5	x2	x0	x9
5	0	0	90

10	10	4	10
x0	x7	x1	x1
0	70	4	10

1	1	0	3
x2	x9	x6	x1
2	9	0	3

0	10	1	10
x4	x5	x6	x2
0	50	6	20

Drill #3

1	0	1	7
x8	x1	x1	x0
8	0	1	0

0	1	10	2
x5	x7	x3	x1
0	7	30	2

5	10	0	10
x1	x8	x3	x6
5	80	0	60

9	10	0	9
x1	x4	x0	x0
9	40	0	0

Drill #4

10	18	10	13
-1	-9	-5	-4
9	9	5	9

4	5	3	15
-3	-2	-1	-7
1	3	2	8

12	7	8	9
-6	-3	-7	-6
6	4	1	3

1	6	2	5
-0	-6	-2	-0
1	0	0	5

Measure the objects in inches. Label each answer.

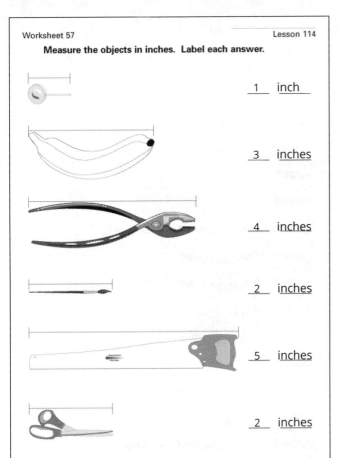

<u>1</u> inch

<u>3</u> inches

<u>4</u> inches

<u>2</u> inches

<u>5</u> inches

<u>2</u> inches

Drill #1

5	9	0	9
+ 0	+ 3	+ 2	+ 8
5	12	2	17
8	6	7	4
+ 1	+ 7	+ 5	+ 1
9	13	12	5
5	1	5	8
+ 8	+ 3	+ 2	+ 7
13	4	7	15
2	6	5	7
+ 2	+ 4	+ 6	+ 9
4	10	11	16

Drill #2

1	5	0	5
x 4	x 2	x 8	x 7
4	10	0	35
4	4	7	9
x 0	x 5	x 1	x 5
0	20	7	45
5	1	5	3
x 6	x 0	x 3	x 0
30	0	15	0
10	5	6	8
x 10	x 5	x 1	x 5
100	25	6	40

Drill #3

6	6	0	5
x 5	x 0	x 9	x 4
30	0	0	20
0	2	1	10
x 7	x 5	x 3	x 5
0	10	3	50
8	3	5	5
x 1	x 5	x 0	x 9
8	15	0	45
2	7	5	1
x 0	x 5	x 8	x 5
0	35	40	5

Drill #4

11	6	8	6
- 9	- 4	- 3	- 2
2	2	5	4
7	14	13	6
- 7	- 7	- 8	- 0
0	7	5	6
5	3	11	16
- 4	- 3	- 5	- 8
1	0	6	8
10	9	2	4
- 9	- 2	- 0	- 1
1	7	2	3

Solve the equations.

$n + 5 = 13$	$n + 6 = 12$	$n + 7 = 16$	$n + 3 = 10$
$- 5 \quad - 5$	$- 6 \quad - 6$	$- 7 \quad - 7$	$- 3 \quad - 3$
$n = 8$	$n = 6$	$n = 9$	$n = 7$
$n + 9 = 14$	$n + 2 = 3$	$n + 0 = 0$	$n + 5 = 10$
$- 9 \quad - 9$	$- 2 \quad - 2$	$- 0 \quad - 0$	$- 5 \quad - 5$
$n = 5$	$n = 1$	$n = 0$	$n = 5$
$n + 4 = 7$	$n + 2 = 11$	$n + 1 = 3$	$n + 9 = 17$
$- 4 \quad - 4$	$- 2 \quad - 2$	$- 1 \quad - 1$	$- 9 \quad - 9$
$n = 3$	$n = 9$	$n = 2$	$n = 8$
$n + 6 = 8$	$n + 0 = 7$	$n + 3 = 9$	$n + 7 = 14$
$- 6 \quad - 6$	$- 0 \quad - 0$	$- 3 \quad - 3$	$- 7 \quad - 7$
$n = 2$	$n = 7$	$n = 6$	$n = 7$
$n + 9 = 16$	$n + 3 = 4$	$n + 7 = 13$	$n + 8 = 17$
$- 9 \quad - 9$	$- 3 \quad - 3$	$- 7 \quad - 7$	$- 8 \quad - 8$
$n = 7$	$n = 1$	$n = 6$	$n = 9$
$n + 8 = 13$	$n + 1 = 5$	$n + 2 = 2$	$n + 6 = 11$
$- 8 \quad - 8$	$- 1 \quad - 1$	$- 2 \quad - 2$	$- 6 \quad - 6$
$n = 5$	$n = 4$	$n = 0$	$n = 5$

Drill #1

2	6	3	0
+ 8	+ 9	+ 7	+ 4
10	15	10	4
6	1	7	8
+ 3	+ 1	+ 7	+ 8
9	2	14	16
0	4	1	0
+ 8	+ 6	+ 5	+ 1
8	10	6	1
1	0	8	6
+ 2	+ 3	+ 7	+ 7
3	3	15	13

Drill #2

7	1	10	6
x 5	x 2	x 10	x 0
35	2	100	0
10	5	2	8
x 5	x 8	x 1	x 5
50	40	2	40
0	0	1	5
x 8	x 0	x 8	x 9
0	0	8	45
5	10	8	1
x 5	x 0	x 1	x 0
25	0	8	0

Drill #3

5	3	4	10
x 1	x 0	x 5	x 8
5	0	20	80
5	1	0	3
x 7	x 5	x 5	x 1
35	5	0	3
9	10	9	0
x 1	x 2	x 0	x 2
9	20	0	0
10	4	5	10
x 3	x 0	x 3	x 6
30	0	15	60

Drill #4

7	12	14	15
- 1	- 8	- 5	- 6
6	4	9	9
10	12	8	8
- 3	- 9	- 5	- 1
7	3	3	7
8	11	9	17
- 8	- 4	- 4	- 8
0	7	5	9
11	9	16	9
- 7	- 7	- 7	- 3
4	2	9	6

Books Read by Students

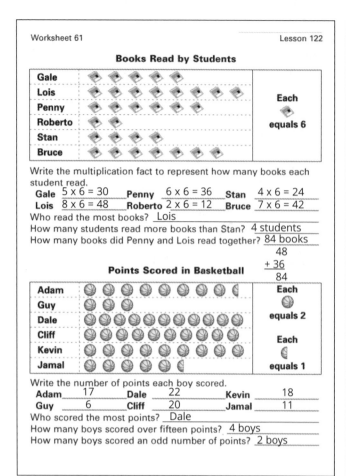

Gale	◈ ◈ ◈ ◈ ◈		
Lois	◈ ◈ ◈ ◈ ◈ ◈ ◈ ◈	Each	
Penny	◈ ◈ ◈ ◈ ◈ ◈	◈	
Roberto	◈ ◈	equals 6	
Stan	◈ ◈ ◈ ◈		
Bruce	◈ ◈ ◈ ◈ ◈ ◈ ◈		

Write the multiplication fact to represent how many books each student read.

Gale   5 x 6 = 30   **Penny**   6 x 6 = 36   **Stan**   4 x 6 = 24

Lois   8 x 6 = 48   **Roberto** 2 x 6 = 12   **Bruce** 7 x 6 = 42

Who read the most books?   Lois

How many students read more books than Stan?   4 students

How many books did Penny and Lois read together?   84 books

48
+ 36
84

Points Scored in Basketball

Adam	🏀🏀🏀🏀🏀🏀🏀🏀◖	Each
Guy	🏀🏀🏀	🏀
Dale	🏀🏀🏀🏀🏀🏀🏀🏀🏀🏀🏀	equals 2
Cliff	🏀🏀🏀🏀🏀🏀🏀🏀🏀🏀	Each
Kevin	🏀🏀🏀🏀🏀🏀🏀🏀🏀	◖
Jamal	🏀🏀🏀🏀🏀◖	equals 1

Write the number of points each boy scored.

Adam   17   **Dale**   22   **Kevin**   18

Guy   6   **Cliff**   20   **Jamal**   11

Who scored the most points?   Dale

How many boys scored over fifteen points?   4 boys

How many boys scored an odd number of points?   2 boys

Draw a line across each ribbon at the given length. Then color the ribbons.

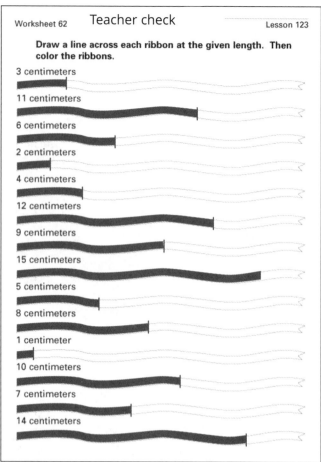

3 centimeters

11 centimeters

6 centimeters

2 centimeters

4 centimeters

12 centimeters

9 centimeters

15 centimeters

5 centimeters

8 centimeters

1 centimeter

10 centimeters

7 centimeters

14 centimeters

Drill #1				Drill #2			
8	7	9	9	6	2	2	10
+ 9	+ 1	+ 2	+ 9	x 2	x 0	x 2	x 7
17	8	11	18	12	0	4	70
7	4	6	1	4	1	9	8
+ 8	+ 3	+ 2	+ 6	x 2	x 4	x 5	x 2
15	7	8	7	8	4	45	16
3	2	5	3	7	10	2	2
+ 3	+ 0	+ 2	+ 4	x 5	x 1	x 3	x 9
6	2	7	7	35	10	6	18
9	3	2	2	2	3	5	0
+ 7	+ 1	+ 7	+ 2	x 7	x 5	x 6	x 4
16	4	9	4	14	15	30	0

Drill #3				Drill #4			
2	0	5	7	9	17	13	11
x 8	x 5	x 8	x 2	- 8	- 9	- 6	- 8
16	0	40	14	1	8	7	3
2	7	3	9	10	10	9	12
x 6	x 1	x 2	x 0	- 8	- 7	- 0	- 5
12	7	6	0	2	3	9	7
5	10	9	4	14	13	11	15
x 4	x 4	x 2	x 1	- 9	- 7	- 3	- 9
20	40	18	4	5	6	8	6
6	1	10	2	10	12	7	14
x 5	x 9	x 3	x 4	- 4	- 4	- 5	- 6
30	9	30	8	6	8	2	8

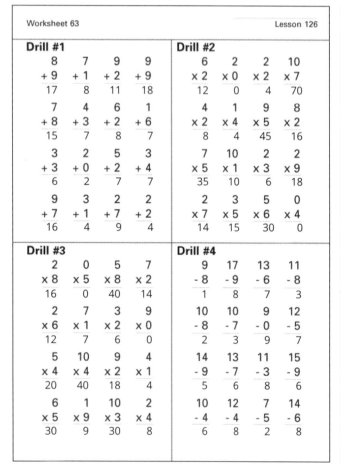

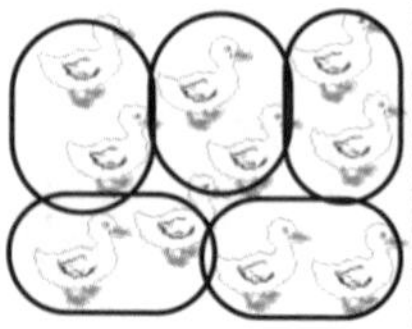

circle sets of 2's
½ of 10 = 5

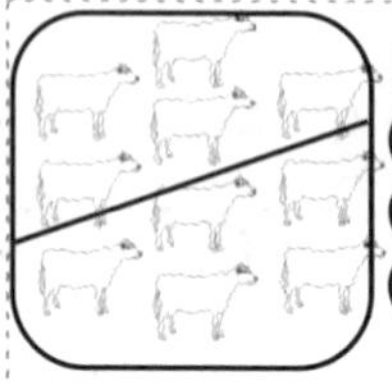

circle sets of 5's
⅕ of 10 = 2

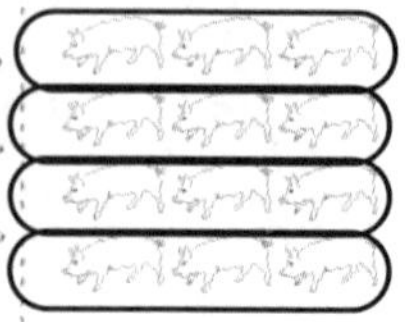

circle sets of 3's
⅓ of 12 = 4

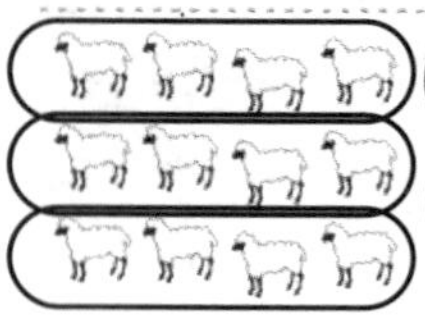

circle sets of 4's
¼ of 12 = 3

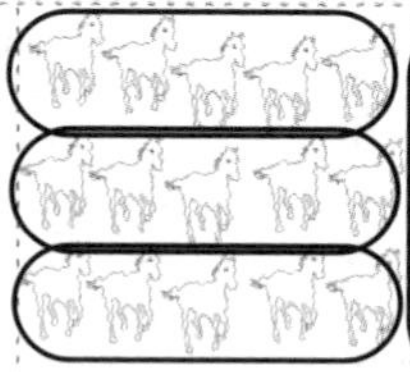

circle sets of 5's
⅕ of 15 = 3

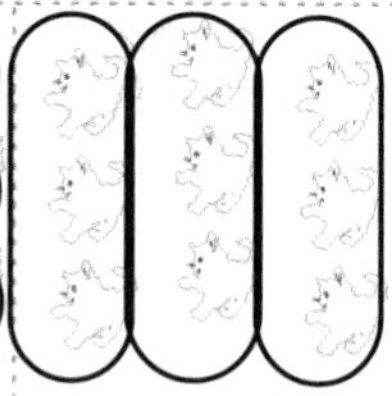

circle sets of 3's
⅓ of 9 = 3

circle sets of 4's
¼ of 16 = 4

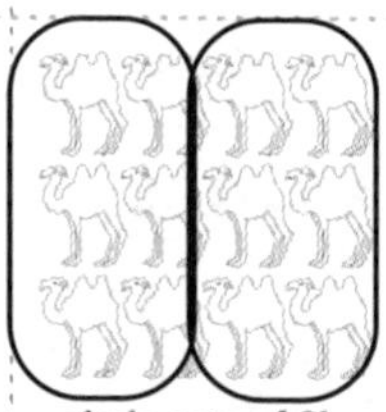

circle sets of 6's
⅙ of 12 = 2

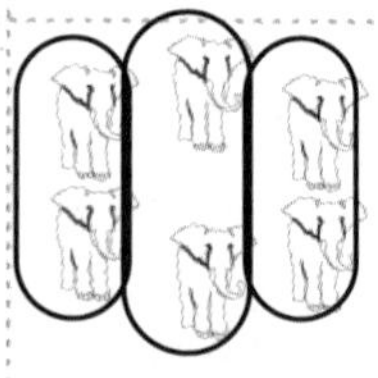

circle sets of 2's
½ of 6 = 3

Drill #1

2	8	9	2
+ 6	+ 1	+ 3	+ 4
8	9	12	6
6	9	9	1
+ 8	+ 1	+ 7	+ 4
14	10	16	5
5	0	9	7
+ 5	+ 9	+ 5	+ 3
10	9	14	10
3	1	4	1
+ 2	+ 2	+ 4	+ 3
5	3	8	4

Drill #2

9	7	7	2
x 2	x 0	x 5	x 7
18	0	35	14
6	1	3	6
x 3	x 6	x 2	x 1
18	6	6	6
5	3	10	6
x 2	x 7	x 10	x 2
10	21	100	12
1	2	0	3
x 7	x 2	x 3	x 5
7	4	0	15

Drill #3

8	8	5	3
x 2	x 3	x 8	x 4
16	24	40	12
6	1	4	10
x 5	x 3	x 2	x 0
30	3	8	0
8	2	5	7
x 0	x 3	x 9	x 2
0	6	45	14
10	1	2	0
x 9	x 1	x 5	x 7
90	1	10	0

Drill #4

5	15	12	6
- 3	- 8	- 7	- 5
2	7	5	1
9	8	1	7
- 1	- 6	- 1	- 2
8	2	0	5
16	14	13	11
- 7	- 9	- 5	- 2
9	5	8	9
3	4	16	10
- 2	- 4	- 9	- 2
1	0	7	8

Find the sum.

$56.20 + $0.86 =
```
  $56.20
+   0.86
  $57.06
```

$10.41 + $14.73 =
```
  $10.41
+  14.73
  $25.14
```

$15.73 + $2.18 =
```
  $15.73
+   2.18
  $17.91
```

$35.65 + $50.15 =
```
  $35.65
+  50.15
  $85.80
```

$92.45 + $1.38 =
```
  $92.45
+   1.38
  $93.83
```

$71.63 + $0.53 =
```
  $71.63
+   0.53
  $72.16
```

$81.36 + $4.58 =
```
  $81.36
+   4.58
  $85.94
```

$42.73 + $3.41 =
```
  $42.73
+   3.41
  $46.14
```

$48.72 + $20.77 =
```
  $48.72
+  20.77
  $69.49
```

$71.18 + $7.62 =
```
  $71.18
+   7.62
  $78.80
```

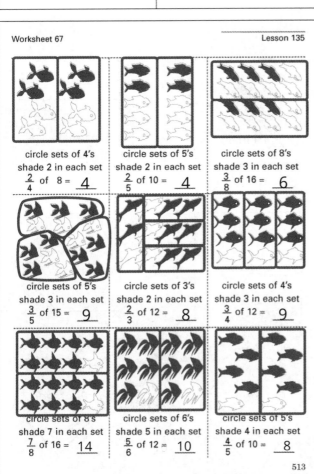

circle sets of 4's
shade 2 in each set
$\frac{2}{4}$ of 8 = 4

circle sets of 5's
shade 2 in each set
$\frac{2}{5}$ of 10 = 4

circle sets of 8's
shade 3 in each set
$\frac{3}{8}$ of 16 = 6

circle sets of 5's
shade 3 in each set
$\frac{3}{5}$ of 15 = 9

circle sets of 3's
shade 2 in each set
$\frac{2}{3}$ of 12 = 8

circle sets of 4's
shade 3 in each set
$\frac{3}{4}$ of 12 = 9

circle sets of 8's
shade 7 in each set
$\frac{7}{8}$ of 16 = 14

circle sets of 6's
shade 5 in each set
$\frac{5}{6}$ of 12 = 10

circle sets of 5's
shade 4 in each set
$\frac{4}{5}$ of 10 = 8

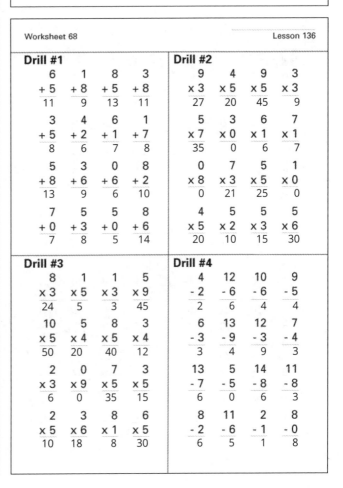

Drill #1

6	1	8	3
+ 5	+ 8	+ 5	+ 8
11	9	13	11
3	4	6	1
+ 5	+ 2	+ 1	+ 7
8	6	7	8
5	3	0	8
+ 8	+ 6	+ 6	+ 2
13	9	6	10
7	5	5	8
+ 0	+ 3	+ 0	+ 6
7	8	5	14

Drill #2

9	4	9	3
x 3	x 5	x 5	x 3
27	20	45	9
5	3	6	7
x 7	x 0	x 1	x 1
35	0	6	7
0	7	5	1
x 8	x 3	x 5	x 0
0	21	25	0
4	5	5	5
x 5	x 2	x 3	x 6
20	10	15	30

Drill #3

8	1	1	5
x 3	x 5	x 3	x 9
24	5	3	45
10	5	8	3
x 5	x 4	x 5	x 4
50	20	40	12
2	0	7	3
x 3	x 9	x 5	x 5
6	0	35	15
2	3	8	6
x 5	x 6	x 1	x 5
10	18	8	30

Drill #4

4	12	10	9
- 2	- 6	- 6	- 5
2	6	4	4
6	13	12	7
- 3	- 9	- 3	- 4
3	4	9	3
13	5	14	11
- 7	- 5	- 8	- 8
6	0	6	3
8	11	2	8
- 2	- 6	- 1	- 0
6	5	1	8

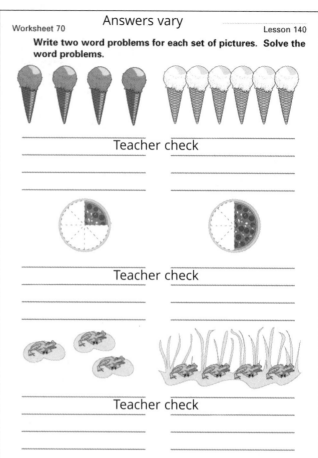

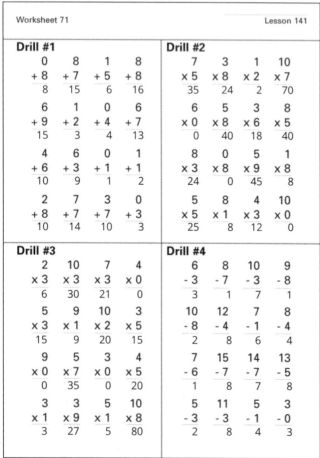

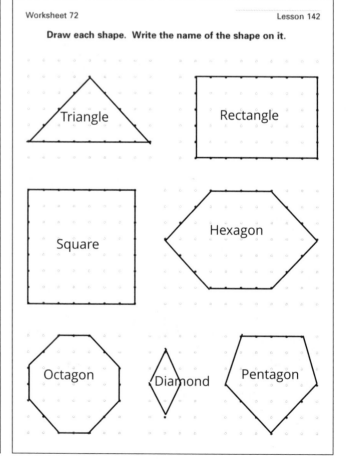

Worksheet 69 — Lesson 139

Answers vary

Draw a line of symmetry on each shape.

515

Worksheet 70 — Lesson 140

Answers vary

Write two word problems for each set of pictures. Solve the word problems.

Teacher check

Teacher check

Teacher check

Worksheet 71 — Lesson 141

Drill #1

0	8	1	8
+ 8	+ 7	+ 5	+ 8
8	15	6	16
6	1	0	6
+ 9	+ 2	+ 4	+ 7
15	3	4	13
4	6	0	1
+ 6	+ 3	+ 1	+ 1
10	9	1	2
2	7	3	0
+ 8	+ 7	+ 7	+ 3
10	14	10	3

Drill #2

7	3	1	10
x 5	x 8	x 2	x 7
35	24	2	70
6	5	3	8
x 0	x 8	x 6	x 5
0	40	18	40
8	0	5	1
x 3	x 8	x 9	x 8
24	0	45	8
5	8	4	10
x 5	x 1	x 3	x 0
25	8	12	0

Drill #3

2	10	7	4
x 3	x 3	x 3	x 0
6	30	21	0
5	9	10	3
x 3	x 1	x 2	x 5
15	9	20	15
9	5	3	4
x 0	x 7	x 0	x 5
0	35	0	20
3	3	5	10
x 1	x 9	x 1	x 8
3	27	5	80

Drill #4

6	8	10	9
- 3	- 7	- 3	- 8
3	1	7	1
10	12	7	8
- 8	- 4	- 1	- 4
2	8	6	4
7	15	14	13
- 6	- 7	- 7	- 5
1	8	7	8
5	11	5	3
- 3	- 3	- 1	- 0
2	8	4	3

Worksheet 72 — Lesson 142

Draw each shape. Write the name of the shape on it.

Triangle

Rectangle

Square

Hexagon

Octagon

Diamond

Pentagon

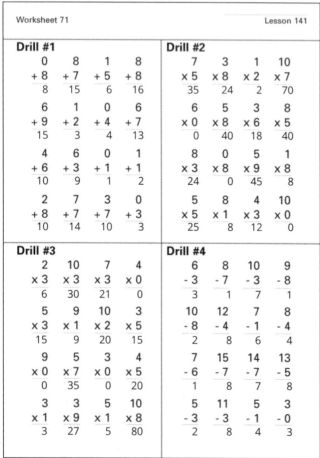

546

Draw the shapes.

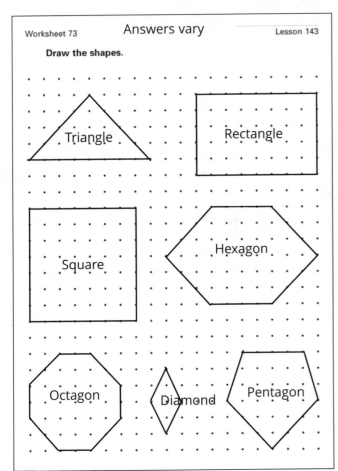

Drill #1

8	2	3	1
+ 9	+ 2	+ 4	+ 6
17	4	7	7
3	7	9	9
+ 3	+ 8	+ 9	+ 7
6	15	18	16
7	3	2	4
+ 1	+ 1	+ 0	+ 6
8	4	2	10
5	6	9	2
+ 2	+ 2	+ 2	+ 7
7	8	11	9

Drill #2

1	9	9	2
x 3	x 3	x 2	x 6
3	27	18	12
5	7	3	6
x 6	x 0	x 3	x 6
30	0	9	36
6	9	7	4
x 3	x 6	x 5	x 3
18	54	35	12
2	0	5	8
x 7	x 6	x 2	x 6
14	0	10	48

Drill #3

3	5	2	3
x 6	x 3	x 3	x 7
18	15	6	21
2	7	1	4
x 2	x 6	x 7	x 6
4	42	7	24
8	1	7	10
x 2	x 6	x 3	x 10
16	6	21	100
0	8	5	10
x 3	x 3	x 8	x 6
0	24	40	60

Drill #4

7	7	6	13
- 4	- 0	- 1	- 9
3	7	5	4
17	11	16	9
- 8	- 5	- 8	- 9
9	6	8	0
6	9	8	12
- 6	- 4	- 2	- 7
0	5	6	5
11	5	14	10
- 7	- 2	- 5	- 0
4	3	9	10

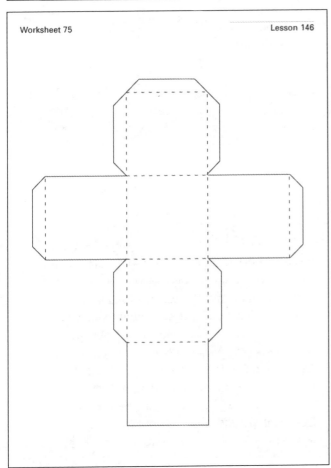

Drill #1

4	2	1	6
+ 3	+ 0	+ 1	+ 5
7	2	2	11
5	9	7	0
+ 1	+ 9	+ 6	+ 8
6	18	13	8
7	6	4	1
+ 2	+ 2	+ 8	+ 7
9	8	12	8
3	8	9	4
+ 0	+ 2	+ 1	+ 1
3	10	10	5

Drill #2

8	6	5	1
x 2	x 3	x 8	x 3
16	18	40	3
6	7	4	3
x 2	x 6	x 2	x 2
12	42	8	6
10	3	5	7
x 0	x 9	x 7	x 2
0	27	35	14
10	5	1	6
x 9	x 3	x 1	x 6
90	15	1	36

Drill #3

2	7	8	4
x 5	x 3	x 0	x 3
10	21	0	12
8	2	6	0
x 6	x 9	x 4	x 7
48	18	24	0
5	3	2	6
x 9	x 3	x 4	x 9
45	9	8	54
2	4	3	5
x 2	x 5	x 8	x 6
4	20	24	30

Drill #4

7	6	2	3
- 6	- 5	- 1	- 3
1	1	1	0
12	16	13	9
- 8	- 9	- 6	- 2
4	7	7	7
15	9	11	11
- 9	- 0	- 9	- 4
6	9	2	7
10	15	14	10
- 1	- 8	- 8	- 5
9	7	6	5

Find the area by adding.

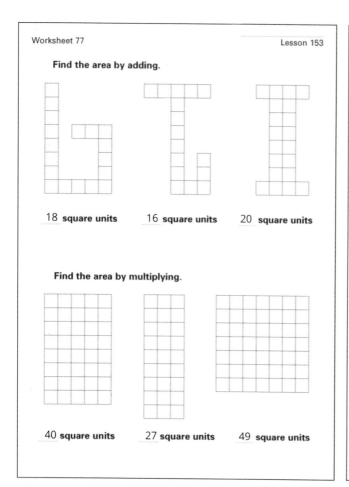

18 square units   16 square units   20 square units

Find the area by multiplying.

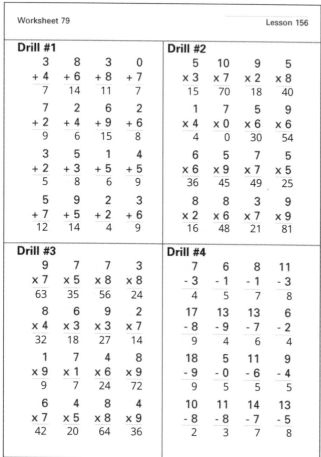

40 square units   27 square units   49 square units

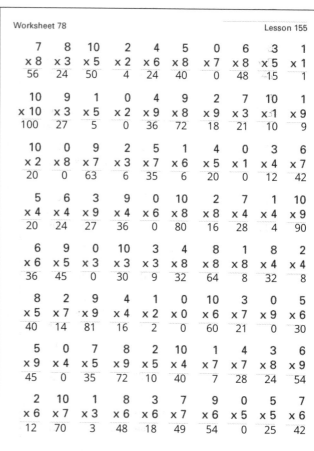

7 ×8 56	8 ×3 24	10 ×5 50	2 ×2 4	4 ×6 24	5 ×8 40	0 ×7 0	6 ×8 48	3 ×5 15	1 ×1 1
10 ×10 100	9 ×3 27	1 ×5 5	0 ×2 0	4 ×9 36	9 ×8 72	2 ×9 18	7 ×3 21	10 ×1 10	1 ×9 9
10 ×2 20	0 ×8 0	9 ×7 63	2 ×3 6	5 ×7 35	1 ×6 6	4 ×5 20	0 ×1 0	3 ×4 12	6 ×7 42
5 ×4 20	6 ×4 24	3 ×9 27	9 ×4 36	0 ×6 0	10 ×8 80	2 ×8 16	7 ×4 28	1 ×4 4	10 ×9 90
6 ×6 36	9 ×5 45	0 ×3 0	10 ×3 30	3 ×3 9	4 ×8 32	8 ×8 64	1 ×8 8	8 ×4 32	2 ×4 8
8 ×5 40	2 ×7 14	9 ×9 81	4 ×4 16	1 ×2 2	0 ×0 0	10 ×6 60	3 ×7 21	0 ×9 0	5 ×6 30
5 ×9 45	0 ×4 0	7 ×5 35	8 ×9 72	2 ×5 10	10 ×4 40	1 ×7 7	4 ×7 28	3 ×8 24	6 ×9 54
2 ×6 12	10 ×7 70	1 ×3 3	8 ×6 48	3 ×6 18	7 ×7 49	9 ×6 54	0 ×5 0	5 ×5 25	7 ×6 42

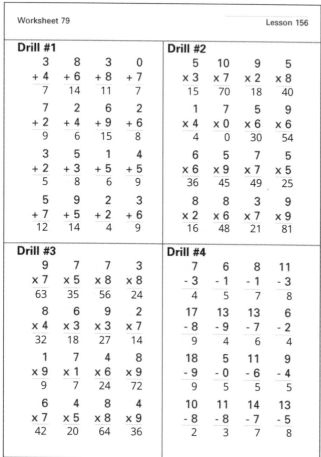

Drill #1

3 +4 7	8 +6 14	3 +8 11	0 +7 7
7 +2 9	2 +4 6	6 +9 15	2 +6 8
3 +2 5	5 +3 8	1 +5 6	4 +5 9
5 +7 12	9 +5 14	2 +2 4	3 +6 9

Drill #2

5 ×3 15	10 ×7 70	9 ×2 18	5 ×8 40
1 ×4 4	7 ×0 0	5 ×6 30	9 ×6 54
6 ×6 36	5 ×9 45	7 ×7 49	5 ×5 25
8 ×2 16	8 ×6 48	3 ×7 21	9 ×9 81

Drill #3

9 ×7 63	7 ×5 35	7 ×8 56	3 ×8 24
8 ×4 32	6 ×3 18	9 ×3 27	2 ×7 14
1 ×9 9	7 ×1 7	4 ×6 24	8 ×9 72
6 ×7 42	4 ×5 20	8 ×8 64	4 ×9 36

Drill #4

7 -3 4	6 -1 5	8 -1 7	11 -3 8
17 -8 9	13 -9 4	13 -7 6	6 -2 4
18 -9 9	5 -0 5	11 -6 5	9 -4 5
10 -8 2	11 -8 3	14 -7 7	13 -5 8

Some Answers Vary.

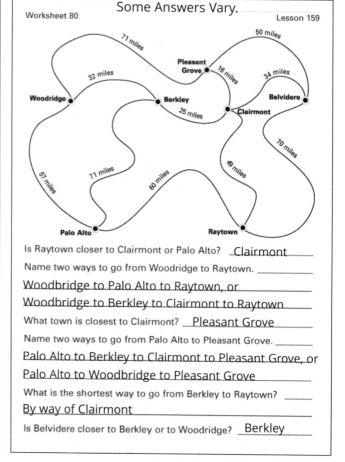

Is Raytown closer to Clairmont or Palo Alto? __Clairmont__

Name two ways to go from Woodridge to Raytown. _____

Woodbridge to Palo Alto to Raytown, or

Woodbridge to Berkley to Clairmont to Raytown

What town is closest to Clairmont? __Pleasant Grove__

Name two ways to go from Palo Alto to Pleasant Grove. _____

Palo Alto to Berkley to Clairmont to Pleasant Grove, or

Palo Alto to Woodbridge to Pleasant Grove

What is the shortest way to go from Berkley to Raytown? _____

By way of Clairmont

Is Belvidere closer to Berkley or to Woodridge? __Berkley__